Anatomy

and

Physiology

openstax™

Anatomy & Physiology

SENIOR CONTRIBUTING AUTHORS

J. Gordon Betts, Tyler Junior College

Peter Desaix, University of North Carolina at Chapel Hill

Eddie Johnson, Central Oregon Community College

Jody E. Johnson, Arapahoe Community College

Oksana Korol, Aims Community College

Dean Kruse, Portland Community College

Brandon Poe, Springfield Technical Community College

James A. Wise, Hampton University

Mark Womble, Youngstown State University

Kelly A. Young, California State University, Long Beach

OpenStax
Rice University
6100 Main Street MS-375
Houston, Texas 77005

To learn more about OpenStax, visit https://openstax.org.
Individual print copies and bulk orders can be purchased through our website.

PRINT BOOK ISBN-10	1-938168-13-5
PRINT BOOK ISBN-13	978-1-938168-13-0
PDF VERSION ISBN-10	1-947172-04-2
PDF VERSION ISBN-13	978-1-947172-04-3
ENHANCED TEXTBOOK ISBN-10	1-938168-30-5
ENHANCED TEXTBOOK ISBN-13	978-1-938168-30-7
Revision Number	AP-2013-003(03/17)-LC
Original Publication Year	2013

OPENSTAX

OpenStax provides free, peer-reviewed, openly licensed textbooks for introductory college and Advanced Placement® courses and low-cost, personalized courseware that helps students learn. A nonprofit ed tech initiative based at Rice University, we're committed to helping students access the tools they need to complete their courses and meet their educational goals.

RICE UNIVERSITY

OpenStax, OpenStax CNX, and OpenStax Tutor are initiatives of Rice University. As a leading research university with a distinctive commitment to undergraduate education, Rice University aspires to path-breaking research, unsurpassed teaching, and contributions to the betterment of our world. It seeks to fulfill this mission by cultivating a diverse community of learning and discovery that produces leaders across the spectrum of human endeavor.

FOUNDATION SUPPORT

OpenStax is grateful for the tremendous support of our sponsors. Without their strong engagement, the goal of free access to high-quality textbooks would remain just a dream.

Laura and John Arnold Foundation (LJAF) actively seeks opportunities to invest in organizations and thought leaders that have a sincere interest in implementing fundamental changes that not only yield immediate gains, but also repair broken systems for future generations. LJAF currently focuses its strategic investments on education, criminal justice, research integrity, and public accountability.

The William and Flora Hewlett Foundation has been making grants since 1967 to help solve social and environmental problems at home and around the world. The Foundation concentrates its resources on activities in education, the environment, global development and population, performing arts, and philanthropy, and makes grants to support disadvantaged communities in the San Francisco Bay Area.

Calvin K. Kazanjian was the founder and president of Peter Paul (Almond Joy), Inc. He firmly believed that the more people understood about basic economics the happier and more prosperous they would be. Accordingly, he established the Calvin K. Kazanjian Economics Foundation Inc, in 1949 as a philanthropic, nonpolitical educational organization to support efforts that enhanced economic understanding.

Guided by the belief that every life has equal value, the Bill & Melinda Gates Foundation works to help all people lead healthy, productive lives. In developing countries, it focuses on improving people's health with vaccines and other life-saving tools and giving them the chance to lift themselves out of hunger and extreme poverty. In the United States, it seeks to significantly improve education so that all young people have the opportunity to reach their full potential. Based in Seattle, Washington, the foundation is led by CEO Jeff Raikes and Co-chair William H. Gates Sr., under the direction of Bill and Melinda Gates and Warren Buffett.

The Maxfield Foundation supports projects with potential for high impact in science, education, sustainability, and other areas of social importance.

Our mission at The Michelson 20MM Foundation is to grow access and success by eliminating unnecessary hurdles to affordability. We support the creation, sharing, and proliferation of more effective, more affordable educational content by leveraging disruptive technologies, open educational resources, and new models for collaboration between for-profit, nonprofit, and public entities.

The Bill and Stephanie Sick Fund supports innovative projects in the areas of Education, Art, Science and Engineering.

Table of Contents

PREFACE

Welcome to *Anatomy and Physiology*, an OpenStax resource. This textbook was written to increase student access to high-quality learning materials, maintaining highest standards of academic rigor at little to no cost.

About OpenStax

OpenStax is a nonprofit based at Rice University, and it's our mission to improve student access to education. Our first openly licensed college textbook was published in 2012, and our library has since scaled to over 25 books for college and AP® courses used by hundreds of thousands of students. Our adaptive learning technology, designed to improve learning outcomes through personalized educational paths, is being piloted in college courses throughout the country. Through our partnerships with philanthropic foundations and our alliance with other educational resource organizations, OpenStax is breaking down the most common barriers to learning and empowering students and instructors to succeed.

About OpenStax Resources

Customization

Anatomy and Physiology is licensed under a Creative Commons Attribution 4.0 International (CC BY) license, which means that you can distribute, remix, and build upon the content, as long as you provide attribution to OpenStax and its content contributors.

Because our books are openly licensed, you are free to use the entire book or pick and choose the sections that are most relevant to the needs of your course. Feel free to remix the content by assigning your students certain chapters and sections in your syllabus, in the order that you prefer. You can even provide a direct link in your syllabus to the sections in the web view of your book.

Instructors also have the option of creating a customized version of their OpenStax book. The custom version can be made available to students in low-cost print or digital form through their campus bookstore. Visit your book page on openstax.org for more information.

Errata

All OpenStax textbooks undergo a rigorous review process. However, like any professional-grade textbook, errors sometimes occur. Since our books are web based, we can make updates periodically when deemed pedagogically necessary. If you have a correction to suggest, submit it through the link on your book page on openstax.org. Subject matter experts review all errata suggestions. OpenStax is committed to remaining transparent about all updates, so you will also find a list of past errata changes on your book page on openstax.org.

Format

You can access this textbook for free in web view or PDF through openstax.org, and in low-cost print and iBooks editions.

About *Anatomy and Physiology*

Coverage and Scope

The units of our *Anatomy and Physiology* textbook adhere to the scope and sequence followed by most two-semester courses nationwide. The development choices for this textbook were made with the guidance of hundreds of faculty who are deeply involved in teaching this course. These choices led to innovations in art, terminology, career orientation, practical applications, and multimedia-based learning, all with a goal of increasing relevance to students. We strove to make the discipline meaningful and memorable to students, so that they can draw from it a working knowledge that will enrich their future studies.

Unit 1: Levels of Organization

Chapters 1–4 provide students with a basic understanding of human anatomy and physiology, including its language, the levels of organization, and the basics of chemistry and cell biology. These chapters provide a foundation for the further study of the body. They also focus particularly on how the body's regions, important chemicals, and cells maintain homeostasis.
Chapter 1 An Introduction to the Human Body
Chapter 2 The Chemical Level of Organization
Chapter 3 The Cellular Level of Organization
Chapter 4 The Tissue Level of Organization

Unit 2: Support and Movement

In Chapters 5–11, students explore the skin, the largest organ of the body, and examine the body's skeletal and muscular systems, following a traditional sequence of topics. This unit is the first to walk students through specific systems of the body, and as it does so, it maintains a focus on homeostasis as well as those diseases and conditions that can disrupt it.

Chapter 5 The Integumentary System
Chapter 6 Bone and Skeletal Tissue
Chapter 7 The Axial Skeleton
Chapter 8 The Appendicular Skeleton
Chapter 9 Joints
Chapter 10 Muscle Tissue
Chapter 11 The Muscular System

Unit 3: Regulation, Integration, and Control

Chapters 12–17 help students answer questions about nervous and endocrine system control and regulation. In a break with the traditional sequence of topics, the special senses are integrated into the chapter on the somatic nervous system. The chapter on the neurological examination offers students a unique approach to understanding nervous system function using five simple but powerful diagnostic tests.

Chapter 12 Introduction to the Nervous System
Chapter 13 The Anatomy of the Nervous System
Chapter 14 The Somatic Nervous System
Chapter 15 The Autonomic Nervous System
Chapter 16 The Neurological Exam
Chapter 17 The Endocrine System

Unit 4: Fluids and Transport

In Chapters 18–21, students examine the principal means of transport for materials needed to support the human body, regulate its internal environment, and provide protection.

Chapter 18 Blood
Chapter 19 The Cardiovascular System: The Heart
Chapter 20 The Cardiovascular System: Blood Vessels and Circulation
Chapter 21 The Lymphatic System and Immunity

Unit 5: Energy, Maintenance, and Environmental Exchange

In Chapters 22–26, students discover the interaction between body systems and the outside environment for the exchange of materials, the capture of energy, the release of waste, and the overall maintenance of the internal systems that regulate the exchange. The explanations and illustrations are particularly focused on how structure relates to function.

Chapter 22 The Respiratory System
Chapter 23 The Digestive System
Chapter 24 Nutrition and Metabolism
Chapter 25 The Urinary System
Chapter 26 Fluid, Electrolyte, and Acid–Base Balance

Unit 6: Human Development and the Continuity of Life

The closing chapters examine the male and female reproductive systems, describe the process of human development and the different stages of pregnancy, and end with a review of the mechanisms of inheritance.

Chapter 27 The Reproductive System
Chapter 28 Development and Genetic Inheritance

Pedagogical Foundation and Features

Anatomy and Physiology is designed to promote scientific literacy. Throughout the text, you will find features that engage the students by taking selected topics a step further.

Homeostatic Imbalances discusses the effects and results of imbalances in the body.

Disorders showcases a disorder that is relevant to the body system at hand. This feature may focus on a specific disorder or a set of related disorders.

Diseases showcases a disease that is relevant to the body system at hand.

Aging explores the effect aging has on a body's system and specific disorders that manifest over time.

Career Connections presents information on the various careers often pursued by allied health students, such as medical technician, medical examiner, and neurophysiologist. Students are introduced to the educational requirements for and day-to-day responsibilities in these careers.

Everyday Connections tie anatomical and physiological concepts to emerging issues and discuss these in terms of everyday life. Topics include "Anabolic Steroids" and "The Effect of Second-Hand Tobacco Smoke."

Interactive Links direct students to online exercises, simulations, animations, and videos to add a fuller context to core content and help improve understanding of the material. Many features include links to the University of Michigan's interactive WebScopes, which allow students to zoom in on micrographs in the collection. These resources were vetted by reviewers and other subject matter experts to ensure that they are effective and accurate. We strongly urge students to explore these links, whether viewing a video or inputting data into a simulation, to gain the fullest experience and to learn how to search for information independently.

Dynamic, Learner-Centered Art

Our unique approach to visuals is designed to emphasize only the components most important in any given illustration. The art style is particularly aimed at focusing student learning through a powerful blend of traditional depictions and instructional innovations.

Much of the art in this book consists of black line illustrations. The strongest line is used to highlight the most important structures, and shading is used to show dimension and shape. Color is used sparingly to highlight and clarify the primary anatomical or functional point of the illustration. This technique is intended to draw students' attention to the critical learning point in the illustration, without distraction from excessive gradients, shadows, and highlights. Full color is used when the structure or process requires it (for example, muscle diagrams and cardiovascular system illustrations).

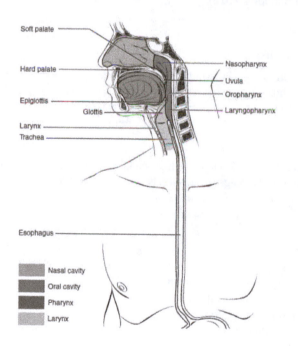

By highlighting the most important portions of the illustration, the artwork helps students focus on the most important points without overwhelming them.

Micrographs

Micrograph magnifications have been calculated based on the objective provided with the image. If a micrograph was recorded at 40×, and the image was magnified an additional 2×, we calculated the final magnification of the micrograph to be 80×.

Please note that, when viewing the textbook electronically, the micrograph magnification provided in the text does not take into account the size and magnification of the screen on your electronic device. There may be some variation.

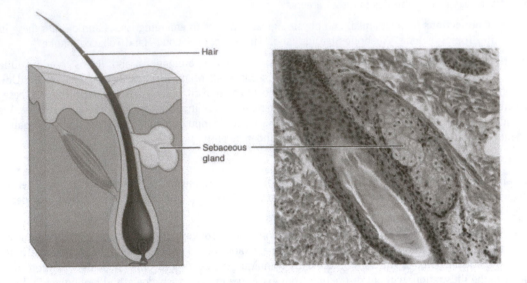

These glands secrete oils that lubricate and protect the skin. LM × 400. (Micrograph provided by the Regents of University of Michigan Medical School © 2012)

Additional Resources

Student and Instructor Resources

We've compiled additional resources for both students and instructors, including Getting Started Guides, an instructor solution guide, and PowerPoint slides. Instructor resources require a verified instructor account, which you can apply for when you log in or create your account on openstax.org. Take advantage of these resources to supplement your OpenStax book.

Partner Resources

OpenStax Partners are our allies in the mission to make high-quality learning materials affordable and accessible to students and instructors everywhere. Their tools integrate seamlessly with our OpenStax titles at a low cost. To access the partner resources for your text, visit your book page on openstax.org.

About the Authors

Senior Contributing Authors

J. Gordon Betts, Tyler Junior College
Peter Desaix, University of North Carolina at Chapel Hill
Eddie Johnson, Central Oregon Community College
Jody E. Johnson, Arapahoe Community College
Oksana Korol, Aims Community College
Dean Kruse, Portland Community College
Brandon Poe, Springfield Technical Community College
James A. Wise, Hampton University
Mark Womble, Youngstown State University
Kelly A. Young, California State University, Long Beach

Advisor

Robin J. Heyden

Contributing Authors

Kim Aaronson, Aquarius Institute; Triton College
Lopamudra Agarwal, Augusta Technical College
Gary Allen, Dalhousie University
Robert Allison, McLennan Community College
Heather Armbruster, Southern Union State Community College

Timothy Ballard, University of North Carolina Wilmington
Matthew Barlow, Eastern New Mexico University
William Blaker, Furman University
Julie Bowers, East Tennessee State University
Emily Bradshaw, Florida Southern College
Nishi Bryska, University of North Carolina, Charlotte
Susan Caley Opsal, Illinois Valley Community College
Boyd Campbell, Southwest College of Naturopathic Medicine and Health Sciences
Ann Caplea, Walsh University
Marnie Chapman, University of Alaska, Sitka
Barbara Christie-Pope, Cornell College
Kenneth Crane, Texarkana College
Maurice Culver, Florida State College at Jacksonville
Heather Cushman, Tacoma Community College
Noelle Cutter, Molloy College
Lynnette Danzl-Tauer, Rock Valley College
Jane Davis, Aurora University
AnnMarie DelliPizzi, Dominican College
Susan Dentel, Washtenaw Community College
Pamela Dobbins, Shelton State Community College
Patty Dolan, Pacific Lutheran University
Sondra Dubowsky, McLennan Community College
Peter Dukehart, Three Rivers Community College
Ellen DuPré, Central College
Elizabeth DuPriest, Warner Pacific College
Pam Elf, University of Minnesota
Sharon Ellerton, Queensborough Community College
Carla Endres, Utah State University - College of Eastern Utah: San Juan Campus
Myriam Feldman, Lake Washington Institute of Technology; Cascadia Community College
Greg Fitch, Avila University
Lynn Gargan, Tarant County College
Michael Giangrande, Oakland Community College
Chaya Gopalan, St. Louis College of Pharmacy
Victor Greco, Chattahoochee Technical College
Susanna Heinze, Skagit Valley College
Ann Henninger, Wartburg College
Dale Horeth, Tidewater Community College
Michael Hortsch, University of Michigan
Rosemary Hubbard, Marymount University
Mark Hubley, Prince George's Community College
Branko Jablanovic, College of Lake County
Norman Johnson, University of Massachusetts Amherst
Mark Jonasson, North Arkansas College
Jeff Keyte, College of Saint Mary
William Kleinelp, Middlesex County College
Leigh Kleinert, Grand Rapids Community College
Brenda Leady, University of Toledo
John Lepri, University of North Carolina, Greensboro
Sarah Leupen, University of Maryland, Baltimore County
Lihua Liang, Johns Hopkins University
Robert Mallet, University of North Texas Health Science Center
Bruce Maring, Daytona State College
Elisabeth Martin, College of Lake County
Natalie Maxwell, Carl Albert State College, Sallisaw
Julie May, William Carey University
Debra McLaughlin, University of Maryland University College
Nicholas Mitchell, St. Bonaventure University
Shobhana Natarajan, Brookhaven College
Phillip Nicotera, St. Petersburg College

Mary Jane Niles, University of San Francisco
Ikemefuna Nwosu, Parkland College; Lake Land College
Betsy Ott, Tyler Junior College
Ivan Paul, John Wood Community College
Aaron Payette, College of Southern Nevada
Scott Payne, Kentucky Wesleyan College
Cameron Perkins, South Georgia College
David Pfeiffer, University of Alaska, Anchorage
Thomas Pilat, Illinois Central College
Eileen Preston, Tarrant County College
Mike Pyle, Olivet Nazarene University
Robert Rawding, Gannon University
Jason Schreer, State University of New York at Potsdam
Laird Sheldahl, Mt. Hood Community College
Brian Shmaefsky, Lone Star College System
Douglas Sizemore, Bevill State Community College
Susan Spencer, Mount Hood Community College
Cynthia Standley, University of Arizona
Robert Sullivan, Marist College
Eric Sun, Middle Georgia State College
Tom Swenson, Ithaca College
Kathleen Tallman, Azusa Pacific University
Rohinton Tarapore, University of Pennsylvania
Elizabeth Tattersall, Western Nevada College
Mark Thomas, University of Northern Colorado
Janis Thompson, Lorain County Community College
Rita Thrasher, Pensacola State College
David Van Wylen, St. Olaf College
Lynn Wandrey, Mott Community College
Margaret Weck, St. Louis College of Pharmacy
Kathleen Weiss, George Fox University
Neil Westergaard, Williston State College
David Wortham, West Georgia Technical College
Umesh Yadav, University of Texas Medical Branch
Tony Yates, Oklahoma Baptist University
Justin York, Glendale Community College
Cheri Zao, North Idaho College
Elena Zoubina, Bridgewater State University; Massasoit Community College
Shobhana Natarajan, Alcon Laboratories, Inc.

Special Thanks

OpenStax wishes to thank the Regents of University of Michigan Medical School for the use of their extensive micrograph collection. Many of the UM micrographs that appear in *Anatomy and Physiology* are interactive WebScopes, which students can explore by zooming in and out.

We also wish to thank the Open Learning Initiative at Carnegie Mellon University, with whom we shared and exchanged resources during the development of *Anatomy and Physiology*.

1 | AN INTRODUCTION TO THE HUMAN BODY

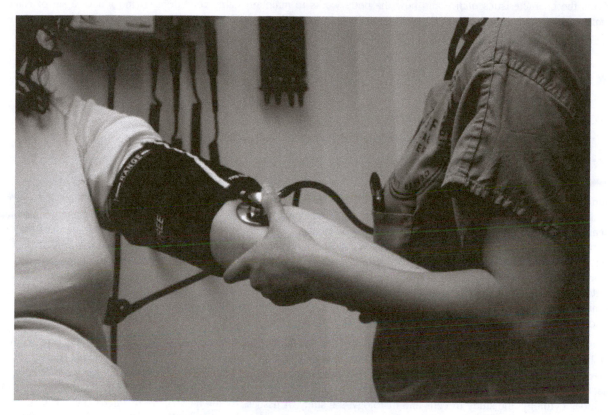

Figure 1.1 Blood Pressure A proficiency in anatomy and physiology is fundamental to any career in the health professions. (credit: Bryan Mason/flickr)

Introduction

Chapter Objectives

After studying this chapter, you will be able to:

- Distinguish between anatomy and physiology, and identify several branches of each
- Describe the structure of the body, from simplest to most complex, in terms of the six levels of organization
- Identify the functional characteristics of human life
- Identify the four requirements for human survival
- Define homeostasis and explain its importance to normal human functioning
- Use appropriate anatomical terminology to identify key body structures, body regions, and directions in the body
- Compare and contrast at least four medical imagining techniques in terms of their function and use in medicine

Though you may approach a course in anatomy and physiology strictly as a requirement for your field of study, the knowledge you gain in this course will serve you well in many aspects of your life. An understanding of anatomy and physiology is not only fundamental to any career in the health professions, but it can also benefit your own health. Familiarity with the human body can help you make healthful choices and prompt you to take appropriate action when signs of illness arise. Your knowledge in this field will help you understand news about nutrition, medications, medical devices, and procedures and help you understand genetic or infectious diseases. At some point, everyone will have a problem with some aspect of his or her body and your knowledge can help you to be a better parent, spouse, partner, friend, colleague, or caregiver.

This chapter begins with an overview of anatomy and physiology and a preview of the body regions and functions. It then covers the characteristics of life and how the body works to maintain stable conditions. It introduces a set of standard terms for body structures and for planes and positions in the body that will serve as a foundation for more comprehensive information covered later in the text. It ends with examples of medical imaging used to see inside the living body.

1.1 | Overview of Anatomy and Physiology

By the end of this section, you will be able to:

- Compare and contrast anatomy and physiology, including their specializations and methods of study
- Discuss the fundamental relationship between anatomy and physiology

Human **anatomy** is the scientific study of the body's structures. Some of these structures are very small and can only be observed and analyzed with the assistance of a microscope. Other larger structures can readily be seen, manipulated, measured, and weighed. The word "anatomy" comes from a Greek root that means "to cut apart." Human anatomy was first studied by observing the exterior of the body and observing the wounds of soldiers and other injuries. Later, physicians were allowed to dissect bodies of the dead to augment their knowledge. When a body is dissected, its structures are cut apart in order to observe their physical attributes and their relationships to one another. Dissection is still used in medical schools, anatomy courses, and in pathology labs. In order to observe structures in living people, however, a number of imaging techniques have been developed. These techniques allow clinicians to visualize structures inside the living body such as a cancerous tumor or a fractured bone.

Like most scientific disciplines, anatomy has areas of specialization. **Gross anatomy** is the study of the larger structures of the body, those visible without the aid of magnification (Figure 1.2a). Macro- means "large," thus, gross anatomy is also referred to as macroscopic anatomy. In contrast, micro- means "small," and **microscopic anatomy** is the study of structures that can be observed only with the use of a microscope or other magnification devices (Figure 1.2b). Microscopic anatomy includes cytology, the study of cells and histology, the study of tissues. As the technology of microscopes has advanced, anatomists have been able to observe smaller and smaller structures of the body, from slices of large structures like the heart, to the three-dimensional structures of large molecules in the body.

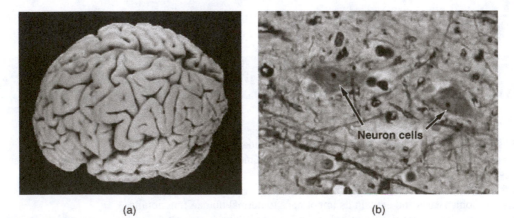

(a)   (b)

Figure 1.2 Gross and Microscopic Anatomy (a) Gross anatomy considers large structures such as the brain. (b) Microscopic anatomy can deal with the same structures, though at a different scale. This is a micrograph of nerve cells from the brain. LM × 1600. (credit a: "WriterHound"/Wikimedia Commons; credit b: Micrograph provided by the Regents of University of Michigan Medical School © 2012)

Anatomists take two general approaches to the study of the body's structures: regional and systemic. **Regional anatomy** is the study of the interrelationships of all of the structures in a specific body region, such as the abdomen. Studying regional anatomy helps us appreciate the interrelationships of body structures, such as how muscles, nerves, blood vessels, and other structures work together to serve a particular body region. In contrast, **systemic anatomy** is the study of the structures that make up a discrete body system—that is, a group of structures that work together to perform a unique body function. For example, a systemic anatomical study of the muscular system would consider all of the skeletal muscles of the body.

Whereas anatomy is about structure, physiology is about function. Human **physiology** is the scientific study of the chemistry and physics of the structures of the body and the ways in which they work together to support the functions of life. Much of the study of physiology centers on the body's tendency toward homeostasis. **Homeostasis** is the state of steady internal conditions maintained by living things. The study of physiology certainly includes observation, both with the naked eye and with microscopes, as well as manipulations and measurements. However, current advances in physiology usually depend on carefully designed laboratory experiments that reveal the functions of the many structures and chemical compounds that make up the human body.

Like anatomists, physiologists typically specialize in a particular branch of physiology. For example, neurophysiology is the study of the brain, spinal cord, and nerves and how these work together to perform functions as complex and diverse as vision, movement, and thinking. Physiologists may work from the organ level (exploring, for example, what different parts of the brain do) to the molecular level (such as exploring how an electrochemical signal travels along nerves).

Form is closely related to function in all living things. For example, the thin flap of your eyelid can snap down to clear away dust particles and almost instantaneously slide back up to allow you to see again. At the microscopic level, the arrangement and function of the nerves and muscles that serve the eyelid allow for its quick action and retreat. At a smaller level of analysis, the function of these nerves and muscles likewise relies on the interactions of specific molecules and ions. Even the three-dimensional structure of certain molecules is essential to their function.

Your study of anatomy and physiology will make more sense if you continually relate the form of the structures you are studying to their function. In fact, it can be somewhat frustrating to attempt to study anatomy without an understanding of the physiology that a body structure supports. Imagine, for example, trying to appreciate the unique arrangement of the bones of the human hand if you had no conception of the function of the hand. Fortunately, your understanding of how the human hand manipulates tools—from pens to cell phones—helps you appreciate the unique alignment of the thumb in opposition to the four fingers, making your hand a structure that allows you to pinch and grasp objects and type text messages.

1.2 | Structural Organization of the Human Body

By the end of this section, you will be able to:

- Describe the structure of the human body in terms of six levels of organization
- List the eleven organ systems of the human body and identify at least one organ and one major function of each

Before you begin to study the different structures and functions of the human body, it is helpful to consider its basic architecture; that is, how its smallest parts are assembled into larger structures. It is convenient to consider the structures of the body in terms of fundamental levels of organization that increase in complexity: subatomic particles, atoms, molecules, organelles, cells, tissues, organs, organ systems, organisms and biosphere (**Figure 1.3**).

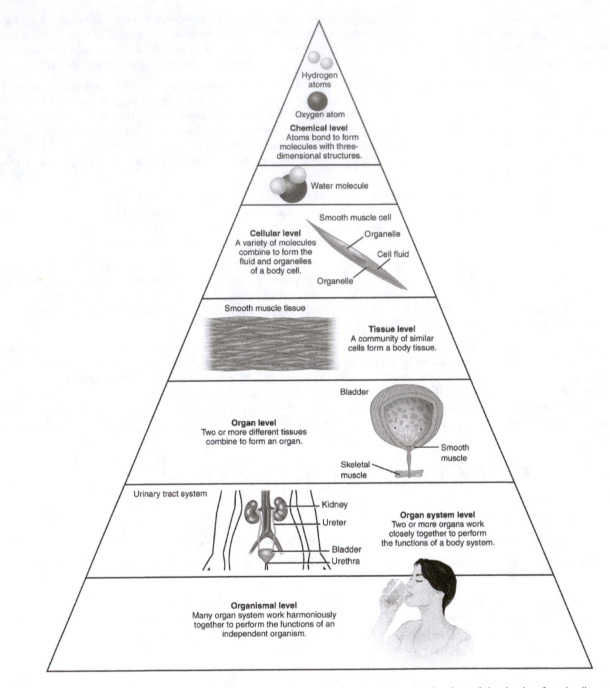

Figure 1.3 Levels of Structural Organization of the Human Body The organization of the body often is discussed in terms of six distinct levels of increasing complexity, from the smallest chemical building blocks to a unique human organism.

The Levels of Organization

To study the chemical level of organization, scientists consider the simplest building blocks of matter: subatomic particles, atoms and molecules. All matter in the universe is composed of one or more unique pure substances called elements, familiar examples of which are hydrogen, oxygen, carbon, nitrogen, calcium, and iron. The smallest unit of any of these pure substances (elements) is an atom. Atoms are made up of subatomic particles such as the proton, electron and neutron. Two or more atoms combine to form a molecule, such as the water molecules, proteins, and sugars found in living things. Molecules are the chemical building blocks of all body structures.

A **cell** is the smallest independently functioning unit of a living organism. Even bacteria, which are extremely small, independently-living organisms, have a cellular structure. Each bacterium is a single cell. All living structures of human anatomy contain cells, and almost all functions of human physiology are performed in cells or are initiated by cells.

A human cell typically consists of flexible membranes that enclose cytoplasm, a water-based cellular fluid together with a variety of tiny functioning units called **organelles**. In humans, as in all organisms, cells perform all functions of life. A **tissue** is a group of many similar cells (though sometimes composed of a few related types) that work together to perform a specific function. An **organ** is an anatomically distinct structure of the body composed of two or more tissue types. Each organ performs one or more specific physiological functions. An **organ system** is a group of organs that work together to perform major functions or meet physiological needs of the body.

This book covers eleven distinct organ systems in the human body (Figure 1.4 and Figure 1.5). Assigning organs to organ systems can be imprecise since organs that "belong" to one system can also have functions integral to another system. In fact, most organs contribute to more than one system.

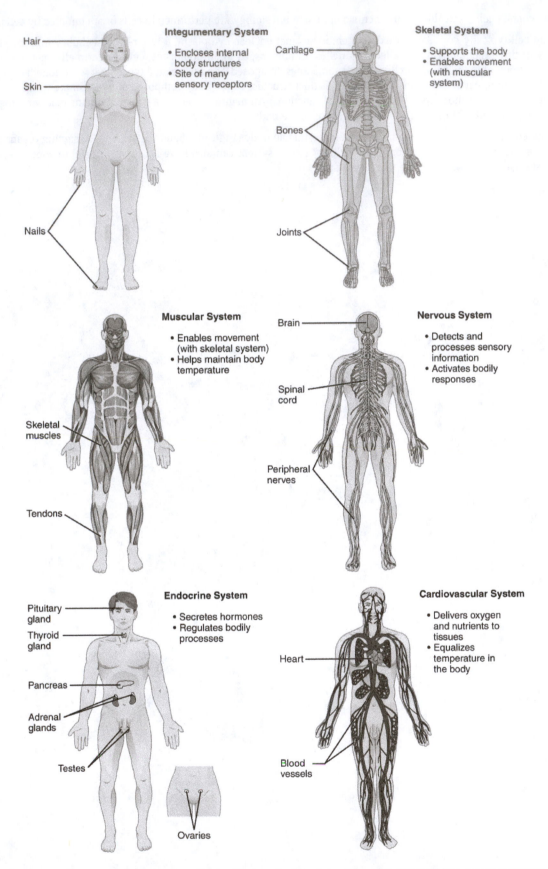

Integumentary System
- Encloses internal body structures
- Site of many sensory receptors

Hair
Skin
Nails

Skeletal System
- Supports the body
- Enables movement (with muscular system)

Cartilage
Bones
Joints

Muscular System
- Enables movement (with skeletal system)
- Helps maintain body temperature

Skeletal muscles
Tendons

Nervous System
- Detects and processes sensory information
- Activates bodily responses

Brain
Spinal cord
Peripheral nerves

Endocrine System
- Secretes hormones
- Regulates bodily processes

Pituitary gland
Thyroid gland
Pancreas
Adrenal glands
Testes
Ovaries

Cardiovascular System
- Delivers oxygen and nutrients to tissues
- Equalizes temperature in the body

Heart
Blood vessels

Figure 1.4 Organ Systems of the Human Body Organs that work together are grouped into organ systems.

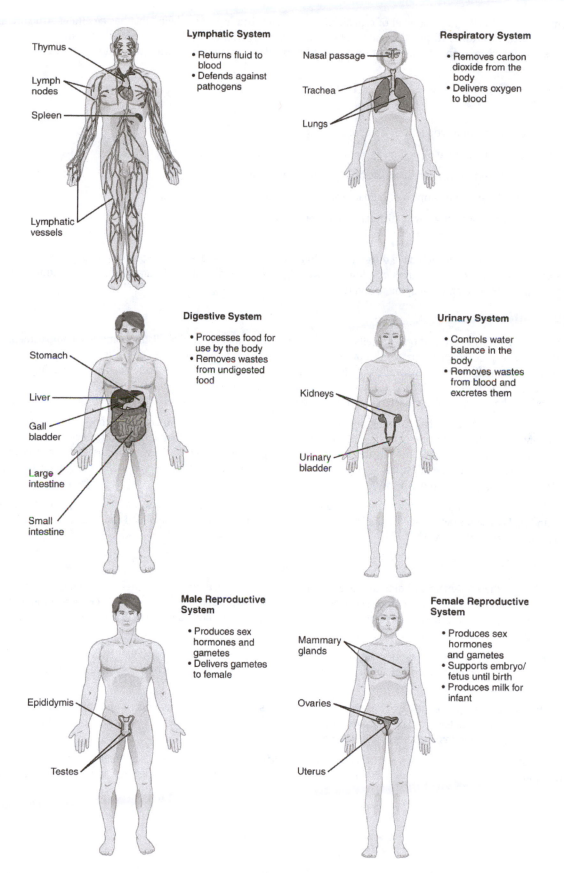

Figure 1.5 Organ Systems of the Human Body (continued) Organs that work together are grouped into organ systems.

The organism level is the highest level of organization. An **organism** is a living being that has a cellular structure and that can independently perform all physiologic functions necessary for life. In multicellular organisms, including humans, all cells, tissues, organs, and organ systems of the body work together to maintain the life and health of the organism.

1.3 | Functions of Human Life

By the end of this section, you will be able to:

- Explain the importance of organization to the function of the human organism
- Distinguish between metabolism, anabolism, and catabolism
- Provide at least two examples of human responsiveness and human movement
- Compare and contrast growth, differentiation, and reproduction

The different organ systems each have different functions and therefore unique roles to perform in physiology. These many functions can be summarized in terms of a few that we might consider definitive of human life: organization, metabolism, responsiveness, movement, development, and reproduction.

Organization

A human body consists of trillions of cells organized in a way that maintains distinct internal compartments. These compartments keep body cells separated from external environmental threats and keep the cells moist and nourished. They also separate internal body fluids from the countless microorganisms that grow on body surfaces, including the lining of certain tracts, or passageways. The intestinal tract, for example, is home to even more bacteria cells than the total of all human cells in the body, yet these bacteria are outside the body and cannot be allowed to circulate freely inside the body.

Cells, for example, have a cell membrane (also referred to as the plasma membrane) that keeps the intracellular environment—the fluids and organelles—separate from the extracellular environment. Blood vessels keep blood inside a closed circulatory system, and nerves and muscles are wrapped in connective tissue sheaths that separate them from surrounding structures. In the chest and abdomen, a variety of internal membranes keep major organs such as the lungs, heart, and kidneys separate from others.

The body's largest organ system is the integumentary system, which includes the skin and its associated structures, such as hair and nails. The surface tissue of skin is a barrier that protects internal structures and fluids from potentially harmful microorganisms and other toxins.

Metabolism

The first law of thermodynamics holds that energy can neither be created nor destroyed—it can only change form. Your basic function as an organism is to consume (ingest) energy and molecules in the foods you eat, convert some of it into fuel for movement, sustain your body functions, and build and maintain your body structures. There are two types of reactions that accomplish this: **anabolism** and **catabolism**.

- **Anabolism** is the process whereby smaller, simpler molecules are combined into larger, more complex substances. Your body can assemble, by utilizing energy, the complex chemicals it needs by combining small molecules derived from the foods you eat

- **Catabolism** is the process by which larger more complex substances are broken down into smaller simpler molecules. Catabolism releases energy. The complex molecules found in foods are broken down so the body can use their parts to assemble the structures and substances needed for life.

Taken together, these two processes are called metabolism. **Metabolism** is the sum of all anabolic and catabolic reactions that take place in the body (**Figure 1.6**). Both anabolism and catabolism occur simultaneously and continuously to keep you alive.

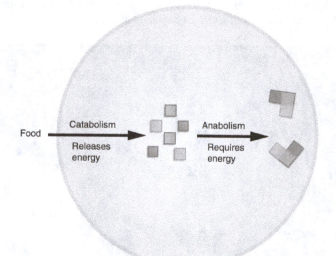

Figure 1.6 Metabolism Anabolic reactions are building reactions, and they consume energy. Catabolic reactions break materials down and release energy. Metabolism includes both anabolic and catabolic reactions.

Every cell in your body makes use of a chemical compound, **adenosine triphosphate (ATP)**, to store and release energy. The cell stores energy in the synthesis (anabolism) of ATP, then moves the ATP molecules to the location where energy is needed to fuel cellular activities. Then the ATP is broken down (catabolism) and a controlled amount of energy is released, which is used by the cell to perform a particular job.

Interactive LINK

View this animation (http://openstaxcollege.org/l/metabolic) to learn more about metabolic processes. What kind of catabolism occurs in the heart?

Responsiveness

Responsiveness is the ability of an organism to adjust to changes in its internal and external environments. An example of responsiveness to external stimuli could include moving toward sources of food and water and away from perceived dangers. Changes in an organism's internal environment, such as increased body temperature, can cause the responses of sweating and the dilation of blood vessels in the skin in order to decrease body temperature, as shown by the runners in Figure 1.7.

Movement

Human movement includes not only actions at the joints of the body, but also the motion of individual organs and even individual cells. As you read these words, red and white blood cells are moving throughout your body, muscle cells are contracting and relaxing to maintain your posture and to focus your vision, and glands are secreting chemicals to regulate body functions. Your body is coordinating the action of entire muscle groups to enable you to move air into and out of your lungs, to push blood throughout your body, and to propel the food you have eaten through your digestive tract. Consciously, of course, you contract your skeletal muscles to move the bones of your skeleton to get from one place to another (as the runners are doing in Figure 1.7), and to carry out all of the activities of your daily life.

Figure 1.7 Marathon Runners Runners demonstrate two characteristics of living humans—responsiveness and movement. Anatomic structures and physiological processes allow runners to coordinate the action of muscle groups and sweat in response to rising internal body temperature. (credit: Phil Roeder/flickr)

Development, growth and reproduction

Development is all of the changes the body goes through in life. Development includes the process of **differentiation**, in which unspecialized cells become specialized in structure and function to perform certain tasks in the body. Development also includes the processes of growth and repair, both of which involve cell differentiation.

Growth is the increase in body size. Humans, like all multicellular organisms, grow by increasing the number of existing cells, increasing the amount of non-cellular material around cells (such as mineral deposits in bone), and, within very narrow limits, increasing the size of existing cells.

Reproduction is the formation of a new organism from parent organisms. In humans, reproduction is carried out by the male and female reproductive systems. Because death will come to all complex organisms, without reproduction, the line of organisms would end.

1.4 | Requirements for Human Life

By the end of this section, you will be able to:

- Discuss the role of oxygen and nutrients in maintaining human survival
- Explain why extreme heat and extreme cold threaten human survival
- Explain how the pressure exerted by gases and fluids influences human survival

Humans have been adapting to life on Earth for at least the past 200,000 years. Earth and its atmosphere have provided us with air to breathe, water to drink, and food to eat, but these are not the only requirements for survival. Although you may rarely think about it, you also cannot live outside of a certain range of temperature and pressure that the surface of our planet and its atmosphere provides. The next sections explore these four requirements of life.

Oxygen

Atmospheric air is only about 20 percent oxygen, but that oxygen is a key component of the chemical reactions that keep the body alive, including the reactions that produce ATP. Brain cells are especially sensitive to lack of oxygen because of their requirement for a high-and-steady production of ATP. Brain damage is likely within five minutes without oxygen, and death is likely within ten minutes.

Nutrients

A **nutrient** is a substance in foods and beverages that is essential to human survival. The three basic classes of nutrients are water, the energy-yielding and body-building nutrients, and the micronutrients (vitamins and minerals).

The most critical nutrient is water. Depending on the environmental temperature and our state of health, we may be able to survive for only a few days without water. The body's functional chemicals are dissolved and transported in water, and the chemical reactions of life take place in water. Moreover, water is the largest component of cells, blood, and the fluid between cells, and water makes up about 70 percent of an adult's body mass. Water also helps regulate our internal temperature and cushions, protects, and lubricates joints and many other body structures.

The energy-yielding nutrients are primarily carbohydrates and lipids, while proteins mainly supply the amino acids that are the building blocks of the body itself. You ingest these in plant and animal foods and beverages, and the digestive system breaks them down into molecules small enough to be absorbed. The breakdown products of carbohydrates and lipids can then be used in the metabolic processes that convert them to ATP. Although you might feel as if you are starving after missing a single meal, you can survive without consuming the energy-yielding nutrients for at least several weeks.

Water and the energy-yielding nutrients are also referred to as macronutrients because the body needs them in large amounts. In contrast, micronutrients are vitamins and minerals. These elements and compounds participate in many essential chemical reactions and processes, such as nerve impulses, and some, such as calcium, also contribute to the body's structure. Your body can store some of the micronutrients in its tissues, and draw on those reserves if you fail to consume them in your diet for a few days or weeks. Some others micronutrients, such as vitamin C and most of the B vitamins, are water-soluble and cannot be stored, so you need to consume them every day or two.

Narrow Range of Temperature

You have probably seen news stories about athletes who died of heat stroke, or hikers who died of exposure to cold. Such deaths occur because the chemical reactions upon which the body depends can only take place within a narrow range of body temperature, from just below to just above 37°C (98.6°F). When body temperature rises well above or drops well below normal, certain proteins (enzymes) that facilitate chemical reactions lose their normal structure and their ability to function and the chemical reactions of metabolism cannot proceed.

That said, the body can respond effectively to short-term exposure to heat (Figure 1.8) or cold. One of the body's responses to heat is, of course, sweating. As sweat evaporates from skin, it removes some thermal energy from the body, cooling it. Adequate water (from the extracellular fluid in the body) is necessary to produce sweat, so adequate fluid intake is essential to balance that loss during the sweat response. Not surprisingly, the sweat response is much less effective in a humid environment because the air is already saturated with water. Thus, the sweat on the skin's surface is not able to evaporate, and internal body temperature can get dangerously high.

Figure 1.8 Extreme Heat Humans adapt to some degree to repeated exposure to high temperatures. (credit: McKay Savage/flickr)

The body can also respond effectively to short-term exposure to cold. One response to cold is shivering, which is random muscle movement that generates heat. Another response is increased breakdown of stored energy to generate heat. When that energy reserve is depleted, however, and the core temperature begins to drop significantly, red blood cells will lose their ability to give up oxygen, denying the brain of this critical component of ATP production. This lack of oxygen can cause confusion, lethargy, and eventually loss of consciousness and death. The body responds to cold by reducing blood circulation to the extremities, the hands and feet, in order to prevent blood from cooling there and so that the body's core can stay warm. Even when core body temperature remains stable, however, tissues exposed to severe cold, especially the fingers and toes, can develop frostbite when blood flow to the extremities has been much reduced. This form of tissue damage can be permanent and lead to gangrene, requiring amputation of the affected region.

Everyday CONNECTION

Controlled Hypothermia

As you have learned, the body continuously engages in coordinated physiological processes to maintain a stable temperature. In some cases, however, overriding this system can be useful, or even life-saving. Hypothermia is the clinical term for an abnormally low body temperature (hypo- = "below" or "under"). Controlled hypothermia is clinically induced hypothermia performed in order to reduce the metabolic rate of an organ or of a person's entire body.

Controlled hypothermia often is used, for example, during open-heart surgery because it decreases the metabolic needs of the brain, heart, and other organs, reducing the risk of damage to them. When controlled hypothermia is used clinically, the patient is given medication to prevent shivering. The body is then cooled to 25–32°C (79–89°F). The heart is stopped and an external heart-lung pump maintains circulation to the patient's body. The heart is cooled further and is maintained at a temperature below 15°C (60°F) for the duration of the surgery. This very cold temperature helps the heart muscle to tolerate its lack of blood supply during the surgery.

Some emergency department physicians use controlled hypothermia to reduce damage to the heart in patients who have suffered a cardiac arrest. In the emergency department, the physician induces coma and lowers the patient's body temperature to approximately 91 degrees. This condition, which is maintained for 24 hours, slows the patient's metabolic rate. Because the patient's organs require less blood to function, the heart's workload is reduced.

Narrow Range of Atmospheric Pressure

Pressure is a force exerted by a substance that is in contact with another substance. Atmospheric pressure is pressure exerted by the mixture of gases (primarily nitrogen and oxygen) in the Earth's atmosphere. Although you may not perceive it, atmospheric pressure is constantly pressing down on your body. This pressure keeps gases within your body, such as the gaseous nitrogen in body fluids, dissolved. If you were suddenly ejected from a space ship above Earth's atmosphere, you would go from a situation of normal pressure to one of very low pressure. The pressure of the nitrogen gas in your blood would be much higher than the pressure of nitrogen in the space surrounding your body. As a result, the nitrogen gas in your blood would expand, forming bubbles that could block blood vessels and even cause cells to break apart.

Atmospheric pressure does more than just keep blood gases dissolved. Your ability to breathe—that is, to take in oxygen and release carbon dioxide—also depends upon a precise atmospheric pressure. Altitude sickness occurs in part because the atmosphere at high altitudes exerts less pressure, reducing the exchange of these gases, and causing shortness of breath, confusion, headache, lethargy, and nausea. Mountain climbers carry oxygen to reduce the effects of both low oxygen levels and low barometric pressure at higher altitudes (Figure 1.9).

Figure 1.9 Harsh Conditions Climbers on Mount Everest must accommodate extreme cold, low oxygen levels, and low barometric pressure in an environment hostile to human life. (credit: Melanie Ko/flickr)

Homeostatic IMBALANCES

Decompression Sickness

Decompression sickness (DCS) is a condition in which gases dissolved in the blood or in other body tissues are no longer dissolved following a reduction in pressure on the body. This condition affects underwater divers who surface from a deep dive too quickly, and it can affect pilots flying at high altitudes in planes with unpressurized cabins. Divers often call this condition "the bends," a reference to joint pain that is a symptom of DCS.

In all cases, DCS is brought about by a reduction in barometric pressure. At high altitude, barometric pressure is much less than on Earth's surface because pressure is produced by the weight of the column of air above the body pressing down on the body. The very great pressures on divers in deep water are likewise from the weight of a column of water pressing down on the body. For divers, DCS occurs at normal barometric pressure (at sea level), but it is brought on by the relatively rapid decrease of pressure as divers rise from the high pressure conditions of deep water to the now low, by comparison, pressure at sea level. Not surprisingly, diving in deep mountain lakes, where barometric pressure at the surface of the lake is less than that at sea level is more likely to result in DCS than diving in water at sea level.

In DCS, gases dissolved in the blood (primarily nitrogen) come rapidly out of solution, forming bubbles in the blood and in other body tissues. This occurs because when pressure of a gas over a liquid is decreased, the amount of gas that can remain dissolved in the liquid also is decreased. It is air pressure that keeps your normal blood gases dissolved in the blood. When pressure is reduced, less gas remains dissolved. You have seen this in effect when you open a carbonated drink. Removing the seal of the bottle reduces the pressure of the gas over the liquid. This in turn causes bubbles as dissolved gases (in this case, carbon dioxide) come out of solution in the liquid.

The most common symptoms of DCS are pain in the joints, with headache and disturbances of vision occurring in 10 percent to 15 percent of cases. Left untreated, very severe DCS can result in death. Immediate treatment is with pure oxygen. The affected person is then moved into a hyperbaric chamber. A hyperbaric chamber is a reinforced, closed chamber that is pressurized to greater than atmospheric pressure. It treats DCS by repressurizing the body so that pressure can then be removed much more gradually. Because the hyperbaric chamber introduces oxygen to the body at high pressure, it increases the concentration of oxygen in the blood. This has the effect of replacing some of the nitrogen in the blood with oxygen, which is easier to tolerate out of solution.

The dynamic pressure of body fluids is also important to human survival. For example, blood pressure, which is the pressure exerted by blood as it flows within blood vessels, must be great enough to enable blood to reach all body tissues, and yet low enough to ensure that the delicate blood vessels can withstand the friction and force of the pulsating flow of pressurized blood.

1.5 | Homeostasis

By the end of this section, you will be able to:

- Discuss the role of homeostasis in healthy functioning
- Contrast negative and positive feedback, giving one physiologic example of each mechanism

Maintaining homeostasis requires that the body continuously monitor its internal conditions. From body temperature to blood pressure to levels of certain nutrients, each physiological condition has a particular set point. A **set point** is the physiological value around which the normal range fluctuates. A **normal range** is the restricted set of values that is optimally healthful and stable. For example, the set point for normal human body temperature is approximately 37°C (98.6°F) Physiological parameters, such as body temperature and blood pressure, tend to fluctuate within a normal range a few degrees above and below that point. Control centers in the brain and other parts of the body monitor and react to deviations from homeostasis using negative feedback. **Negative feedback** is a mechanism that reverses a deviation from the set point. Therefore, negative feedback maintains body parameters within their normal range. The maintenance of homeostasis by negative feedback goes on throughout the body at all times, and an understanding of negative feedback is thus fundamental to an understanding of human physiology.

Negative Feedback

A negative feedback system has three basic components (**Figure 1.10a**). A **sensor**, also referred to a receptor, is a component of a feedback system that monitors a physiological value. This value is reported to the control center. The **control center** is the component in a feedback system that compares the value to the normal range. If the value deviates too much from the set point, then the control center activates an effector. An **effector** is the component in a feedback system that causes a change to reverse the situation and return the value to the normal range.

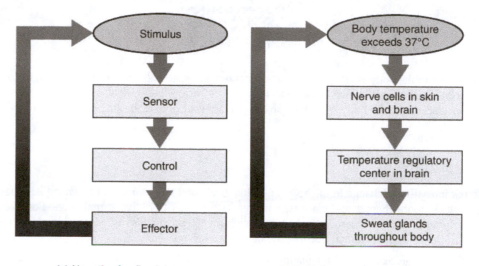

(a) Negative feedback loop   (b) Body temperature regulation

Figure 1.10 Negative Feedback Loop In a negative feedback loop, a stimulus—a deviation from a set point—is resisted through a physiological process that returns the body to homeostasis. (a) A negative feedback loop has four basic parts. (b) Body temperature is regulated by negative feedback.

In order to set the system in motion, a stimulus must drive a physiological parameter beyond its normal range (that is, beyond homeostasis). This stimulus is "heard" by a specific sensor. For example, in the control of blood glucose, specific endocrine cells in the pancreas detect excess glucose (the stimulus) in the bloodstream. These pancreatic beta cells respond to the increased level of blood glucose by releasing the hormone insulin into the bloodstream. The insulin signals skeletal muscle fibers, fat cells (adipocytes), and liver cells to take up the excess glucose, removing it from the bloodstream. As glucose concentration in the bloodstream drops, the decrease in concentration—the actual negative feedback—is detected by pancreatic alpha cells, and insulin release stops. This prevents blood sugar levels from continuing to drop below the normal range.

Humans have a similar temperature regulation feedback system that works by promoting either heat loss or heat gain (**Figure 1.10b**). When the brain's temperature regulation center receives data from the sensors indicating that the body's temperature exceeds its normal range, it stimulates a cluster of brain cells referred to as the "heat-loss center." This stimulation has three major effects:

- Blood vessels in the skin begin to dilate allowing more blood from the body core to flow to the surface of the skin allowing the heat to radiate into the environment.

- As blood flow to the skin increases, sweat glands are activated to increase their output. As the sweat evaporates from the skin surface into the surrounding air, it takes heat with it.

- The depth of respiration increases, and a person may breathe through an open mouth instead of through the nasal passageways. This further increases heat loss from the lungs.

In contrast, activation of the brain's heat-gain center by exposure to cold reduces blood flow to the skin, and blood returning from the limbs is diverted into a network of deep veins. This arrangement traps heat closer to the body core and restricts heat loss. If heat loss is severe, the brain triggers an increase in random signals to skeletal muscles, causing them to contract and producing shivering. The muscle contractions of shivering release heat while using up ATP. The brain triggers the thyroid gland in the endocrine system to release thyroid hormone, which increases metabolic activity and heat production in cells throughout the body. The brain also signals the adrenal glands to release epinephrine (adrenaline), a hormone that causes the breakdown of glycogen into glucose, which can be used as an energy source. The breakdown of glycogen into glucose also results in increased metabolism and heat production.

Interactive LINK

Water concentration in the body is critical for proper functioning. A person's body retains very tight control on water levels without conscious control by the person. Watch this **video (http://openstaxcollege.org/l/H2Ocon)** to learn more about water concentration in the body. Which organ has primary control over the amount of water in the body?

Positive Feedback

Positive feedback intensifies a change in the body's physiological condition rather than reversing it. A deviation from the normal range results in more change, and the system moves farther away from the normal range. Positive feedback in the body is normal only when there is a definite end point. Childbirth and the body's response to blood loss are two examples of positive feedback loops that are normal but are activated only when needed.

Childbirth at full term is an example of a situation in which the maintenance of the existing body state is not desired. Enormous changes in the mother's body are required to expel the baby at the end of pregnancy. And the events of childbirth, once begun, must progress rapidly to a conclusion or the life of the mother and the baby are at risk. The extreme muscular work of labor and delivery are the result of a positive feedback system (**Figure 1.11**).

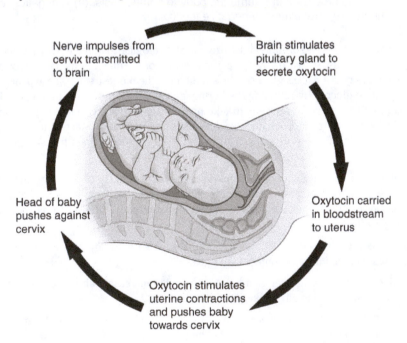

Figure 1.11 Positive Feedback Loop Normal childbirth is driven by a positive feedback loop. A positive feedback loop results in a change in the body's status, rather than a return to homeostasis.

The first contractions of labor (the stimulus) push the baby toward the cervix (the lowest part of the uterus). The cervix contains stretch-sensitive nerve cells that monitor the degree of stretching (the sensors). These nerve cells send messages to the brain, which in turn causes the pituitary gland at the base of the brain to release the hormone oxytocin into the bloodstream. Oxytocin causes stronger contractions of the smooth muscles in of the uterus (the effectors), pushing the baby further down the birth canal. This causes even greater stretching of the cervix. The cycle of stretching, oxytocin release, and increasingly more forceful contractions stops only when the baby is born. At this point, the stretching of the cervix halts, stopping the release of oxytocin.

A second example of positive feedback centers on reversing extreme damage to the body. Following a penetrating wound, the most immediate threat is excessive blood loss. Less blood circulating means reduced blood pressure and reduced perfusion (penetration of blood) to the brain and other vital organs. If perfusion is severely reduced, vital organs will shut down and the person will die. The body responds to this potential catastrophe by releasing substances in the injured blood vessel wall that begin the process of blood clotting. As each step of clotting occurs, it stimulates the release of more clotting substances. This accelerates the processes of clotting and sealing off the damaged area. Clotting is contained in a local area based on the tightly controlled availability of clotting proteins. This is an adaptive, life-saving cascade of events.

1.6 | Anatomical Terminology

By the end of this section, you will be able to:

- Demonstrate the anatomical position
- Describe the human body using directional and regional terms
- Identify three planes most commonly used in the study of anatomy
- Distinguish between the posterior (dorsal) and the anterior (ventral) body cavities, identifying their subdivisions and representative organs found in each
- Describe serous membrane and explain its function

Anatomists and health care providers use terminology that can be bewildering to the uninitiated. However, the purpose of this language is not to confuse, but rather to increase precision and reduce medical errors. For example, is a scar "above the wrist" located on the forearm two or three inches away from the hand? Or is it at the base of the hand? Is it on the palm-side or back-side? By using precise anatomical terminology, we eliminate ambiguity. Anatomical terms derive from ancient Greek and Latin words. Because these languages are no longer used in everyday conversation, the meaning of their words does not change.

Anatomical terms are made up of roots, prefixes, and suffixes. The root of a term often refers to an organ, tissue, or condition, whereas the prefix or suffix often describes the root. For example, in the disorder hypertension, the prefix "hyper-" means "high" or "over," and the root word "tension" refers to pressure, so the word "hypertension" refers to abnormally high blood pressure.

Anatomical Position

To further increase precision, anatomists standardize the way in which they view the body. Just as maps are normally oriented with north at the top, the standard body "map," or **anatomical position**, is that of the body standing upright, with the feet at shoulder width and parallel, toes forward. The upper limbs are held out to each side, and the palms of the hands face forward as illustrated in Figure 1.12. Using this standard position reduces confusion. It does not matter how the body being described is oriented, the terms are used as if it is in anatomical position. For example, a scar in the "anterior (front) carpal (wrist) region" would be present on the palm side of the wrist. The term "anterior" would be used even if the hand were palm down on a table.

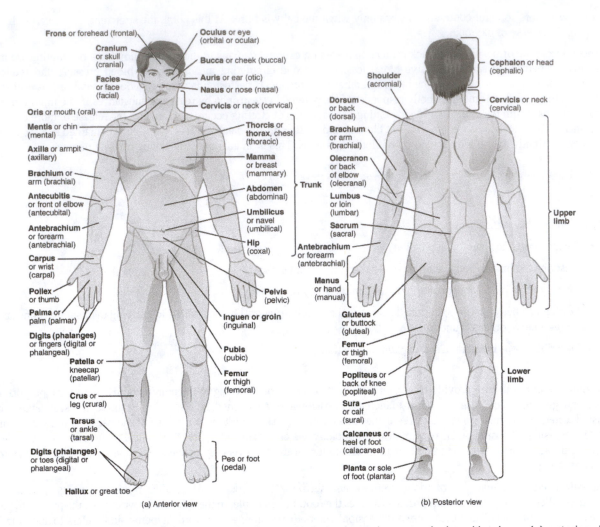

Figure 1.12 Regions of the Human Body The human body is shown in anatomical position in an (a) anterior view and a (b) posterior view. The regions of the body are labeled in boldface.

A body that is lying down is described as either prone or supine. **Prone** describes a face-down orientation, and **supine** describes a face up orientation. These terms are sometimes used in describing the position of the body during specific physical examinations or surgical procedures.

Regional Terms

The human body's numerous regions have specific terms to help increase precision (see Figure 1.12). Notice that the term "brachium" or "arm" is reserved for the "upper arm" and "antebrachium" or "forearm" is used rather than "lower arm." Similarly, "femur" or "thigh" is correct, and "leg" or "crus" is reserved for the portion of the lower limb between the knee and the ankle. You will be able to describe the body's regions using the terms from the figure.

Directional Terms

Certain directional anatomical terms appear throughout this and any other anatomy textbook (Figure 1.13). These terms are essential for describing the relative locations of different body structures. For instance, an anatomist might describe one band of tissue as "inferior to" another or a physician might describe a tumor as "superficial to" a deeper body structure. Commit these terms to memory to avoid confusion when you are studying or describing the locations of particular body parts.

- **Anterior** (or **ventral**) Describes the front or direction toward the front of the body. The toes are anterior to the foot.

- **Posterior** (or **dorsal**) Describes the back or direction toward the back of the body. The popliteus is posterior to the patella.

- **Superior** (or **cranial**) describes a position above or higher than another part of the body proper. The orbits are superior to the oris.

- **Inferior** (or **caudal**) describes a position below or lower than another part of the body proper; near or toward the tail (in humans, the coccyx, or lowest part of the spinal column). The pelvis is inferior to the abdomen.

- **Lateral** describes the side or direction toward the side of the body. The thumb (pollex) is lateral to the digits.

- **Medial** describes the middle or direction toward the middle of the body. The hallux is the medial toe.

- **Proximal** describes a position in a limb that is nearer to the point of attachment or the trunk of the body. The brachium is proximal to the antebrachium.

- **Distal** describes a position in a limb that is farther from the point of attachment or the trunk of the body. The crus is distal to the femur.

- **Superficial** describes a position closer to the surface of the body. The skin is superficial to the bones.

- **Deep** describes a position farther from the surface of the body. The brain is deep to the skull.

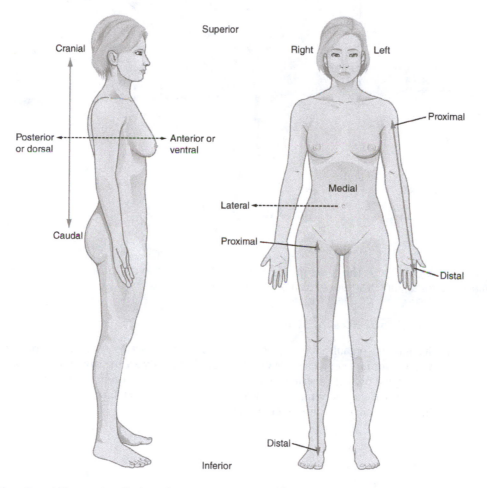

Figure 1.13 Directional Terms Applied to the Human Body Paired directional terms are shown as applied to the human body.

Body Planes

A **section** is a two-dimensional surface of a three-dimensional structure that has been cut. Modern medical imaging devices enable clinicians to obtain "virtual sections" of living bodies. We call these scans. Body sections and scans can be correctly interpreted, however, only if the viewer understands the plane along which the section was made. A **plane** is an imaginary two-dimensional surface that passes through the body. There are three planes commonly referred to in anatomy and medicine, as illustrated in **Figure 1.14**.

- The **sagittal plane** is the plane that divides the body or an organ vertically into right and left sides. If this vertical plane runs directly down the middle of the body, it is called the midsagittal or median plane. If it divides the body into unequal right and left sides, it is called a parasagittal plane or less commonly a longitudinal section.

- The **frontal plane** is the plane that divides the body or an organ into an anterior (front) portion and a posterior (rear) portion. The frontal plane is often referred to as a coronal plane. ("Corona" is Latin for "crown.")

- The **transverse plane** is the plane that divides the body or organ horizontally into upper and lower portions. Transverse planes produce images referred to as cross sections.

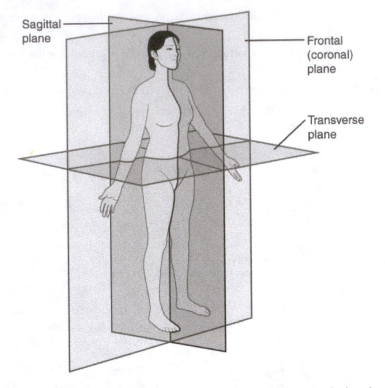

Figure 1.14 Planes of the Body The three planes most commonly used in anatomical and medical imaging are the sagittal, frontal (or coronal), and transverse plane.

Body Cavities and Serous Membranes

The body maintains its internal organization by means of membranes, sheaths, and other structures that separate compartments. The **dorsal (posterior) cavity** and the **ventral (anterior) cavity** are the largest body compartments (Figure 1.15). These cavities contain and protect delicate internal organs, and the ventral cavity allows for significant changes in the size and shape of the organs as they perform their functions. The lungs, heart, stomach, and intestines, for example, can expand and contract without distorting other tissues or disrupting the activity of nearby organs.

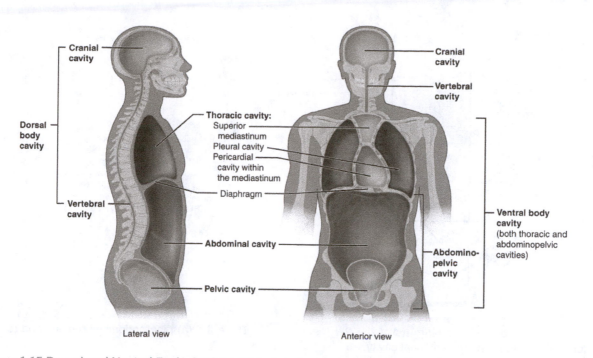

Figure 1.15 Dorsal and Ventral Body Cavities The ventral cavity includes the thoracic and abdominopelvic cavities and their subdivisions. The dorsal cavity includes the cranial and spinal cavities.

Subdivisions of the Posterior (Dorsal) and Anterior (Ventral) Cavities

The posterior (dorsal) and anterior (ventral) cavities are each subdivided into smaller cavities. In the posterior (dorsal) cavity, the **cranial cavity** houses the brain, and the **spinal cavity** (or vertebral cavity) encloses the spinal cord. Just as the brain and spinal cord make up a continuous, uninterrupted structure, the cranial and spinal cavities that house them are also continuous. The brain and spinal cord are protected by the bones of the skull and vertebral column and by cerebrospinal fluid, a colorless fluid produced by the brain, which cushions the brain and spinal cord within the posterior (dorsal) cavity.

The anterior (ventral) cavity has two main subdivisions: the thoracic cavity and the abdominopelvic cavity (see **Figure 1.15**). The **thoracic cavity** is the more superior subdivision of the anterior cavity, and it is enclosed by the rib cage. The thoracic cavity contains the lungs and the heart, which is located in the mediastinum. The diaphragm forms the floor of the thoracic cavity and separates it from the more inferior abdominopelvic cavity. The **abdominopelvic cavity** is the largest cavity in the body. Although no membrane physically divides the abdominopelvic cavity, it can be useful to distinguish between the abdominal cavity, the division that houses the digestive organs, and the pelvic cavity, the division that houses the organs of reproduction.

Abdominal Regions and Quadrants

To promote clear communication, for instance about the location of a patient's abdominal pain or a suspicious mass, health care providers typically divide up the cavity into either nine regions or four quadrants (**Figure 1.16**).

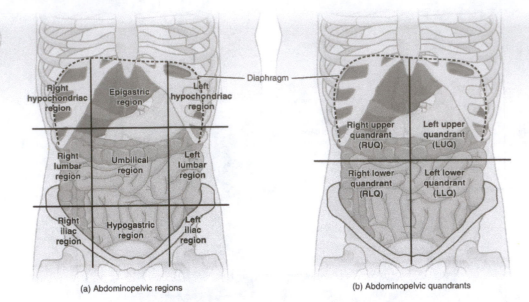

(a) Abdominopelvic regions   (b) Abdominopelvic quadrants

Figure 1.16 Regions and Quadrants of the Peritoneal Cavity There are (a) nine abdominal regions and (b) four abdominal quadrants in the peritoneal cavity.

The more detailed regional approach subdivides the cavity with one horizontal line immediately inferior to the ribs and one immediately superior to the pelvis, and two vertical lines drawn as if dropped from the midpoint of each clavicle (collarbone). There are nine resulting regions. The simpler quadrants approach, which is more commonly used in medicine, subdivides the cavity with one horizontal and one vertical line that intersect at the patient's umbilicus (navel).

Membranes of the Anterior (Ventral) Body Cavity

A **serous membrane** (also referred to a serosa) is one of the thin membranes that cover the walls and organs in the thoracic and abdominopelvic cavities. The parietal layers of the membranes line the walls of the body cavity (pariet- refers to a cavity wall). The visceral layer of the membrane covers the organs (the viscera). Between the parietal and visceral layers is a very thin, fluid-filled serous space, or cavity (**Figure 1.17**).

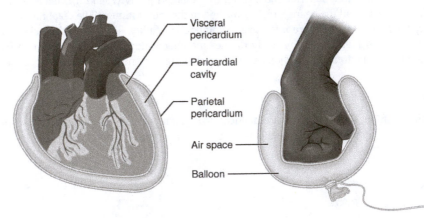

Figure 1.17 Serous Membrane Serous membrane lines the pericardial cavity and reflects back to cover the heart—much the same way that an underinflated balloon would form two layers surrounding a fist.

There are three serous cavities and their associated membranes. The **pleura** is the serous membrane that surrounds the lungs in the pleural cavity; the **pericardium** is the serous membrane that surrounds the heart in the pericardial cavity; and the **peritoneum** is the serous membrane that surrounds several organs in the abdominopelvic cavity.The serous membranes form fluid-filled sacs, or cavities, that are meant to cushion and reduce friction on internal organs when they move, such as when the lungs inflate or the heart beats. Both the parietal and visceral serosa secrete the thin, slippery serous fluid located within the serous cavities. The pleural cavity reduces friction between the lungs and the body wall. Likewise, the pericardial cavity reduces friction between the heart and the wall of the pericardium. The peritoneal cavity reduces friction between the abdominal and pelvic organs and the body wall. Therefore, serous membranes provide additional protection to the viscera they enclose by reducing friction that could lead to inflammation of the organs.

1.7 | Medical Imaging

By the end of this section, you will be able to:

- Discuss the uses and drawbacks of X-ray imaging
- Identify four modern medical imaging techniques and how they are used

For thousands of years, fear of the dead and legal sanctions limited the ability of anatomists and physicians to study the internal structures of the human body. An inability to control bleeding, infection, and pain made surgeries infrequent, and those that were performed—such as wound suturing, amputations, tooth and tumor removals, skull drilling, and cesarean births—did not greatly advance knowledge about internal anatomy. Theories about the function of the body and about disease were therefore largely based on external observations and imagination. During the fourteenth and fifteenth centuries, however, the detailed anatomical drawings of Italian artist and anatomist Leonardo da Vinci and Flemish anatomist Andreas Vesalius were published, and interest in human anatomy began to increase. Medical schools began to teach anatomy using human dissection; although some resorted to grave robbing to obtain corpses. Laws were eventually passed that enabled students to dissect the corpses of criminals and those who donated their bodies for research. Still, it was not until the late nineteenth century that medical researchers discovered non-surgical methods to look inside the living body.

X-Rays

German physicist Wilhelm Röntgen (1845–1923) was experimenting with electrical current when he discovered that a mysterious and invisible "ray" would pass through his flesh but leave an outline of his bones on a screen coated with a metal compound. In 1895, Röntgen made the first durable record of the internal parts of a living human: an "X-ray" image (as it came to be called) of his wife's hand. Scientists around the world quickly began their own experiments with X-rays, and by 1900, X-rays were widely used to detect a variety of injuries and diseases. In 1901, Röntgen was awarded the first Nobel Prize for physics for his work in this field.

The **X-ray** is a form of high energy electromagnetic radiation with a short wavelength capable of penetrating solids and ionizing gases. As they are used in medicine, X-rays are emitted from an X-ray machine and directed toward a specially treated metallic plate placed behind the patient's body. The beam of radiation results in darkening of the X-ray plate. X-rays are slightly impeded by soft tissues, which show up as gray on the X-ray plate, whereas hard tissues, such as bone, largely block the rays, producing a light-toned "shadow." Thus, X-rays are best used to visualize hard body structures such as teeth and bones (Figure 1.18). Like many forms of high energy radiation, however, X-rays are capable of damaging cells and initiating changes that can lead to cancer. This danger of excessive exposure to X-rays was not fully appreciated for many years after their widespread use.

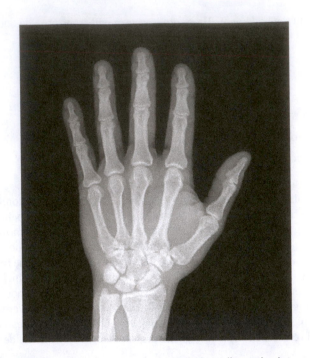

Figure 1.18 X-Ray of a Hand High energy electromagnetic radiation allows the internal structures of the body, such as bones, to be seen in X-rays like these. (credit: Trace Meek/flickr)

Refinements and enhancements of X-ray techniques have continued throughout the twentieth and twenty-first centuries. Although often supplanted by more sophisticated imaging techniques, the X-ray remains a "workhorse" in medical imaging, especially for viewing fractures and for dentistry. The disadvantage of irradiation to the patient and the operator is now attenuated by proper shielding and by limiting exposure.

Modern Medical Imaging

X-rays can depict a two-dimensional image of a body region, and only from a single angle. In contrast, more recent medical imaging technologies produce data that is integrated and analyzed by computers to produce three-dimensional images or images that reveal aspects of body functioning.

Computed Tomography

Tomography refers to imaging by sections. **Computed tomography (CT)** is a noninvasive imaging technique that uses computers to analyze several cross-sectional X-rays in order to reveal minute details about structures in the body (Figure 1.19a). The technique was invented in the 1970s and is based on the principle that, as X-rays pass through the body, they are absorbed or reflected at different levels. In the technique, a patient lies on a motorized platform while a computerized axial tomography (CAT) scanner rotates 360 degrees around the patient, taking X-ray images. A computer combines these images into a two-dimensional view of the scanned area, or "slice."

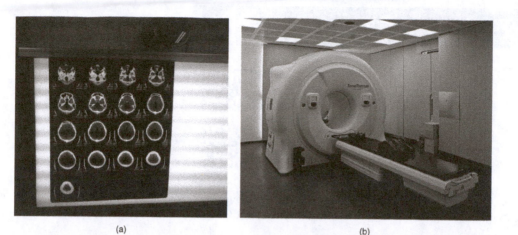

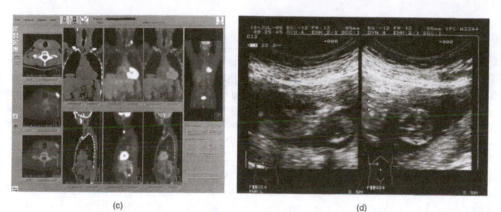

Figure 1.19 Medical Imaging Techniques (a) The results of a CT scan of the head are shown as successive transverse sections. (b) An MRI machine generates a magnetic field around a patient. (c) PET scans use radiopharmaceuticals to create images of active blood flow and physiologic activity of the organ or organs being targeted. (d) Ultrasound technology is used to monitor pregnancies because it is the least invasive of imaging techniques and uses no electromagnetic radiation. (credit a: Akira Ohgaki/flickr; credit b: "Digital Cate"/flickr; credit c: "Raziel"/Wikimedia Commons; credit d: "Isis"/Wikimedia Commons)

Since 1970, the development of more powerful computers and more sophisticated software has made CT scanning routine for many types of diagnostic evaluations. It is especially useful for soft tissue scanning, such as of the brain and the thoracic and abdominal viscera. Its level of detail is so precise that it can allow physicians to measure the size of a mass down to a millimeter. The main disadvantage of CT scanning is that it exposes patients to a dose of radiation many times higher than that of X-rays. In fact, children who undergo CT scans are at increased risk of developing cancer, as are adults who have multiple CT scans.

A CT or CAT scan relies on a circling scanner that revolves around the patient's body. Watch this video (http://openstaxcollege.org/l/CATscan) to learn more about CT and CAT scans. What type of radiation does a CT scanner use?

Magnetic Resonance Imaging

Magnetic resonance imaging (MRI) is a noninvasive medical imaging technique based on a phenomenon of nuclear physics discovered in the 1930s, in which matter exposed to magnetic fields and radio waves was found to emit radio signals. In 1970, a physician and researcher named Raymond Damadian noticed that malignant (cancerous) tissue gave off different signals than normal body tissue. He applied for a patent for the first MRI scanning device, which was in use clinically by the early 1980s. The early MRI scanners were crude, but advances in digital computing and electronics led to their advancement over any other technique for precise imaging, especially to discover tumors. MRI also has the major advantage of not exposing patients to radiation.

Drawbacks of MRI scans include their much higher cost, and patient discomfort with the procedure. The MRI scanner subjects the patient to such powerful electromagnets that the scan room must be shielded. The patient must be enclosed in a metal tube-like device for the duration of the scan (see Figure 1.19b), sometimes as long as thirty minutes, which can be uncomfortable and impractical for ill patients. The device is also so noisy that, even with earplugs, patients can become anxious or even fearful. These problems have been overcome somewhat with the development of "open" MRI scanning, which does not require the patient to be entirely enclosed in the metal tube. Patients with iron-containing metallic implants (internal sutures, some prosthetic devices, and so on) cannot undergo MRI scanning because it can dislodge these implants.

Functional MRIs (fMRIs), which detect the concentration of blood flow in certain parts of the body, are increasingly being used to study the activity in parts of the brain during various body activities. This has helped scientists learn more about the locations of different brain functions and more about brain abnormalities and diseases.

A patient undergoing an MRI is surrounded by a tube-shaped scanner. Watch this video (http://openstaxcollege.org/l/MRI) to learn more about MRIs. What is the function of magnets in an MRI?

Positron Emission Tomography

Positron emission tomography (PET) is a medical imaging technique involving the use of so-called radiopharmaceuticals, substances that emit radiation that is short-lived and therefore relatively safe to administer to the body. Although the first PET scanner was introduced in 1961, it took 15 more years before radiopharmaceuticals were combined with the technique and revolutionized its potential. The main advantage is that PET (see Figure 1.19c) can illustrate physiologic activity—including nutrient metabolism and blood flow—of the organ or organs being targeted, whereas CT and MRI scans can only show static images. PET is widely used to diagnose a multitude of conditions, such as heart disease, the spread of cancer, certain forms of infection, brain abnormalities, bone disease, and thyroid disease.

PET relies on radioactive substances administered several minutes before the scan. Watch this video (http://openstaxcollege.org/l/PET) to learn more about PET. How is PET used in chemotherapy?

Ultrasonography

Ultrasonography is an imaging technique that uses the transmission of high-frequency sound waves into the body to generate an echo signal that is converted by a computer into a real-time image of anatomy and physiology (see Figure 1.19d). Ultrasonography is the least invasive of all imaging techniques, and it is therefore used more freely in sensitive situations such as pregnancy. The technology was first developed in the 1940s and 1950s. Ultrasonography is used to study heart function, blood flow in the neck or extremities, certain conditions such as gallbladder disease, and fetal growth and development. The main disadvantages of ultrasonography are that the image quality is heavily operator-dependent and that it is unable to penetrate bone and gas.

KEY TERMS

abdominopelvic cavity division of the anterior (ventral) cavity that houses the abdominal and pelvic viscera

anabolism assembly of more complex molecules from simpler molecules

anatomical position standard reference position used for describing locations and directions on the human body

anatomy science that studies the form and composition of the body's structures

anterior describes the front or direction toward the front of the body; also referred to as ventral

anterior cavity larger body cavity located anterior to the posterior (dorsal) body cavity; includes the serous membrane-lined pleural cavities for the lungs, pericardial cavity for the heart, and peritoneal cavity for the abdominal and pelvic organs; also referred to as ventral cavity

catabolism breaking down of more complex molecules into simpler molecules

caudal describes a position below or lower than another part of the body proper; near or toward the tail (in humans, the coccyx, or lowest part of the spinal column); also referred to as inferior

cell smallest independently functioning unit of all organisms; in animals, a cell contains cytoplasm, composed of fluid and organelles

computed tomography (CT) medical imaging technique in which a computer-enhanced cross-sectional X-ray image is obtained

control center compares values to their normal range; deviations cause the activation of an effector

cranial describes a position above or higher than another part of the body proper; also referred to as superior

cranial cavity division of the posterior (dorsal) cavity that houses the brain

deep describes a position farther from the surface of the body

development changes an organism goes through during its life

differentiation process by which unspecialized cells become specialized in structure and function

distal describes a position farther from the point of attachment or the trunk of the body

dorsal describes the back or direction toward the back of the body; also referred to as posterior

dorsal cavity posterior body cavity that houses the brain and spinal cord; also referred to the posterior body cavity

effector organ that can cause a change in a value

frontal plane two-dimensional, vertical plane that divides the body or organ into anterior and posterior portions

gross anatomy study of the larger structures of the body, typically with the unaided eye; also referred to macroscopic anatomy

growth process of increasing in size

homeostasis steady state of body systems that living organisms maintain

inferior describes a position below or lower than another part of the body proper; near or toward the tail (in humans, the coccyx, or lowest part of the spinal column); also referred to as caudal

lateral describes the side or direction toward the side of the body

magnetic resonance imaging (MRI) medical imaging technique in which a device generates a magnetic field to obtain detailed sectional images of the internal structures of the body

medial describes the middle or direction toward the middle of the body

metabolism sum of all of the body's chemical reactions

microscopic anatomy study of very small structures of the body using magnification

negative feedback homeostatic mechanism that tends to stabilize an upset in the body's physiological condition by preventing an excessive response to a stimulus, typically as the stimulus is removed

normal range range of values around the set point that do not cause a reaction by the control center

nutrient chemical obtained from foods and beverages that is critical to human survival

organ functionally distinct structure composed of two or more types of tissues

organ system group of organs that work together to carry out a particular function

organism living being that has a cellular structure and that can independently perform all physiologic functions necessary for life

pericardium sac that encloses the heart

peritoneum serous membrane that lines the abdominopelvic cavity and covers the organs found there

physiology science that studies the chemistry, biochemistry, and physics of the body's functions

plane imaginary two-dimensional surface that passes through the body

pleura serous membrane that lines the pleural cavity and covers the lungs

positive feedback mechanism that intensifies a change in the body's physiological condition in response to a stimulus

positron emission tomography (PET) medical imaging technique in which radiopharmaceuticals are traced to reveal metabolic and physiological functions in tissues

posterior describes the back or direction toward the back of the body; also referred to as dorsal

posterior cavity posterior body cavity that houses the brain and spinal cord; also referred to as dorsal cavity

pressure force exerted by a substance in contact with another substance

prone face down

proximal describes a position nearer to the point of attachment or the trunk of the body

regional anatomy study of the structures that contribute to specific body regions

renewal process by which worn-out cells are replaced

reproduction process by which new organisms are generated

responsiveness ability of an organisms or a system to adjust to changes in conditions

sagittal plane two-dimensional, vertical plane that divides the body or organ into right and left sides

section in anatomy, a single flat surface of a three-dimensional structure that has been cut through

sensor (also, receptor) reports a monitored physiological value to the control center

serosa membrane that covers organs and reduces friction; also referred to as serous membrane

serous membrane membrane that covers organs and reduces friction; also referred to as serosa

set point ideal value for a physiological parameter; the level or small range within which a physiological parameter such as blood pressure is stable and optimally healthful, that is, within its parameters of homeostasis

spinal cavity division of the dorsal cavity that houses the spinal cord; also referred to as vertebral cavity

superficial describes a position nearer to the surface of the body

superior describes a position above or higher than another part of the body proper; also referred to as cranial

supine face up

systemic anatomy study of the structures that contribute to specific body systems

thoracic cavity division of the anterior (ventral) cavity that houses the heart, lungs, esophagus, and trachea

tissue group of similar or closely related cells that act together to perform a specific function

transverse plane two-dimensional, horizontal plane that divides the body or organ into superior and inferior portions

ultrasonography application of ultrasonic waves to visualize subcutaneous body structures such as tendons and organs

ventral describes the front or direction toward the front of the body; also referred to as anterior

ventral cavity larger body cavity located anterior to the posterior (dorsal) body cavity; includes the serous membrane-lined pleural cavities for the lungs, pericardial cavity for the heart, and peritoneal cavity for the abdominal and pelvic organs; also referred to as anterior body cavity

X-ray form of high energy electromagnetic radiation with a short wavelength capable of penetrating solids and ionizing gases; used in medicine as a diagnostic aid to visualize body structures such as bones

CHAPTER REVIEW

1.1 Overview of Anatomy and Physiology

Human anatomy is the scientific study of the body's structures. In the past, anatomy has primarily been studied via observing injuries, and later by the dissection of anatomical structures of cadavers, but in the past century, computer-assisted imaging techniques have allowed clinicians to look inside the living body. Human physiology is the scientific study of the chemistry and physics of the structures of the body. Physiology explains how the structures of the body work together to maintain life. It is difficult to study structure (anatomy) without knowledge of function (physiology). The two disciplines are typically studied together because form and function are closely related in all living things.

1.2 Structural Organization of the Human Body

Life processes of the human body are maintained at several levels of structural organization. These include the chemical, cellular, tissue, organ, organ system, and the organism level. Higher levels of organization are built from lower levels. Therefore, molecules combine to form cells, cells combine to form tissues, tissues combine to form organs, organs combine to form organ systems, and organ systems combine to form organisms.

1.3 Functions of Human Life

Most processes that occur in the human body are not consciously controlled. They occur continuously to build, maintain, and sustain life. These processes include: organization, in terms of the maintenance of essential body boundaries; metabolism, including energy transfer via anabolic and catabolic reactions; responsiveness; movement; and growth, differentiation, reproduction, and renewal.

1.4 Requirements for Human Life

Humans cannot survive for more than a few minutes without oxygen, for more than several days without water, and for more than several weeks without carbohydrates, lipids, proteins, vitamins, and minerals. Although the body can respond to high temperatures by sweating and to low temperatures by shivering and increased fuel consumption, long-term exposure to extreme heat and cold is not compatible with survival. The body requires a precise atmospheric pressure to maintain its gases in solution and to facilitate respiration—the intake of oxygen and the release of carbon dioxide. Humans also require blood pressure high enough to ensure that blood reaches all body tissues but low enough to avoid damage to blood vessels.

1.5 Homeostasis

Homeostasis is the activity of cells throughout the body to maintain the physiological state within a narrow range that is compatible with life. Homeostasis is regulated by negative feedback loops and, much less frequently, by positive feedback loops. Both have the same components of a stimulus, sensor, control center, and effector; however, negative feedback loops work to prevent an excessive response to the stimulus, whereas positive feedback loops intensify the response until an end point is reached.

1.6 Anatomical Terminology

Ancient Greek and Latin words are used to build anatomical terms. A standard reference position for mapping the body's structures is the normal anatomical position. Regions of the body are identified using terms such as "occipital" that are more precise than common words and phrases such as "the back of the head." Directional terms such as anterior and posterior are essential for accurately describing the relative locations of body structures. Images of the body's interior commonly align along one of three planes: the sagittal, frontal, or transverse. The body's organs are organized in one of two main cavities—dorsal (also referred to posterior) and ventral (also referred to anterior)—which are further sub-divided according to the structures present in each area. The serous membranes have two layers—parietal and visceral—surrounding a fluid filled space. Serous membranes cover the lungs (pleural serosa), heart (pericardial serosa), and some abdominopelvic organs (peritoneal serosa).

1.7 Medical Imaging

Detailed anatomical drawings of the human body first became available in the fifteenth and sixteenth centuries; however, it was not until the end of the nineteenth century, and the discovery of X-rays, that anatomists and physicians discovered non-surgical methods to look inside a living body. Since then, many other techniques, including CT scans, MRI scans, PET scans, and ultrasonography, have been developed, providing more accurate and detailed views of the form and function of the human body.

INTERACTIVE LINK QUESTIONS

1. View this animation (http://openstaxcollege.org/l/metabolic) to learn more about metabolic processes. What kind of catabolism occurs in the heart?

2. Water concentration in the body is critical for proper functioning. A person's body retains very tight control on water levels without conscious control by the person. Watch this video (http://openstaxcollege.org/l/H2Ocon) to learn more about water concentration in the body. Which organ has primary control over the amount of water in the body?

3. A CT or CAT scan relies on a circling scanner that revolves around the patient's body. Watch this video (http://openstaxcollege.org/l/CATscan) to learn more about CT and CAT scans. What type of radiation does a CT scanner use?

4. A patient undergoing an MRI is surrounded by a tube-shaped scanner. Watch this video (http://openstaxcollege.org/l/MRI) to learn more about MRIs. What is the function of magnets in an MRI?

5. PET relies on radioactive substances administered several minutes before the scan. Watch this video (http://openstaxcollege.org/l/PET) to learn more about PET. How is PET used in chemotherapy?

REVIEW QUESTIONS

6. Which of the following specialties might focus on studying all of the structures of the ankle and foot?

    a. microscopic anatomy
    b. muscle anatomy
    c. regional anatomy
    d. systemic anatomy

7. A scientist wants to study how the body uses foods and fluids during a marathon run. This scientist is most likely a(n) _____.

    a. exercise physiologist
    b. microscopic anatomist
    c. regional physiologist
    d. systemic anatomist

8. The smallest independently functioning unit of an organism is a(n) _____.
   a. cell
   b. molecule
   c. organ
   d. tissue

9. A collection of similar tissues that performs a specific function is an _____.
   a. organ
   b. organelle
   c. organism
   d. organ system

10. The body system responsible for structural support and movement is the _____.
   a. cardiovascular system
   b. endocrine system
   c. muscular system
   d. skeletal system

11. Metabolism can be defined as the _____.
   a. adjustment by an organism to external or internal changes
   b. process whereby all unspecialized cells become specialized to perform distinct functions
   c. process whereby new cells are formed to replace worn-out cells
   d. sum of all chemical reactions in an organism

12. Adenosine triphosphate (ATP) is an important molecule because it _____.
   a. is the result of catabolism
   b. release energy in uncontrolled bursts
   c. stores energy for use by body cells
   d. All of the above

13. Cancer cells can be characterized as "generic" cells that perform no specialized body function. Thus cancer cells lack _____.
   a. differentiation
   b. reproduction
   c. responsiveness
   d. both reproduction and responsiveness

14. Humans have the most urgent need for a continuous supply of _____.
   a. food
   b. nitrogen
   c. oxygen
   d. water

15. Which of the following statements about nutrients is true?
   a. All classes of nutrients are essential to human survival.
   b. Because the body cannot store any micronutrients, they need to be consumed nearly every day.
   c. Carbohydrates, lipids, and proteins are micronutrients.
   d. Macronutrients are vitamins and minerals.

16. C.J. is stuck in her car during a bitterly cold blizzard. Her body responds to the cold by _____.
   a. increasing the blood to her hands and feet
   b. becoming lethargic to conserve heat
   c. breaking down stored energy
   d. significantly increasing blood oxygen levels

17. After you eat lunch, nerve cells in your stomach respond to the distension (the stimulus) resulting from the food. They relay this information to _____.
   a. a control center
   b. a set point
   c. effectors
   d. sensors

18. Stimulation of the heat-loss center causes _____.
   a. blood vessels in the skin to constrict
   b. breathing to become slow and shallow
   c. sweat glands to increase their output
   d. All of the above

19. Which of the following is an example of a normal physiologic process that uses a positive feedback loop?
   a. blood pressure regulation
   b. childbirth
   c. regulation of fluid balance
   d. temperature regulation

20. What is the position of the body when it is in the "normal anatomical position?"
   a. The person is prone with upper limbs, including palms, touching sides and lower limbs touching at sides.
   b. The person is standing facing the observer, with upper limbs extended out at a ninety-degree angle from the torso and lower limbs in a wide stance with feet pointing laterally
   c. The person is supine with upper limbs, including palms, touching sides and lower limbs touching at sides.
   d. None of the above

21. To make a banana split, you halve a banana into two long, thin, right and left sides along the _____.
   a. coronal plane
   b. longitudinal plane
   c. midsagittal plane
   d. transverse plane

22. The lumbar region is _____.
   a. inferior to the gluteal region
   b. inferior to the umbilical region
   c. superior to the cervical region
   d. superior to the popliteal region

23. The heart is within the _____.
   a. cranial cavity
   b. mediastinum
   c. posterior (dorsal) cavity
   d. All of the above

24. In 1901, Wilhelm Röntgen was the first person to win the Nobel Prize for physics. For what discovery did he win?

    a. nuclear physics
    b. radiopharmaceuticals
    c. the link between radiation and cancer
    d. X-rays

25. Which of the following imaging techniques would be best to use to study the uptake of nutrients by rapidly multiplying cancer cells?

    a. CT
    b. MRI
    c. PET
    d. ultrasonography

26. Which of the following imaging studies can be used most safely during pregnancy?

    a. CT scans
    b. PET scans
    c. ultrasounds
    d. X-rays

27. What are two major disadvantages of MRI scans?

    a. release of radiation and poor quality images
    b. high cost and the need for shielding from the magnetic signals
    c. can only view metabolically active tissues and inadequate availability of equipment
    d. release of radiation and the need for a patient to be confined to metal tube for up to 30 minutes

CRITICAL THINKING QUESTIONS

28. Name at least three reasons to study anatomy and physiology.

29. For whom would an appreciation of the structural characteristics of the human heart come more easily: an alien who lands on Earth, abducts a human, and dissects his heart, or an anatomy and physiology student performing a dissection of the heart on her very first day of class? Why?

30. Name the six levels of organization of the human body.

31. The female ovaries and the male testes are a part of which body system? Can these organs be members of more than one organ system? Why or why not?

32. Explain why the smell of smoke when you are sitting at a campfire does not trigger alarm, but the smell of smoke in your residence hall does.

33. Identify three different ways that growth can occur in the human body.

34. When you open a bottle of sparkling water, the carbon dioxide gas in the bottle form bubbles. If the bottle is left open, the water will eventually "go flat." Explain these phenomena in terms of atmospheric pressure.

35. On his midsummer trek through the desert, Josh ran out of water. Why is this particularly dangerous?

36. Identify the four components of a negative feedback loop and explain what would happen if secretion of a body chemical controlled by a negative feedback system became too great.

37. What regulatory processes would your body use if you were trapped by a blizzard in an unheated, uninsulated cabin in the woods?

38. In which direction would an MRI scanner move to produce sequential images of the body in the frontal plane, and in which direction would an MRI scanner move to produce sequential images of the body in the sagittal plane?

39. If a bullet were to penetrate a lung, which three anterior thoracic body cavities would it enter, and which layer of the serous membrane would it encounter first?

40. Which medical imaging technique is most dangerous to use repeatedly, and why?

41. Explain why ultrasound imaging is the technique of choice for studying fetal growth and development.

2 | THE CHEMICAL LEVEL OF ORGANIZATION

Figure 2.1 Human DNA Human DNA is described as a double helix that resembles a molecular spiral staircase. In humans the DNA is organized into 46 chromosomes.

Introduction

Chapter Objectives

After studying this chapter, you will be able to:

- Describe the fundamental composition of matter
- Identify the three subatomic particles
- Identify the four most abundant elements in the body
- Explain the relationship between an atom's number of electrons and its relative stability
- Distinguish between ionic bonds, covalent bonds, and hydrogen bonds
- Explain how energy is invested, stored, and released via chemical reactions, particularly those reactions that are critical to life
- Explain the importance of the inorganic compounds that contribute to life, such as water, salts, acids, and

bases
- Compare and contrast the four important classes of organic (carbon-based) compounds—proteins, carbohydrates, lipids and nucleic acids—according to their composition and functional importance to human life

The smallest, most fundamental material components of the human body are basic chemical elements. In fact, chemicals called nucleotide bases are the foundation of the genetic code with the instructions on how to build and maintain the human body from conception through old age. There are about three billion of these base pairs in human DNA.

Human chemistry includes organic molecules (carbon-based) and biochemicals (those produced by the body). Human chemistry also includes elements. In fact, life cannot exist without many of the elements that are part of the earth. All of the elements that contribute to chemical reactions, to the transformation of energy, and to electrical activity and muscle contraction—elements that include phosphorus, carbon, sodium, and calcium, to name a few—originated in stars.

These elements, in turn, can form both the inorganic and organic chemical compounds important to life, including, for example, water, glucose, and proteins. This chapter begins by examining elements and how the structures of atoms, the basic units of matter, determine the characteristics of elements by the number of protons, neutrons, and electrons in the atoms. The chapter then builds the framework of life from there.

2.1 | Elements and Atoms: The Building Blocks of Matter

By the end of this section, you will be able to:

- Discuss the relationships between matter, mass, elements, compounds, atoms, and subatomic particles
- Distinguish between atomic number and mass number
- Identify the key distinction between isotopes of the same element
- Explain how electrons occupy electron shells and their contribution to an atom's relative stability

The substance of the universe—from a grain of sand to a star—is called **matter**. Scientists define matter as anything that occupies space and has mass. An object's mass and its weight are related concepts, but not quite the same. An object's mass is the amount of matter contained in the object, and the object's mass is the same whether that object is on Earth or in the zero-gravity environment of outer space. An object's weight, on the other hand, is its mass as affected by the pull of gravity. Where gravity strongly pulls on an object's mass its weight is greater than it is where gravity is less strong. An object of a certain mass weighs less on the moon, for example, than it does on Earth because the gravity of the moon is less than that of Earth. In other words, weight is variable, and is influenced by gravity. A piece of cheese that weighs a pound on Earth weighs only a few ounces on the moon.

Elements and Compounds

All matter in the natural world is composed of one or more of the 92 fundamental substances called elements. An **element** is a pure substance that is distinguished from all other matter by the fact that it cannot be created or broken down by ordinary chemical means. While your body can assemble many of the chemical compounds needed for life from their constituent elements, it cannot make elements. They must come from the environment. A familiar example of an element that you must take in is calcium (Ca^{++}). Calcium is essential to the human body; it is absorbed and used for a number of processes, including strengthening bones. When you consume dairy products your digestive system breaks down the food into components small enough to cross into the bloodstream. Among these is calcium, which, because it is an element, cannot be broken down further. The elemental calcium in cheese, therefore, is the same as the calcium that forms your bones. Some other elements you might be familiar with are oxygen, sodium, and iron. The elements in the human body are shown in Figure 2.2, beginning with the most abundant: oxygen (O), carbon (C), hydrogen (H), and nitrogen (N). Each element's name can be replaced by a one- or two-letter symbol; you will become familiar with some of these during this course. All the elements in your body are derived from the foods you eat and the air you breathe.

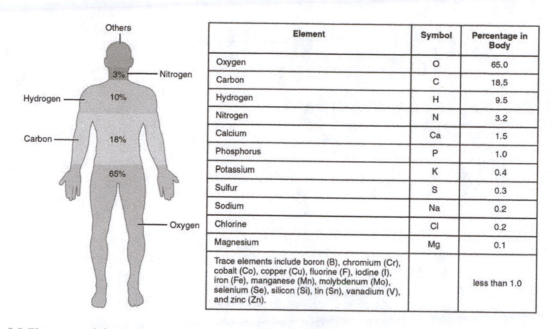

Element	Symbol	Percentage in Body
Oxygen	O	65.0
Carbon	C	18.5
Hydrogen	H	9.5
Nitrogen	N	3.2
Calcium	Ca	1.5
Phosphorus	P	1.0
Potassium	K	0.4
Sulfur	S	0.3
Sodium	Na	0.2
Chlorine	Cl	0.2
Magnesium	Mg	0.1
Trace elements include boron (B), chromium (Cr), cobalt (Co), copper (Cu), fluorine (F), iodine (I), iron (Fe), manganese (Mn), molybdenum (Mo), selenium (Se), silicon (Si), tin (Sn), vanadium (V), and zinc (Zn).		less than 1.0

Figure 2.2 Elements of the Human Body The main elements that compose the human body are shown from most abundant to least abundant.

In nature, elements rarely occur alone. Instead, they combine to form compounds. A **compound** is a substance composed of two or more elements joined by chemical bonds. For example, the compound glucose is an important body fuel. It is always composed of the same three elements: carbon, hydrogen, and oxygen. Moreover, the elements that make up any given compound always occur in the same relative amounts. In glucose, there are always six carbon and six oxygen units for every twelve hydrogen units. But what, exactly, are these "units" of elements?

Atoms and Subatomic Particles

An **atom** is the smallest quantity of an element that retains the unique properties of that element. In other words, an atom of hydrogen is a unit of hydrogen—the smallest amount of hydrogen that can exist. As you might guess, atoms are almost unfathomably small. The period at the end of this sentence is millions of atoms wide.

Atomic Structure and Energy

Atoms are made up of even smaller subatomic particles, three types of which are important: the **proton**, **neutron**, and **electron**. The number of positively-charged protons and non-charged ("neutral") neutrons, gives mass to the atom, and the number of each in the nucleus of the atom determine the element. The number of negatively-charged electrons that "spin" around the nucleus at close to the speed of light equals the number of protons. An electron has about 1/2000th the mass of a proton or neutron.

Figure 2.3 shows two models that can help you imagine the structure of an atom—in this case, helium (He). In the planetary model, helium's two electrons are shown circling the nucleus in a fixed orbit depicted as a ring. Although this model is helpful in visualizing atomic structure, in reality, electrons do not travel in fixed orbits, but whiz around the nucleus erratically in a so-called electron cloud.

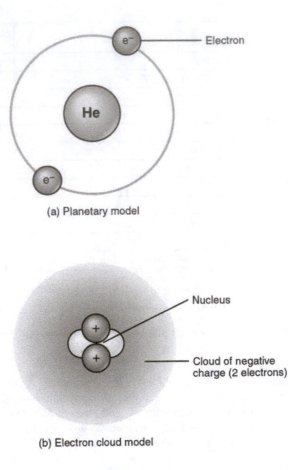

(a) Planetary model

(b) Electron cloud model

Figure 2.3 Two Models of Atomic Structure (a) In the planetary model, the electrons of helium are shown in fixed orbits, depicted as rings, at a precise distance from the nucleus, somewhat like planets orbiting the sun. (b) In the electron cloud model, the electrons of carbon are shown in the variety of locations they would have at different distances from the nucleus over time.

An atom's protons and electrons carry electrical charges. Protons, with their positive charge, are designated p^+. Electrons, which have a negative charge, are designated e^-. An atom's neutrons have no charge: they are electrically neutral. Just as a magnet sticks to a steel refrigerator because their opposite charges attract, the positively charged protons attract the negatively charged electrons. This mutual attraction gives the atom some structural stability. The attraction by the positively charged nucleus helps keep electrons from straying far. The number of protons and electrons within a neutral atom are equal, thus, the atom's overall charge is balanced.

Atomic Number and Mass Number

An atom of carbon is unique to carbon, but a proton of carbon is not. One proton is the same as another, whether it is found in an atom of carbon, sodium (Na), or iron (Fe). The same is true for neutrons and electrons. So, what gives an element its distinctive properties—what makes carbon so different from sodium or iron? The answer is the unique quantity of protons each contains. Carbon by definition is an element whose atoms contain six protons. No other element has exactly six protons in its atoms. Moreover, *all* atoms of carbon, whether found in your liver or in a lump of coal, contain six protons. Thus, the **atomic number**, which is the number of protons in the nucleus of the atom, identifies the element. Because an atom usually has the same number of electrons as protons, the atomic number identifies the usual number of electrons as well.

In their most common form, many elements also contain the same number of neutrons as protons. The most common form of carbon, for example, has six neutrons as well as six protons, for a total of 12 subatomic particles in its nucleus. An element's **mass number** is the sum of the number of protons and neutrons in its nucleus. So the most common form of carbon's mass number is 12. (Electrons have so little mass that they do not appreciably contribute to the mass of an atom.) Carbon is a relatively light element. Uranium (U), in contrast, has a mass number of 238 and is referred to as a heavy metal. Its atomic number is 92 (it has 92 protons) but it contains 146 neutrons; it has the most mass of all the naturally occurring elements.

The **periodic table of the elements**, shown in Figure 2.4, is a chart identifying the 92 elements found in nature, as well as several larger, unstable elements discovered experimentally. The elements are arranged in order of their atomic number, with hydrogen and helium at the top of the table, and the more massive elements below. The periodic table is a useful device because for each element, it identifies the chemical symbol, the atomic number, and the mass number, while organizing elements according to their propensity to react with other elements. The number of protons and electrons in an element are equal. The number of protons and neutrons may be equal for some elements, but are not equal for all.

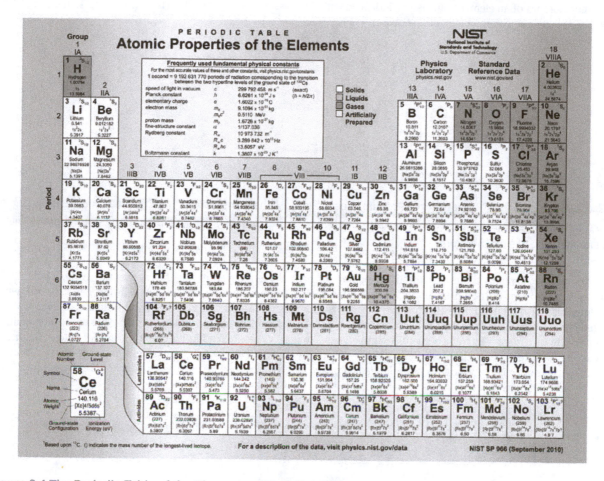

Figure 2.4 The Periodic Table of the Elements   (credit: R.A. Dragoset, A. Musgrove, C.W. Clark, W.C. Martin)

Visit this website (http://openstaxcollege.org/l/ptable) to view the periodic table. In the periodic table of the elements, elements in a single column have the same number of electrons that can participate in a chemical reaction. These electrons are known as "valence electrons." For example, the elements in the first column all have a single valence electron, an electron that can be "donated" in a chemical reaction with another atom. What is the meaning of a mass number shown in parentheses?

Isotopes

Although each element has a unique number of protons, it can exist as different isotopes. An **isotope** is one of the different forms of an element, distinguished from one another by different numbers of neutrons. The standard isotope of carbon is ^{12}C, commonly called carbon twelve. ^{12}C has six protons and six neutrons, for a mass number of twelve. All of the isotopes of carbon have the same number of protons; therefore, ^{13}C has seven neutrons, and ^{14}C has eight neutrons. The different isotopes of an element can also be indicated with the mass number hyphenated (for example, C-12 instead of ^{12}C). Hydrogen has three common isotopes, shown in Figure 2.5.

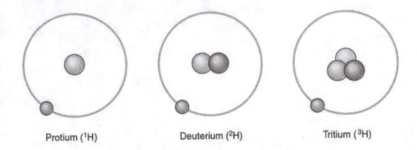

Protium (^{1}H)   Deuterium (^{2}H)   Tritium (^{3}H)

Figure 2.5 Isotopes of Hydrogen Protium, designated ^{1}H, has one proton and no neutrons. It is by far the most abundant isotope of hydrogen in nature. Deuterium, designated ^{2}H, has one proton and one neutron. Tritium, designated ^{3}H, has two neutrons.

An isotope that contains more than the usual number of neutrons is referred to as a heavy isotope. An example is ^{14}C. Heavy isotopes tend to be unstable, and unstable isotopes are radioactive. A **radioactive isotope** is an isotope whose nucleus readily decays, giving off subatomic particles and electromagnetic energy. Different radioactive isotopes (also called radioisotopes) differ in their half-life, the time it takes for half of any size sample of an isotope to decay. For example, the half-life of tritium—a radioisotope of hydrogen—is about 12 years, indicating it takes 12 years for half of the tritium nuclei in a sample to decay. Excessive exposure to radioactive isotopes can damage human cells and even cause cancer and birth defects, but when exposure is controlled, some radioactive isotopes can be useful in medicine. For more information, see the Career Connections.

Career CONNECTION

Interventional Radiologist

The controlled use of radioisotopes has advanced medical diagnosis and treatment of disease. Interventional radiologists are physicians who treat disease by using minimally invasive techniques involving radiation. Many conditions that could once only be treated with a lengthy and traumatic operation can now be treated non-surgically, reducing the cost, pain, length of hospital stay, and recovery time for patients. For example, in the past, the only options for a patient with one or more tumors in the liver were surgery and chemotherapy (the administration of drugs to treat cancer). Some liver tumors, however, are difficult to access surgically, and others could require the surgeon to remove too much of the liver. Moreover, chemotherapy is highly toxic to the liver, and certain tumors do not respond well to it anyway. In some such cases, an interventional radiologist can treat the tumors by disrupting their blood supply, which they need if they are to continue to grow. In this procedure, called radioembolization, the radiologist accesses the liver with a fine needle, threaded through one of the patient's blood vessels. The radiologist then inserts tiny radioactive "seeds" into the blood vessels that supply the tumors. In the days and weeks following the procedure, the radiation emitted from the seeds destroys the vessels and directly kills the tumor cells in the vicinity of the treatment.

Radioisotopes emit subatomic particles that can be detected and tracked by imaging technologies. One of the most advanced uses of radioisotopes in medicine is the positron emission tomography (PET) scanner, which detects the activity in the body of a very small injection of radioactive glucose, the simple sugar that cells use for energy. The PET camera reveals to the medical team which of the patient's tissues are taking up the most glucose. Thus, the most metabolically active tissues show up as bright "hot spots" on the images (Figure 2.6). PET can reveal some cancerous masses because cancer cells consume glucose at a high rate to fuel their rapid reproduction.

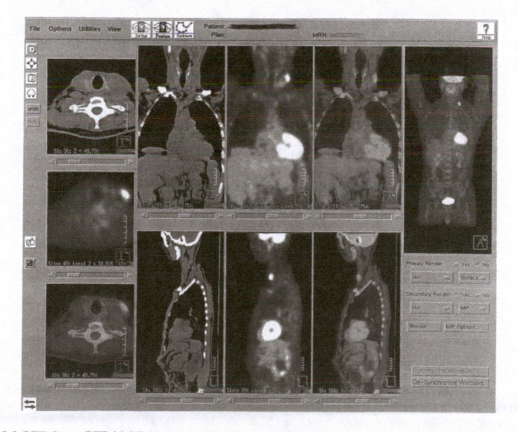

Figure 2.6 PET Scan PET highlights areas in the body where there is relatively high glucose use, which is characteristic of cancerous tissue. This PET scan shows sites of the spread of a large primary tumor to other sites.

The Behavior of Electrons

In the human body, atoms do not exist as independent entities. Rather, they are constantly reacting with other atoms to form and to break down more complex substances. To fully understand anatomy and physiology you must grasp how atoms participate in such reactions. The key is understanding the behavior of electrons.

Although electrons do not follow rigid orbits a set distance away from the atom's nucleus, they do tend to stay within certain regions of space called electron shells. An **electron shell** is a layer of electrons that encircle the nucleus at a distinct energy level.

The atoms of the elements found in the human body have from one to five electron shells, and all electron shells hold eight electrons except the first shell, which can only hold two. This configuration of electron shells is the same for all atoms. The precise number of shells depends on the number of electrons in the atom. Hydrogen and helium have just one and two electrons, respectively. If you take a look at the periodic table of the elements, you will notice that hydrogen and helium are placed alone on either sides of the top row; they are the only elements that have just one electron shell (Figure 2.7). A second shell is necessary to hold the electrons in all elements larger than hydrogen and helium.

Lithium (Li), whose atomic number is 3, has three electrons. Two of these fill the first electron shell, and the third spills over into a second shell. The second electron shell can accommodate as many as eight electrons. Carbon, with its six electrons, entirely fills its first shell, and half-fills its second. With ten electrons, neon (Ne) entirely fills its two electron shells. Again, a look at the periodic table reveals that all of the elements in the second row, from lithium to neon, have just two electron shells. Atoms with more than ten electrons require more than two shells. These elements occupy the third and subsequent rows of the periodic table.

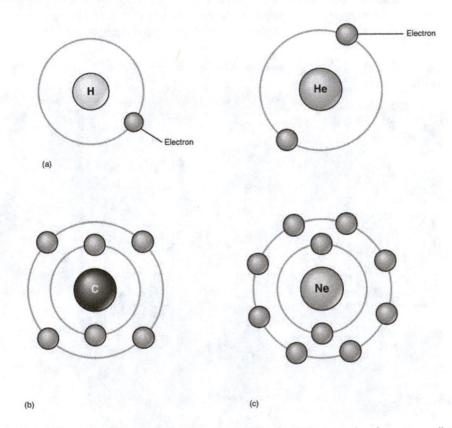

Figure 2.7 Electron Shells Electrons orbit the atomic nucleus at distinct levels of energy called electron shells. (a) With one electron, hydrogen only half-fills its electron shell. Helium also has a single shell, but its two electrons completely fill it. (b) The electrons of carbon completely fill its first electron shell, but only half-fills its second. (c) Neon, an element that does not occur in the body, has 10 electrons, filling both of its electron shells.

The factor that most strongly governs the tendency of an atom to participate in chemical reactions is the number of electrons in its valence shell. A **valence shell** is an atom's outermost electron shell. If the valence shell is full, the atom is stable; meaning its electrons are unlikely to be pulled away from the nucleus by the electrical charge of other atoms. If the valence shell is not full, the atom is reactive; meaning it will tend to react with other atoms in ways that make the valence shell full. Consider hydrogen, with its one electron only half-filling its valence shell. This single electron is likely to be drawn into relationships with the atoms of other elements, so that hydrogen's single valence shell can be stabilized.

All atoms (except hydrogen and helium with their single electron shells) are most stable when there are exactly eight electrons in their valence shell. This principle is referred to as the octet rule, and it states that an atom will give up, gain, or share electrons with another atom so that it ends up with eight electrons in its own valence shell. For example, oxygen, with six electrons in its valence shell, is likely to react with other atoms in a way that results in the addition of two electrons to oxygen's valence shell, bringing the number to eight. When two hydrogen atoms each share their single electron with oxygen, covalent bonds are formed, resulting in a molecule of water, H_2O.

In nature, atoms of one element tend to join with atoms of other elements in characteristic ways. For example, carbon commonly fills its valence shell by linking up with four atoms of hydrogen. In so doing, the two elements form the simplest of organic molecules, methane, which also is one of the most abundant and stable carbon-containing compounds on Earth. As stated above, another example is water; oxygen needs two electrons to fill its valence shell. It commonly interacts with two atoms of hydrogen, forming H_2O. Incidentally, the name "hydrogen" reflects its contribution to water (hydro- = "water"; -gen = "maker"). Thus, hydrogen is the "water maker."

2.2 | Chemical Bonds

By the end of this section, you will be able to:

- Explain the relationship between molecules and compounds
- Distinguish between ions, cations, and anions
- Identify the key difference between ionic and covalent bonds
- Distinguish between nonpolar and polar covalent bonds
- Explain how water molecules link via hydrogen bonds

Atoms separated by a great distance cannot link; rather, they must come close enough for the electrons in their valence shells to interact. But do atoms ever actually touch one another? Most physicists would say no, because the negatively charged electrons in their valence shells repel one another. No force within the human body—or anywhere in the natural world—is strong enough to overcome this electrical repulsion. So when you read about atoms linking together or colliding, bear in mind that the atoms are not merging in a physical sense.

Instead, atoms link by forming a chemical bond. A **bond** is a weak or strong electrical attraction that holds atoms in the same vicinity. The new grouping is typically more stable—less likely to react again—than its component atoms were when they were separate. A more or less stable grouping of two or more atoms held together by chemical bonds is called a **molecule**. The bonded atoms may be of the same element, as in the case of H_2, which is called molecular hydrogen or hydrogen gas. When a molecule is made up of two or more atoms of different elements, it is called a chemical **compound**. Thus, a unit of water, or H_2O, is a compound, as is a single molecule of the gas methane, or CH_4.

Three types of chemical bonds are important in human physiology, because they hold together substances that are used by the body for critical aspects of homeostasis, signaling, and energy production, to name just a few important processes. These are ionic bonds, covalent bonds, and hydrogen bonds.

Ions and Ionic Bonds

Recall that an atom typically has the same number of positively charged protons and negatively charged electrons. As long as this situation remains, the atom is electrically neutral. But when an atom participates in a chemical reaction that results in the donation or acceptance of one or more electrons, the atom will then become positively or negatively charged. This happens frequently for most atoms in order to have a full valence shell, as described previously. This can happen either by gaining electrons to fill a shell that is more than half-full, or by giving away electrons to empty a shell than is less than half-full, thereby leaving the next smaller electron shell as the new, full, valence shell. An atom that has an electrical charge—whether positive or negative—is an **ion**.

Interactive LINK

Visit this **website (http://openstaxcollege.org/l/electenergy)** to learn about electrical energy and the attraction/repulsion of charges. What happens to the charged electroscope when a conductor is moved between its plastic sheets, and why?

Potassium (K), for instance, is an important element in all body cells. Its atomic number is 19. It has just one electron in its valence shell. This characteristic makes potassium highly likely to participate in chemical reactions in which it donates one electron. (It is easier for potassium to donate one electron than to gain seven electrons.) The loss will cause the positive charge of potassium's protons to be more influential than the negative charge of potassium's electrons. In other words, the resulting potassium ion will be slightly positive. A potassium ion is written K^+, indicating that it has lost a single electron. A positively charged ion is known as a **cation**.

Now consider fluorine (F), a component of bones and teeth. Its atomic number is nine, and it has seven electrons in its valence shell. Thus, it is highly likely to bond with other atoms in such a way that fluorine accepts one electron (it is easier for fluorine to gain one electron than to donate seven electrons). When it does, its electrons will outnumber its protons by one, and it will have an overall negative charge. The ionized form of fluorine is called fluoride, and is written as F^-. A negatively charged ion is known as an **anion**.

Atoms that have more than one electron to donate or accept will end up with stronger positive or negative charges. A cation that has donated two electrons has a net charge of +2. Using magnesium (Mg) as an example, this can be written Mg^{++} or Mg^{2+}. An anion that has accepted two electrons has a net charge of –2. The ionic form of selenium (Se), for example, is typically written Se^{2-}.

The opposite charges of cations and anions exert a moderately strong mutual attraction that keeps the atoms in close proximity forming an ionic bond. An **ionic bond** is an ongoing, close association between ions of opposite charge. The table salt you sprinkle on your food owes its existence to ionic bonding. As shown in **Figure 2.8**, sodium commonly donates an electron to chlorine, becoming the cation Na^+. When chlorine accepts the electron, it becomes the chloride anion, Cl^-. With their opposing charges, these two ions strongly attract each other.

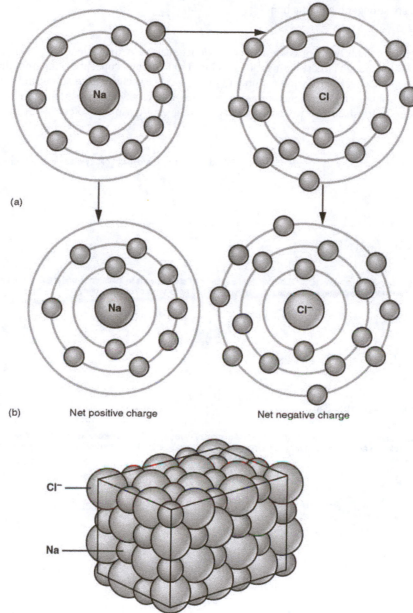

Figure 2.8 Ionic Bonding (a) Sodium readily donates the solitary electron in its valence shell to chlorine, which needs only one electron to have a full valence shell. (b) The opposite electrical charges of the resulting sodium cation and chloride anion result in the formation of a bond of attraction called an ionic bond. (c) The attraction of many sodium and chloride ions results in the formation of large groupings called crystals.

Water is an essential component of life because it is able to break the ionic bonds in salts to free the ions. In fact, in biological fluids, most individual atoms exist as ions. These dissolved ions produce electrical charges within the body. The behavior of these ions produces the tracings of heart and brain function observed as waves on an electrocardiogram (EKG or ECG) or an electroencephalogram (EEG). The electrical activity that derives from the interactions of the charged ions is why they are also called electrolytes.

Covalent Bonds

Unlike ionic bonds formed by the attraction between a cation's positive charge and an anion's negative charge, molecules formed by a **covalent bond** share electrons in a mutually stabilizing relationship. Like next-door neighbors whose kids hang out first at one home and then at the other, the atoms do not lose or gain electrons permanently. Instead, the electrons move back and forth between the elements. Because of the close sharing of pairs of electrons (one electron from each of two atoms), covalent bonds are stronger than ionic bonds.

Nonpolar Covalent Bonds

Figure 2.9 shows several common types of covalent bonds. Notice that the two covalently bonded atoms typically share just one or two electron pairs, though larger sharings are possible. The important concept to take from this is that in covalent bonds, electrons in the outermost valence shell are shared to fill the valence shells of both atoms, ultimately stabilizing both of the atoms involved. In a single covalent bond, a single electron is shared between two atoms, while in a double covalent bond, two pairs of electrons are shared between two atoms. There even are triple covalent bonds, where three atoms are shared.

(a) A single covalent bond: hydrogen gas (H—H). Two atoms of hydrogen each share their solitary electron in a single covalent bond.

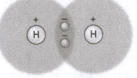

(b) A double covalent bond: oxygen gas (O=O). An atom of oxygen has six electrons in its valence shell; thus, two more would make it stable. Two atoms of oxygen achieve stability by sharing two pairs of electrons in a double covalent bond.

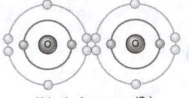

Molecule of oxygen gas (O_2)

(c) Two double covalent bonds: carbon dioxide (O=C=O). An atom of carbon has four electrons in its valence shell; thus, four more would make it stable. An atom of carbon and two atoms of oxygen achieve stability by sharing two electron pairs each, in two double covalent bonds.

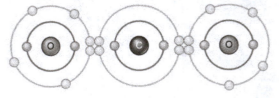

Figure 2.9 Covalent Bonding

You can see that the covalent bonds shown in Figure 2.9 are balanced. The sharing of the negative electrons is relatively equal, as is the electrical pull of the positive protons in the nucleus of the atoms involved. This is why covalently bonded molecules that are electrically balanced in this way are described as nonpolar; that is, no region of the molecule is either more positive or more negative than any other.

Polar Covalent Bonds

Groups of legislators with completely opposite views on a particular issue are often described as "polarized" by news writers. In chemistry, a **polar molecule** is a molecule that contains regions that have opposite electrical charges. Polar molecules occur when atoms share electrons unequally, in polar covalent bonds.

The most familiar example of a polar molecule is water (Figure 2.10). The molecule has three parts: one atom of oxygen, the nucleus of which contains eight protons, and two hydrogen atoms, whose nuclei each contain only one proton. Because every proton exerts an identical positive charge, a nucleus that contains eight protons exerts a charge eight times greater than a nucleus that contains one proton. This means that the negatively charged electrons present in the water molecule are more strongly attracted to the oxygen nucleus than to the hydrogen nuclei. Each hydrogen atom's single negative electron therefore migrates toward the oxygen atom, making the oxygen end of their bond slightly more negative than the hydrogen end of their bond.

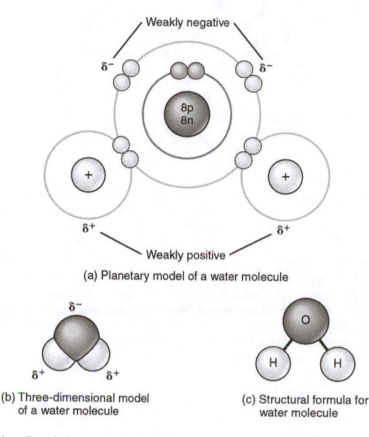

Weakly negative

δ^- δ^-

8p
8n

$+$ $+$

δ^+ δ^+

Weakly positive

(a) Planetary model of a water molecule

δ^-

δ^+ δ^+

(b) Three-dimensional model
of a water molecule

O

H   H

(c) Structural formula for
water molecule

Figure 2.10 Polar Covalent Bonds in a Water Molecule

What is true for the bonds is true for the water molecule as a whole; that is, the oxygen region has a slightly negative charge and the regions of the hydrogen atoms have a slightly positive charge. These charges are often referred to as "partial charges" because the strength of the charge is less than one full electron, as would occur in an ionic bond. As shown in Figure 2.10, regions of weak polarity are indicated with the Greek letter delta (δ) and a plus ($+$) or minus ($-$) sign.

Even though a single water molecule is unimaginably tiny, it has mass, and the opposing electrical charges on the molecule pull that mass in such a way that it creates a shape somewhat like a triangular tent (see Figure 2.10b). This dipole, with the positive charges at one end formed by the hydrogen atoms at the "bottom" of the tent and the negative charge at the opposite end (the oxygen atom at the "top" of the tent) makes the charged regions highly likely to interact with charged regions of other polar molecules. For human physiology, the resulting bond is one of the most important formed by water—the hydrogen bond.

Hydrogen Bonds

A **hydrogen bond** is formed when a weakly positive hydrogen atom already bonded to one electronegative atom (for example, the oxygen in the water molecule) is attracted to another electronegative atom from another molecule. In other words, hydrogen bonds always include hydrogen that is already part of a polar molecule.

The most common example of hydrogen bonding in the natural world occurs between molecules of water. It happens before your eyes whenever two raindrops merge into a larger bead, or a creek spills into a river. Hydrogen bonding occurs because the weakly negative oxygen atom in one water molecule is attracted to the weakly positive hydrogen atoms of two other water molecules (Figure 2.11).

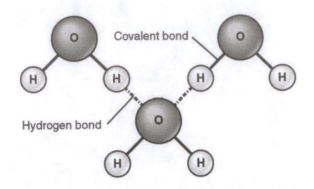

Figure 2.11 Hydrogen Bonds between Water Molecules   Notice that the bonds occur between the weakly positive charge on the hydrogen atoms and the weakly negative charge on the oxygen atoms. Hydrogen bonds are relatively weak, and therefore are indicated with a dotted (rather than a solid) line.

Water molecules also strongly attract other types of charged molecules as well as ions. This explains why "table salt," for example, actually is a molecule called a "salt" in chemistry, which consists of equal numbers of positively-charged sodium (Na^+) and negatively-charged chloride (Cl^-), dissolves so readily in water, in this case forming dipole-ion bonds between the water and the electrically-charged ions (electrolytes). Water molecules also repel molecules with nonpolar covalent bonds, like fats, lipids, and oils. You can demonstrate this with a simple kitchen experiment: pour a teaspoon of vegetable oil, a compound formed by nonpolar covalent bonds, into a glass of water. Instead of instantly dissolving in the water, the oil forms a distinct bead because the polar water molecules repel the nonpolar oil.

2.3 | Chemical Reactions

By the end of this section, you will be able to:

- Distinguish between kinetic and potential energy, and between exergonic and endergonic chemical reactions
- Identify four forms of energy important in human functioning
- Describe the three basic types of chemical reactions
- Identify several factors influencing the rate of chemical reactions

One characteristic of a living organism is metabolism, which is the sum total of all of the chemical reactions that go on to maintain that organism's health and life. The bonding processes you have learned thus far are anabolic chemical reactions; that is, they form larger molecules from smaller molecules or atoms. But recall that metabolism can proceed in another direction: in catabolic chemical reactions, bonds between components of larger molecules break, releasing smaller molecules or atoms. Both types of reaction involve exchanges not only of matter, but of energy.

The Role of Energy in Chemical Reactions

Chemical reactions require a sufficient amount of energy to cause the matter to collide with enough precision and force that old chemical bonds can be broken and new ones formed. In general, **kinetic energy** is the form of energy powering any type of matter in motion. Imagine you are building a brick wall. The energy it takes to lift and place one brick atop another is kinetic energy—the energy matter possesses because of its motion. Once the wall is in place, it stores potential energy. **Potential energy** is the energy of position, or the energy matter possesses because of the positioning or structure of its components. If the brick wall collapses, the stored potential energy is released as kinetic energy as the bricks fall.

In the human body, potential energy is stored in the bonds between atoms and molecules. **Chemical energy** is the form of potential energy in which energy is stored in chemical bonds. When those bonds are formed, chemical energy is invested, and when they break, chemical energy is released. Notice that chemical energy, like all energy, is neither created nor destroyed; rather, it is converted from one form to another. When you eat an energy bar before heading out the door for a hike, the honey, nuts, and other foods the bar contains are broken down and rearranged by your body into molecules that your muscle cells convert to kinetic energy.

Chemical reactions that release more energy than they absorb are characterized as exergonic. The catabolism of the foods in your energy bar is an example. Some of the chemical energy stored in the bar is absorbed into molecules your body uses for fuel, but some of it is released—for example, as heat. In contrast, chemical reactions that absorb more energy than they release are endergonic. These reactions require energy input, and the resulting molecule stores not only the chemical energy in the original components, but also the energy that fueled the reaction. Because energy is neither created nor destroyed, where does the energy needed for endergonic reactions come from? In many cases, it comes from exergonic reactions.

Forms of Energy Important in Human Functioning

You have already learned that chemical energy is absorbed, stored, and released by chemical bonds. In addition to chemical energy, mechanical, radiant, and electrical energy are important in human functioning.

- Mechanical energy, which is stored in physical systems such as machines, engines, or the human body, directly powers the movement of matter. When you lift a brick into place on a wall, your muscles provide the mechanical energy that moves the brick.

- Radiant energy is energy emitted and transmitted as waves rather than matter. These waves vary in length from long radio waves and microwaves to short gamma waves emitted from decaying atomic nuclei. The full spectrum of radiant energy is referred to as the electromagnetic spectrum. The body uses the ultraviolet energy of sunlight to convert a compound in skin cells to vitamin D, which is essential to human functioning. The human eye evolved to see the wavelengths that comprise the colors of the rainbow, from red to violet, so that range in the spectrum is called "visible light."

- Electrical energy, supplied by electrolytes in cells and body fluids, contributes to the voltage changes that help transmit impulses in nerve and muscle cells.

Characteristics of Chemical Reactions

All chemical reactions begin with a **reactant**, the general term for the one or more substances that enter into the reaction. Sodium and chloride ions, for example, are the reactants in the production of table salt. The one or more substances produced by a chemical reaction are called the **product**.

In chemical reactions, the components of the reactants—the elements involved and the number of atoms of each—are all present in the product(s). Similarly, there is nothing present in the products that are not present in the reactants. This is because chemical reactions are governed by the law of conservation of mass, which states that matter cannot be created or destroyed in a chemical reaction.

Just as you can express mathematical calculations in equations such as $2 + 7 = 9$, you can use chemical equations to show how reactants become products. As in math, chemical equations proceed from left to right, but instead of an equal sign, they employ an arrow or arrows indicating the direction in which the chemical reaction proceeds. For example, the chemical reaction in which one atom of nitrogen and three atoms of hydrogen produce ammonia would be written as $N + 3H \rightarrow NH_3$. Correspondingly, the breakdown of ammonia into its components would be written as $NH_3 \rightarrow N + 3H$.

Notice that, in the first example, a nitrogen (N) atom and three hydrogen (H) atoms bond to form a compound. This anabolic reaction requires energy, which is then stored within the compound's bonds. Such reactions are referred to as synthesis reactions. A **synthesis reaction** is a chemical reaction that results in the synthesis (joining) of components that were formerly separate (Figure 2.12a). Again, nitrogen and hydrogen are reactants in a synthesis reaction that yields ammonia as the product. The general equation for a synthesis reaction is $A + B \rightarrow AB$.

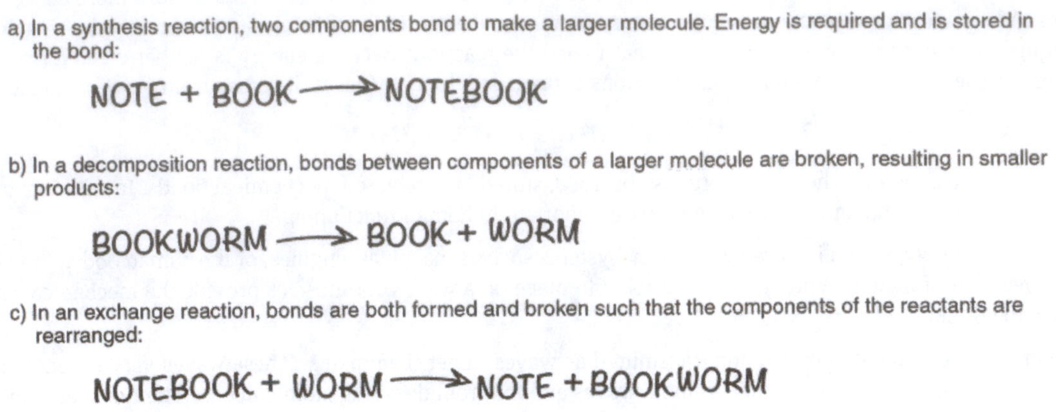

a) In a synthesis reaction, two components bond to make a larger molecule. Energy is required and is stored in the bond:

NOTE + BOOK ⟶ NOTEBOOK

b) In a decomposition reaction, bonds between components of a larger molecule are broken, resulting in smaller products:

BOOKWORM ⟶ BOOK + WORM

c) In an exchange reaction, bonds are both formed and broken such that the components of the reactants are rearranged:

NOTEBOOK + WORM ⟶ NOTE + BOOKWORM

Figure 2.12 The Three Fundamental Chemical Reactions The atoms and molecules involved in the three fundamental chemical reactions can be imagined as words.

In the second example, ammonia is catabolized into its smaller components, and the potential energy that had been stored in its bonds is released. Such reactions are referred to as decomposition reactions. A **decomposition reaction** is a chemical reaction that breaks down or "de-composes" something larger into its constituent parts (see Figure 2.12b). The general equation for a decomposition reaction is: $AB \rightarrow A + B$.

An **exchange reaction** is a chemical reaction in which both synthesis and decomposition occur, chemical bonds are both formed and broken, and chemical energy is absorbed, stored, and released (see Figure 2.12c). The simplest form of an exchange reaction might be: $A + BC \rightarrow AB + C$. Notice that, to produce these products, B and C had to break apart in a decomposition reaction, whereas A and B had to bond in a synthesis reaction. A more complex exchange reaction might be: $AB + CD \rightarrow AC + BD$. Another example might be: $AB + CD \rightarrow AD + BC$.

In theory, any chemical reaction can proceed in either direction under the right conditions. Reactants may synthesize into a product that is later decomposed. Reversibility is also a quality of exchange reactions. For instance, $A + BC \rightarrow AB + C$ could then reverse to $AB + C \rightarrow A + BC$. This reversibility of a chemical reaction is indicated with a double arrow: $A + BC \rightleftarrows AB + C$. Still, in the human body, many chemical reactions do proceed in a predictable direction, either one way or the other. You can think of this more predictable path as the path of least resistance because, typically, the alternate direction requires more energy.

Factors Influencing the Rate of Chemical Reactions

If you pour vinegar into baking soda, the reaction is instantaneous; the concoction will bubble and fizz. But many chemical reactions take time. A variety of factors influence the rate of chemical reactions. This section, however, will consider only the most important in human functioning.

Properties of the Reactants

If chemical reactions are to occur quickly, the atoms in the reactants have to have easy access to one another. Thus, the greater the surface area of the reactants, the more readily they will interact. When you pop a cube of cheese into your mouth, you chew it before you swallow it. Among other things, chewing increases the surface area of the food so that digestive chemicals can more easily get at it. As a general rule, gases tend to react faster than liquids or solids, again because it takes energy to separate particles of a substance, and gases by definition already have space between their particles. Similarly, the larger the molecule, the greater the number of total bonds, so reactions involving smaller molecules, with fewer total bonds, would be expected to proceed faster.

In addition, recall that some elements are more reactive than others. Reactions that involve highly reactive elements like hydrogen proceed more quickly than reactions that involve less reactive elements. Reactions involving stable elements like helium are not likely to happen at all.

Temperature

Nearly all chemical reactions occur at a faster rate at higher temperatures. Recall that kinetic energy is the energy of matter in motion. The kinetic energy of subatomic particles increases in response to increases in thermal energy. The higher the temperature, the faster the particles move, and the more likely they are to come in contact and react.

Concentration and Pressure

If just a few people are dancing at a club, they are unlikely to step on each other's toes. But as more and more people get up to dance—especially if the music is fast—collisions are likely to occur. It is the same with chemical reactions: the more particles present within a given space, the more likely those particles are to bump into one another. This means that chemists can speed up chemical reactions not only by increasing the **concentration** of particles—the number of particles in the space—but also by decreasing the volume of the space, which would correspondingly increase the pressure. If there were 100 dancers in that club, and the manager abruptly moved the party to a room half the size, the concentration of the dancers would double in the new space, and the likelihood of collisions would increase accordingly.

Enzymes and Other Catalysts

For two chemicals in nature to react with each other they first have to come into contact, and this occurs through random collisions. Because heat helps increase the kinetic energy of atoms, ions, and molecules, it promotes their collision. But in the body, extremely high heat—such as a very high fever—can damage body cells and be life-threatening. On the other hand, normal body temperature is not high enough to promote the chemical reactions that sustain life. That is where catalysts come in.

In chemistry, a **catalyst** is a substance that increases the rate of a chemical reaction without itself undergoing any change. You can think of a catalyst as a chemical change agent. They help increase the rate and force at which atoms, ions, and molecules collide, thereby increasing the probability that their valence shell electrons will interact.

The most important catalysts in the human body are enzymes. An **enzyme** is a catalyst composed of protein or ribonucleic acid (RNA), both of which will be discussed later in this chapter. Like all catalysts, enzymes work by lowering the level of energy that needs to be invested in a chemical reaction. A chemical reaction's **activation energy** is the "threshold" level of energy needed to break the bonds in the reactants. Once those bonds are broken, new arrangements can form. Without an enzyme to act as a catalyst, a much larger investment of energy is needed to ignite a chemical reaction (**Figure 2.13**).

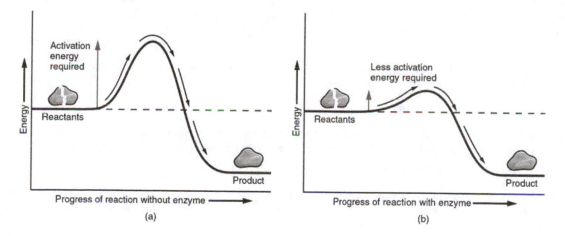

Figure 2.13 Enzymes Enzymes decrease the activation energy required for a given chemical reaction to occur. (a) Without an enzyme, the energy input needed for a reaction to begin is high. (b) With the help of an enzyme, less energy is needed for a reaction to begin.

Enzymes are critical to the body's healthy functioning. They assist, for example, with the breakdown of food and its conversion to energy. In fact, most of the chemical reactions in the body are facilitated by enzymes.

2.4 | Inorganic Compounds Essential to Human Functioning

By the end of this section, you will be able to:

- Compare and contrast inorganic and organic compounds
- Identify the properties of water that make it essential to life
- Explain the role of salts in body functioning
- Distinguish between acids and bases, and explain their role in pH
- Discuss the role of buffers in helping the body maintain pH homeostasis

The concepts you have learned so far in this chapter govern all forms of matter, and would work as a foundation for geology as well as biology. This section of the chapter narrows the focus to the chemistry of human life; that is, the compounds important for the body's structure and function. In general, these compounds are either inorganic or organic.

- An **inorganic compound** is a substance that does not contain both carbon and hydrogen. A great many inorganic compounds do contain hydrogen atoms, such as water (H_2O) and the hydrochloric acid (HCl) produced by your stomach. In contrast, only a handful of inorganic compounds contain carbon atoms. Carbon dioxide (CO_2) is one of the few examples.
- An **organic compound**, then, is a substance that contains both carbon and hydrogen. Organic compounds are synthesized via covalent bonds within living organisms, including the human body. Recall that carbon and hydrogen are the second and third most abundant elements in your body. You will soon discover how these two elements combine in the foods you eat, in the compounds that make up your body structure, and in the chemicals that fuel your functioning.

The following section examines the three groups of inorganic compounds essential to life: water, salts, acids, and bases. Organic compounds are covered later in the chapter.

Water

As much as 70 percent of an adult's body weight is water. This water is contained both within the cells and between the cells that make up tissues and organs. Its several roles make water indispensable to human functioning.

Water as a Lubricant and Cushion

Water is a major component of many of the body's lubricating fluids. Just as oil lubricates the hinge on a door, water in synovial fluid lubricates the actions of body joints, and water in pleural fluid helps the lungs expand and recoil with breathing. Watery fluids help keep food flowing through the digestive tract, and ensure that the movement of adjacent abdominal organs is friction free.

Water also protects cells and organs from physical trauma, cushioning the brain within the skull, for example, and protecting the delicate nerve tissue of the eyes. Water cushions a developing fetus in the mother's womb as well.

Water as a Heat Sink

A heat sink is a substance or object that absorbs and dissipates heat but does not experience a corresponding increase in temperature. In the body, water absorbs the heat generated by chemical reactions without greatly increasing in temperature. Moreover, when the environmental temperature soars, the water stored in the body helps keep the body cool. This cooling effect happens as warm blood from the body's core flows to the blood vessels just under the skin and is transferred to the environment. At the same time, sweat glands release warm water in sweat. As the water evaporates into the air, it carries away heat, and then the cooler blood from the periphery circulates back to the body core.

Water as a Component of Liquid Mixtures

A mixture is a combination of two or more substances, each of which maintains its own chemical identity. In other words, the constituent substances are not chemically bonded into a new, larger chemical compound. The concept is easy to imagine if you think of powdery substances such as flour and sugar; when you stir them together in a bowl, they obviously do not bond to form a new compound. The room air you breathe is a gaseous mixture, containing three discrete elements—nitrogen, oxygen, and argon—and one compound, carbon dioxide. There are three types of liquid mixtures, all of which contain water as a key component. These are solutions, colloids, and suspensions.

For cells in the body to survive, they must be kept moist in a water-based liquid called a solution. In chemistry, a liquid **solution** consists of a solvent that dissolves a substance called a solute. An important characteristic of solutions is that they are homogeneous; that is, the solute molecules are distributed evenly throughout the solution. If you were to stir a teaspoon of sugar into a glass of water, the sugar would dissolve into sugar molecules separated by water molecules. The ratio of sugar to water in the left side of the glass would be the same as the ratio of sugar to water in the right side of the glass. If you were to add more sugar, the ratio of sugar to water would change, but the distribution—provided you had stirred well—would still be even.

Water is considered the "universal solvent" and it is believed that life cannot exist without water because of this. Water is certainly the most abundant solvent in the body; essentially all of the body's chemical reactions occur among compounds dissolved in water. Because water molecules are polar, with regions of positive and negative electrical charge, water readily dissolves ionic compounds and polar covalent compounds. Such compounds are referred to as hydrophilic, or "water-loving." As mentioned above, sugar dissolves well in water. This is because sugar molecules contain regions of hydrogen-oxygen polar bonds, making it hydrophilic. Nonpolar molecules, which do not readily dissolve in water, are called hydrophobic, or "water-fearing."

Concentrations of Solutes

Various mixtures of solutes and water are described in chemistry. The concentration of a given solute is the number of particles of that solute in a given space (oxygen makes up about 21 percent of atmospheric air). In the bloodstream of humans, glucose concentration is usually measured in milligram (mg) per deciliter (dL), and in a healthy adult averages about 100 mg/dL. Another method of measuring the concentration of a solute is by its molarilty—which is moles (M) of the molecules per liter (L). The mole of an element is its atomic weight, while a mole of a compound is the sum of the atomic weights of its components, called the molecular weight. An often-used example is calculating a mole of glucose, with the chemical formula $C_6H_{12}O_6$. Using the periodic table, the atomic weight of carbon (C) is 12.011 grams (g), and there are six carbons in glucose, for a total atomic weight of 72.066 g. Doing the same calculations for hydrogen (H) and oxygen (O), the molecular weight equals 180.156g (the "gram molecular weight" of glucose). When water is added to make one liter of solution, you have one mole (1M) of glucose. This is particularly useful in chemistry because of the relationship of moles to "Avogadro's number." A mole of any solution has the same number of particles in it: 6.02×10^{23}. Many substances in the bloodstream and other tissue of the body are measured in thousandths of a mole, or millimoles (mM).

A **colloid** is a mixture that is somewhat like a heavy solution. The solute particles consist of tiny clumps of molecules large enough to make the liquid mixture opaque (because the particles are large enough to scatter light). Familiar examples of colloids are milk and cream. In the thyroid glands, the thyroid hormone is stored as a thick protein mixture also called a colloid.

A **suspension** is a liquid mixture in which a heavier substance is suspended temporarily in a liquid, but over time, settles out. This separation of particles from a suspension is called sedimentation. An example of sedimentation occurs in the blood test that establishes sedimentation rate, or sed rate. The test measures how quickly red blood cells in a test tube settle out of the watery portion of blood (known as plasma) over a set period of time. Rapid sedimentation of blood cells does not normally happen in the healthy body, but aspects of certain diseases can cause blood cells to clump together, and these heavy clumps of blood cells settle to the bottom of the test tube more quickly than do normal blood cells.

The Role of Water in Chemical Reactions

Two types of chemical reactions involve the creation or the consumption of water: dehydration synthesis and hydrolysis.

- In dehydration synthesis, one reactant gives up an atom of hydrogen and another reactant gives up a hydroxyl group (OH) in the synthesis of a new product. In the formation of their covalent bond, a molecule of water is released as a byproduct (Figure 2.14). This is also sometimes referred to as a condensation reaction.

- In hydrolysis, a molecule of water disrupts a compound, breaking its bonds. The water is itself split into H and OH. One portion of the severed compound then bonds with the hydrogen atom, and the other portion bonds with the hydroxyl group.

These reactions are reversible, and play an important role in the chemistry of organic compounds (which will be discussed shortly).

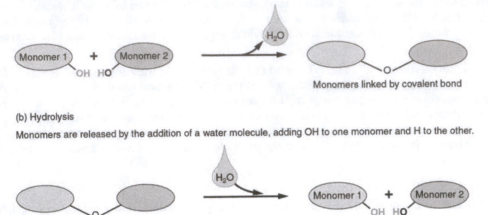

(a) Dehydration synthesis

Monomers are joined by removal of OH from one monomer and removal of H from the other at the site of bond formation.

(b) Hydrolysis

Monomers are released by the addition of a water molecule, adding OH to one monomer and H to the other.

Figure 2.14 Dehydration Synthesis and Hydrolysis Monomers, the basic units for building larger molecules, form polymers (two or more chemically-bonded monomers). (a) In dehydration synthesis, two monomers are covalently bonded in a reaction in which one gives up a hydroxyl group and the other a hydrogen atom. A molecule of water is released as a byproduct during dehydration reactions. (b) In hydrolysis, the covalent bond between two monomers is split by the addition of a hydrogen atom to one and a hydroxyl group to the other, which requires the contribution of one molecule of water.

Salts

Recall that salts are formed when ions form ionic bonds. In these reactions, one atom gives up one or more electrons, and thus becomes positively charged, whereas the other accepts one or more electrons and becomes negatively charged. You can now define a salt as a substance that, when dissolved in water, dissociates into ions other than H^+ or OH^-. This fact is important in distinguishing salts from acids and bases, discussed next.

A typical salt, NaCl, dissociates completely in water (Figure 2.15). The positive and negative regions on the water molecule (the hydrogen and oxygen ends respectively) attract the negative chloride and positive sodium ions, pulling them away from each other. Again, whereas nonpolar and polar covalently bonded compounds break apart into molecules in solution, salts dissociate into ions. These ions are electrolytes; they are capable of conducting an electrical current in solution. This property is critical to the function of ions in transmitting nerve impulses and prompting muscle contraction.

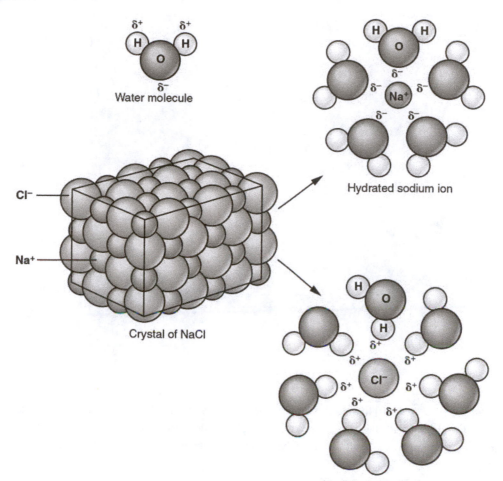

Figure 2.15 Dissociation of Sodium Chloride in Water Notice that the crystals of sodium chloride dissociate not into molecules of NaCl, but into Na^+ cations and Cl^- anions, each completely surrounded by water molecules.

Many other salts are important in the body. For example, bile salts produced by the liver help break apart dietary fats, and calcium phosphate salts form the mineral portion of teeth and bones.

Acids and Bases

Acids and bases, like salts, dissociate in water into electrolytes. Acids and bases can very much change the properties of the solutions in which they are dissolved.

Acids

An **acid** is a substance that releases hydrogen ions (H^+) in solution (**Figure 2.16a**). Because an atom of hydrogen has just one proton and one electron, a positively charged hydrogen ion is simply a proton. This solitary proton is highly likely to participate in chemical reactions. Strong acids are compounds that release all of their H^+ in solution; that is, they ionize completely. Hydrochloric acid (HCl), which is released from cells in the lining of the stomach, is a strong acid because it releases all of its H^+ in the stomach's watery environment. This strong acid aids in digestion and kills ingested microbes. Weak acids do not ionize completely; that is, some of their hydrogen ions remain bonded within a compound in solution. An example of a weak acid is vinegar, or acetic acid; it is called acetate after it gives up a proton.

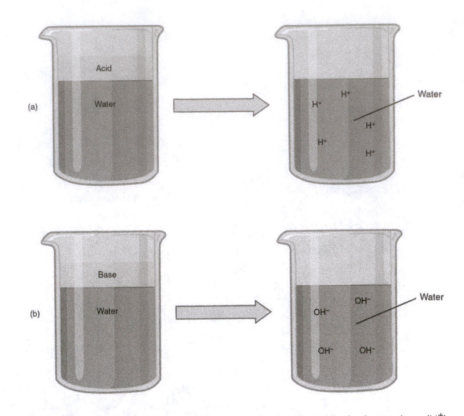

Figure 2.16 Acids and Bases (a) In aqueous solution, an acid dissociates into hydrogen ions (H^+) and anions. Nearly every molecule of a strong acid dissociates, producing a high concentration of H^+. (b) In aqueous solution, a base dissociates into hydroxyl ions (OH^-) and cations. Nearly every molecule of a strong base dissociates, producing a high concentration of OH^-.

Bases

A **base** is a substance that releases hydroxyl ions (OH^-) in solution, or one that accepts H^+ already present in solution (see Figure 2.16**b**). The hydroxyl ions (also known as hydroxide ions) or other basic substances combine with H^+ present to form a water molecule, thereby removing H^+ and reducing the solution's acidity. Strong bases release most or all of their hydroxyl ions; weak bases release only some hydroxyl ions or absorb only a few H^+. Food mixed with hydrochloric acid from the stomach would burn the small intestine, the next portion of the digestive tract after the stomach, if it were not for the release of bicarbonate (HCO_3^-), a weak base that attracts H^+. Bicarbonate accepts some of the H^+ protons, thereby reducing the acidity of the solution.

The Concept of pH

The relative acidity or alkalinity of a solution can be indicated by its pH. A solution's **pH** is the negative, base-10 logarithm of the hydrogen ion (H^+) concentration of the solution. As an example, a pH 4 solution has an H^+ concentration that is ten times greater than that of a pH 5 solution. That is, a solution with a pH of 4 is ten times more acidic than a solution with a pH of 5. The concept of pH will begin to make more sense when you study the pH scale, like that shown in Figure 2.17. The scale consists of a series of increments ranging from 0 to 14. A solution with a pH of 7 is considered neutral—neither acidic nor basic. Pure water has a pH of 7. The lower the number below 7, the more acidic the solution, or the greater the concentration of H^+. The concentration of hydrogen ions at each pH value is 10 times different than the next pH. For instance, a pH value of 4 corresponds to a proton concentration of 10^{-4} M, or 0.0001M, while a pH value of 5 corresponds to a proton concentration of 10^{-5} M, or 0.00001M. The higher the number above 7, the more basic (alkaline) the solution, or the lower the concentration of H^+. Human urine, for example, is ten times more acidic than pure water, and HCl is 10,000,000 times more acidic than water.

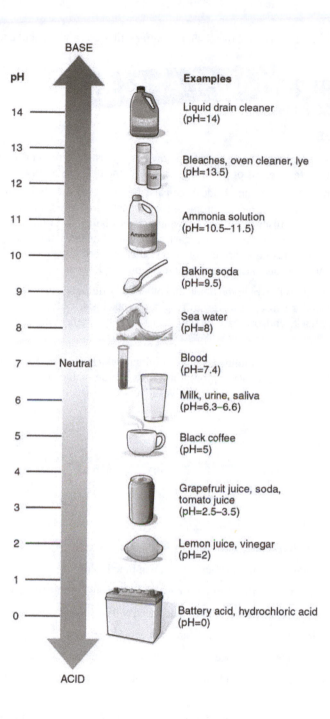

Figure 2.17 The pH Scale

Buffers

The pH of human blood normally ranges from 7.35 to 7.45, although it is typically identified as pH 7.4. At this slightly basic pH, blood can reduce the acidity resulting from the carbon dioxide (CO_2) constantly being released into the bloodstream by the trillions of cells in the body. Homeostatic mechanisms (along with exhaling CO_2 while breathing) normally keep the pH of blood within this narrow range. This is critical, because fluctuations—either too acidic or too alkaline—can lead to life-threatening disorders.

All cells of the body depend on homeostatic regulation of acid–base balance at a pH of approximately 7.4. The body therefore has several mechanisms for this regulation, involving breathing, the excretion of chemicals in urine, and the internal release of chemicals collectively called buffers into body fluids. A **buffer** is a solution of a weak acid and its conjugate base. A buffer can neutralize small amounts of acids or bases in body fluids. For example, if there is even a slight decrease below 7.35 in the pH of a bodily fluid, the buffer in the fluid—in this case, acting as a weak base—will bind the excess hydrogen ions. In contrast, if pH rises above 7.45, the buffer will act as a weak acid and contribute hydrogen ions.

Homeostatic IMBALANCES

Acids and Bases

Excessive acidity of the blood and other body fluids is known as acidosis. Common causes of acidosis are situations and disorders that reduce the effectiveness of breathing, especially the person's ability to exhale fully, which causes a buildup of CO_2 (and H^+) in the bloodstream. Acidosis can also be caused by metabolic problems that reduce the level or function of buffers that act as bases, or that promote the production of acids. For instance, with severe diarrhea, too much bicarbonate can be lost from the body, allowing acids to build up in body fluids. In people with poorly managed diabetes (ineffective regulation of blood sugar), acids called ketones are produced as a form of body fuel. These can build up in the blood, causing a serious condition called diabetic ketoacidosis. Kidney failure, liver failure, heart failure, cancer, and other disorders also can prompt metabolic acidosis.

In contrast, alkalosis is a condition in which the blood and other body fluids are too alkaline (basic). As with acidosis, respiratory disorders are a major cause; however, in respiratory alkalosis, carbon dioxide levels fall too low. Lung disease, aspirin overdose, shock, and ordinary anxiety can cause respiratory alkalosis, which reduces the normal concentration of H^+.

Metabolic alkalosis often results from prolonged, severe vomiting, which causes a loss of hydrogen and chloride ions (as components of HCl). Medications also can prompt alkalosis. These include diuretics that cause the body to lose potassium ions, as well as antacids when taken in excessive amounts, for instance by someone with persistent heartburn or an ulcer.

2.5 | Organic Compounds Essential to Human Functioning

By the end of this section, you will be able to:

- Identify four types of organic molecules essential to human functioning
- Explain the chemistry behind carbon's affinity for covalently bonding in organic compounds
- Provide examples of three types of carbohydrates, and identify the primary functions of carbohydrates in the body
- Discuss four types of lipids important in human functioning
- Describe the structure of proteins, and discuss their importance to human functioning
- Identify the building blocks of nucleic acids, and the roles of DNA, RNA, and ATP in human functioning

Organic compounds typically consist of groups of carbon atoms covalently bonded to hydrogen, usually oxygen, and often other elements as well. Created by living things, they are found throughout the world, in soils and seas, commercial products, and every cell of the human body. The four types most important to human structure and function are carbohydrates, lipids, proteins, and nucleotides. Before exploring these compounds, you need to first understand the chemistry of carbon.

The Chemistry of Carbon

What makes organic compounds ubiquitous is the chemistry of their carbon core. Recall that carbon atoms have four electrons in their valence shell, and that the octet rule dictates that atoms tend to react in such a way as to complete their valence shell with eight electrons. Carbon atoms do not complete their valence shells by donating or accepting four electrons. Instead, they readily share electrons via covalent bonds.

Commonly, carbon atoms share with other carbon atoms, often forming a long carbon chain referred to as a carbon skeleton. When they do share, however, they do not share all their electrons exclusively with each other. Rather, carbon atoms tend to share electrons with a variety of other elements, one of which is always hydrogen. Carbon and hydrogen groupings are called hydrocarbons. If you study the figures of organic compounds in the remainder of this chapter, you will see several with chains of hydrocarbons in one region of the compound.

Many combinations are possible to fill carbon's four "vacancies." Carbon may share electrons with oxygen or nitrogen or other atoms in a particular region of an organic compound. Moreover, the atoms to which carbon atoms bond may also be part of a functional group. A **functional group** is a group of atoms linked by strong covalent bonds and tending to function in chemical reactions as a single unit. You can think of functional groups as tightly knit "cliques" whose members are unlikely to be parted. Five functional groups are important in human physiology; these are the hydroxyl, carboxyl, amino, methyl and phosphate groups (Table 2.1).

Functional Groups Important in Human Physiology

Functional group	Structural formula	Importance
Hydroxyl	$-O-H$	Hydroxyl groups are polar. They are components of all four types of organic compounds discussed in this chapter. They are involved in dehydration synthesis and hydrolysis reactions.
Carboxyl	$O-C-OH$	Carboxyl groups are found within fatty acids, amino acids, and many other acids.
Amino	$-N-H_2$	Amino groups are found within amino acids, the building blocks of proteins.
Methyl	$-C-H_3$	Methyl groups are found within amino acids.
Phosphate	$-P-O_4^{2-}$	Phosphate groups are found within phospholipids and nucleotides.

Table 2.1

Carbon's affinity for covalent bonding means that many distinct and relatively stable organic molecules nevertheless readily form larger, more complex molecules. Any large molecule is referred to as **macromolecule** (macro- = "large"), and the organic compounds in this section all fit this description. However, some macromolecules are made up of several "copies" of single units called monomer (mono- = "one"; -mer = "part"). Like beads in a long necklace, these monomers link by covalent bonds to form long polymers (poly- = "many"). There are many examples of monomers and polymers among the organic compounds.

Monomers form polymers by engaging in dehydration synthesis (see Figure 2.14). As was noted earlier, this reaction results in the release of a molecule of water. Each monomer contributes: One gives up a hydrogen atom and the other gives up a hydroxyl group. Polymers are split into monomers by hydrolysis (-lysis = "rupture"). The bonds between their monomers are broken, via the donation of a molecule of water, which contributes a hydrogen atom to one monomer and a hydroxyl group to the other.

Carbohydrates

The term carbohydrate means "hydrated carbon." Recall that the root hydro- indicates water. A **carbohydrate** is a molecule composed of carbon, hydrogen, and oxygen; in most carbohydrates, hydrogen and oxygen are found in the same two-to-one relative proportions they have in water. In fact, the chemical formula for a "generic" molecule of carbohydrate is $(CH_2O)_n$.

Carbohydrates are referred to as saccharides, a word meaning "sugars." Three forms are important in the body. Monosaccharides are the monomers of carbohydrates. Disaccharides (di- = "two") are made up of two monomers. **Polysaccharides** are the polymers, and can consist of hundreds to thousands of monomers.

Monosaccharides

A **monosaccharide** is a monomer of carbohydrates. Five monosaccharides are important in the body. Three of these are the hexose sugars, so called because they each contain six atoms of carbon. These are glucose, fructose, and galactose, shown in Figure 2.18a. The remaining monosaccharides are the two pentose sugars, each of which contains five atoms of carbon. They are ribose and deoxyribose, shown in Figure 2.18b.

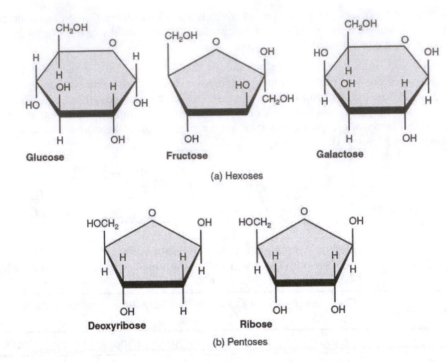

Figure 2.18 Five Important Monosaccharides

Disaccharides

A **disaccharide** is a pair of monosaccharides. Disaccharides are formed via dehydration synthesis, and the bond linking them is referred to as a glycosidic bond (glyco- = "sugar"). Three disaccharides (shown in Figure 2.19) are important to humans. These are sucrose, commonly referred to as table sugar; lactose, or milk sugar; and maltose, or malt sugar. As you can tell from their common names, you consume these in your diet; however, your body cannot use them directly. Instead, in the digestive tract, they are split into their component monosaccharides via hydrolysis.

(a) The monosaccharides glucose and fructose bond to form sucrose

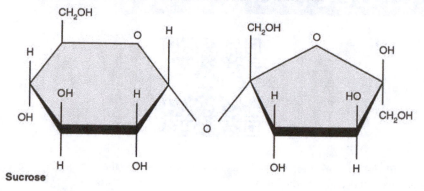

Sucrose

(b) The monosaccharides galactose and glucose bond to form lactose.

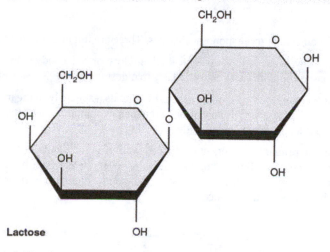

Lactose

(c) Two glucose monosaccharides bond to form maltose.

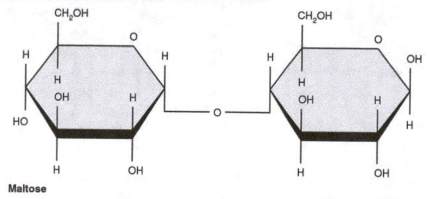

Maltose

Figure 2.19 Three Important Disaccharides   All three important disaccharides form by dehydration synthesis.

Interactive LINK

Watch this video (http://openstaxcollege.org/l/disaccharide) to observe the formation of a disaccharide. What happens when water encounters a glycosidic bond?

Polysaccharides

Polysaccharides can contain a few to a thousand or more monosaccharides. Three are important to the body (Figure 2.20):

- Starches are polymers of glucose. They occur in long chains called amylose or branched chains called amylopectin, both of which are stored in plant-based foods and are relatively easy to digest.

- Glycogen is also a polymer of glucose, but it is stored in the tissues of animals, especially in the muscles and liver. It is not considered a dietary carbohydrate because very little glycogen remains in animal tissues after slaughter; however, the human body stores excess glucose as glycogen, again, in the muscles and liver.

- Cellulose, a polysaccharide that is the primary component of the cell wall of green plants, is the component of plant food referred to as "fiber". In humans, cellulose/fiber is not digestible; however, dietary fiber has many health benefits. It helps you feel full so you eat less, it promotes a healthy digestive tract, and a diet high in fiber is thought to reduce the risk of heart disease and possibly some forms of cancer.

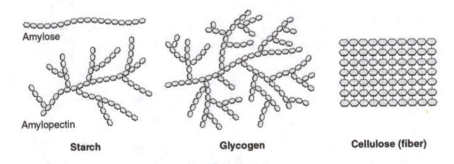

Amylose

Amylopectin

Starch   **Glycogen**   **Cellulose (fiber)**

Figure 2.20 Three Important Polysaccharides Three important polysaccharides are starches, glycogen, and fiber.

Functions of Carbohydrates

The body obtains carbohydrates from plant-based foods. Grains, fruits, and legumes and other vegetables provide most of the carbohydrate in the human diet, although lactose is found in dairy products.

Although most body cells can break down other organic compounds for fuel, all body cells can use glucose. Moreover, nerve cells (neurons) in the brain, spinal cord, and through the peripheral nervous system, as well as red blood cells, can use only glucose for fuel. In the breakdown of glucose for energy, molecules of adenosine triphosphate, better known as ATP, are produced. **Adenosine triphosphate (ATP)** is composed of a ribose sugar, an adenine base, and three phosphate groups. ATP releases free energy when its phosphate bonds are broken, and thus supplies ready energy to the cell. More ATP is produced in the presence of oxygen (O_2) than in pathways that do not use oxygen. The overall reaction for the conversion of the energy in glucose to energy stored in ATP can be written:

$$C_6H_{12}O_6 + 6\,O_2 \;\rightarrow\; 6\,CO_2 + 6\,H_2O + ATP$$

In addition to being a critical fuel source, carbohydrates are present in very small amounts in cells' structure. For instance, some carbohydrate molecules bind with proteins to produce glycoproteins, and others combine with lipids to produce glycolipids, both of which are found in the membrane that encloses the contents of body cells.

Lipids

A **lipid** is one of a highly diverse group of compounds made up mostly of hydrocarbons. The few oxygen atoms they contain are often at the periphery of the molecule. Their nonpolar hydrocarbons make all lipids hydrophobic. In water, lipids do not form a true solution, but they may form an emulsion, which is the term for a mixture of solutions that do not mix well.

Triglycerides

A **triglyceride** is one of the most common dietary lipid groups, and the type found most abundantly in body tissues. This compound, which is commonly referred to as a fat, is formed from the synthesis of two types of molecules (**Figure 2.21**):

- A glycerol backbone at the core of triglycerides, consists of three carbon atoms.

- Three fatty acids, long chains of hydrocarbons with a carboxyl group and a methyl group at opposite ends, extend from each of the carbons of the glycerol.

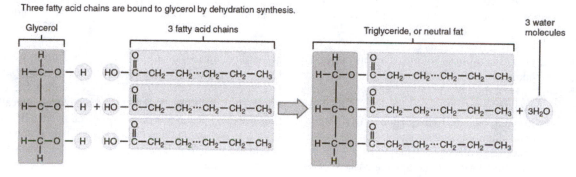

Figure 2.21 Triglycerides   Triglycerides are composed of glycerol attached to three fatty acids via dehydration synthesis. Notice that glycerol gives up a hydrogen atom, and the carboxyl groups on the fatty acids each give up a hydroxyl group.

Triglycerides form via dehydration synthesis. Glycerol gives up hydrogen atoms from its hydroxyl groups at each bond, and the carboxyl group on each fatty acid chain gives up a hydroxyl group. A total of three water molecules are thereby released.

Fatty acid chains that have no double carbon bonds anywhere along their length and therefore contain the maximum number of hydrogen atoms are called saturated fatty acids. These straight, rigid chains pack tightly together and are solid or semi-solid at room temperature (**Figure 2.22a**). Butter and lard are examples, as is the fat found on a steak or in your own body. In contrast, fatty acids with one double carbon bond are kinked at that bond (**Figure 2.22b**). These monounsaturated fatty acids are therefore unable to pack together tightly, and are liquid at room temperature. Polyunsaturated fatty acids contain two or more double carbon bonds, and are also liquid at room temperature. Plant oils such as olive oil typically contain both mono- and polyunsaturated fatty acids.

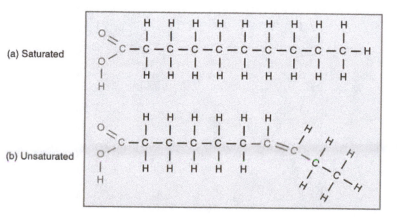

Figure 2.22 Fatty Acid Shapes   The level of saturation of a fatty acid affects its shape. (a) Saturated fatty acid chains are straight. (b) Unsaturated fatty acid chains are kinked.

Whereas a diet high in saturated fatty acids increases the risk of heart disease, a diet high in unsaturated fatty acids is thought to reduce the risk. This is especially true for the omega-3 unsaturated fatty acids found in cold-water fish such as salmon. These fatty acids have their first double carbon bond at the third hydrocarbon from the methyl group (referred to as the omega end of the molecule).

Finally, *trans* fatty acids found in some processed foods, including some stick and tub margarines, are thought to be even more harmful to the heart and blood vessels than saturated fatty acids. *Trans* fats are created from unsaturated fatty acids (such as corn oil) when chemically treated to produce partially hydrogenated fats.

As a group, triglycerides are a major fuel source for the body. When you are resting or asleep, a majority of the energy used to keep you alive is derived from triglycerides stored in your fat (adipose) tissues. Triglycerides also fuel long, slow physical activity such as gardening or hiking, and contribute a modest percentage of energy for vigorous physical activity. Dietary fat also assists the absorption and transport of the nonpolar fat-soluble vitamins A, D, E, and K. Additionally, stored body fat protects and cushions the body's bones and internal organs, and acts as insulation to retain body heat.

Fatty acids are also components of glycolipids, which are sugar-fat compounds found in the cell membrane. Lipoproteins are compounds in which the hydrophobic triglycerides are packaged in protein envelopes for transport in body fluids.

Phospholipids

As its name suggests, a **phospholipid** is a bond between the glycerol component of a lipid and a phosphorous molecule. In fact, phospholipids are similar in structure to triglycerides. However, instead of having three fatty acids, a phospholipid is generated from a diglyceride, a glycerol with just two fatty acid chains (Figure 2.23). The third binding site on the glycerol is taken up by the phosphate group, which in turn is attached to a polar "head" region of the molecule. Recall that triglycerides are nonpolar and hydrophobic. This still holds for the fatty acid portion of a phospholipid compound. However, the head of a phospholipid contains charges on the phosphate groups, as well as on the nitrogen atom. These charges make the phospholipid head hydrophilic. Therefore, phospholipids are said to have hydrophobic tails, containing the neutral fatty acids, and hydrophilic heads, containing the charged phosphate groups and nitrogen atom.

(a) Phospholipids

Two fatty acid chains and a phosphorus-containing group are attached to the glycerol backbone.

Example: Phosphatidylcholine

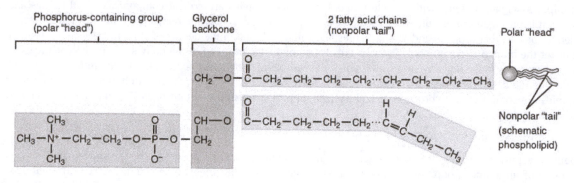

(b) Sterols

Four interlocking hydrocarbon rings from a steroid.

Example: Cholesterol (cholesterol is the basis for all steroids formed in the body)

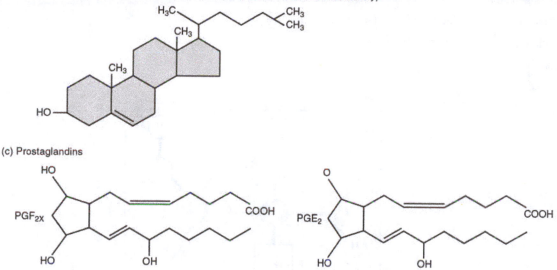

(c) Prostaglandins

Figure 2.23 Other Important Lipids (a) Phospholipids are composed of two fatty acids, glycerol, and a phosphate group. (b) Sterols are ring-shaped lipids. Shown here is cholesterol. (c) Prostaglandins are derived from unsaturated fatty acids. Prostaglandin E2 (PGE2) includes hydroxyl and carboxyl groups.

Steroids

A **steroid** compound (referred to as a sterol) has as its foundation a set of four hydrocarbon rings bonded to a variety of other atoms and molecules (see Figure 2.23b). Although both plants and animals synthesize sterols, the type that makes the most important contribution to human structure and function is cholesterol, which is synthesized by the liver in humans and animals and is also present in most animal-based foods. Like other lipids, cholesterol's hydrocarbons make it hydrophobic; however, it has a polar hydroxyl head that is hydrophilic. Cholesterol is an important component of bile acids, compounds that help emulsify dietary fats. In fact, the word root chole- refers to bile. Cholesterol is also a building block of many hormones, signaling molecules that the body releases to regulate processes at distant sites. Finally, like phospholipids, cholesterol molecules are found in the cell membrane, where their hydrophobic and hydrophilic regions help regulate the flow of substances into and out of the cell.

Prostaglandins

Like a hormone, a **prostaglandin** is one of a group of signaling molecules, but prostaglandins are derived from unsaturated fatty acids (see Figure 2.23c). One reason that the omega-3 fatty acids found in fish are beneficial is that they stimulate the production of certain prostaglandins that help regulate aspects of blood pressure and inflammation, and thereby reduce the risk for heart disease. Prostaglandins also sensitize nerves to pain. One class of pain-relieving medications called nonsteroidal anti-inflammatory drugs (NSAIDs) works by reducing the effects of prostaglandins.

Proteins

You might associate proteins with muscle tissue, but in fact, proteins are critical components of all tissues and organs. A **protein** is an organic molecule composed of amino acids linked by peptide bonds. Proteins include the keratin in the epidermis of skin that protects underlying tissues, the collagen found in the dermis of skin, in bones, and in the meninges that cover the brain and spinal cord. Proteins are also components of many of the body's functional chemicals, including digestive enzymes in the digestive tract, antibodies, the neurotransmitters that neurons use to communicate with other cells, and the peptide-based hormones that regulate certain body functions (for instance, growth hormone). While carbohydrates and lipids are composed of hydrocarbons and oxygen, all proteins also contain nitrogen (N), and many contain sulfur (S), in addition to carbon, hydrogen, and oxygen.

Microstructure of Proteins

Proteins are polymers made up of nitrogen-containing monomers called amino acids. An **amino acid** is a molecule composed of an amino group and a carboxyl group, together with a variable side chain. Just 20 different amino acids contribute to nearly all of the thousands of different proteins important in human structure and function. Body proteins contain a unique combination of a few dozen to a few hundred of these 20 amino acid monomers. All 20 of these amino acids share a similar structure (Figure 2.24). All consist of a central carbon atom to which the following are bonded:

- a hydrogen atom
- an alkaline (basic) amino group NH_2 (see Table 2.1)
- an acidic carboxyl group COOH (see Table 2.1)
- a variable group

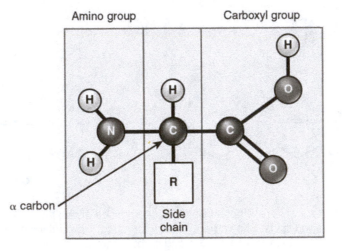

Figure 2.24 Structure of an Amino Acid

Notice that all amino acids contain both an acid (the carboxyl group) and a base (the amino group) (amine = "nitrogen-containing"). For this reason, they make excellent buffers, helping the body regulate acid–base balance. What distinguishes the 20 amino acids from one another is their variable group, which is referred to as a side chain or an R-group. This group can vary in size and can be polar or nonpolar, giving each amino acid its unique characteristics. For example, the side chains of two amino acids—cysteine and methionine—contain sulfur. Sulfur does not readily participate in hydrogen bonds, whereas all other amino acids do. This variation influences the way that proteins containing cysteine and methionine are assembled.

Amino acids join via dehydration synthesis to form protein polymers (Figure 2.25). The unique bond holding amino acids together is called a peptide bond. A **peptide bond** is a covalent bond between two amino acids that forms by dehydration synthesis. A peptide, in fact, is a very short chain of amino acids. Strands containing fewer than about 100 amino acids are generally referred to as polypeptides rather than proteins.

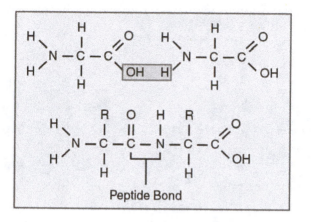

Figure 2.25 Peptide Bond Different amino acids join together to form peptides, polypeptides, or proteins via dehydration synthesis. The bonds between the amino acids are peptide bonds.

The body is able to synthesize most of the amino acids from components of other molecules; however, nine cannot be synthesized and have to be consumed in the diet. These are known as the essential amino acids.

Free amino acids available for protein construction are said to reside in the amino acid pool within cells. Structures within cells use these amino acids when assembling proteins. If a particular essential amino acid is not available in sufficient quantities in the amino acid pool, however, synthesis of proteins containing it can slow or even cease.

Shape of Proteins

Just as a fork cannot be used to eat soup and a spoon cannot be used to spear meat, a protein's shape is essential to its function. A protein's shape is determined, most fundamentally, by the sequence of amino acids of which it is made (**Figure 2.26a**). The sequence is called the primary structure of the protein.

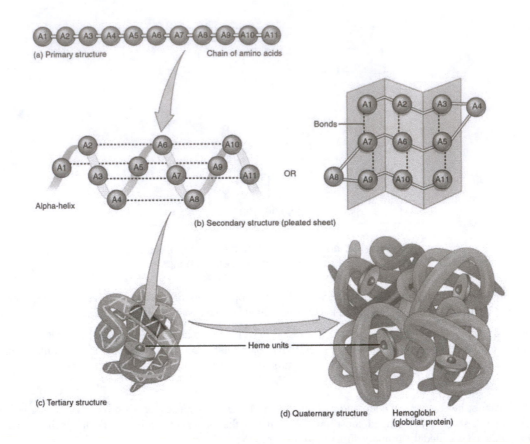

Figure 2.26 The Shape of Proteins (a) The primary structure is the sequence of amino acids that make up the polypeptide chain. (b) The secondary structure, which can take the form of an alpha-helix or a beta-pleated sheet, is maintained by hydrogen bonds between amino acids in different regions of the original polypeptide strand. (c) The tertiary structure occurs as a result of further folding and bonding of the secondary structure. (d) The quaternary structure occurs as a result of interactions between two or more tertiary subunits. The example shown here is hemoglobin, a protein in red blood cells which transports oxygen to body tissues.

Although some polypeptides exist as linear chains, most are twisted or folded into more complex secondary structures that form when bonding occurs between amino acids with different properties at different regions of the polypeptide. The most common secondary structure is a spiral called an alpha-helix. If you were to take a length of string and simply twist it into a spiral, it would not hold the shape. Similarly, a strand of amino acids could not maintain a stable spiral shape without the help of hydrogen bonds, which create bridges between different regions of the same strand (see Figure 2.26b). Less commonly, a polypeptide chain can form a beta-pleated sheet, in which hydrogen bonds form bridges between different regions of a single polypeptide that has folded back upon itself, or between two or more adjacent polypeptide chains.

The secondary structure of proteins further folds into a compact three-dimensional shape, referred to as the protein's tertiary structure (see Figure 2.26c). In this configuration, amino acids that had been very distant in the primary chain can be brought quite close via hydrogen bonds or, in proteins containing cysteine, via disulfide bonds. A **disulfide bond** is a covalent bond between sulfur atoms in a polypeptide. Often, two or more separate polypeptides bond to form an even larger protein with a quaternary structure (see Figure 2.26d). The polypeptide subunits forming a quaternary structure can be identical or different. For instance, hemoglobin, the protein found in red blood cells is composed of four tertiary polypeptides, two of which are called alpha chains and two of which are called beta chains.

When they are exposed to extreme heat, acids, bases, and certain other substances, proteins will denature. **Denaturation** is a change in the structure of a molecule through physical or chemical means. Denatured proteins lose their functional shape and are no longer able to carry out their jobs. An everyday example of protein denaturation is the curdling of milk when acidic lemon juice is added.

The contribution of the shape of a protein to its function can hardly be exaggerated. For example, the long, slender shape of protein strands that make up muscle tissue is essential to their ability to contract (shorten) and relax (lengthen). As another example, bones contain long threads of a protein called collagen that acts as scaffolding upon which bone minerals are deposited. These elongated proteins, called fibrous proteins, are strong and durable and typically hydrophobic.

In contrast, globular proteins are globes or spheres that tend to be highly reactive and are hydrophilic. The hemoglobin proteins packed into red blood cells are an example (see Figure 2.26d); however, globular proteins are abundant throughout the body, playing critical roles in most body functions. Enzymes, introduced earlier as protein catalysts, are examples of this. The next section takes a closer look at the action of enzymes.

Proteins Function as Enzymes

If you were trying to type a paper, and every time you hit a key on your laptop there was a delay of six or seven minutes before you got a response, you would probably get a new laptop. In a similar way, without enzymes to catalyze chemical reactions, the human body would be nonfunctional. It functions only because enzymes function.

Enzymatic reactions—chemical reactions catalyzed by enzymes—begin when substrates bind to the enzyme. A **substrate** is a reactant in an enzymatic reaction. This occurs on regions of the enzyme known as active sites (Figure 2.27). Any given enzyme catalyzes just one type of chemical reaction. This characteristic, called specificity, is due to the fact that a substrate with a particular shape and electrical charge can bind only to an active site corresponding to that substrate.

Due to this jigsaw puzzle-like match between an enzyme and its substrates, enzymes are known for their specificity. In fact, as an enzyme binds to its substrate(s), the enzyme structure changes slightly to find the best fit between the transition state (a structural intermediate between the substrate and product) and the active site, just as a rubber glove molds to a hand inserted into it. This active-site modification in the presence of substrate, along with the simultaneous formation of the transition state, is called induced fit. Overall, there is a specifically matched enzyme for each substrate and, thus, for each chemical reaction; however, there is some flexibility as well. Some enzymes have the ability to act on several different structurally related substrates.

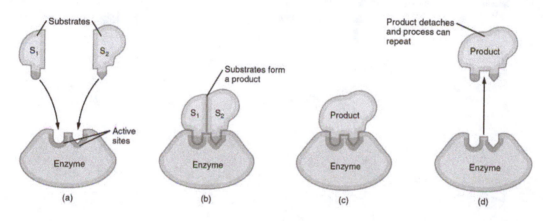

Figure 2.27 Steps in an Enzymatic Reaction According to the induced-fit model, the active site of the enzyme undergoes conformational changes upon binding with the substrate.(a) Substrates approach active sites on enzyme. (b) Substrates bind to active sites, producing an enzyme–substrate complex. (c) Changes internal to the enzyme–substrate complex facilitate interaction of the substrates. (d) Products are released and the enzyme returns to its original form, ready to facilitate another enzymatic reaction.

Binding of a substrate produces an enzyme–substrate complex. It is likely that enzymes speed up chemical reactions in part because the enzyme–substrate complex undergoes a set of temporary and reversible changes that cause the substrates to be oriented toward each other in an optimal position to facilitate their interaction. This promotes increased reaction speed. The enzyme then releases the product(s), and resumes its original shape. The enzyme is then free to engage in the process again, and will do so as long as substrate remains.

Other Functions of Proteins

Advertisements for protein bars, powders, and shakes all say that protein is important in building, repairing, and maintaining muscle tissue, but the truth is that proteins contribute to all body tissues, from the skin to the brain cells. Also, certain proteins act as hormones, chemical messengers that help regulate body functions. For example, growth hormone is important for skeletal growth, among other roles.

As was noted earlier, the basic and acidic components enable proteins to function as buffers in maintaining acid–base balance, but they also help regulate fluid–electrolyte balance. Proteins attract fluid, and a healthy concentration of proteins in the blood, the cells, and the spaces between cells helps ensure a balance of fluids in these various "compartments." Moreover, proteins in the cell membrane help to transport electrolytes in and out of the cell, keeping these ions in a healthy balance. Like lipids, proteins can bind with carbohydrates. They can thereby produce glycoproteins or proteoglycans, both of which have many functions in the body.

The body can use proteins for energy when carbohydrate and fat intake is inadequate, and stores of glycogen and adipose tissue become depleted. However, since there is no storage site for protein except functional tissues, using protein for energy causes tissue breakdown, and results in body wasting.

Nucleotides

The fourth type of organic compound important to human structure and function are the nucleotides (Figure 2.28). A **nucleotide** is one of a class of organic compounds composed of three subunits:

- one or more phosphate groups
- a pentose sugar: either deoxyribose or ribose
- a nitrogen-containing base: adenine, cytosine, guanine, thymine, or uracil

Nucleotides can be assembled into nucleic acids (DNA or RNA) or the energy compound adenosine triphosphate.

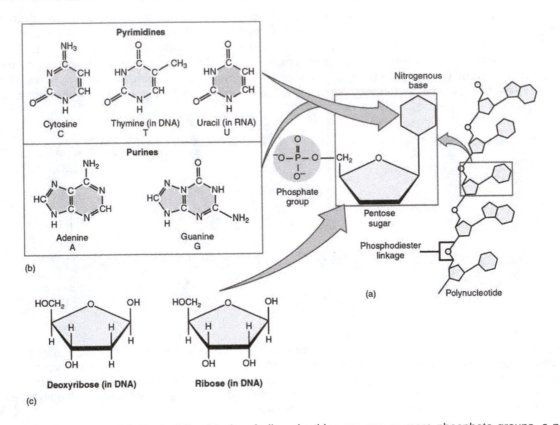

Figure 2.28 Nucleotides (a) The building blocks of all nucleotides are one or more phosphate groups, a pentose sugar, and a nitrogen-containing base. (b) The nitrogen-containing bases of nucleotides. (c) The two pentose sugars of DNA and RNA.

Nucleic Acids

The nucleic acids differ in their type of pentose sugar. **Deoxyribonucleic acid (DNA)** is nucleotide that stores genetic information. DNA contains deoxyribose (so-called because it has one less atom of oxygen than ribose) plus one phosphate group and one nitrogen-containing base. The "choices" of base for DNA are adenine, cytosine, guanine, and thymine. **Ribonucleic acid (RNA)** is a ribose-containing nucleotide that helps manifest the genetic code as protein. RNA contains ribose, one phosphate group, and one nitrogen-containing base, but the "choices" of base for RNA are adenine, cytosine, guanine, and uracil.

The nitrogen-containing bases adenine and guanine are classified as purines. A **purine** is a nitrogen-containing molecule with a double ring structure, which accommodates several nitrogen atoms. The bases cytosine, thymine (found in DNA only) and uracil (found in RNA only) are pyramidines. A **pyramidine** is a nitrogen-containing base with a single ring structure

Bonds formed by dehydration synthesis between the pentose sugar of one nucleic acid monomer and the phosphate group of another form a "backbone," from which the components' nitrogen-containing bases protrude. In DNA, two such backbones attach at their protruding bases via hydrogen bonds. These twist to form a shape known as a double helix (Figure 2.29). The sequence of nitrogen-containing bases within a strand of DNA form the genes that act as a molecular code instructing cells in the assembly of amino acids into proteins. Humans have almost 22,000 genes in their DNA, locked up in the 46 chromosomes inside the nucleus of each cell (except red blood cells which lose their nuclei during development). These genes carry the genetic code to build one's body, and are unique for each individual except identical twins.

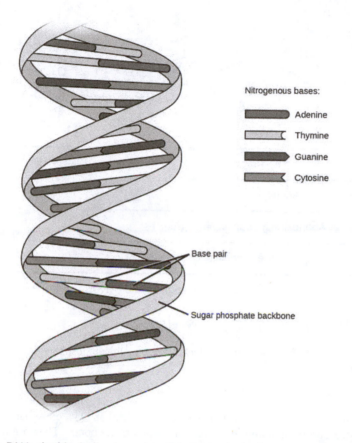

Figure 2.29 DNA In the DNA double helix, two strands attach via hydrogen bonds between the bases of the component nucleotides.

In contrast, RNA consists of a single strand of sugar-phosphate backbone studded with bases. Messenger RNA (mRNA) is created during protein synthesis to carry the genetic instructions from the DNA to the cell's protein manufacturing plants in the cytoplasm, the ribosomes.

Adenosine Triphosphate

The nucleotide adenosine triphosphate (ATP), is composed of a ribose sugar, an adenine base, and three phosphate groups (Figure 2.30). ATP is classified as a high energy compound because the two covalent bonds linking its three phosphates store a significant amount of potential energy. In the body, the energy released from these high energy bonds helps fuel the body's activities, from muscle contraction to the transport of substances in and out of cells to anabolic chemical reactions.

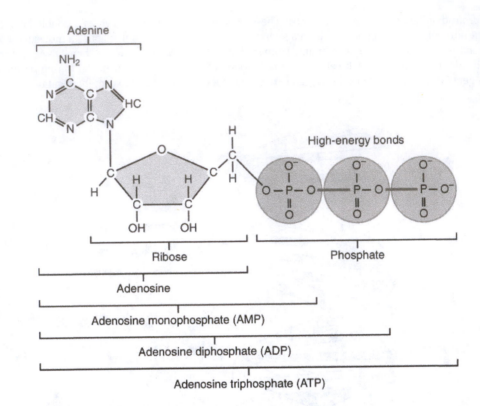

Figure 2.30 Structure of Adenosine Triphosphate (ATP)

When a phosphate group is cleaved from ATP, the products are adenosine diphosphate (ADP) and inorganic phosphate (P_i). This hydrolysis reaction can be written:

$$ATP + H_2O \rightarrow ADP + P_i + energy$$

Removal of a second phosphate leaves adenosine monophosphate (AMP) and two phosphate groups. Again, these reactions also liberate the energy that had been stored in the phosphate-phosphate bonds. They are reversible, too, as when ADP undergoes phosphorylation. **Phosphorylation** is the addition of a phosphate group to an organic compound, in this case, resulting in ATP. In such cases, the same level of energy that had been released during hydrolysis must be reinvested to power dehydration synthesis.

Cells can also transfer a phosphate group from ATP to another organic compound. For example, when glucose first enters a cell, a phosphate group is transferred from ATP, forming glucose phosphate ($C_6H_{12}O_6$—P) and ADP. Once glucose is phosphorylated in this way, it can be stored as glycogen or metabolized for immediate energy.

KEY TERMS

acid compound that releases hydrogen ions (H^+) in solution

activation energy amount of energy greater than the energy contained in the reactants, which must be overcome for a reaction to proceed

adenosine triphosphate (ATP) nucleotide containing ribose and an adenine base that is essential in energy transfer

amino acid building block of proteins; characterized by an amino and carboxyl functional groups and a variable side-chain

anion atom with a negative charge

atom smallest unit of an element that retains the unique properties of that element

atomic number number of protons in the nucleus of an atom

base compound that accepts hydrogen ions (H^+) in solution

bond electrical force linking atoms

buffer solution containing a weak acid or a weak base that opposes wide fluctuations in the pH of body fluids

carbohydrate class of organic compounds built from sugars, molecules containing carbon, hydrogen, and oxygen in a 1-2-1 ratio

catalyst substance that increases the rate of a chemical reaction without itself being changed in the process

cation atom with a positive charge

chemical energy form of energy that is absorbed as chemical bonds form, stored as they are maintained, and released as they are broken

colloid liquid mixture in which the solute particles consist of clumps of molecules large enough to scatter light

compound substance composed of two or more different elements joined by chemical bonds

concentration number of particles within a given space

covalent bond chemical bond in which two atoms share electrons, thereby completing their valence shells

decomposition reaction type of catabolic reaction in which one or more bonds within a larger molecule are broken, resulting in the release of smaller molecules or atoms

denaturation change in the structure of a molecule through physical or chemical means

deoxyribonucleic acid (DNA) deoxyribose-containing nucleotide that stores genetic information

disaccharide pair of carbohydrate monomers bonded by dehydration synthesis via a glycosidic bond

disulfide bond covalent bond formed within a polypeptide between sulfide groups of sulfur-containing amino acids, for example, cysteine

electron subatomic particle having a negative charge and nearly no mass; found orbiting the atom's nucleus

electron shell area of space a given distance from an atom's nucleus in which electrons are grouped

element substance that cannot be created or broken down by ordinary chemical means

enzyme protein or RNA that catalyzes chemical reactions

exchange reaction type of chemical reaction in which bonds are both formed and broken, resulting in the transfer of components

functional group group of atoms linked by strong covalent bonds that tends to behave as a distinct unit in chemical reactions with other atoms

hydrogen bond dipole-dipole bond in which a hydrogen atom covalently bonded to an electronegative atom is weakly attracted to a second electronegative atom

inorganic compound substance that does not contain both carbon and hydrogen

ion atom with an overall positive or negative charge

ionic bond attraction between an anion and a cation

isotope one of the variations of an element in which the number of neutrons differ from each other

kinetic energy energy that matter possesses because of its motion

lipid class of nonpolar organic compounds built from hydrocarbons and distinguished by the fact that they are not soluble in water

macromolecule large molecule formed by covalent bonding

mass number sum of the number of protons and neutrons in the nucleus of an atom

matter physical substance; that which occupies space and has mass

molecule two or more atoms covalently bonded together

monosaccharide monomer of carbohydrate; also known as a simple sugar

neutron heavy subatomic particle having no electrical charge and found in the atom's nucleus

nucleotide class of organic compounds composed of one or more phosphate groups, a pentose sugar, and a base

organic compound substance that contains both carbon and hydrogen

peptide bond covalent bond formed by dehydration synthesis between two amino acids

periodic table of the elements arrangement of the elements in a table according to their atomic number; elements having similar properties because of their electron arrangements compose columns in the table, while elements having the same number of valence shells compose rows in the table

pH negative logarithm of the hydrogen ion (H^+) concentration of a solution

phospholipid a lipid compound in which a phosphate group is combined with a diglyceride

phosphorylation addition of one or more phosphate groups to an organic compound

polar molecule molecule with regions that have opposite charges resulting from uneven numbers of electrons in the nuclei of the atoms participating in the covalent bond

polysaccharide compound consisting of more than two carbohydrate monomers bonded by dehydration synthesis via glycosidic bonds

potential energy stored energy matter possesses because of the positioning or structure of its components

product one or more substances produced by a chemical reaction

prostaglandin lipid compound derived from fatty acid chains and important in regulating several body processes

protein class of organic compounds that are composed of many amino acids linked together by peptide bonds

proton heavy subatomic particle having a positive charge and found in the atom's nucleus

purine nitrogen-containing base with a double ring structure; adenine and guanine

pyrimidine nitrogen-containing base with a single ring structure; cytosine, thiamine, and uracil

radioactive isotope unstable, heavy isotope that gives off subatomic particles, or electromagnetic energy, as it decays; also called radioisotopes

reactant one or more substances that enter into the reaction

ribonucleic acid (RNA) ribose-containing nucleotide that helps manifest the genetic code as protein

solution homogeneous liquid mixture in which a solute is dissolved into molecules within a solvent

steroid (also, sterol) lipid compound composed of four hydrocarbon rings bonded to a variety of other atoms and molecules

substrate reactant in an enzymatic reaction

suspension liquid mixture in which particles distributed in the liquid settle out over time

synthesis reaction type of anabolic reaction in which two or more atoms or molecules bond, resulting in the formation of a larger molecule

triglyceride lipid compound composed of a glycerol molecule bonded with three fatty acid chains

valence shell outermost electron shell of an atom

CHAPTER REVIEW

2.1 Elements and Atoms: The Building Blocks of Matter

The human body is composed of elements, the most abundant of which are oxygen (O), carbon (C), hydrogen (H) and nitrogen (N). You obtain these elements from the foods you eat and the air you breathe. The smallest unit of an element that retains all of the properties of that element is an atom. But, atoms themselves contain many subatomic particles, the three most important of which are protons, neutrons, and electrons. These particles do not vary in quality from one element to another; rather, what gives an element its distinctive identification is the quantity of its protons, called its atomic number. Protons and neutrons contribute nearly all of an atom's mass; the number of protons and neutrons is an element's mass number. Heavier and lighter versions of the same element can occur in nature because these versions have different numbers of neutrons. Different versions of an element are called isotopes.

The tendency of an atom to be stable or to react readily with other atoms is largely due to the behavior of the electrons within the atom's outermost electron shell, called its valence shell. Helium, as well as larger atoms with eight electrons in their valence shell, is unlikely to participate in chemical reactions because they are stable. All other atoms tend to accept, donate, or share electrons in a process that brings the electrons in their valence shell to eight (or in the case of hydrogen, to two).

2.2 Chemical Bonds

Each moment of life, atoms of oxygen, carbon, hydrogen, and the other elements of the human body are making and breaking chemical bonds. Ions are charged atoms that form when an atom donates or accepts one or more negatively charged electrons. Cations (ions with a positive charge) are attracted to anions (ions with a negative charge). This attraction is called an ionic bond. In covalent bonds, the participating atoms do not lose or gain electrons, but rather share them. Molecules with nonpolar covalent bonds are electrically balanced, and have a linear three-dimensional shape. Molecules with polar covalent bonds have "poles"—regions of weakly positive and negative charge—and have a triangular three-dimensional shape. An atom of oxygen and two atoms of hydrogen form water molecules by means of polar covalent bonds. Hydrogen bonds link hydrogen atoms already participating in polar covalent bonds to anions or electronegative regions of other polar molecules. Hydrogen bonds link water molecules, resulting in the properties of water that are important to living things.

2.3 Chemical Reactions

Chemical reactions, in which chemical bonds are broken and formed, require an initial investment of energy. Kinetic energy, the energy of matter in motion, fuels the collisions of atoms, ions, and molecules that are necessary if their old bonds are to break and new ones to form. All molecules store potential energy, which is released when their bonds are broken.

Four forms of energy essential to human functioning are: chemical energy, which is stored and released as chemical bonds are formed and broken; mechanical energy, which directly powers physical activity; radiant energy, emitted as waves such as in sunlight; and electrical energy, the power of moving electrons.

Chemical reactions begin with reactants and end with products. Synthesis reactions bond reactants together, a process that requires energy, whereas decomposition reactions break the bonds within a reactant and thereby release energy. In exchange reactions, bonds are both broken and formed, and energy is exchanged.

The rate at which chemical reactions occur is influenced by several properties of the reactants: temperature, concentration and pressure, and the presence or absence of a catalyst. An enzyme is a catalytic protein that speeds up chemical reactions in the human body.

2.4 Inorganic Compounds Essential to Human Functioning

Inorganic compounds essential to human functioning include water, salts, acids, and bases. These compounds are inorganic; that is, they do not contain both hydrogen and carbon. Water is a lubricant and cushion, a heat sink, a component of liquid mixtures, a byproduct of dehydration synthesis reactions, and a reactant in hydrolysis reactions. Salts are compounds that, when dissolved in water, dissociate into ions other than H^+ or OH^-. In contrast, acids release H^+ in solution, making it more acidic. Bases accept H^+, thereby making the solution more alkaline (caustic).

The pH of any solution is its relative concentration of H^+. A solution with pH 7 is neutral. Solutions with pH below 7 are acids, and solutions with pH above 7 are bases. A change in a single digit on the pH scale (e.g., from 7 to 8) represents a ten-fold increase or decrease in the concentration of H^+. In a healthy adult, the pH of blood ranges from 7.35 to 7.45. Homeostatic control mechanisms important for keeping blood in a healthy pH range include chemicals called buffers, weak acids and weak bases released when the pH of blood or other body fluids fluctuates in either direction outside of this normal range.

2.5 Organic Compounds Essential to Human Functioning

Organic compounds essential to human functioning include carbohydrates, lipids, proteins, and nucleotides. These compounds are said to be organic because they contain both carbon and hydrogen. Carbon atoms in organic compounds readily share electrons with hydrogen and other atoms, usually oxygen, and sometimes nitrogen. Carbon atoms also may bond with one or more functional groups such as carboxyls, hydroxyls, aminos, or phosphates. Monomers are single units of organic compounds. They bond by dehydration synthesis to form polymers, which can in turn be broken by hydrolysis.

Carbohydrate compounds provide essential body fuel. Their structural forms include monosaccharides such as glucose, disaccharides such as lactose, and polysaccharides, including starches (polymers of glucose), glycogen (the storage form of glucose), and fiber. All body cells can use glucose for fuel. It is converted via an oxidation-reduction reaction to ATP.

Lipids are hydrophobic compounds that provide body fuel and are important components of many biological compounds. Triglycerides are the most abundant lipid in the body, and are composed of a glycerol backbone attached to three fatty acid chains. Phospholipids are compounds composed of a diglyceride with a phosphate group attached at the molecule's head. The result is a molecule with polar and nonpolar regions. Steroids are lipids formed of four hydrocarbon rings. The most important is cholesterol. Prostaglandins are signaling molecules derived from unsaturated fatty acids.

Proteins are critical components of all body tissues. They are made up of monomers called amino acids, which contain nitrogen, joined by peptide bonds. Protein shape is critical to its function. Most body proteins are globular. An example is enzymes, which catalyze chemical reactions.

Nucleotides are compounds with three building blocks: one or more phosphate groups, a pentose sugar, and a nitrogen-containing base. DNA and RNA are nucleic acids that function in protein synthesis. ATP is the body's fundamental molecule of energy transfer. Removal or addition of phosphates releases or invests energy.

INTERACTIVE LINK QUESTIONS

1. Visit this website (http://openstaxcollege.org/l/ptable) to view the periodic table. In the periodic table of the elements, elements in a single column have the same number of electrons that can participate in a chemical reaction. These electrons are known as "valence electrons." For example, the elements in the first column all have a single valence electron—an electron that can be "donated" in a chemical reaction with another atom. What is the meaning of a mass number shown in parentheses?

2. Visit this website (http://openstaxcollege.org/l/electenergy) to learn about electrical energy and the attraction/repulsion of charges. What happens to the charged electroscope when a conductor is moved between its plastic sheets, and why?

3. Watch this video (http://openstaxcollege.org/l/disaccharide) to observe the formation of a disaccharide. What happens when water encounters a glycosidic bond?

REVIEW QUESTIONS

4. Together, just four elements make up more than 95 percent of the body's mass. These include _____.

    a. calcium, magnesium, iron, and carbon
    b. oxygen, calcium, iron, and nitrogen
    c. sodium, chlorine, carbon, and hydrogen
    d. oxygen, carbon, hydrogen, and nitrogen

5. The smallest unit of an element that still retains the distinctive behavior of that element is an _____.

    a. electron
    b. atom
    c. elemental particle
    d. isotope

6. The characteristic that gives an element its distinctive properties is its number of _____.
    a. protons
    b. neutrons
    c. electrons
    d. atoms

7. On the periodic table of the elements, mercury (Hg) has an atomic number of 80 and a mass number of 200.59. It has seven stable isotopes. The most abundant of these probably have _____.
    a. about 80 neutrons each
    b. fewer than 80 neutrons each
    c. more than 80 neutrons each
    d. more electrons than neutrons

8. Nitrogen has an atomic number of seven. How many electron shells does it likely have?
    a. one
    b. two
    c. three
    d. four

9. Which of the following is a molecule, but *not* a compound?
    a. H_2O
    b. ^2H
    c. H_2
    d. H^+

10. A molecule of ammonia contains one atom of nitrogen and three atoms of hydrogen. These are linked with _____.

    a. ionic bonds
    b. nonpolar covalent bonds
    c. polar covalent bonds
    d. hydrogen bonds

11. When an atom donates an electron to another atom, it becomes
    a. an ion
    b. an anion
    c. nonpolar
    d. all of the above

12. A substance formed of crystals of equal numbers of cations and anions held together by ionic bonds is called a(n) _____.
    a. noble gas
    b. salt
    c. electrolyte
    d. dipole

13. Which of the following statements about chemical bonds is true?
    a. Covalent bonds are stronger than ionic bonds.
    b. Hydrogen bonds occur between two atoms of hydrogen.
    c. Bonding readily occurs between nonpolar and polar molecules.
    d. A molecule of water is unlikely to bond with an ion.

14. The energy stored in a foot of snow on a steep roof is _____.

    a. potential energy
    b. kinetic energy
    c. radiant energy
    d. activation energy

15. The bonding of calcium, phosphorus, and other elements produces mineral crystals that are found in bone. This is an example of a(n) _____ reaction.
    a. catabolic
    b. synthesis
    c. decomposition
    d. exchange

16. $AB \rightarrow A + B$ is a general notation for a(n) _____ reaction.
   a. anabolic
   b. endergonic
   c. decomposition
   d. exchange

17. _____ reactions release energy.
   a. Catabolic
   b. Exergonic
   c. Decomposition
   d. Catabolic, exergonic, and decomposition

18. Which of the following combinations of atoms is *most likely* to result in a chemical reaction?
   a. hydrogen and hydrogen
   b. hydrogen and helium
   c. helium and helium
   d. neon and helium

19. Chewing a bite of bread mixes it with saliva and facilitates its chemical breakdown. This is *most likely* due to the fact that _____.
   a. the inside of the mouth maintains a very high temperature
   b. chewing stores potential energy
   c. chewing facilitates synthesis reactions
   d. saliva contains enzymes

20. CH_4 is methane. This compound is _____.

   a. inorganic
   b. organic
   c. reactive
   d. a crystal

21. Which of the following is most likely to be found evenly distributed in water in a homogeneous solution?

   a. sodium ions and chloride ions
   b. NaCl molecules
   c. salt crystals
   d. red blood cells

22. Jenny mixes up a batch of pancake batter, then stirs in some chocolate chips. As she is waiting for the first few pancakes to cook, she notices the chocolate chips sinking to the bottom of the clear glass mixing bowl. The chocolate-chip batter is an example of a _____.
   a. solvent
   b. solute
   c. solution
   d. suspension

23. A substance dissociates into K^+ and Cl^- in solution. The substance is a(n) _____.
   a. acid
   b. base
   c. salt
   d. buffer

24. Ty is three years old and as a result of a "stomach bug" has been vomiting for about 24 hours. His blood pH is 7.48. What does this mean?
   a. Ty's blood is slightly acidic.
   b. Ty's blood is slightly alkaline.
   c. Ty's blood is highly acidic.
   d. Ty's blood is within the normal range

25. $C_6H_{12}O_6$ is the chemical formula for a _____.

   a. polymer of carbohydrate
   b. pentose monosaccharide
   c. hexose monosaccharide
   d. all of the above

26. What organic compound do brain cells primarily rely on for fuel?
   a. glucose
   b. glycogen
   c. galactose
   d. glycerol

27. Which of the following is a functional group that is part of a building block of proteins?
   a. phosphate
   b. adenine
   c. amino
   d. ribose

28. A pentose sugar is a part of the monomer used to build which type of macromolecule?
   a. polysaccharides
   b. nucleic acids
   c. phosphorylated glucose
   d. glycogen

29. A phospholipid _____.
   a. has both polar and nonpolar regions
   b. is made up of a triglyceride bonded to a phosphate group
   c. is a building block of ATP
   d. can donate both cations and anions in solution

30. In DNA, nucleotide bonding forms a compound with a characteristic shape known as a(n) _____.
   a. beta chain
   b. pleated sheet
   c. alpha helix
   d. double helix

31. Uracil _____.
   a. contains nitrogen
   b. is a pyrimidine
   c. is found in RNA
   d. all of the above

32. The ability of an enzyme's active sites to bind only substrates of compatible shape and charge is known as _____.
   a. selectivity
   b. specificity
   c. subjectivity
   d. specialty

CRITICAL THINKING QUESTIONS

33. The most abundant elements in the foods and beverages you consume are oxygen, carbon, hydrogen, and nitrogen. Why might having these elements in consumables be useful?

34. Oxygen, whose atomic number is eight, has three stable isotopes: ^{16}O, ^{17}O, and ^{18}O. Explain what this means in terms of the number of protons and neutrons.

35. Magnesium is an important element in the human body, especially in bones. Magnesium's atomic number is 12. Is it stable or reactive? Why? If it were to react with another atom, would it be more likely to accept or to donate one or more electrons?

36. Explain why CH_4 is one of the most common molecules found in nature. Are the bonds between the atoms ionic or covalent?

37. In a hurry one day, you merely rinse your lunch dishes with water. As you are drying your salad bowl, you notice that it still has an oily film. Why was the water alone not effective in cleaning the bowl?

38. Could two atoms of oxygen engage in ionic bonding? Why or why not?

39. $AB + CD \rightarrow AD + BE$ Is this a legitimate example of an exchange reaction? Why or why not?

40. When you do a load of laundry, why do you not just drop a bar of soap into the washing machine? In other words, why is laundry detergent sold as a liquid or powder?

41. The pH of lemon juice is 2, and the pH of orange juice is 4. Which of these is more acidic, and by how much? What does this mean?

42. During a party, Eli loses a bet and is forced to drink a bottle of lemon juice. Not long thereafter, he begins complaining of having difficulty breathing, and his friends take him to the local emergency room. There, he is given an intravenous solution of bicarbonate. Why?

43. If the disaccharide maltose is formed from two glucose monosaccharides, which are hexose sugars, how many atoms of carbon, hydrogen, and oxygen does maltose contain and why?

44. Once dietary fats are digested and absorbed, why can they not be released directly into the bloodstream?

3 | THE CELLULAR LEVEL OF ORGANIZATION

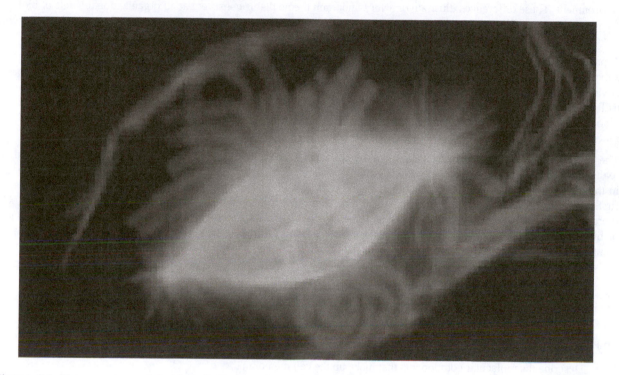

Figure 3.1 Fluorescence-stained Cell Undergoing Mitosis A lung cell from a newt, commonly studied for its similarity to human lung cells, is stained with fluorescent dyes. The green stain reveals mitotic spindles, red is the cell membrane and part of the cytoplasm, and the structures that appear light blue are chromosomes. This cell is in anaphase of mitosis. (credit: "Mortadelo2005"/Wikimedia Commons)

Introduction

Chapter Objectives

After studying this chapter, you will be able to:

- Describe the structure and function of the cell membrane, including its regulation of materials into and out of the cell
- Describe the functions of the various cytoplasmic organelles
- Explain the structure and contents of the nucleus, as well as the process of DNA replication
- Explain the process by which a cell builds proteins using the DNA code
- List the stages of the cell cycle in order, including the steps of cell division in somatic cells
- Discuss how a cell differentiates and becomes more specialized
- List the morphological and physiological characteristics of some representative cell types in the human body

You developed from a single fertilized egg cell into the complex organism containing trillions of cells that you see when you look in a mirror. During this developmental process, early, undifferentiated cells differentiate and become specialized in their structure and function. These different cell types form specialized tissues that work in concert to perform all of the functions necessary for the living organism. Cellular and developmental biologists study how the continued division of a single cell leads to such complexity and differentiation.

Consider the difference between a structural cell in the skin and a nerve cell. A structural skin cell may be shaped like a flat plate (squamous) and live only for a short time before it is shed and replaced. Packed tightly into rows and sheets, the squamous skin cells provide a protective barrier for the cells and tissues that lie beneath. A nerve cell, on the other hand, may be shaped something like a star, sending out long processes up to a meter in length and may live for the entire lifetime of the organism. With their long winding appendages, nerve cells can communicate with one another and with other types of body cells and send rapid signals that inform the organism about its environment and allow it to interact with that environment. These differences illustrate one very important theme that is consistent at all organizational levels of biology: the form of a structure is optimally suited to perform particular functions assigned to that structure. Keep this theme in mind as you tour the inside of a cell and are introduced to the various types of cells in the body.

A primary responsibility of each cell is to contribute to homeostasis. Homeostasis is a term used in biology that refers to a dynamic state of balance within parameters that are compatible with life. For example, living cells require a water-based environment to survive in, and there are various physical (anatomical) and physiological mechanisms that keep all of the trillions of living cells in the human body moist. This is one aspect of homeostasis. When a particular parameter, such as blood pressure or blood oxygen content, moves far enough *out* of homeostasis (generally becoming too high or too low), illness or disease—and sometimes death—inevitably results.

The concept of a cell started with microscopic observations of dead cork tissue by scientist Robert Hooke in 1665. Without realizing their function or importance, Hook coined the term "cell" based on the resemblance of the small subdivisions in the cork to the rooms that monks inhabited, called cells. About ten years later, Antonie van Leeuwenhoek became the first person to observe living and moving cells under a microscope. In the century that followed, the theory that cells represented the basic unit of life would develop. These tiny fluid-filled sacs house components responsible for the thousands of biochemical reactions necessary for an organism to grow and survive. In this chapter, you will learn about the major components and functions of a prototypical, generalized cell and discover some of the different types of cells in the human body.

3.1 | The Cell Membrane

By the end of this section, you will be able to:
- Describe the molecular components that make up the cell membrane
- Explain the major features and properties of the cell membrane
- Differentiate between materials that can and cannot diffuse through the lipid bilayer
- Compare and contrast different types of passive transport with active transport, providing examples of each

Despite differences in structure and function, all living cells in multicellular organisms have a surrounding cell membrane. As the outer layer of your skin separates your body from its environment, the cell membrane (also known as the plasma membrane) separates the inner contents of a cell from its exterior environment. This cell membrane provides a protective barrier around the cell and regulates which materials can pass in or out.

Structure and Composition of the Cell Membrane

The **cell membrane** is an extremely pliable structure composed primarily of back-to-back phospholipids (a "bilayer"). Cholesterol is also present, which contributes to the fluidity of the membrane, and there are various proteins embedded within the membrane that have a variety of functions.

A single phospholipid molecule has a phosphate group on one end, called the "head," and two side-by-side chains of fatty acids that make up the lipid tails (**Figure 3.2**). The phosphate group is negatively charged, making the head polar and hydrophilic—or "water loving." A **hydrophilic** molecule (or region of a molecule) is one that is attracted to water. The phosphate heads are thus attracted to the water molecules of both the extracellular and intracellular environments. The lipid tails, on the other hand, are uncharged, or nonpolar, and are hydrophobic—or "water fearing." A **hydrophobic** molecule (or region of a molecule) repels and is repelled by water. Some lipid tails consist of saturated fatty acids and some contain unsaturated fatty acids. This combination adds to the fluidity of the tails that are constantly in motion. Phospholipids are thus amphipathic molecules. An **amphipathic** molecule is one that contains both a hydrophilic and a hydrophobic region. In fact, soap works to remove oil and grease stains because it has amphipathic properties. The hydrophilic portion can dissolve in water while the hydrophobic portion can trap grease in micelles that then can be washed away.

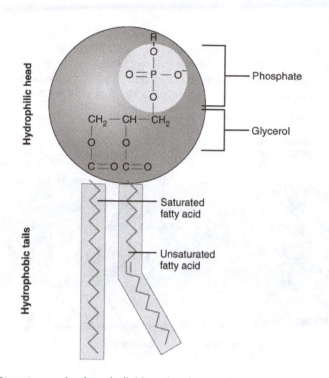

Figure 3.2 Phospholipid Structure A phospholipid molecule consists of a polar phosphate "head," which is hydrophilic and a non-polar lipid "tail," which is hydrophobic. Unsaturated fatty acids result in kinks in the hydrophobic tails.

The cell membrane consists of two adjacent layers of phospholipids. The lipid tails of one layer face the lipid tails of the other layer, meeting at the interface of the two layers. The phospholipid heads face outward, one layer exposed to the interior of the cell and one layer exposed to the exterior (Figure 3.3). Because the phosphate groups are polar and hydrophilic, they are attracted to water in the intracellular fluid. **Intracellular fluid (ICF)** is the fluid interior of the cell. The phosphate groups are also attracted to the extracellular fluid. **Extracellular fluid (ECF)** is the fluid environment outside the enclosure of the cell membrane. **Interstitial fluid (IF)** is the term given to extracellular fluid not contained within blood vessels. Because the lipid tails are hydrophobic, they meet in the inner region of the membrane, excluding watery intracellular and extracellular fluid from this space. The cell membrane has many proteins, as well as other lipids (such as cholesterol), that are associated with the phospholipid bilayer. An important feature of the membrane is that it remains fluid; the lipids and proteins in the cell membrane are not rigidly locked in place.

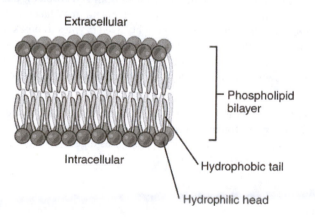

Figure 3.3 Phospolipid Bilayer The phospholipid bilayer consists of two adjacent sheets of phospholipids, arranged tail to tail. The hydrophobic tails associate with one another, forming the interior of the membrane. The polar heads contact the fluid inside and outside of the cell.

Membrane Proteins

The lipid bilayer forms the basis of the cell membrane, but it is peppered throughout with various proteins. Two different types of proteins that are commonly associated with the cell membrane are the integral proteins and peripheral protein (Figure 3.4). As its name suggests, an **integral protein** is a protein that is embedded in the membrane. A **channel protein** is an example of an integral protein that selectively allows particular materials, such as certain ions, to pass into or out of the cell.

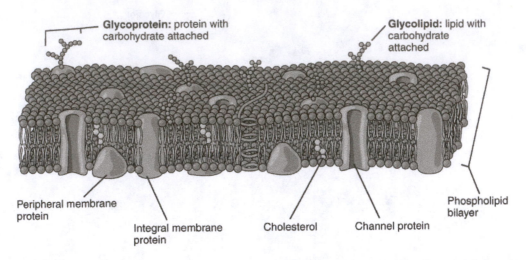

Figure 3.4 Cell Membrane The cell membrane of the cell is a phospholipid bilayer containing many different molecular components, including proteins and cholesterol, some with carbohydrate groups attached.

Another important group of integral proteins are cell recognition proteins, which serve to mark a cell's identity so that it can be recognized by other cells. A **receptor** is a type of recognition protein that can selectively bind a specific molecule outside the cell, and this binding induces a chemical reaction within the cell. A **ligand** is the specific molecule that binds to and activates a receptor. Some integral proteins serve dual roles as both a receptor and an ion channel. One example of a receptor-ligand interaction is the receptors on nerve cells that bind neurotransmitters, such as dopamine. When a dopamine molecule binds to a dopamine receptor protein, a channel within the transmembrane protein opens to allow certain ions to flow into the cell.

Some integral membrane proteins are glycoproteins. A **glycoprotein** is a protein that has carbohydrate molecules attached, which extend into the extracellular matrix. The attached carbohydrate tags on glycoproteins aid in cell recognition. The carbohydrates that extend from membrane proteins and even from some membrane lipids collectively form the glycocalyx. The **glycocalyx** is a fuzzy-appearing coating around the cell formed from glycoproteins and other carbohydrates attached to the cell membrane. The glycocalyx can have various roles. For example, it may have molecules that allow the cell to bind to another cell, it may contain receptors for hormones, or it might have enzymes to break down nutrients. The glycocalyces found in a person's body are products of that person's genetic makeup. They give each of the individual's trillions of cells the "identity" of belonging in the person's body. This identity is the primary way that a person's immune defense cells "know" not to attack the person's own body cells, but it also is the reason organs donated by another person might be rejected.

Peripheral proteins are typically found on the inner or outer surface of the lipid bilayer but can also be attached to the internal or external surface of an integral protein. These proteins typically perform a specific function for the cell. Some peripheral proteins on the surface of intestinal cells, for example, act as digestive enzymes to break down nutrients to sizes that can pass through the cells and into the bloodstream.

Transport across the Cell Membrane

One of the great wonders of the cell membrane is its ability to regulate the concentration of substances inside the cell. These substances include ions such as Ca^{++}, Na^+, K^+, and Cl^-; nutrients including sugars, fatty acids, and amino acids; and waste products, particularly carbon dioxide (CO_2), which must leave the cell.

The membrane's lipid bilayer structure provides the first level of control. The phospholipids are tightly packed together, and the membrane has a hydrophobic interior. This structure causes the membrane to be selectively permeable. A membrane that has **selective permeability** allows only substances meeting certain criteria to pass through it unaided. In the case of the cell membrane, only relatively small, nonpolar materials can move through the lipid bilayer (remember, the lipid tails of the membrane are nonpolar). Some examples of these are other lipids, oxygen and carbon dioxide gases, and alcohol. However, water-soluble materials—like glucose, amino acids, and electrolytes—need some assistance to cross the membrane because they are repelled by the hydrophobic tails of the phospholipid bilayer. All substances that move through the membrane do so by one of two general methods, which are categorized based on whether or not energy is required. **Passive transport** is the movement of substances across the membrane without the expenditure of cellular energy. In contrast, **active transport** is the movement of substances across the membrane using energy from adenosine triphosphate (ATP).

Passive Transport

In order to understand *how* substances move passively across a cell membrane, it is necessary to understand concentration gradients and diffusion. A **concentration gradient** is the difference in concentration of a substance across a space. Molecules (or ions) will spread/diffuse from where they are more concentrated to where they are less concentrated until they are equally distributed in that space. (When molecules move in this way, they are said to move *down* their concentration gradient.) **Diffusion** is the movement of particles from an area of higher concentration to an area of lower concentration. A couple of common examples will help to illustrate this concept. Imagine being inside a closed bathroom. If a bottle of perfume were sprayed, the scent molecules would naturally diffuse from the spot where they left the bottle to all corners of the bathroom, and this diffusion would go on until no more concentration gradient remains. Another example is a spoonful of sugar placed in a cup of tea. Eventually the sugar will diffuse throughout the tea until no concentration gradient remains. In both cases, if the room is warmer or the tea hotter, diffusion occurs even faster as the molecules are bumping into each other and spreading out faster than at cooler temperatures. Having an internal body temperature around 98.6° F thus also aids in diffusion of particles within the body.

Visit this link (http://openstaxcollege.org/l/diffusion) to see diffusion and how it is propelled by the kinetic energy of molecules in solution. How does temperature affect diffusion rate, and why?

Whenever a substance exists in greater concentration on one side of a semipermeable membrane, such as the cell membranes, any substance that can move down its concentration gradient across the membrane will do so. Consider substances that can easily diffuse through the lipid bilayer of the cell membrane, such as the gases oxygen (O_2) and CO_2. O_2 generally diffuses into cells because it is more concentrated outside of them, and CO_2 typically diffuses out of cells because it is more concentrated inside of them. Neither of these examples requires any energy on the part of the cell, and therefore they use passive transport to move across the membrane.

Before moving on, you need to review the gases that can diffuse across a cell membrane. Because cells rapidly use up oxygen during metabolism, there is typically a lower concentration of O_2 inside the cell than outside. As a result, oxygen will diffuse from the interstitial fluid directly through the lipid bilayer of the membrane and into the cytoplasm within the cell. On the other hand, because cells produce CO_2 as a byproduct of metabolism, CO_2 concentrations rise within the cytoplasm; therefore, CO_2 will move from the cell through the lipid bilayer and into the interstitial fluid, where its concentration is lower. This mechanism of molecules moving across a cell membrane from the side where they are more concentrated to the side where they are less concentrated is a form of passive transport called simple diffusion (Figure 3.5).

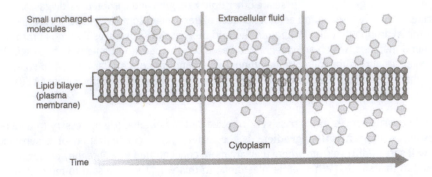

Figure 3.5 Simple Diffusion across the Cell (Plasma) Membrane The structure of the lipid bilayer allows small, uncharged substances such as oxygen and carbon dioxide, and hydrophobic molecules such as lipids, to pass through the cell membrane, down their concentration gradient, by simple diffusion.

Large polar or ionic molecules, which are hydrophilic, cannot easily cross the phospholipid bilayer. Very small polar molecules, such as water, can cross via simple diffusion due to their small size. Charged atoms or molecules of any size cannot cross the cell membrane via simple diffusion as the charges are repelled by the hydrophobic tails in the interior of the phospholipid bilayer. Solutes dissolved in water on either side of the cell membrane will tend to diffuse down their concentration gradients, but because most substances cannot pass freely through the lipid bilayer of the cell membrane, their movement is restricted to protein channels and specialized transport mechanisms in the membrane. **Facilitated diffusion** is the diffusion process used for those substances that cannot cross the lipid bilayer due to their size, charge, and/or polarity (Figure 3.6). A common example of facilitated diffusion is the movement of glucose into the cell, where it is used to make ATP. Although glucose can be more concentrated outside of a cell, it cannot cross the lipid bilayer via simple diffusion because it is both large and polar. To resolve this, a specialized carrier protein called the glucose transporter will transfer glucose molecules into the cell to facilitate its inward diffusion.

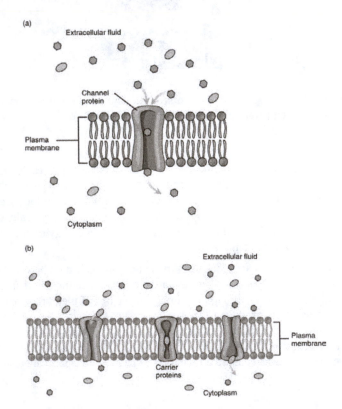

Figure 3.6 Facilitated Diffusion (a) Facilitated diffusion of substances crossing the cell (plasma) membrane takes place with the help of proteins such as channel proteins and carrier proteins. Channel proteins are less selective than carrier proteins, and usually mildly discriminate between their cargo based on size and charge. (b) Carrier proteins are more selective, often only allowing one particular type of molecule to cross.

As an example, even though sodium ions (Na$^+$) are highly concentrated outside of cells, these electrolytes are charged and cannot pass through the nonpolar lipid bilayer of the membrane. Their diffusion is facilitated by membrane proteins that form sodium channels (or "pores"), so that Na$^+$ ions can move down their concentration gradient from outside the cells to inside the cells. There are many other solutes that must undergo facilitated diffusion to move into a cell, such as amino acids, or to move out of a cell, such as wastes. Because facilitated diffusion is a passive process, it does not require energy expenditure by the cell.

Water also can move freely across the cell membrane of all cells, either through protein channels or by slipping between the lipid tails of the membrane itself. **Osmosis** is the diffusion of water through a semipermeable membrane (**Figure 3.7**).

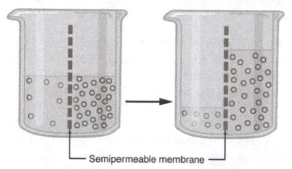

Semipermeable membrane

Figure 3.7 Osmosis   Osmosis is the diffusion of water through a semipermeable membrane down its concentration gradient. If a membrane is permeable to water, though not to a solute, water will equalize its own concentration by diffusing to the side of lower water concentration (and thus the side of higher solute concentration). In the beaker on the left, the solution on the right side of the membrane is hypertonic.

The movement of water molecules is not itself regulated by cells, so it is important that cells are exposed to an environment in which the concentration of solutes outside of the cells (in the extracellular fluid) is equal to the concentration of solutes inside the cells (in the cytoplasm). Two solutions that have the same concentration of solutes are said to be **isotonic** (equal tension). When cells and their extracellular environments are isotonic, the concentration of water molecules is the same outside and inside the cells, and the cells maintain their normal shape (and function).

Osmosis occurs when there is an imbalance of solutes outside of a cell versus inside the cell. A solution that has a higher concentration of solutes than another solution is said to be **hypertonic**, and water molecules tend to diffuse into a hypertonic solution (**Figure 3.8**). Cells in a hypertonic solution will shrivel as water leaves the cell via osmosis. In contrast, a solution that has a lower concentration of solutes than another solution is said to be **hypotonic**, and water molecules tend to diffuse out of a hypotonic solution. Cells in a hypotonic solution will take on too much water and swell, with the risk of eventually bursting. A critical aspect of homeostasis in living things is to create an internal environment in which all of the body's cells are in an isotonic solution. Various organ systems, particularly the kidneys, work to maintain this homeostasis.

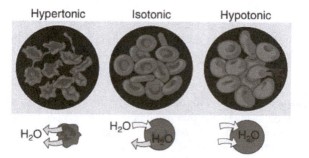

Figure 3.8 Concentration of Solutions   A hypertonic solution has a solute concentration higher than another solution. An isotonic solution has a solute concentration equal to another solution. A hypotonic solution has a solute concentration lower than another solution.

Another mechanism besides diffusion to passively transport materials between compartments is filtration. Unlike diffusion of a substance from where it is more concentrated to less concentrated, filtration uses a hydrostatic pressure gradient that pushes the fluid—and the solutes within it—from a higher pressure area to a lower pressure area. Filtration is an extremely important process in the body. For example, the circulatory system uses filtration to move plasma and substances across the endothelial lining of capillaries and into surrounding tissues, supplying cells with the nutrients. Filtration pressure in the kidneys provides the mechanism to remove wastes from the bloodstream.

Active Transport

For all of the transport methods described above, the cell expends no energy. Membrane proteins that aid in the passive transport of substances do so without the use of ATP. During active transport, ATP is required to move a substance across a membrane, often with the help of protein carriers, and usually *against* its concentration gradient.

One of the most common types of active transport involves proteins that serve as pumps. The word "pump" probably conjures up thoughts of using energy to pump up the tire of a bicycle or a basketball. Similarly, energy from ATP is required for these membrane proteins to transport substances—molecules or ions—across the membrane, usually against their concentration gradients (from an area of low concentration to an area of high concentration).

The **sodium-potassium pump**, which is also called Na^+/K^+ ATPase, transports sodium out of a cell while moving potassium into the cell. The Na^+/K^+ pump is an important ion pump found in the membranes of many types of cells. These pumps are particularly abundant in nerve cells, which are constantly pumping out sodium ions and pulling in potassium ions to maintain an electrical gradient across their cell membranes. An **electrical gradient** is a difference in electrical charge across a space. In the case of nerve cells, for example, the electrical gradient exists between the inside and outside of the cell, with the inside being negatively-charged (at around -70 mV) relative to the outside. The negative electrical gradient is maintained because each Na^+/K^+ pump moves three Na^+ ions out of the cell and two K^+ ions into the cell for each ATP molecule that is used (Figure 3.9). This process is so important for nerve cells that it accounts for the majority of their ATP usage.

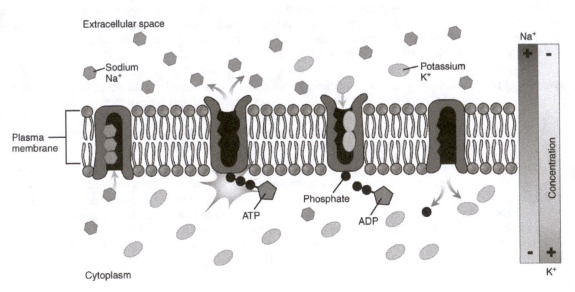

Figure 3.9 Sodium-Potassium Pump The sodium-potassium pump is found in many cell (plasma) membranes. Powered by ATP, the pump moves sodium and potassium ions in opposite directions, each against its concentration gradient. In a single cycle of the pump, three sodium ions are extruded from and two potassium ions are imported into the cell.

Active transport pumps can also work together with other active or passive transport systems to move substances across the membrane. For example, the sodium-potassium pump maintains a high concentration of sodium ions outside of the cell. Therefore, if the cell needs sodium ions, all it has to do is open a passive sodium channel, as the concentration gradient of the sodium ions will drive them to diffuse into the cell. In this way, the action of an active transport pump (the sodium-potassium pump) powers the passive transport of sodium ions by creating a concentration gradient. When active transport powers the transport of another substance in this way, it is called secondary active transport.

Symporters are secondary active transporters that move two substances in the same direction. For example, the sodium-glucose symporter uses sodium ions to "pull" glucose molecules into the cell. Because cells store glucose for energy, glucose is typically at a higher concentration inside of the cell than outside. However, due to the action of the sodium-potassium pump, sodium ions will easily diffuse into the cell when the symporter is opened. The flood of sodium ions through the symporter provides the energy that allows glucose to move through the symporter and into the cell, against its concentration gradient.

Conversely, antiporters are secondary active transport systems that transport substances in opposite directions. For example, the sodium-hydrogen ion antiporter uses the energy from the inward flood of sodium ions to move hydrogen ions (H+) out of the cell. The sodium-hydrogen antiporter is used to maintain the pH of the cell's interior.

Other forms of active transport do not involve membrane carriers. **Endocytosis** (bringing "into the cell") is the process of a cell ingesting material by enveloping it in a portion of its cell membrane, and then pinching off that portion of membrane (**Figure 3.10**). Once pinched off, the portion of membrane and its contents becomes an independent, intracellular vesicle. A **vesicle** is a membranous sac—a spherical and hollow organelle bounded by a lipid bilayer membrane. Endocytosis often brings materials into the cell that must to be broken down or digested. **Phagocytosis** ("cell eating") is the endocytosis of large particles. Many immune cells engage in phagocytosis of invading pathogens. Like little Pac-men, their job is to patrol body tissues for unwanted matter, such as invading bacterial cells, phagocytize them, and digest them. In contrast to phagocytosis, **pinocytosis** ("cell drinking") brings fluid containing dissolved substances into a cell through membrane vesicles.

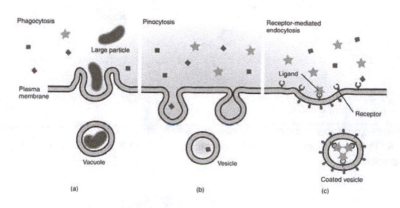

Figure 3.10 Three Forms of Endocytosis Endocytosis is a form of active transport in which a cell envelopes extracellular materials using its cell membrane. (a) In phagocytosis, which is relatively nonselective, the cell takes in a large particle. (b) In pinocytosis, the cell takes in small particles in fluid. (c) In contrast, receptor-mediated endocytosis is quite selective. When external receptors bind a specific ligand, the cell responds by endocytosing the ligand.

Phagocytosis and pinocytosis take in large portions of extracellular material, and they are typically not highly selective in the substances they bring in. Cells regulate the endocytosis of specific substances via receptor-mediated endocytosis. **Receptor-mediated endocytosis** is endocytosis by a portion of the cell membrane that contains many receptors that are specific for a certain substance. Once the surface receptors have bound sufficient amounts of the specific substance (the receptor's ligand), the cell will endocytose the part of the cell membrane containing the receptor-ligand complexes. Iron, a required component of hemoglobin, is endocytosed by red blood cells in this way. Iron is bound to a protein called transferrin in the blood. Specific transferrin receptors on red blood cell surfaces bind the iron-transferrin molecules, and the cell endocytoses the receptor-ligand complexes.

In contrast with endocytosis, **exocytosis** (taking "out of the cell") is the process of a cell exporting material using vesicular transport (**Figure 3.11**). Many cells manufacture substances that must be secreted, like a factory manufacturing a product for export. These substances are typically packaged into membrane-bound vesicles within the cell. When the vesicle membrane fuses with the cell membrane, the vesicle releases it contents into the interstitial fluid. The vesicle membrane then becomes part of the cell membrane. Cells of the stomach and pancreas produce and secrete digestive enzymes through exocytosis (**Figure 3.12**). Endocrine cells produce and secrete hormones that are sent throughout the body, and certain immune cells produce and secrete large amounts of histamine, a chemical important for immune responses.

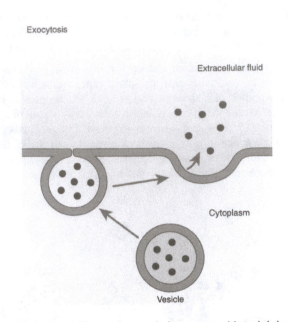

Figure 3.11 Exocytosis Exocytosis is much like endocytosis in reverse. Material destined for export is packaged into a vesicle inside the cell. The membrane of the vesicle fuses with the cell membrane, and the contents are released into the extracellular space.

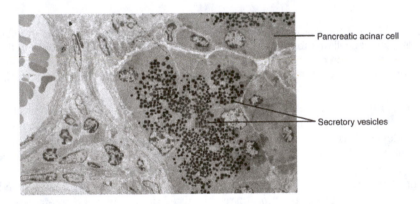

Figure 3.12 Pancreatic Cells' Enzyme Products The pancreatic acinar cells produce and secrete many enzymes that digest food. The tiny black granules in this electron micrograph are secretory vesicles filled with enzymes that will be exported from the cells via exocytosis. LM × 2900. (Micrograph provided by the Regents of University of Michigan Medical School © 2012)

View the University of Michigan WebScope at http://virtualslides.med.umich.edu/Histology/EMsmallCharts/3%20Image%20Scope%20finals/226%20-%20Pancreas_001.svs/view.apml (http://openstaxcollege.org/l/pcells)

to explore the tissue sample in greater detail.

Cell: Cystic Fibrosis

Cystic fibrosis (CF) affects approximately 30,000 people in the United States, with about 1,000 new cases reported each year. The genetic disease is most well known for its damage to the lungs, causing breathing difficulties and chronic lung infections, but it also affects the liver, pancreas, and intestines. Only about 50 years ago, the prognosis for children born with CF was very grim—a life expectancy rarely over 10 years. Today, with advances in medical treatment, many CF patients live into their 30s.

The symptoms of CF result from a malfunctioning membrane ion channel called the cystic fibrosis transmembrane conductance regulator, or CFTR. In healthy people, the CFTR protein is an integral membrane protein that transports Cl^- ions out of the cell. In a person who has CF, the gene for the CFTR is mutated, thus, the cell manufactures a defective channel protein that typically is not incorporated into the membrane, but is instead degraded by the cell.

The CFTR requires ATP in order to function, making its Cl^- transport a form of active transport. This characteristic puzzled researchers for a long time because the Cl^- ions are actually flowing *down* their concentration gradient when transported out of cells. Active transport generally pumps ions *against* their concentration gradient, but the CFTR presents an exception to this rule.

In normal lung tissue, the movement of Cl^- out of the cell maintains a Cl^--rich, negatively charged environment immediately outside of the cell. This is particularly important in the epithelial lining of the respiratory system. Respiratory epithelial cells secrete mucus, which serves to trap dust, bacteria, and other debris. A cilium (plural = cilia) is one of the hair-like appendages found on certain cells. Cilia on the epithelial cells move the mucus and its trapped particles up the airways away from the lungs and toward the outside. In order to be effectively moved upward, the mucus cannot be too viscous; rather it must have a thin, watery consistency. The transport of Cl^- and the maintenance of an electronegative environment outside of the cell attract positive ions such as Na^+ to the extracellular space. The accumulation of both Cl^- and Na^+ ions in the extracellular space creates solute-rich mucus, which has a low concentration of water molecules. As a result, through osmosis, water moves from cells and extracellular matrix into the mucus, "thinning" it out. This is how, in a normal respiratory system, the mucus is kept sufficiently watered-down to be propelled out of the respiratory system.

If the CFTR channel is absent, Cl^- ions are not transported out of the cell in adequate numbers, thus preventing them from drawing positive ions. The absence of ions in the secreted mucus results in the lack of a normal water concentration gradient. Thus, there is no osmotic pressure pulling water into the mucus. The resulting mucus is thick and sticky, and the ciliated epithelia cannot effectively remove it from the respiratory system. Passageways in the lungs become blocked with mucus, along with the debris it carries. Bacterial infections occur more easily because bacterial cells are not effectively carried away from the lungs.

3.2 | The Cytoplasm and Cellular Organelles

By the end of this section, you will be able to:

- Describe the structure and function of the cellular organelles associated with the endomembrane system, including the endoplasmic reticulum, Golgi apparatus, and lysosomes
- Describe the structure and function of mitochondria and peroxisomes
- Explain the three components of the cytoskeleton, including their composition and functions

Now that you have learned that the cell membrane surrounds all cells, you can dive inside of a prototypical human cell to learn about its internal components and their functions. All living cells in multicellular organisms contain an internal cytoplasmic compartment, and a nucleus within the cytoplasm. **Cytosol**, the jelly-like substance within the cell, provides the fluid medium necessary for biochemical reactions. Eukaryotic cells, including all animal cells, also contain various cellular organelles. An **organelle** ("little organ") is one of several different types of membrane-enclosed bodies in the cell, each performing a unique function. Just as the various bodily organs work together in harmony to perform all of a human's functions, the many different cellular organelles work together to keep the cell healthy and performing all of its important functions. The organelles and cytosol, taken together, compose the cell's **cytoplasm**. The **nucleus** is a cell's central organelle, which contains the cell's DNA (Figure 3.13).

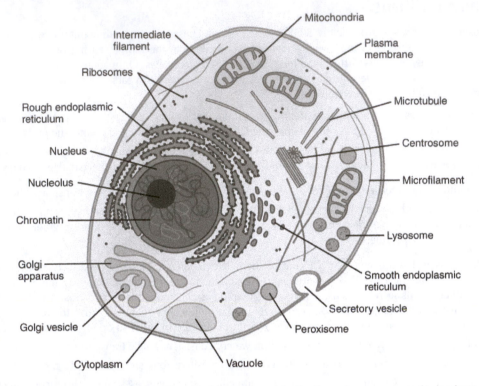

Figure 3.13 Prototypical Human Cell While this image is not indicative of any one particular human cell, it is a prototypical example of a cell containing the primary organelles and internal structures.

Organelles of the Endomembrane System

A set of three major organelles together form a system within the cell called the endomembrane system. These organelles work together to perform various cellular jobs, including the task of producing, packaging, and exporting certain cellular products. The organelles of the endomembrane system include the endoplasmic reticulum, Golgi apparatus, and vesicles.

Endoplasmic Reticulum

The **endoplasmic reticulum (ER)** is a system of channels that is continuous with the nuclear membrane (or "envelope") covering the nucleus and composed of the same lipid bilayer material. The ER can be thought of as a series of winding thoroughfares similar to the waterway canals in Venice. The ER provides passages throughout much of the cell that function in transporting, synthesizing, and storing materials. The winding structure of the ER results in a large membranous surface area that supports its many functions (Figure 3.14).

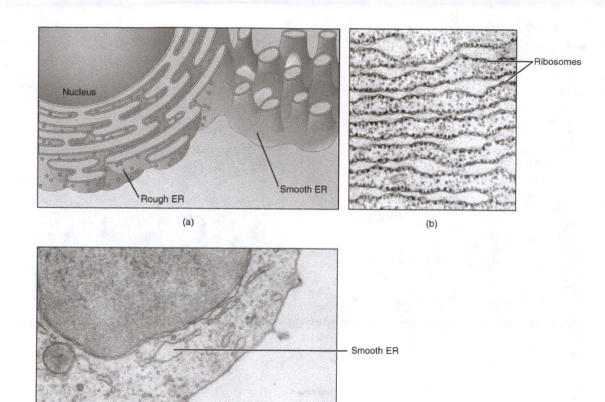

Figure 3.14 Endoplasmic Reticulum (ER) (a) The ER is a winding network of thin membranous sacs found in close association with the cell nucleus. The smooth and rough endoplasmic reticula are very different in appearance and function (source: mouse tissue). (b) Rough ER is studded with numerous ribosomes, which are sites of protein synthesis (source: mouse tissue). EM × 110,000. (c) Smooth ER synthesizes phospholipids, steroid hormones, regulates the concentration of cellular Ca^{++}, metabolizes some carbohydrates, and breaks down certain toxins (source: mouse tissue). EM × 110,510. (Micrographs provided by the Regents of University of Michigan Medical School © 2012)

Endoplasmic reticulum can exist in two forms: rough ER and smooth ER. These two types of ER perform some very different functions and can be found in very different amounts depending on the type of cell. Rough ER (RER) is so-called because its membrane is dotted with embedded granules—organelles called ribosomes, giving the RER a bumpy appearance. A **ribosome** is an organelle that serves as the site of protein synthesis. It is composed of two ribosomal RNA subunits that wrap around mRNA to start the process of translation, followed by protein synthesis. Smooth ER (SER) lacks these ribosomes.

One of the main functions of the smooth ER is in the synthesis of lipids. The smooth ER synthesizes phospholipids, the main component of biological membranes, as well as steroid hormones. For this reason, cells that produce large quantities of such hormones, such as those of the female ovaries and male testes, contain large amounts of smooth ER. In addition to lipid synthesis, the smooth ER also sequesters (i.e., stores) and regulates the concentration of cellular Ca^{++}, a function extremely important in cells of the nervous system where Ca^{++} is the trigger for neurotransmitter release. The smooth ER additionally metabolizes some carbohydrates and performs a detoxification role, breaking down certain toxins.

In contrast with the smooth ER, the primary job of the rough ER is the synthesis and modification of proteins destined for the cell membrane or for export from the cell. For this protein synthesis, many ribosomes attach to the ER (giving it the studded appearance of rough ER). Typically, a protein is synthesized within the ribosome and released inside the channel of the rough ER, where sugars can be added to it (by a process called glycosylation) before it is transported within a vesicle to the next stage in the packaging and shipping process: the Golgi apparatus.

The Golgi Apparatus

The **Golgi apparatus** is responsible for sorting, modifying, and shipping off the products that come from the rough ER, much like a post-office. The Golgi apparatus looks like stacked flattened discs, almost like stacks of oddly shaped pancakes. Like the ER, these discs are membranous. The Golgi apparatus has two distinct sides, each with a different role. One side of the apparatus receives products in vesicles. These products are sorted through the apparatus, and then they are released from the opposite side after being repackaged into new vesicles. If the product is to be exported from the cell, the vesicle migrates to the cell surface and fuses to the cell membrane, and the cargo is secreted (Figure 3.15).

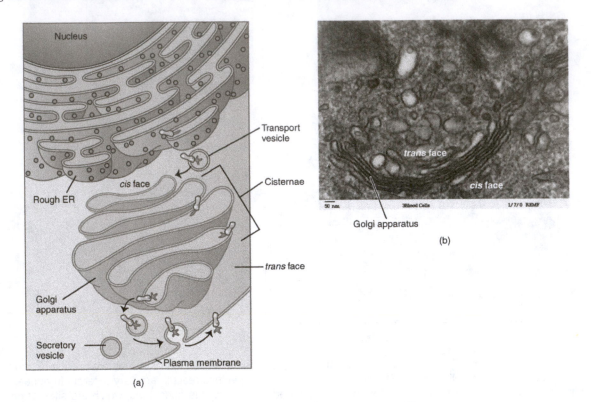

Figure 3.15 Golgi Apparatus (a) The Golgi apparatus manipulates products from the rough ER, and also produces new organelles called lysosomes. Proteins and other products of the ER are sent to the Golgi apparatus, which organizes, modifies, packages, and tags them. Some of these products are transported to other areas of the cell and some are exported from the cell through exocytosis. Enzymatic proteins are packaged as new lysosomes (or packaged and sent for fusion with existing lysosomes). (b) An electron micrograph of the Golgi apparatus.

Lysosomes

Some of the protein products packaged by the Golgi include digestive enzymes that are meant to remain inside the cell for use in breaking down certain materials. The enzyme-containing vesicles released by the Golgi may form new lysosomes, or fuse with existing, lysosomes. A **lysosome** is an organelle that contains enzymes that break down and digest unneeded cellular components, such as a damaged organelle. (A lysosome is similar to a wrecking crew that takes down old and unsound buildings in a neighborhood.) **Autophagy** ("self-eating") is the process of a cell digesting its own structures. Lysosomes are also important for breaking down foreign material. For example, when certain immune defense cells (white blood cells) phagocytize bacteria, the bacterial cell is transported into a lysosome and digested by the enzymes inside. As one might imagine, such phagocytic defense cells contain large numbers of lysosomes.

Under certain circumstances, lysosomes perform a more grand and dire function. In the case of damaged or unhealthy cells, lysosomes can be triggered to open up and release their digestive enzymes into the cytoplasm of the cell, killing the cell. This "self-destruct" mechanism is called **autolysis**, and makes the process of cell death controlled (a mechanism called "apoptosis").

Interactive LINK

Watch this **video (http://openstaxcollege.org/l/endomembrane1)** to learn about the endomembrane system, which includes the rough and smooth ER and the Golgi body as well as lysosomes and vesicles. What is the primary role of the endomembrane system?

Organelles for Energy Production and Detoxification

In addition to the jobs performed by the endomembrane system, the cell has many other important functions. Just as you must consume nutrients to provide yourself with energy, so must each of your cells take in nutrients, some of which convert to chemical energy that can be used to power biochemical reactions. Another important function of the cell is detoxification. Humans take in all sorts of toxins from the environment and also produce harmful chemicals as byproducts of cellular processes. Cells called hepatocytes in the liver detoxify many of these toxins.

Mitochondria

A **mitochondrion** (plural = mitochondria) is a membranous, bean-shaped organelle that is the "energy transformer" of the cell. Mitochondria consist of an outer lipid bilayer membrane as well as an additional inner lipid bilayer membrane (**Figure 3.16**). The inner membrane is highly folded into winding structures with a great deal of surface area, called cristae. It is along this inner membrane that a series of proteins, enzymes, and other molecules perform the biochemical reactions of cellular respiration. These reactions convert energy stored in nutrient molecules (such as glucose) into adenosine triphosphate (ATP), which provides usable cellular energy to the cell. Cells use ATP constantly, and so the mitochondria are constantly at work. Oxygen molecules are required during cellular respiration, which is why you must constantly breathe it in. One of the organ systems in the body that uses huge amounts of ATP is the muscular system because ATP is required to sustain muscle contraction. As a result, muscle cells are packed full of mitochondria. Nerve cells also need large quantities of ATP to run their sodium-potassium pumps. Therefore, an individual neuron will be loaded with over a thousand mitochondria. On the other hand, a bone cell, which is not nearly as metabolically-active, might only have a couple hundred mitochondria.

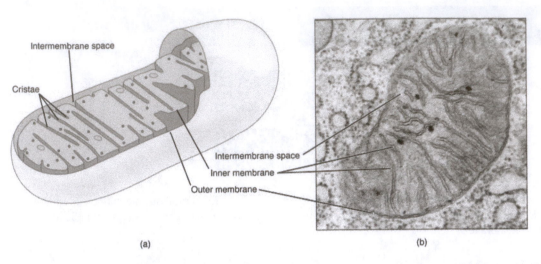

Figure 3.16 Mitochondrion The mitochondria are the energy-conversion factories of the cell. (a) A mitochondrion is composed of two separate lipid bilayer membranes. Along the inner membrane are various molecules that work together to produce ATP, the cell's major energy currency. (b) An electron micrograph of mitochondria. EM × 236,000. (Micrograph provided by the Regents of University of Michigan Medical School © 2012)

Peroxisomes

Like lysosomes, a **peroxisome** is a membrane-bound cellular organelle that contains mostly enzymes (Figure 3.17). Peroxisomes perform a couple of different functions, including lipid metabolism and chemical detoxification. In contrast to the digestive enzymes found in lysosomes, the enzymes within peroxisomes serve to transfer hydrogen atoms from various molecules to oxygen, producing hydrogen peroxide (H_2O_2). In this way, peroxisomes neutralize poisons such as alcohol. In order to appreciate the importance of peroxisomes, it is necessary to understand the concept of reactive oxygen species.

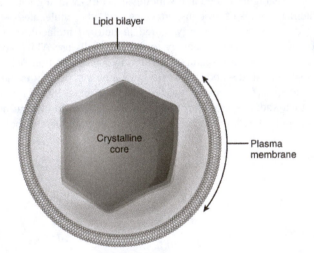

Figure 3.17 Peroxisome Peroxisomes are membrane-bound organelles that contain an abundance of enzymes for detoxifying harmful substances and lipid metabolism.

Reactive oxygen species (ROS) such as peroxides and free radicals are the highly reactive products of many normal cellular processes, including the mitochondrial reactions that produce ATP and oxygen metabolism. Examples of ROS include the hydroxyl radical OH, H_2O_2, and superoxide (O_2^-). Some ROS are important for certain cellular functions, such as cell signaling processes and immune responses against foreign substances. Free radicals are reactive because they contain free unpaired electrons; they can easily oxidize other molecules throughout the cell, causing cellular damage and even cell death. Free radicals are thought to play a role in many destructive processes in the body, from cancer to coronary artery disease.

Peroxisomes, on the other hand, oversee reactions that neutralize free radicals. Peroxisomes produce large amounts of the toxic H_2O_2 in the process, but peroxisomes contain enzymes that convert H_2O_2 into water and oxygen. These byproducts are safely released into the cytoplasm. Like miniature sewage treatment plants, peroxisomes neutralize harmful toxins so that they do not wreak havoc in the cells. The liver is the organ primarily responsible for detoxifying the blood before it travels throughout the body, and liver cells contain an exceptionally high number of peroxisomes.

Defense mechanisms such as detoxification within the peroxisome and certain cellular antioxidants serve to neutralize many of these molecules. Some vitamins and other substances, found primarily in fruits and vegetables, have antioxidant properties. Antioxidants work by being oxidized themselves, halting the destructive reaction cascades initiated by the free radicals. Sometimes though, ROS accumulate beyond the capacity of such defenses.

Oxidative stress is the term used to describe damage to cellular components caused by ROS. Due to their characteristic unpaired electrons, ROS can set off chain reactions where they remove electrons from other molecules, which then become oxidized and reactive, and do the same to other molecules, causing a chain reaction. ROS can cause permanent damage to cellular lipids, proteins, carbohydrates, and nucleic acids. Damaged DNA can lead to genetic mutations and even cancer. A **mutation** is a change in the nucleotide sequence in a gene within a cell's DNA, potentially altering the protein coded by that gene. Other diseases believed to be triggered or exacerbated by ROS include Alzheimer's disease, cardiovascular diseases, diabetes, Parkinson's disease, arthritis, Huntington's disease, and schizophrenia, among many others. It is noteworthy that these diseases are largely age-related. Many scientists believe that oxidative stress is a major contributor to the aging process.

Aging AND THE...

Cell: The Free Radical Theory

The free radical theory on aging was originally proposed in the 1950s, and still remains under debate. Generally speaking, the free radical theory of aging suggests that accumulated cellular damage from oxidative stress contributes to the physiological and anatomical effects of aging. There are two significantly different versions of this theory: one states that the aging process itself is a result of oxidative damage, and the other states that oxidative damage causes age-related disease and disorders. The latter version of the theory is more widely accepted than the former. However, many lines of evidence suggest that oxidative damage does contribute to the aging process. Research has shown that reducing oxidative damage can result in a longer lifespan in certain organisms such as yeast, worms, and fruit flies. Conversely, increasing oxidative damage can shorten the lifespan of mice and worms. Interestingly, a manipulation called calorie-restriction (moderately restricting the caloric intake) has been shown to increase life span in some laboratory animals. It is believed that this increase is at least in part due to a reduction of oxidative stress. However, a long-term study of primates with calorie-restriction showed no increase in their lifespan. A great deal of additional research will be required to better understand the link between reactive oxygen species and aging.

The Cytoskeleton

Much like the bony skeleton structurally supports the human body, the cytoskeleton helps the cells to maintain their structural integrity. The **cytoskeleton** is a group of fibrous proteins that provide structural support for cells, but this is only one of the functions of the cytoskeleton. Cytoskeletal components are also critical for cell motility, cell reproduction, and transportation of substances within the cell.

The cytoskeleton forms a complex thread-like network throughout the cell consisting of three different kinds of protein-based filaments: microfilaments, intermediate filaments, and microtubules (Figure 3.18). The thickest of the three is the **microtubule**, a structural filament composed of subunits of a protein called tubulin. Microtubules maintain cell shape and structure, help resist compression of the cell, and play a role in positioning the organelles within the cell. Microtubules also make up two types of cellular appendages important for motion: cilia and flagella. **Cilia** are found on many cells of the body, including the epithelial cells that line the airways of the respiratory system. Cilia move rhythmically; they beat constantly, moving waste materials such as dust, mucus, and bacteria upward through the airways, away from the lungs and toward the mouth. Beating cilia on cells in the female fallopian tubes move egg cells from the ovary towards the uterus. A **flagellum** (plural = flagella) is an appendage larger than a cilium and specialized for cell locomotion. The only flagellated cell in humans is the sperm cell that must propel itself towards female egg cells.

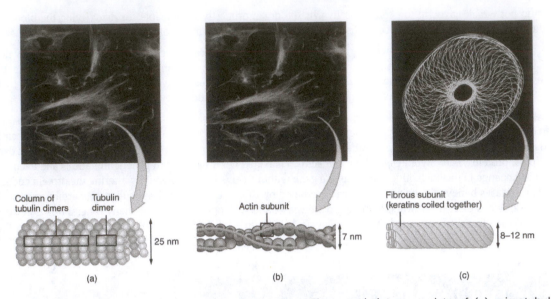

Figure 3.18 The Three Components of the Cytoskeleton The cytoskeleton consists of (a) microtubules, (b) microfilaments, and (c) intermediate filaments. The cytoskeleton plays an important role in maintaining cell shape and structure, promoting cellular movement, and aiding cell division.

A very important function of microtubules is to set the paths (somewhat like railroad tracks) along which the genetic material can be pulled (a process requiring ATP) during cell division, so that each new daughter cell receives the appropriate set of chromosomes. Two short, identical microtubule structures called centrioles are found near the nucleus of cells. A **centriole** can serve as the cellular origin point for microtubules extending outward as cilia or flagella or can assist with the separation of DNA during cell division. Microtubules grow out from the centrioles by adding more tubulin subunits, like adding additional links to a chain.

In contrast with microtubules, the **microfilament** is a thinner type of cytoskeletal filament (see **Figure 3.18b**). Actin, a protein that forms chains, is the primary component of these microfilaments. Actin fibers, twisted chains of actin filaments, constitute a large component of muscle tissue and, along with the protein myosin, are responsible for muscle contraction. Like microtubules, actin filaments are long chains of single subunits (called actin subunits). In muscle cells, these long actin strands, called thin filaments, are "pulled" by thick filaments of the myosin protein to contract the cell.

Actin also has an important role during cell division. When a cell is about to split in half during cell division, actin filaments work with myosin to create a cleavage furrow that eventually splits the cell down the middle, forming two new cells from the original cell.

The final cytoskeletal filament is the intermediate filament. As its name would suggest, an **intermediate filament** is a filament intermediate in thickness between the microtubules and microfilaments (see **Figure 3.18c**). Intermediate filaments are made up of long fibrous subunits of a protein called keratin that are wound together like the threads that compose a rope. Intermediate filaments, in concert with the microtubules, are important for maintaining cell shape and structure. Unlike the microtubules, which resist compression, intermediate filaments resist tension—the forces that pull apart cells. There are many cases in which cells are prone to tension, such as when epithelial cells of the skin are compressed, tugging them in different directions. Intermediate filaments help anchor organelles together within a cell and also link cells to other cells by forming special cell-to-cell junctions.

3.3 | The Nucleus and DNA Replication

By the end of this section, you will be able to:

- Describe the structure and features of the nuclear membrane
- List the contents of the nucleus
- Explain the organization of the DNA molecule within the nucleus
- Describe the process of DNA replication

The nucleus is the largest and most prominent of a cell's organelles (Figure 3.19). The nucleus is generally considered the control center of the cell because it stores all of the genetic instructions for manufacturing proteins. Interestingly, some cells in the body, such as muscle cells, contain more than one nucleus (Figure 3.20), which is known as multinucleated. Other cells, such as mammalian red blood cells (RBCs), do not contain nuclei at all. RBCs eject their nuclei as they mature, making space for the large numbers of hemoglobin molecules that carry oxygen throughout the body (Figure 3.21). Without nuclei, the life span of RBCs is short, and so the body must produce new ones constantly.

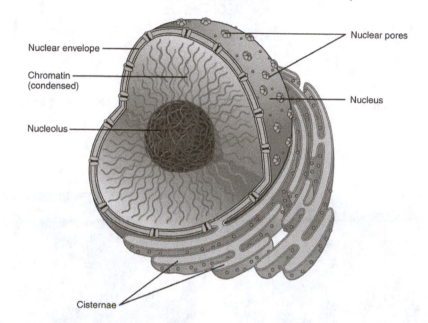

Figure 3.19 The Nucleus The nucleus is the control center of the cell. The nucleus of living cells contains the genetic material that determines the entire structure and function of that cell.

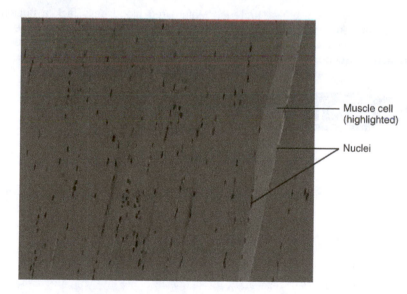

Figure 3.20 Multinucleate Muscle Cell Unlike cardiac muscle cells and smooth muscle cells, which have a single nucleus, a skeletal muscle cell contains many nuclei, and is referred to as "multinucleated." These muscle cells are long and fibrous (often referred to as muscle fibers). During development, many smaller cells fuse to form a mature muscle fiber. The nuclei of the fused cells are conserved in the mature cell, thus imparting a multinucleate characteristic to mature muscle cells. LM × 104.3. (Micrograph provided by the Regents of University of Michigan Medical School © 2012)

Interactive LINK

View the University of Michigan WebScope at http://141.214.65.171/Histology/Basic%20Tissues/Muscle/058thin_HISTO_83X.svs/view.apml (http://openstaxcollege.org/l/mnucleate) to explore the tissue sample in greater detail.

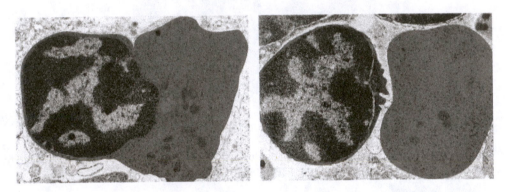

Figure 3.21 Red Blood Cell Extruding Its Nucleus Mature red blood cells lack a nucleus. As they mature, erythroblasts extrude their nucleus, making room for more hemoglobin. The two panels here show an erythroblast before and after ejecting its nucleus, respectively. (credit: modification of micrograph provided by the Regents of University of Michigan Medical School © 2012)

Interactive LINK

View the University of Michigan WebScope at http://virtualslides.med.umich.edu/Histology/EMsmallCharts/3%20Image%20Scope%20finals/139%20-%20Erythroblast_001.svs/view.apml (http://openstaxcollege.org/l/RBC) to explore the tissue sample in greater detail.

Inside the nucleus lies the blueprint that dictates everything a cell will do and all of the products it will make. This information is stored within DNA. The nucleus sends "commands" to the cell via molecular messengers that translate the information from DNA. Each cell in your body (with the exception of germ cells) contains the complete set of your DNA. When a cell divides, the DNA must be duplicated so that the each new cell receives a full complement of DNA. The following section will explore the structure of the nucleus and its contents, as well as the process of DNA replication.

Organization of the Nucleus and Its DNA

Like most other cellular organelles, the nucleus is surrounded by a membrane called the **nuclear envelope**. This membranous covering consists of two adjacent lipid bilayers with a thin fluid space in between them. Spanning these two bilayers are nuclear pores. A **nuclear pore** is a tiny passageway for the passage of proteins, RNA, and solutes between the nucleus and the cytoplasm. Proteins called pore complexes lining the nuclear pores regulate the passage of materials into and out of the nucleus.

Inside the nuclear envelope is a gel-like nucleoplasm with solutes that include the building blocks of nucleic acids. There also can be a dark-staining mass often visible under a simple light microscope, called a **nucleolus** (plural = nucleoli). The nucleolus is a region of the nucleus that is responsible for manufacturing the RNA necessary for construction of ribosomes. Once synthesized, newly made ribosomal subunits exit the cell's nucleus through the nuclear pores.

The genetic instructions that are used to build and maintain an organism are arranged in an orderly manner in strands of DNA. Within the nucleus are threads of **chromatin** composed of DNA and associated proteins (Figure 3.22). Along the chromatin threads, the DNA is wrapped around a set of **histone** proteins. A **nucleosome** is a single, wrapped DNA-histone complex. Multiple nucleosomes along the entire molecule of DNA appear like a beaded necklace, in which the string is the DNA and the beads are the associated histones. When a cell is in the process of division, the chromatin condenses into chromosomes, so that the DNA can be safely transported to the "daughter cells." The **chromosome** is composed of DNA and proteins; it is the condensed form of chromatin. It is estimated that humans have almost 22,000 genes distributed on 46 chromosomes.

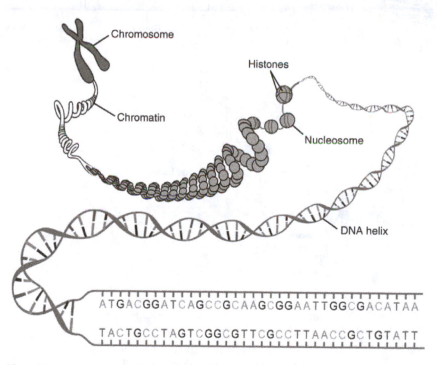

Figure 3.22 DNA Macrostructure Strands of DNA are wrapped around supporting histones. These proteins are increasingly bundled and condensed into chromatin, which is packed tightly into chromosomes when the cell is ready to divide.

DNA Replication

In order for an organism to grow, develop, and maintain its health, cells must reproduce themselves by dividing to produce two new daughter cells, each with the full complement of DNA as found in the original cell. Billions of new cells are produced in an adult human every day. Only very few cell types in the body do not divide, including nerve cells, skeletal muscle fibers, and cardiac muscle cells. The division time of different cell types varies. Epithelial cells of the skin and gastrointestinal lining, for instance, divide very frequently to replace those that are constantly being rubbed off of the surface by friction.

A DNA molecule is made of two strands that "complement" each other in the sense that the molecules that compose the strands fit together and bind to each other, creating a double-stranded molecule that looks much like a long, twisted ladder. Each side rail of the DNA ladder is composed of alternating sugar and phosphate groups (Figure 3.23). The two sides of the ladder are not identical, but are complementary. These two backbones are bonded to each other across pairs of protruding bases, each bonded pair forming one "rung," or cross member. The four DNA bases are adenine (A), thymine (T), cytosine (C), and guanine (G). Because of their shape and charge, the two bases that compose a pair always bond together. Adenine always binds with thymine, and cytosine always binds with guanine. The particular sequence of bases along the DNA molecule determines the genetic code. Therefore, if the two complementary strands of DNA were pulled apart, you could infer the order of the bases in one strand from the bases in the other, complementary strand. For example, if one strand has a region with the sequence AGTGCCT, then the sequence of the complementary strand would be TCACGGA.

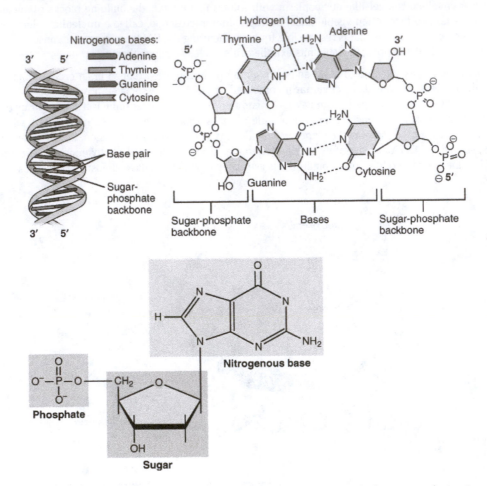

Figure 3.23 Molecular Structure of DNA The DNA double helix is composed of two complementary strands. The strands are bonded together via their nitrogenous base pairs using hydrogen bonds.

DNA replication is the copying of DNA that occurs before cell division can take place. After a great deal of debate and experimentation, the general method of DNA replication was deduced in 1958 by two scientists in California, Matthew Meselson and Franklin Stahl. This method is illustrated in **Figure 3.24** and described below.

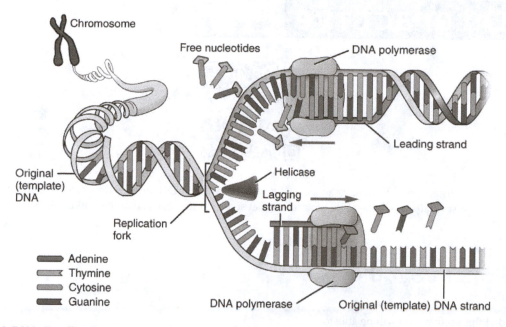

Figure 3.24 DNA Replication   DNA replication faithfully duplicates the entire genome of the cell. During DNA replication, a number of different enzymes work together to pull apart the two strands so each strand can be used as a template to synthesize new complementary strands. The two new daughter DNA molecules each contain one pre-existing strand and one newly synthesized strand. Thus, DNA replication is said to be "semiconservative."

Stage 1: Initiation. The two complementary strands are separated, much like unzipping a zipper. Special enzymes, including **helicase**, untwist and separate the two strands of DNA.

Stage 2: Elongation. Each strand becomes a template along which a new complementary strand is built. **DNA polymerase** brings in the correct bases to complement the template strand, synthesizing a new strand base by base. A DNA polymerase is an enzyme that adds free nucleotides to the end of a chain of DNA, making a new double strand. This growing strand continues to be built until it has fully complemented the template strand.

Stage 3: Termination. Once the two original strands are bound to their own, finished, complementary strands, DNA replication is stopped and the two new identical DNA molecules are complete.

Each new DNA molecule contains one strand from the original molecule and one newly synthesized strand. The term for this mode of replication is "semiconservative," because half of the original DNA molecule is conserved in each new DNA molecule. This process continues until the cell's entire **genome**, the entire complement of an organism's DNA, is replicated. As you might imagine, it is very important that DNA replication take place precisely so that new cells in the body contain the exact same genetic material as their parent cells. Mistakes made during DNA replication, such as the accidental addition of an inappropriate nucleotide, have the potential to render a gene dysfunctional or useless. Fortunately, there are mechanisms in place to minimize such mistakes. A DNA proofreading process enlists the help of special enzymes that scan the newly synthesized molecule for mistakes and corrects them. Once the process of DNA replication is complete, the cell is ready to divide. You will explore the process of cell division later in the chapter.

☞Interactive LINK

Watch this **video (http://openstaxcollege.org/l/DNArep)** to learn about DNA replication. DNA replication proceeds simultaneously at several sites on the same molecule. What separates the base pair at the start of DNA replication?

3.4 | Protein Synthesis

By the end of this section, you will be able to:

- Explain how the genetic code stored within DNA determines the protein that will form
- Describe the process of transcription
- Describe the process of translation
- Discuss the function of ribosomes

It was mentioned earlier that DNA provides a "blueprint" for the cell structure and physiology. This refers to the fact that DNA contains the information necessary for the cell to build one very important type of molecule: the protein. Most structural components of the cell are made up, at least in part, by proteins and virtually all the functions that a cell carries out are completed with the help of proteins. One of the most important classes of proteins is enzymes, which help speed up necessary biochemical reactions that take place inside the cell. Some of these critical biochemical reactions include building larger molecules from smaller components (such as occurs during DNA replication or synthesis of microtubules) and breaking down larger molecules into smaller components (such as when harvesting chemical energy from nutrient molecules). Whatever the cellular process may be, it is almost sure to involve proteins. Just as the cell's genome describes its full complement of DNA, a cell's **proteome** is its full complement of proteins. Protein synthesis begins with genes. A **gene** is a functional segment of DNA that provides the genetic information necessary to build a protein. Each particular gene provides the code necessary to construct a particular protein. **Gene expression**, which transforms the information coded in a gene to a final gene product, ultimately dictates the structure and function of a cell by determining which proteins are made.

The interpretation of genes works in the following way. Recall that proteins are polymers, or chains, of many amino acid building blocks. The sequence of bases in a gene (that is, its sequence of A, T, C, G nucleotides) translates to an amino acid sequence. A **triplet** is a section of three DNA bases in a row that codes for a specific amino acid. Similar to the way in which the three-letter code *d-o-g* signals the image of a dog, the three-letter DNA base code signals the use of a particular amino acid. For example, the DNA triplet CAC (cytosine, adenine, and cytosine) specifies the amino acid valine. Therefore, a gene, which is composed of multiple triplets in a unique sequence, provides the code to build an entire protein, with multiple amino acids in the proper sequence (**Figure 3.25**). The mechanism by which cells turn the DNA code into a protein product is a two-step process, with an RNA molecule as the intermediate.

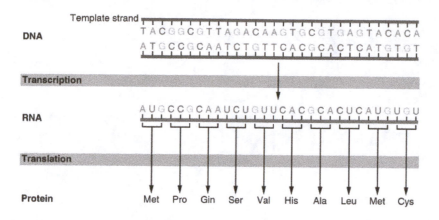

Figure 3.25 The Genetic Code DNA holds all of the genetic information necessary to build a cell's proteins. The nucleotide sequence of a gene is ultimately translated into an amino acid sequence of the gene's corresponding protein.

From DNA to RNA: Transcription

DNA is housed within the nucleus, and protein synthesis takes place in the cytoplasm, thus there must be some sort of intermediate messenger that leaves the nucleus and manages protein synthesis. This intermediate messenger is **messenger RNA (mRNA)**, a single-stranded nucleic acid that carries a copy of the genetic code for a single gene out of the nucleus and into the cytoplasm where it is used to produce proteins.

There are several different types of RNA, each having different functions in the cell. The structure of RNA is similar to DNA with a few small exceptions. For one thing, unlike DNA, most types of RNA, including mRNA, are single-stranded and contain no complementary strand. Second, the ribose sugar in RNA contains an additional oxygen atom compared with DNA. Finally, instead of the base thymine, RNA contains the base uracil. This means that adenine will always pair up with uracil during the protein synthesis process.

Gene expression begins with the process called **transcription**, which is the synthesis of a strand of mRNA that is complementary to the gene of interest. This process is called transcription because the mRNA is like a transcript, or copy, of the gene's DNA code. Transcription begins in a fashion somewhat like DNA replication, in that a region of DNA unwinds and the two strands separate, however, only that small portion of the DNA will be split apart. The triplets within the gene on this section of the DNA molecule are used as the template to transcribe the complementary strand of RNA (**Figure 3.26**). A **codon** is a three-base sequence of mRNA, so-called because they directly encode amino acids. Like DNA replication, there are three stages to transcription: initiation, elongation, and termination.

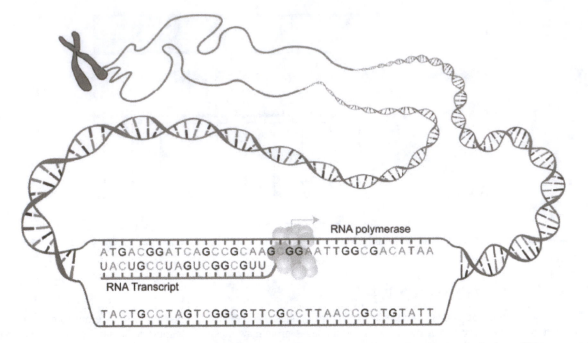

Figure 3.26 Transcription: from DNA to mRNA In the first of the two stages of making protein from DNA, a gene on the DNA molecule is transcribed into a complementary mRNA molecule.

Stage 1: Initiation. A region at the beginning of the gene called a **promoter**—a particular sequence of nucleotides—triggers the start of transcription.

Stage 2: Elongation. Transcription starts when RNA polymerase unwinds the DNA segment. One strand, referred to as the coding strand, becomes the template with the genes to be coded. The polymerase then aligns the correct nucleic acid (A, C, G, or U) with its complementary base on the coding strand of DNA. **RNA polymerase** is an enzyme that adds new nucleotides to a growing strand of RNA. This process builds a strand of mRNA.

Stage 3: Termination. When the polymerase has reached the end of the gene, one of three specific triplets (UAA, UAG, or UGA) codes a "stop" signal, which triggers the enzymes to terminate transcription and release the mRNA transcript.

Before the mRNA molecule leaves the nucleus and proceeds to protein synthesis, it is modified in a number of ways. For this reason, it is often called a pre-mRNA at this stage. For example, your DNA, and thus complementary mRNA, contains long regions called non-coding regions that do not code for amino acids. Their function is still a mystery, but the process called **splicing** removes these non-coding regions from the pre-mRNA transcript (Figure 3.27). A **spliceosome**—a structure composed of various proteins and other molecules—attaches to the mRNA and "splices" or cuts out the non-coding regions. The removed segment of the transcript is called an **intron**. The remaining exons are pasted together. An **exon** is a segment of RNA that remains after splicing. Interestingly, some introns that are removed from mRNA are not always non-coding. When different coding regions of mRNA are spliced out, different variations of the protein will eventually result, with differences in structure and function. This process results in a much larger variety of possible proteins and protein functions. When the mRNA transcript is ready, it travels out of the nucleus and into the cytoplasm.

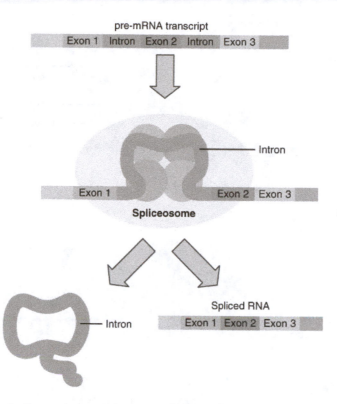

Figure 3.27 Splicing DNA In the nucleus, a structure called a spliceosome cuts out introns (noncoding regions) within a pre-mRNA transcript and reconnects the exons.

From RNA to Protein: Translation

Like translating a book from one language into another, the codons on a strand of mRNA must be translated into the amino acid alphabet of proteins. **Translation** is the process of synthesizing a chain of amino acids called a **polypeptide**. Translation requires two major aids: first, a "translator," the molecule that will conduct the translation, and second, a substrate on which the mRNA strand is translated into a new protein, like the translator's "desk." Both of these requirements are fulfilled by other types of RNA. The substrate on which translation takes place is the ribosome.

Remember that many of a cell's ribosomes are found associated with the rough ER, and carry out the synthesis of proteins destined for the Golgi apparatus. **Ribosomal RNA (rRNA)** is a type of RNA that, together with proteins, composes the structure of the ribosome. Ribosomes exist in the cytoplasm as two distinct components, a small and a large subunit. When an mRNA molecule is ready to be translated, the two subunits come together and attach to the mRNA. The ribosome provides a substrate for translation, bringing together and aligning the mRNA molecule with the molecular "translators" that must decipher its code.

The other major requirement for protein synthesis is the translator molecules that physically "read" the mRNA codons. **Transfer RNA (tRNA)** is a type of RNA that ferries the appropriate corresponding amino acids to the ribosome, and attaches each new amino acid to the last, building the polypeptide chain one-by-one. Thus tRNA transfers specific amino acids from the cytoplasm to a growing polypeptide. The tRNA molecules must be able to recognize the codons on mRNA and match them with the correct amino acid. The tRNA is modified for this function. On one end of its structure is a binding site for a specific amino acid. On the other end is a base sequence that matches the codon specifying its particular amino acid. This sequence of three bases on the tRNA molecule is called an **anticodon**. For example, a tRNA responsible for shuttling the amino acid glycine contains a binding site for glycine on one end. On the other end it contains an anticodon that complements the glycine codon (GGA is a codon for glycine, and so the tRNAs anticodon would read CCU). Equipped with its particular cargo and matching anticodon, a tRNA molecule can read its recognized mRNA codon and bring the corresponding amino acid to the growing chain (**Figure 3.28**).

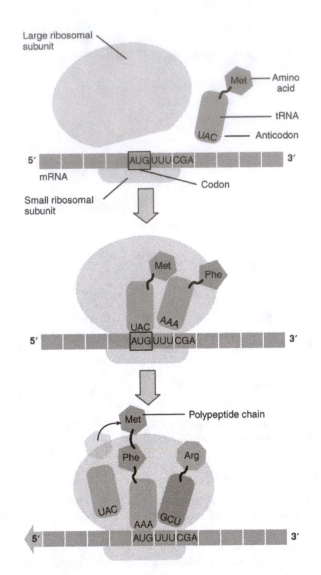

Figure 3.28 Translation from RNA to Protein During translation, the mRNA transcript is "read" by a functional complex consisting of the ribosome and tRNA molecules. tRNAs bring the appropriate amino acids in sequence to the growing polypeptide chain by matching their anti-codons with codons on the mRNA strand.

Much like the processes of DNA replication and transcription, translation consists of three main stages: initiation, elongation, and termination. Initiation takes place with the binding of a ribosome to an mRNA transcript. The elongation stage involves the recognition of a tRNA anticodon with the next mRNA codon in the sequence. Once the anticodon and codon sequences are bound (remember, they are complementary base pairs), the tRNA presents its amino acid cargo and the growing polypeptide strand is attached to this next amino acid. This attachment takes place with the assistance of various enzymes and requires energy. The tRNA molecule then releases the mRNA strand, the mRNA strand shifts one codon over in the ribosome, and the next appropriate tRNA arrives with its matching anticodon. This process continues until the final codon on the mRNA is reached which provides a "stop" message that signals termination of translation and triggers the release of the complete, newly synthesized protein. Thus, a gene within the DNA molecule is transcribed into mRNA, which is then translated into a protein product (Figure 3.29).

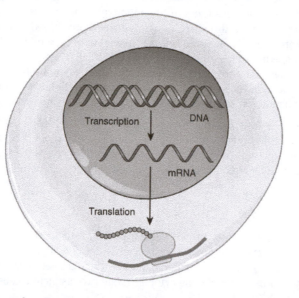

Figure 3.29 From DNA to Protein: Transcription through Translation Transcription within the cell nucleus produces an mRNA molecule, which is modified and then sent into the cytoplasm for translation. The transcript is decoded into a protein with the help of a ribosome and tRNA molecules.

Commonly, an mRNA transcription will be translated simultaneously by several adjacent ribosomes. This increases the efficiency of protein synthesis. A single ribosome might translate an mRNA molecule in approximately one minute; so multiple ribosomes aboard a single transcript could produce multiple times the number of the same protein in the same minute. A **polyribosome** is a string of ribosomes translating a single mRNA strand.

Watch this **video (http://openstaxcollege.org/l/ribosome)** to learn about ribosomes. The ribosome binds to the mRNA molecule to start translation of its code into a protein. What happens to the small and large ribosomal subunits at the end of translation?

3.5 | Cell Growth and Division

By the end of this section, you will be able to:

- Describe the stages of the cell cycle
- Discuss how the cell cycle is regulated
- Describe the implications of losing control over the cell cycle
- Describe the stages of mitosis and cytokinesis, in order

So far in this chapter, you have read numerous times of the importance and prevalence of cell division. While there are a few cells in the body that do not undergo cell division (such as gametes, red blood cells, most neurons, and some muscle cells), most somatic cells divide regularly. A **somatic cell** is a general term for a body cell, and all human cells, except for the cells that produce eggs and sperm (which are referred to as germ cells), are somatic cells. Somatic cells contain *two* copies of each of their chromosomes (one copy received from each parent). A **homologous** pair of chromosomes is the two copies of a single chromosome found in each somatic cell. The human is a **diploid** organism, having 23 homologous pairs of chromosomes in each of the somatic cells. The condition of having pairs of chromosomes is known as diploidy.

Cells in the body replace themselves over the lifetime of a person. For example, the cells lining the gastrointestinal tract must be frequently replaced when constantly "worn off" by the movement of food through the gut. But what triggers a cell to divide, and how does it prepare for and complete cell division? The **cell cycle** is the sequence of events in the life of the cell from the moment it is created at the end of a previous cycle of cell division until it then divides itself, generating two new cells.

The Cell Cycle

One "turn" or cycle of the cell cycle consists of two general phases: interphase, followed by mitosis and cytokinesis. **Interphase** is the period of the cell cycle during which the cell is not dividing. The majority of cells are in interphase most of the time. **Mitosis** is the division of genetic material, during which the cell nucleus breaks down and two new, fully functional, nuclei are formed. **Cytokinesis** divides the cytoplasm into two distinctive cells.

Interphase

A cell grows and carries out all normal metabolic functions and processes in a period called G_1 (Figure 3.30). G_1 **phase** (gap 1 phase) is the first gap, or growth phase in the cell cycle. For cells that will divide again, G_1 is followed by replication of the DNA, during the S phase. The **S phase** (synthesis phase) is period during which a cell replicates its DNA.

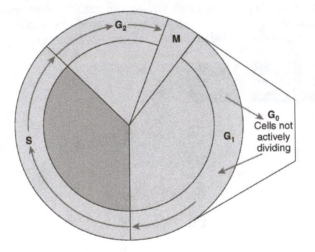

Figure 3.30 Cell Cycle The two major phases of the cell cycle include mitosis (cell division), and interphase, when the cell grows and performs all of its normal functions. Interphase is further subdivided into G_1, S, and G_2 phases.

After the synthesis phase, the cell proceeds through the G_2 phase. The G_2 **phase** is a second gap phase, during which the cell continues to grow and makes the necessary preparations for mitosis. Between G_1, S, and G_2 phases, cells will vary the most in their duration of the G1 phase. It is here that a cell might spend a couple of hours, or many days. The S phase typically lasts between 8-10 hours and the G_2 phase approximately 5 hours. In contrast to these phases, the G_0 **phase** is a resting phase of the cell cycle. Cells that have temporarily stopped dividing and are resting (a common condition) and cells that have permanently ceased dividing (like nerve cells) are said to be in G_0.

The Structure of Chromosomes

Billions of cells in the human body divide every day. During the synthesis phase (S, for DNA synthesis) of interphase, the amount of DNA within the cell precisely doubles. Therefore, after DNA replication but before cell division, each cell actually contains *two* copies of each chromosome. Each copy of the chromosome is referred to as a **sister chromatid** and is physically bound to the other copy. The **centromere** is the structure that attaches one sister chromatid to another. Because a human cell has 46 chromosomes, during this phase, there are 92 chromatids (46×2) in the cell. Make sure not to confuse the concept of a pair of chromatids (one chromosome and its exact copy attached during mitosis) and a homologous pair of chromosomes (two paired chromosomes which were inherited separately, one from each parent) (Figure 3.31).

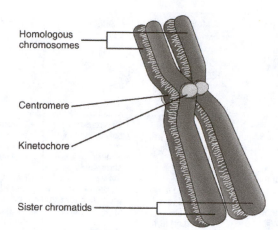

Homologous chromosomes

Centromere

Kinetochore

Sister chromatids

Figure 3.31 A Homologous Pair of Chromosomes with their Attached Sister Chromatids   The red and blue colors correspond to a homologous pair of chromosomes. Each member of the pair was separately inherited from one parent. Each chromosome in the homologous pair is also bound to an identical sister chromatid, which is produced by DNA replication, and results in the familiar "X" shape.

Mitosis and Cytokinesis

The **mitotic phase** of the cell typically takes between 1 and 2 hours. During this phase, a cell undergoes two major processes. First, it completes mitosis, during which the contents of the nucleus are equitably pulled apart and distributed between its two halves. Cytokinesis then occurs, dividing the cytoplasm and cell body into two new cells. Mitosis is divided into four major stages that take place after interphase (Figure 3.32) and in the following order: prophase, metaphase, anaphase, and telophase. The process is then followed by cytokinesis.

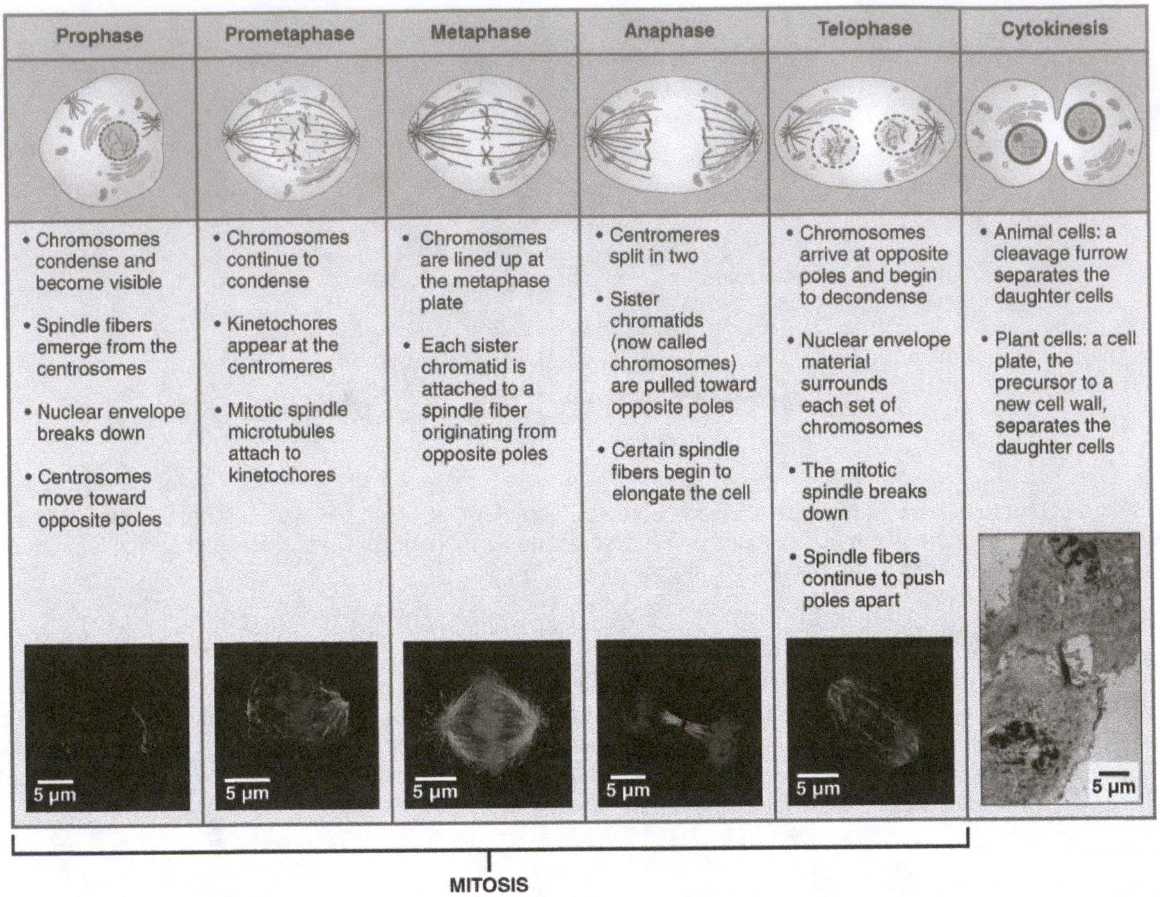

Prophase	Prometaphase	Metaphase	Anaphase	Telophase	Cytokinesis
• Chromosomes condense and become visible • Spindle fibers emerge from the centrosomes • Nuclear envelope breaks down • Centrosomes move toward opposite poles	• Chromosomes continue to condense • Kinetochores appear at the centromeres • Mitotic spindle microtubules attach to kinetochores	• Chromosomes are lined up at the metaphase plate • Each sister chromatid is attached to a spindle fiber originating from opposite poles	• Centromeres split in two • Sister chromatids (now called chromosomes) are pulled toward opposite poles • Certain spindle fibers begin to elongate the cell	• Chromosomes arrive at opposite poles and begin to decondense • Nuclear envelope material surrounds each set of chromosomes • The mitotic spindle breaks down • Spindle fibers continue to push poles apart	• Animal cells: a cleavage furrow separates the daughter cells • Plant cells: a cell plate, the precursor to a new cell wall, separates the daughter cells

MITOSIS

Figure 3.32 Cell Division: Mitosis Followed by Cytokinesis The stages of cell division oversee the separation of identical genetic material into two new nuclei, followed by the division of the cytoplasm.

Prophase is the first phase of mitosis, during which the loosely packed chromatin coils and condenses into visible chromosomes. During prophase, each chromosome becomes visible with its identical partner attached, forming the familiar X-shape of sister chromatids. The nucleolus disappears early during this phase, and the nuclear envelope also disintegrates.

A major occurrence during prophase concerns a very important structure that contains the origin site for microtubule growth. Recall the cellular structures called centrioles that serve as origin points from which microtubules extend. These tiny structures also play a very important role during mitosis. A **centrosome** is a pair of centrioles together. The cell contains two centrosomes side-by-side, which begin to move apart during prophase. As the centrosomes migrate to two different sides of the cell, microtubules begin to extend from each like long fingers from two hands extending toward each other. The **mitotic spindle** is the structure composed of the centrosomes and their emerging microtubules.

Near the end of prophase there is an invasion of the nuclear area by microtubules from the mitotic spindle. The nuclear membrane has disintegrated, and the microtubules attach themselves to the centromeres that adjoin pairs of sister chromatids. The **kinetochore** is a protein structure on the centromere that is the point of attachment between the mitotic spindle and the sister chromatids. This stage is referred to as late prophase or "prometaphase" to indicate the transition between prophase and metaphase.

Metaphase is the second stage of mitosis. During this stage, the sister chromatids, with their attached microtubules, line up along a linear plane in the middle of the cell. A metaphase plate forms between the centrosomes that are now located at either end of the cell. The **metaphase plate** is the name for the plane through the center of the spindle on which the sister chromatids are positioned. The microtubules are now poised to pull apart the sister chromatids and bring one from each pair to each side of the cell.

Anaphase is the third stage of mitosis. Anaphase takes place over a few minutes, when the pairs of sister chromatids are separated from one another, forming individual chromosomes once again. These chromosomes are pulled to opposite ends of the cell by their kinetochores, as the microtubules shorten. Each end of the cell receives one partner from each pair of sister chromatids, ensuring that the two new daughter cells will contain identical genetic material.

Telophase is the final stage of mitosis. Telophase is characterized by the formation of two new daughter nuclei at either end of the dividing cell. These newly formed nuclei surround the genetic material, which uncoils such that the chromosomes return to loosely packed chromatin. Nucleoli also reappear within the new nuclei, and the mitotic spindle breaks apart, each new cell receiving its own complement of DNA, organelles, membranes, and centrioles. At this point, the cell is already beginning to split in half as cytokinesis begins.

The **cleavage furrow** is a contractile band made up of microfilaments that forms around the midline of the cell during cytokinesis. (Recall that microfilaments consist of actin.) This contractile band squeezes the two cells apart until they finally separate. Two new cells are now formed. One of these cells (the "stem cell") enters its own cell cycle; able to grow and divide again at some future time. The other cell transforms into the functional cell of the tissue, typically replacing an "old" cell there.

Imagine a cell that completed mitosis but never underwent cytokinesis. In some cases, a cell may divide its genetic material and grow in size, but fail to undergo cytokinesis. This results in larger cells with more than one nucleus. Usually this is an unwanted aberration and can be a sign of cancerous cells.

Cell Cycle Control

A very elaborate and precise system of regulation controls direct the way cells proceed from one phase to the next in the cell cycle and begin mitosis. The control system involves molecules within the cell as well as external triggers. These internal and external control triggers provide "stop" and "advance" signals for the cell. Precise regulation of the cell cycle is critical for maintaining the health of an organism, and loss of cell cycle control can lead to cancer.

Mechanisms of Cell Cycle Control

As the cell proceeds through its cycle, each phase involves certain processes that must be completed before the cell should advance to the next phase. A **checkpoint** is a point in the cell cycle at which the cycle can be signaled to move forward or stopped. At each of these checkpoints, different varieties of molecules provide the stop or go signals, depending on certain conditions within the cell. A **cyclin** is one of the primary classes of cell cycle control molecules (**Figure 3.33**). A **cyclin-dependent kinase (CDK)** is one of a group of molecules that work together with cyclins to determine progression past cell checkpoints. By interacting with many additional molecules, these triggers push the cell cycle forward unless prevented from doing so by "stop" signals, if for some reason the cell is not ready. At the G_1 checkpoint, the cell must be ready for DNA synthesis to occur. At the G_2 checkpoint the cell must be fully prepared for mitosis. Even during mitosis, a crucial stop and go checkpoint in metaphase ensures that the cell is fully prepared to complete cell division. The metaphase checkpoint ensures that all sister chromatids are properly attached to their respective microtubules and lined up at the metaphase plate before the signal is given to separate them during anaphase.

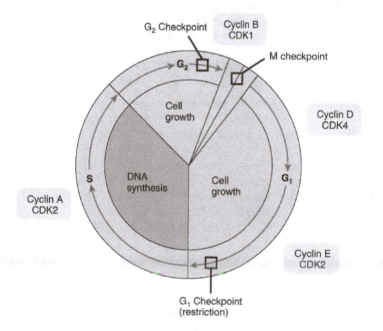

Figure 3.33 Control of the Cell Cycle Cells proceed through the cell cycle under the control of a variety of molecules, such as cyclins and cyclin-dependent kinases. These control molecules determine whether or not the cell is prepared to move into the following stage.

The Cell Cycle Out of Control: Implications

Most people understand that cancer or tumors are caused by abnormal cells that multiply continuously. If the abnormal cells continue to divide unstopped, they can damage the tissues around them, spread to other parts of the body, and eventually result in death. In healthy cells, the tight regulation mechanisms of the cell cycle prevent this from happening, while failures of cell cycle control can cause unwanted and excessive cell division. Failures of control may be caused by inherited genetic abnormalities that compromise the function of certain "stop" and "go" signals. Environmental insult that damages DNA can also cause dysfunction in those signals. Often, a combination of both genetic predisposition and environmental factors lead to cancer.

The process of a cell escaping its normal control system and becoming cancerous may actually happen throughout the body quite frequently. Fortunately, certain cells of the immune system are capable of recognizing cells that have become cancerous and destroying them. However, in certain cases the cancerous cells remain undetected and continue to proliferate. If the resulting tumor does not pose a threat to surrounding tissues, it is said to be benign and can usually be easily removed. If capable of damage, the tumor is considered malignant and the patient is diagnosed with cancer.

Homeostatic IMBALANCES

Cancer Arises from Homeostatic Imbalances

Cancer is an extremely complex condition, capable of arising from a wide variety of genetic and environmental causes. Typically, mutations or aberrations in a cell's DNA that compromise normal cell cycle control systems lead to cancerous tumors. Cell cycle control is an example of a homeostatic mechanism that maintains proper cell function and health. While progressing through the phases of the cell cycle, a large variety of intracellular molecules provide stop and go signals to regulate movement forward to the next phase. These signals are maintained in an intricate balance so that the cell only proceeds to the next phase when it is ready. This homeostatic control of the cell cycle can be thought of like a car's cruise control. Cruise control will continually apply just the right amount of acceleration to maintain a desired speed, unless the driver hits the brakes, in which case the car will slow down. Similarly, the cell includes molecular messengers, such as cyclins, that push the cell forward in its cycle.

In addition to cyclins, a class of proteins that are encoded by genes called proto-oncogenes provide important signals that regulate the cell cycle and move it forward. Examples of proto-oncogene products include cell-surface receptors for growth factors, or cell-signaling molecules, two classes of molecules that can promote DNA replication and cell division. In contrast, a second class of genes known as tumor suppressor genes sends stop signals during a cell cycle. For example, certain protein products of tumor suppressor genes signal potential problems with the DNA and thus stop the cell from dividing, while other proteins signal the cell to die if it is damaged beyond repair. Some tumor suppressor proteins also signal a sufficient surrounding cellular density, which indicates that the cell need not presently divide. The latter function is uniquely important in preventing tumor growth: normal cells exhibit a phenomenon called "contact inhibition;" thus, extensive cellular contact with neighboring cells causes a signal that stops further cell division.

These two contrasting classes of genes, proto-oncogenes and tumor suppressor genes, are like the accelerator and brake pedal of the cell's own "cruise control system," respectively. Under normal conditions, these stop and go signals are maintained in a homeostatic balance. Generally speaking, there are two ways that the cell's cruise control can lose control: a malfunctioning (overactive) accelerator, or a malfunctioning (underactive) brake. When compromised through a mutation, or otherwise altered, proto-oncogenes can be converted to oncogenes, which produce oncoproteins that push a cell forward in its cycle and stimulate cell division even when it is undesirable to do so. For example, a cell that should be programmed to self-destruct (a process called apoptosis) due to extensive DNA damage might instead be triggered to proliferate by an oncoprotein. On the other hand, a dysfunctional tumor suppressor gene may fail to provide the cell with a necessary stop signal, also resulting in unwanted cell division and proliferation.

A delicate homeostatic balance between the many proto-oncogenes and tumor suppressor genes delicately controls the cell cycle and ensures that only healthy cells replicate. Therefore, a disruption of this homeostatic balance can cause aberrant cell division and cancerous growths.

Interactive LINK

Visit this link (http://openstaxcollege.org/l/mitosis) to learn about mitosis. Mitosis results in two identical diploid cells. What structures forms during prophase?

3.6 | Cellular Differentiation

By the end of this section, you will be able to:

- Discuss how the generalized cells of a developing embryo or the stem cells of an adult organism become differentiated into specialized cells
- Distinguish between the categories of stem cells

How does a complex organism such as a human develop from a single cell—a fertilized egg—into the vast array of cell types such as nerve cells, muscle cells, and epithelial cells that characterize the adult? Throughout development and adulthood, the process of cellular differentiation leads cells to assume their final morphology and physiology. Differentiation is the process by which unspecialized cells become specialized to carry out distinct functions.

Stem Cells

A **stem cell** is an unspecialized cell that can divide without limit as needed and can, under specific conditions, differentiate into specialized cells. Stem cells are divided into several categories according to their potential to differentiate.

The first embryonic cells that arise from the division of the zygote are the ultimate stem cells; these stems cells are described as **totipotent** because they have the potential to differentiate into any of the cells needed to enable an organism to grow and develop.

The embryonic cells that develop from totipotent stem cells and are precursors to the fundamental tissue layers of the embryo are classified as pluripotent. A **pluripotent** stem cell is one that has the potential to differentiate into any type of human tissue but cannot support the full development of an organism. These cells then become slightly more specialized, and are referred to as multipotent cells.

A **multipotent** stem cell has the potential to differentiate into different types of cells within a given cell lineage or small number of lineages, such as a red blood cell or white blood cell.

Finally, multipotent cells can become further specialized oligopotent cells. An **oligopotent** stem cell is limited to becoming one of a few different cell types. In contrast, a **unipotent** cell is fully specialized and can only reproduce to generate more of its own specific cell type.

Stem cells are unique in that they can also continually divide and regenerate new stem cells instead of further specializing. There are different stem cells present at different stages of a human's life. They include the embryonic stem cells of the embryo, fetal stem cells of the fetus, and adult stem cells in the adult. One type of adult stem cell is the epithelial stem cell, which gives rise to the keratinocytes in the multiple layers of epithelial cells in the epidermis of skin. Adult bone marrow has three distinct types of stem cells: hematopoietic stem cells, which give rise to red blood cells, white blood cells, and platelets (Figure 3.34); endothelial stem cells, which give rise to the endothelial cell types that line blood and lymph vessels; and mesenchymal stem cells, which give rise to the different types of muscle cells.

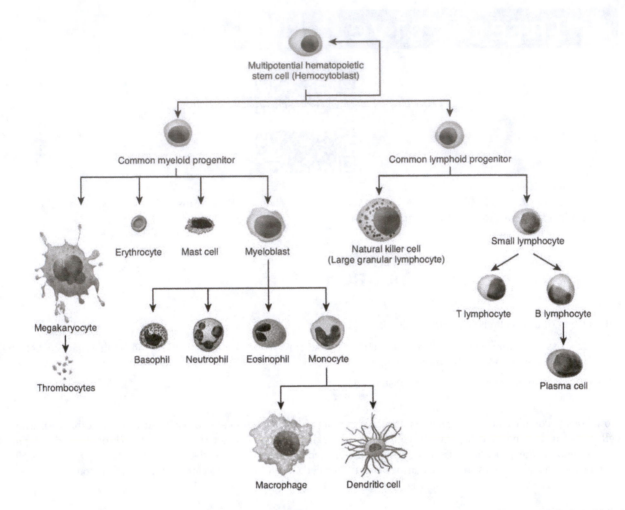

Figure 3.34 Hematopoiesis The process of hematopoiesis involves the differentiation of multipotent cells into blood and immune cells. The multipotent hematopoietic stem cells give rise to many different cell types, including the cells of the immune system and red blood cells.

Differentiation

When a cell differentiates (becomes more specialized), it may undertake major changes in its size, shape, metabolic activity, and overall function. Because all cells in the body, beginning with the fertilized egg, contain the same DNA, how do the different cell types come to be so different? The answer is analogous to a movie script. The different actors in a movie all read from the same script, however, they are each only reading their own part of the script. Similarly, all cells contain the same full complement of DNA, but each type of cell only "reads" the portions of DNA that are relevant to its own function. In biology, this is referred to as the unique genetic expression of each cell.

In order for a cell to differentiate into its specialized form and function, it need only manipulate those genes (and thus those proteins) that will be expressed, and not those that will remain silent. The primary mechanism by which genes are turned "on" or "off" is through transcription factors. A **transcription factor** is one of a class of proteins that bind to specific genes on the DNA molecule and either promote or inhibit their transcription (**Figure 3.35**).

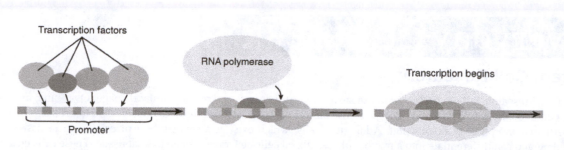

Figure 3.35 Transcription Factors Regulate Gene Expression While each body cell contains the organism's entire genome, different cells regulate gene expression with the use of various transcription factors. Transcription factors are proteins that affect the binding of RNA polymerase to a particular gene on the DNA molecule.

Everyday CONNECTION

Stem Cell Research

Stem cell research aims to find ways to use stem cells to regenerate and repair cellular damage. Over time, most adult cells undergo the wear and tear of aging and lose their ability to divide and repair themselves. Stem cells do not display a particular morphology or function. Adult stem cells, which exist as a small subset of cells in most tissues, keep dividing and can differentiate into a number of specialized cells generally formed by that tissue. These cells enable the body to renew and repair body tissues.

The mechanisms that induce a non-differentiated cell to become a specialized cell are poorly understood. In a laboratory setting, it is possible to induce stem cells to differentiate into specialized cells by changing the physical and chemical conditions of growth. Several sources of stem cells are used experimentally and are classified according to their origin and potential for differentiation. Human embryonic stem cells (hESCs) are extracted from embryos and are pluripotent. The adult stem cells that are present in many organs and differentiated tissues, such as bone marrow and skin, are multipotent, being limited in differentiation to the types of cells found in those tissues. The stem cells isolated from umbilical cord blood are also multipotent, as are cells from deciduous teeth (baby teeth). Researchers have recently developed induced pluripotent stem cells (iPSCs) from mouse and human adult stem cells. These cells are genetically reprogrammed multipotent adult cells that function like embryonic stem cells; they are capable of generating cells characteristic of all three germ layers.

Because of their capacity to divide and differentiate into specialized cells, stem cells offer a potential treatment for diseases such as diabetes and heart disease (Figure 3.36). Cell-based therapy refers to treatment in which stem cells induced to differentiate in a growth dish are injected into a patient to repair damaged or destroyed cells or tissues. Many obstacles must be overcome for the application of cell-based therapy. Although embryonic stem cells have a nearly unlimited range of differentiation potential, they are seen as foreign by the patient's immune system and may trigger rejection. Also, the destruction of embryos to isolate embryonic stem cells raises considerable ethical and legal questions.

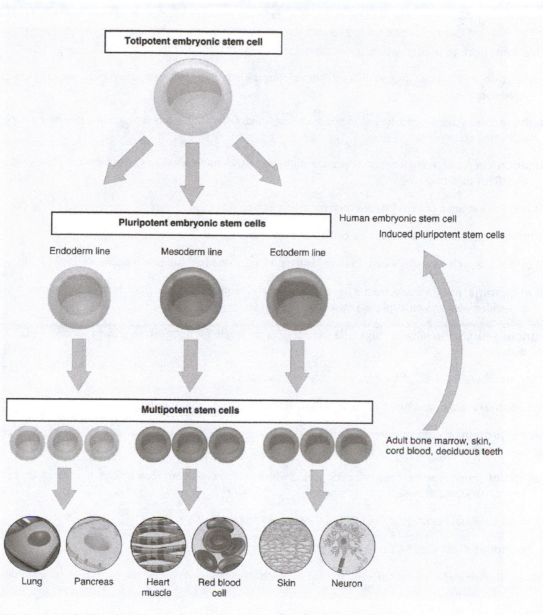

Figure 3.36 Stem Cells The capacity of stem cells to differentiate into specialized cells make them potentially valuable in therapeutic applications designed to replace damaged cells of different body tissues.

In contrast, adult stem cells isolated from a patient are not seen as foreign by the body, but they have a limited range of differentiation. Some individuals bank the cord blood or deciduous teeth of their child, storing away those sources of stem cells for future use, should their child need it. Induced pluripotent stem cells are considered a promising advance in the field because using them avoids the legal, ethical, and immunological pitfalls of embryonic stem cells.

KEY TERMS

active transport form of transport across the cell membrane that requires input of cellular energy

amphipathic describes a molecule that exhibits a difference in polarity between its two ends, resulting in a difference in water solubility

anaphase third stage of mitosis (and meiosis), during which sister chromatids separate into two new nuclear regions of a dividing cell

anticodon consecutive sequence of three nucleotides on a tRNA molecule that is complementary to a specific codon on an mRNA molecule

autolysis breakdown of cells by their own enzymatic action

autophagy lysosomal breakdown of a cell's own components

cell cycle life cycle of a single cell, from its birth until its division into two new daughter cells

cell membrane membrane surrounding all animal cells, composed of a lipid bilayer interspersed with various molecules; also known as plasma membrane

centriole small, self-replicating organelle that provides the origin for microtubule growth and moves DNA during cell division

centromere region of attachment for two sister chromatids

centrosome cellular structure that organizes microtubules during cell division

channel protein membrane-spanning protein that has an inner pore which allows the passage of one or more substances

checkpoint progress point in the cell cycle during which certain conditions must be met in order for the cell to proceed to a subsequence phase

chromatin substance consisting of DNA and associated proteins

chromosome condensed version of chromatin

cilia small appendage on certain cells formed by microtubules and modified for movement of materials across the cellular surface

cleavage furrow contractile ring that forms around a cell during cytokinesis that pinches the cell into two halves

codon consecutive sequence of three nucleotides on an mRNA molecule that corresponds to a specific amino acid

concentration gradient difference in the concentration of a substance between two regions

cyclin one of a group of proteins that function in the progression of the cell cycle

cyclin-dependent kinase (CDK) one of a group of enzymes associated with cyclins that help them perform their functions

cytokinesis final stage in cell division, where the cytoplasm divides to form two separate daughter cells

cytoplasm internal material between the cell membrane and nucleus of a cell, mainly consisting of a water-based fluid called cytosol, within which are all the other organelles and cellular solute and suspended materials

cytoskeleton "skeleton" of a cell; formed by rod-like proteins that support the cell's shape and provide, among other functions, locomotive abilities

cytosol clear, semi-fluid medium of the cytoplasm, made up mostly of water

diffusion movement of a substance from an area of higher concentration to one of lower concentration

diploid condition marked by the presence of a double complement of genetic material (two sets of chromosomes, one set inherited from each of two parents)

DNA polymerase enzyme that functions in adding new nucleotides to a growing strand of DNA during DNA replication

DNA replication process of duplicating a molecule of DNA

electrical gradient difference in the electrical charge (potential) between two regions

endocytosis import of material into the cell by formation of a membrane-bound vesicle

endoplasmic reticulum (ER) cellular organelle that consists of interconnected membrane-bound tubules, which may or may not be associated with ribosomes (rough type or smooth type, respectively)

exocytosis export of a substance out of a cell by formation of a membrane-bound vesicle

exon one of the coding regions of an mRNA molecule that remain after splicing

extracellular fluid (ECF) fluid exterior to cells; includes the interstitial fluid, blood plasma, and fluid found in other reservoirs in the body

facilitated diffusion diffusion of a substance with the aid of a membrane protein

flagellum appendage on certain cells formed by microtubules and modified for movement

G_0 phase phase of the cell cycle, usually entered from the G_1 phase; characterized by long or permanent periods where the cell does not move forward into the DNA synthesis phase

G_1 phase first phase of the cell cycle, after a new cell is born

G_2 phase third phase of the cell cycle, after the DNA synthesis phase

gene functional length of DNA that provides the genetic information necessary to build a protein

gene expression active interpretation of the information coded in a gene to produce a functional gene product

genome entire complement of an organism's DNA; found within virtually every cell

glycocalyx coating of sugar molecules that surrounds the cell membrane

glycoprotein protein that has one or more carbohydrates attached

Golgi apparatus cellular organelle formed by a series of flattened, membrane-bound sacs that functions in protein modification, tagging, packaging, and transport

helicase enzyme that functions to separate the two DNA strands of a double helix during DNA replication

histone family of proteins that associate with DNA in the nucleus to form chromatin

homologous describes two copies of the same chromosome (not identical), one inherited from each parent

hydrophilic describes a substance or structure attracted to water

hydrophobic describes a substance or structure repelled by water

hypertonic describes a solution concentration that is higher than a reference concentration

hypotonic describes a solution concentration that is lower than a reference concentration

integral protein membrane-associated protein that spans the entire width of the lipid bilayer

intermediate filament type of cytoskeletal filament made of keratin, characterized by an intermediate thickness, and playing a role in resisting cellular tension

interphase entire life cycle of a cell, excluding mitosis

interstitial fluid (IF) fluid in the small spaces between cells not contained within blood vessels

intracellular fluid (ICF) fluid in the cytosol of cells

intron non-coding regions of a pre-mRNA transcript that may be removed during splicing

isotonic describes a solution concentration that is the same as a reference concentration

kinetochore region of a centromere where microtubules attach to a pair of sister chromatids

ligand molecule that binds with specificity to a specific receptor molecule

lysosome membrane-bound cellular organelle originating from the Golgi apparatus and containing digestive enzymes

messenger RNA (mRNA) nucleotide molecule that serves as an intermediate in the genetic code between DNA and protein

metaphase second stage of mitosis (and meiosis), characterized by the linear alignment of sister chromatids in the center of the cell

metaphase plate linear alignment of sister chromatids in the center of the cell, which takes place during metaphase

microfilament the thinnest of the cytoskeletal filaments; composed of actin subunits that function in muscle contraction and cellular structural support

microtubule the thickest of the cytoskeletal filaments, composed of tubulin subunits that function in cellular movement and structural support

mitochondrion one of the cellular organelles bound by a double lipid bilayer that function primarily in the production of cellular energy (ATP)

mitosis division of genetic material, during which the cell nucleus breaks down and two new, fully functional, nuclei are formed

mitotic phase phase of the cell cycle in which a cell undergoes mitosis

mitotic spindle network of microtubules, originating from centrioles, that arranges and pulls apart chromosomes during mitosis

multipotent describes the condition of being able to differentiate into different types of cells within a given cell lineage or small number of lineages, such as a red blood cell or white blood cell

mutation change in the nucleotide sequence in a gene within a cell's DNA

nuclear envelope membrane that surrounds the nucleus; consisting of a double lipid-bilayer

nuclear pore one of the small, protein-lined openings found scattered throughout the nuclear envelope

nucleolus small region of the nucleus that functions in ribosome synthesis

nucleosome unit of chromatin consisting of a DNA strand wrapped around histone proteins

nucleus cell's central organelle; contains the cell's DNA

oligopotent describes the condition of being more specialized than multipotency; the condition of being able to differentiate into one of a few possible cell types

organelle any of several different types of membrane-enclosed specialized structures in the cell that perform specific functions for the cell

osmosis diffusion of water molecules down their concentration gradient across a selectively permeable membrane

passive transport form of transport across the cell membrane that does not require input of cellular energy

peripheral protein membrane-associated protein that does not span the width of the lipid bilayer, but is attached peripherally to integral proteins, membrane lipids, or other components of the membrane

peroxisome membrane-bound organelle that contains enzymes primarily responsible for detoxifying harmful substances

phagocytosis endocytosis of large particles

pinocytosis endocytosis of fluid

pluripotent describes the condition of being able to differentiate into a large variety of cell types

polypeptide chain of amino acids linked by peptide bonds

polyribosome simultaneous translation of a single mRNA transcript by multiple ribosomes

promoter region of DNA that signals transcription to begin at that site within the gene

prophase first stage of mitosis (and meiosis), characterized by breakdown of the nuclear envelope and condensing of the chromatin to form chromosomes

proteome full complement of proteins produced by a cell (determined by the cell's specific gene expression)

reactive oxygen species (ROS) a group of extremely reactive peroxides and oxygen-containing radicals that may contribute to cellular damage

receptor protein molecule that contains a binding site for another specific molecule (called a ligand)

receptor-mediated endocytosis endocytosis of ligands attached to membrane-bound receptors

ribosomal RNA (rRNA) RNA that makes up the subunits of a ribosome

ribosome cellular organelle that functions in protein synthesis

RNA polymerase enzyme that unwinds DNA and then adds new nucleotides to a growing strand of RNA for the transcription phase of protein synthesis

S phase stage of the cell cycle during which DNA replication occurs

selective permeability feature of any barrier that allows certain substances to cross but excludes others

sister chromatid one of a pair of identical chromosomes, formed during DNA replication

sodium-potassium pump (also, Na^+/K^+ ATP-ase) membrane-embedded protein pump that uses ATP to move Na^+ out of a cell and K^+ into the cell

somatic cell all cells of the body excluding gamete cells

spliceosome complex of enzymes that serves to splice out the introns of a pre-mRNA transcript

splicing the process of modifying a pre-mRNA transcript by removing certain, typically non-coding, regions

stem cell cell that is oligo-, multi-, or pleuripotent that has the ability to produce additional stem cells rather than becoming further specialized

telophase final stage of mitosis (and meiosis), preceding cytokinesis, characterized by the formation of two new daughter nuclei

totipotent embryonic cells that have the ability to differentiate into any type of cell and organ in the body

transcription process of producing an mRNA molecule that is complementary to a particular gene of DNA

transcription factor one of the proteins that regulate the transcription of genes

transfer RNA (tRNA) molecules of RNA that serve to bring amino acids to a growing polypeptide strand and properly place them into the sequence

translation process of producing a protein from the nucleotide sequence code of an mRNA transcript

triplet consecutive sequence of three nucleotides on a DNA molecule that, when transcribed into an mRNA codon, corresponds to a particular amino acid

unipotent describes the condition of being committed to a single specialized cell type

vesicle membrane-bound structure that contains materials within or outside of the cell

CHAPTER REVIEW

3.1 The Cell Membrane

The cell membrane provides a barrier around the cell, separating its internal components from the extracellular environment. It is composed of a phospholipid bilayer, with hydrophobic internal lipid "tails" and hydrophilic external phosphate "heads." Various membrane proteins are scattered throughout the bilayer, both inserted within it and attached to it peripherally. The cell membrane is selectively permeable, allowing only a limited number of materials to diffuse through its lipid bilayer. All materials that cross the membrane do so using passive (non energy-requiring) or active (energy-requiring) transport processes. During passive transport, materials move by simple diffusion or by facilitated diffusion through the membrane, down their concentration gradient. Water passes through the membrane in a diffusion process called osmosis. During active transport, energy is expended to assist material movement across the membrane in a direction against their concentration gradient. Active transport may take place with the help of protein pumps or through the use of vesicles.

3.2 The Cytoplasm and Cellular Organelles

The internal environmental of a living cell is made up of a fluid, jelly-like substance called cytosol, which consists mainly of water, but also contains various dissolved nutrients and other molecules. The cell contains an array of cellular organelles, each one performing a unique function and helping to maintain the health and activity of the cell. The cytosol and organelles together compose the cell's cytoplasm. Most organelles are surrounded by a lipid membrane similar to the cell membrane of the cell. The endoplasmic reticulum (ER), Golgi apparatus, and lysosomes share a functional connectivity and are collectively referred to as the endomembrane system. There are two types of ER: smooth and rough. While the smooth ER performs many functions, including lipid synthesis and ion storage, the rough ER is mainly responsible for protein synthesis using its associated ribosomes. The rough ER sends newly made proteins to the Golgi apparatus where they are modified and packaged for delivery to various locations within or outside of the cell. Some of these protein products are enzymes destined to break down unwanted material and are packaged as lysosomes for use inside the cell.

Cells also contain mitochondria and peroxisomes, which are the organelles responsible for producing the cell's energy supply and detoxifying certain chemicals, respectively. Biochemical reactions within mitochondria transform energy-carrying molecules into the usable form of cellular energy known as ATP. Peroxisomes contain enzymes that transform harmful substances such as free radicals into oxygen and water. Cells also contain a miniaturized "skeleton" of protein filaments that extend throughout its interior. Three different kinds of filaments compose this cytoskeleton (in order of increasing thickness): microfilaments, intermediate filaments, and microtubules. Each cytoskeletal component performs unique functions as well as provides a supportive framework for the cell.

3.3 The Nucleus and DNA Replication

The nucleus is the command center of the cell, containing the genetic instructions for all of the materials a cell will make (and thus all of its functions it can perform). The nucleus is encased within a membrane of two interconnected lipid bilayers, side-by-side. This nuclear envelope is studded with protein-lined pores that allow materials to be trafficked into and out of the nucleus. The nucleus contains one or more nucleoli, which serve as sites for ribosome synthesis. The nucleus houses the genetic material of the cell: DNA. DNA is normally found as a loosely contained structure called chromatin within the nucleus, where it is wound up and associated with a variety of histone proteins. When a cell is about to divide, the chromatin coils tightly and condenses to form chromosomes.

There is a pool of cells constantly dividing within your body. The result is billions of new cells being created each day. Before any cell is ready to divide, it must replicate its DNA so that each new daughter cell will receive an exact copy of the organism's genome. A variety of enzymes are enlisted during DNA replication. These enzymes unwind the DNA molecule, separate the two strands, and assist with the building of complementary strands along each parent strand. The original DNA strands serve as templates from which the nucleotide sequence of the new strands are determined and synthesized. When replication is completed, two identical DNA molecules exist. Each one contains one original strand and one newly synthesized complementary strand.

3.4 Protein Synthesis

DNA stores the information necessary for instructing the cell to perform all of its functions. Cells use the genetic code stored within DNA to build proteins, which ultimately determine the structure and function of the cell. This genetic code lies in the particular sequence of nucleotides that make up each gene along the DNA molecule. To "read" this code, the cell must perform two sequential steps. In the first step, transcription, the DNA code is converted into a RNA code. A molecule of messenger RNA that is complementary to a specific gene is synthesized in a process similar to DNA replication. The molecule of mRNA provides the code to synthesize a protein. In the process of translation, the mRNA attaches to a ribosome. Next, tRNA molecules shuttle the appropriate amino acids to the ribosome, one-by-one, coded by sequential triplet codons on the mRNA, until the protein is fully synthesized. When completed, the mRNA detaches from the ribosome, and the protein is released. Typically, multiple ribosomes attach to a single mRNA molecule at once such that multiple proteins can be manufactured from the mRNA concurrently.

3.5 Cell Growth and Division

The life of cell consists of stages that make up the cell cycle. After a cell is born, it passes through an interphase before it is ready to replicate itself and produce daughter cells. This interphase includes two gap phases (G_1 and G_2), as well as an S phase, during which its DNA is replicated in preparation for cell division. The cell cycle is under precise regulation by chemical messengers both inside and outside the cell that provide "stop" and "go" signals for movement from one phase to the next. Failures of these signals can result in cells that continue to divide uncontrollably, which can lead to cancer.

Once a cell has completed interphase and is ready for cell division, it proceeds through four separate stages of mitosis (prophase, metaphase, anaphase, and telophase). Telophase is followed by the division of the cytoplasm (cytokinesis), which generates two daughter cells. This process takes place in all normally dividing cells of the body except for the germ cells that produce eggs and sperm.

3.6 Cellular Differentiation

One of the major areas of research in biology is that of how cells specialize to assume their unique structures and functions, since all cells essentially originate from a single fertilized egg. Cell differentiation is the process of cells becoming specialized as they body develops. A stem cell is an unspecialized cell that can divide without limit as needed and can, under specific conditions, differentiate into specialized cells. Stem cells are divided into several categories according to their potential to differentiate. While all somatic cells contain the exact same genome, different cell types only express some of those genes at any given time. These differences in gene expression ultimately dictate a cell's unique morphological and physiological characteristics. The primary mechanism that determines which genes will be expressed and which ones will not is through the use of different transcription factor proteins, which bind to DNA and promote or hinder the transcription of different genes. Through the action of these transcription factors, cells specialize into one of hundreds of different cell types in the human body.

INTERACTIVE LINK QUESTIONS

1. Visit this link (http://openstaxcollege.org/l/diffusion) to see diffusion and how it is propelled by the kinetic energy of molecules in solution. How does temperature affect diffusion rate, and why?

2. Watch this video (http://openstaxcollege.org/l/endomembrane1) to learn about the endomembrane system, which includes the rough and smooth ER and the Golgi body as well as lysosomes and vesicles. What is the primary role of the endomembrane system?

3. Watch this video (http://openstaxcollege.org/l/DNArep) to learn about DNA replication. DNA replication proceeds simultaneously at several sites on the same molecule. What separates the base pair at the start of DNA replication?

4. Watch this video (http://openstaxcollege.org/l/ribosome) to learn about ribosomes. The ribosome binds to the mRNA molecule to start translation of its code into a protein. What happens to the small and large ribosomal subunits at the end of translation?

5. Visit this link (http://openstaxcollege.org/l/mitosis) to learn about mitosis. Mitosis results in two identical diploid cells. What structures form during prophase?

REVIEW QUESTIONS

6. Because they are embedded within the membrane, ion channels are examples of _____.
    a. receptor proteins
    b. integral proteins
    c. peripheral proteins
    d. glycoproteins

7. The diffusion of substances within a solution tends to move those substances _____ their _____ gradient.

    a. up; electrical
    b. up; electrochemical
    c. down; pressure
    d. down; concentration

8. Ion pumps and phagocytosis are both examples of _____.
    a. endocytosis
    b. passive transport
    c. active transport
    d. facilitated diffusion

9. Choose the answer that best completes the following analogy: Diffusion is to _____ as endocytosis is to _____.
    a. filtration; phagocytosis
    b. osmosis; pinocytosis
    c. solutes; fluid
    d. gradient; chemical energy

10. Choose the term that best completes the following analogy: Cytoplasm is to cytosol as a swimming pool containing chlorine and flotation toys is to _____.
    a. the walls of the pool
    b. the chlorine
    c. the flotation toys
    d. the water

11. The rough ER has its name due to what associated structures?
    a. Golgi apparatus
    b. ribosomes
    c. lysosomes
    d. proteins

12. Which of the following is a function of the rough ER?

    a. production of proteins
    b. detoxification of certain substances
    c. synthesis of steroid hormones
    d. regulation of intracellular calcium concentration

13. Which of the following is a feature common to all three components of the cytoskeleton?
    a. They all serve to scaffold the organelles within the cell.
    b. They are all characterized by roughly the same diameter.
    c. They are all polymers of protein subunits.
    d. They all help the cell resist compression and tension.

14. Which of the following organelles produces large quantities of ATP when both glucose and oxygen are available to the cell?
    a. mitochondria
    b. peroxisomes
    c. lysosomes
    d. ER

15. The nucleus and mitochondria share which of the following features?
    a. protein-lined membrane pores
    b. a double cell membrane
    c. the synthesis of ribosomes
    d. the production of cellular energy

16. Which of the following structures could be found within the nucleolus?
    a. chromatin
    b. histones
    c. ribosomes
    d. nucleosomes

17. Which of the following sequences on a DNA molecule would be complementary to GCTTATAT?
    a. TAGGCGCG
    b. ATCCGCGC
    c. CGAATATA
    d. TGCCTCTC

18. Place the following structures in order from least to most complex organization: chromatin, nucleosome, DNA, chromosome
    a. DNA, nucleosome, chromatin, chromosome
    b. nucleosome, DNA, chromosome, chromatin
    c. DNA, chromatin, nucleosome, chromosome
    d. nucleosome, chromatin, DNA, chromosome

19. Which of the following is part of the elongation step of DNA synthesis?
    a. pulling apart the two DNA strands
    b. attaching complementary nucleotides to the template strand
    c. untwisting the DNA helix
    d. none of the above

20. Which of the following is *not* a difference between DNA and RNA?
   a. DNA contains thymine whereas RNA contains uracil
   b. DNA contains deoxyribose and RNA contains ribose
   c. DNA contains alternating sugar-phosphate molecules whereas RNA does not contain sugars
   d. RNA is single stranded and DNA is double stranded

21. Transcription and translation take place in the _____ and _____, respectively.
   a. nucleus; cytoplasm
   b. nucleolus; nucleus
   c. nucleolus; cytoplasm
   d. cytoplasm; nucleus

22. How many "letters" of an RNA molecule, in sequence, does it take to provide the code for a single amino acid?

   a. 1
   b. 2
   c. 3
   d. 4

23. Which of the following is *not* made out of RNA?

   a. the carriers that shuffle amino acids to a growing polypeptide strand
   b. the ribosome
   c. the messenger molecule that provides the code for protein synthesis
   d. the intron

24. Which of the following phases is characterized by preparation for DNA synthesis?
   a. G_0
   b. G_1
   c. G_2
   d. S

25. A mutation in the gene for a cyclin protein might result in which of the following?
   a. a cell with additional genetic material than normal
   b. cancer
   c. a cell with less genetic material than normal
   d. any of the above

26. What is a primary function of tumor suppressor genes?

   a. stop all cells from dividing
   b. stop certain cells from dividing
   c. help oncogenes produce oncoproteins
   d. allow the cell to skip certain phases of the cell cycle

27. Arrange the following terms in order of increasing specialization: oligopotency, pleuripotency, unipotency, multipotency.
   a. multipotency, pleuripotency, oligopotency, unipotency
   b. pleuripotency, oligopotency, multipotency unipotency
   c. oligopotency, pleuripotency, unipotency, multipotency
   d. pleuripotency, multipotency, oligopotency, unipotency

28. Which type of stem cell gives rise to red and white blood cells?
   a. endothelial
   b. epithelial
   c. hematopoietic
   d. mesenchymal

29. What multipotent stem cells from children sometimes banked by parents?
   a. fetal stem cells
   b. embryonic stem cells
   c. cells from the umbilical cord and from baby teeth
   d. hematopoietic stem cells from red and white blood cells

CRITICAL THINKING QUESTIONS

30. What materials can easily diffuse through the lipid bilayer, and why?

31. Why is receptor-mediated endocytosis said to be more selective than phagocytosis or pinocytosis?

32. What do osmosis, diffusion, filtration, and the movement of ions away from like charge all have in common? In what way do they differ?

33. Explain why the structure of the ER, mitochondria, and Golgi apparatus assist their respective functions.

34. Compare and contrast lysosomes with peroxisomes: name at least two similarities and one difference.

35. Explain in your own words why DNA replication is said to be "semiconservative"?

36. Why is it important that DNA replication take place before cell division? What would happen if cell division of a body cell took place without DNA replication, or when DNA replication was incomplete?

37. Briefly explain the similarities between transcription and DNA replication.

38. Contrast transcription and translation. Name at least three differences between the two processes.

39. What would happen if anaphase proceeded even though the sister chromatids were not properly attached to their respective microtubules and lined up at the metaphase plate?

40. What are cyclins and cyclin-dependent kinases, and how do they interact?

41. Explain how a transcription factor ultimately determines whether or not a protein will be present in a given cell?

42. Discuss two reasons why the therapeutic use of embryonic stem cells can present a problem.

4 | THE TISSUE LEVEL OF ORGANIZATION

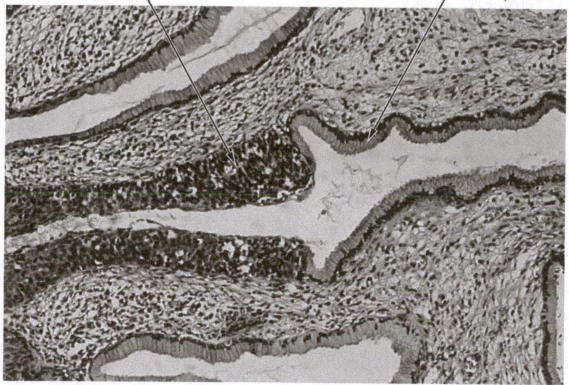

Figure 4.1 Micrograph of Cervical Tissue This figure is a view of the regular architecture of normal tissue contrasted with the irregular arrangement of cancerous cells. (credit: "Haymanj"/Wikimedia Commons)

Introduction

Chapter Objectives

After studying this chapter, you will be able to:

- Identify the main tissue types and discuss their roles in the human body
- Identify the four types of tissue membranes and the characteristics of each that make them functional
- Explain the functions of various epithelial tissues and how their forms enable their functions
- Explain the functions of various connective tissues and how their forms enable their functions
- Describe the characteristics of muscle tissue and how these enable function
- Discuss the characteristics of nervous tissue and how these enable information processing and control of muscular and glandular activities

The body contains at least 200 distinct cell types. These cells contain essentially the same internal structures yet they vary enormously in shape and function. The different types of cells are not randomly distributed throughout the body; rather they occur in organized layers, a level of organization referred to as tissue. The micrograph that opens this chapter shows the high degree of organization among different types of cells in the tissue of the cervix. You can also see how that organization breaks down when cancer takes over the regular mitotic functioning of a cell.

The variety in shape reflects the many different roles that cells fulfill in your body. The human body starts as a single cell at fertilization. As this fertilized egg divides, it gives rise to trillions of cells, each built from the same blueprint, but organizing into tissues and becoming irreversibly committed to a developmental pathway.

4.1 | Types of Tissues

By the end of this section, you will be able to:

- Identify the four main tissue types
- Discuss the functions of each tissue type
- Relate the structure of each tissue type to their function
- Discuss the embryonic origin of tissue
- Identify the three major germ layers
- Identify the main types of tissue membranes

The term **tissue** is used to describe a group of cells found together in the body. The cells within a tissue share a common embryonic origin. Microscopic observation reveals that the cells in a tissue share morphological features and are arranged in an orderly pattern that achieves the tissue's functions. From the evolutionary perspective, tissues appear in more complex organisms. For example, multicellular protists, ancient eukaryotes, do not have cells organized into tissues.

Although there are many types of cells in the human body, they are organized into four broad categories of tissues: epithelial, connective, muscle, and nervous. Each of these categories is characterized by specific functions that contribute to the overall health and maintenance of the body. A disruption of the structure is a sign of injury or disease. Such changes can be detected through **histology**, the microscopic study of tissue appearance, organization, and function.

The Four Types of Tissues

Epithelial tissue, also referred to as epithelium, refers to the sheets of cells that cover exterior surfaces of the body, lines internal cavities and passageways, and forms certain glands. **Connective tissue**, as its name implies, binds the cells and organs of the body together and functions in the protection, support, and integration of all parts of the body. **Muscle tissue** is excitable, responding to stimulation and contracting to provide movement, and occurs as three major types: skeletal (voluntary) muscle, smooth muscle, and cardiac muscle in the heart. **Nervous tissue** is also excitable, allowing the propagation of electrochemical signals in the form of nerve impulses that communicate between different regions of the body (Figure 4.2).

The next level of organization is the organ, where several types of tissues come together to form a working unit. Just as knowing the structure and function of cells helps you in your study of tissues, knowledge of tissues will help you understand how organs function. The epithelial and connective tissues are discussed in detail in this chapter. Muscle and nervous tissues will be discussed only briefly in this chapter.

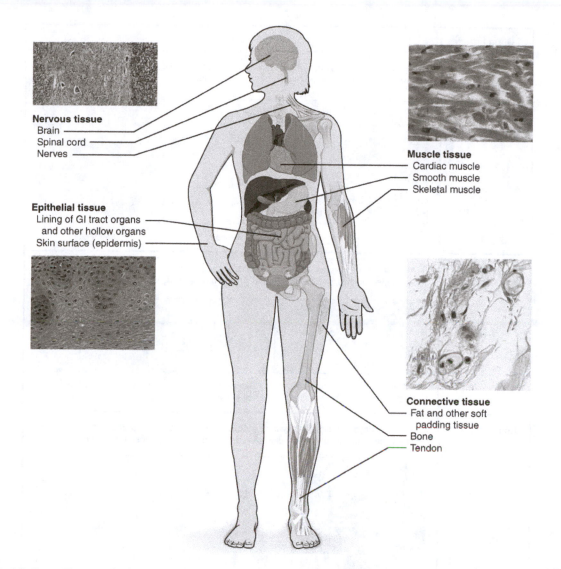

Figure 4.2 Four Types of Tissue: Body The four types of tissues are exemplified in nervous tissue, stratified squamous epithelial tissue, cardiac muscle tissue, and connective tissue in small intestine. Clockwise from nervous tissue, LM × 872, LM × 282, LM × 460, LM × 800. (Micrographs provided by the Regents of University of Michigan Medical School © 2012)

Embryonic Origin of Tissues

The zygote, or fertilized egg, is a single cell formed by the fusion of an egg and sperm. After fertilization the zygote gives rise to rapid mitotic cycles, generating many cells to form the embryo. The first embryonic cells generated have the ability to differentiate into any type of cell in the body and, as such, are called **totipotent**, meaning each has the capacity to divide, differentiate, and develop into a new organism. As cell proliferation progresses, three major cell lineages are established within the embryo. As explained in a later chapter, each of these lineages of embryonic cells forms the distinct germ layers from which all the tissues and organs of the human body eventually form. Each germ layer is identified by its relative position: **ectoderm** (ecto- = "outer"), **mesoderm** (meso- = "middle"), and **endoderm** (endo- = "inner"). Figure 4.3 shows the types of tissues and organs associated with the each of the three germ layers. Note that epithelial tissue originates in all three layers, whereas nervous tissue derives primarily from the ectoderm and muscle tissue from mesoderm.

Germ Layer	Gives rise to:
Ectoderm	Epidermis, glands on skin, some cranial bones, pituitary and adrenal medulla, the nervous system, the mouth between cheek and gums, the anus Skin cells — Neurons — Pigment cell
Mesoderm	Connective tissues proper, bone, cartilage, blood, endothelium of blood vessels, muscle, synovial membranes, serous membranes lining body cavities, kidneys, lining of gonads Cardiac muscle — Skeletal muscle — Tubule cell of kidney — Red blood cells — Smooth muscle
Endoderm	Lining of airways and digestive system except the mouth and distal part of digestive system (rectum and anal canal); glands (digestive glands, endocrine glands, adrenal cortex) Lung cell — Thyroid cell — Pancreatic cell

Figure 4.3 Embryonic Origin of Tissues and Major Organs

Interactive LINK

View this slideshow (http://openstaxcollege.org/l/stemcells) to learn more about stem cells. How do somatic stem cells differ from embryonic stem cells?

Tissue Membranes

A **tissue membrane** is a thin layer or sheet of cells that covers the outside of the body (for example, skin), the organs (for example, pericardium), internal passageways that lead to the exterior of the body (for example, abdominal mesenteries), and the lining of the moveable joint cavities. There are two basic types of tissue membranes: connective tissue and epithelial membranes (**Figure 4.4**).

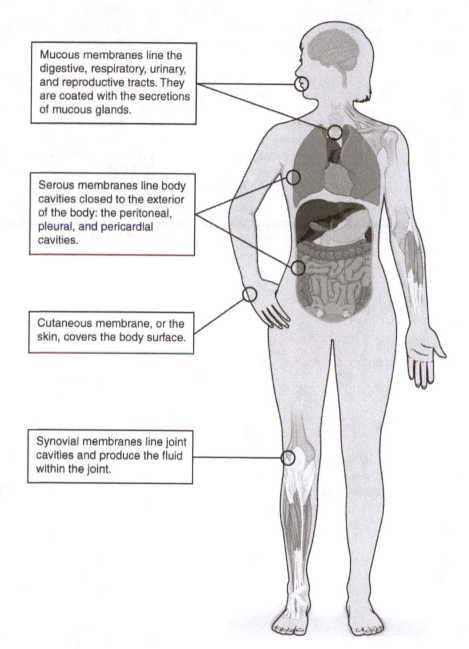

Mucous membranes line the digestive, respiratory, urinary, and reproductive tracts. They are coated with the secretions of mucous glands.

Serous membranes line body cavities closed to the exterior of the body: the peritoneal, pleural, and pericardial cavities.

Cutaneous membrane, or the skin, covers the body surface.

Synovial membranes line joint cavities and produce the fluid within the joint.

Figure 4.4 Tissue Membranes   The two broad categories of tissue membranes in the body are (1) connective tissue membranes, which include synovial membranes, and (2) epithelial membranes, which include mucous membranes, serous membranes, and the cutaneous membrane, in other words, the skin.

Connective Tissue Membranes

The **connective tissue membrane** is formed solely from connective tissue. These membranes encapsulate organs, such as the kidneys, and line our movable joints. A **synovial membrane** is a type of connective tissue membrane that lines the cavity of a freely movable joint. For example, synovial membranes surround the joints of the shoulder, elbow, and knee. Fibroblasts in the inner layer of the synovial membrane release hyaluronan into the joint cavity. The hyaluronan effectively traps available water to form the synovial fluid, a natural lubricant that enables the bones of a joint to move freely against one another without much friction. This synovial fluid readily exchanges water and nutrients with blood, as do all body fluids.

Epithelial Membranes

The **epithelial membrane** is composed of epithelium attached to a layer of connective tissue, for example, your skin. The **mucous membrane** is also a composite of connective and epithelial tissues. Sometimes called mucosae, these epithelial membranes line the body cavities and hollow passageways that open to the external environment, and include the digestive, respiratory, excretory, and reproductive tracts. Mucous, produced by the epithelial exocrine glands, covers the epithelial layer. The underlying connective tissue, called the **lamina propria** (literally "own layer"), help support the fragile epithelial layer.

A **serous membrane** is an epithelial membrane composed of mesodermally derived epithelium called the mesothelium that is supported by connective tissue. These membranes line the coelomic cavities of the body, that is, those cavities that do not open to the outside, and they cover the organs located within those cavities. They are essentially membranous bags, with mesothelium lining the inside and connective tissue on the outside. Serous fluid secreted by the cells of the thin squamous mesothelium lubricates the membrane and reduces abrasion and friction between organs. Serous membranes are identified according locations. Three serous membranes line the thoracic cavity; the two pleura that cover the lungs and the pericardium that covers the heart. A fourth, the peritoneum, is the serous membrane in the abdominal cavity that covers abdominal organs and forms double sheets of mesenteries that suspend many of the digestive organs.

The skin is an epithelial membrane also called the **cutaneous membrane**. It is a stratified squamous epithelial membrane resting on top of connective tissue. The apical surface of this membrane is exposed to the external environment and is covered with dead, keratinized cells that help protect the body from desiccation and pathogens.

4.2 | Epithelial Tissue

By the end of this section, you will be able to:

- Explain the structure and function of epithelial tissue
- Distinguish between tight junctions, anchoring junctions, and gap junctions
- Distinguish between simple epithelia and stratified epithelia, as well as between squamous, cuboidal, and columnar epithelia
- Describe the structure and function of endocrine and exocrine glands and their respective secretions

Most epithelial tissues are essentially large sheets of cells covering all the surfaces of the body exposed to the outside world and lining the outside of organs. Epithelium also forms much of the glandular tissue of the body. Skin is not the only area of the body exposed to the outside. Other areas include the airways, the digestive tract, as well as the urinary and reproductive systems, all of which are lined by an epithelium. Hollow organs and body cavities that do not connect to the exterior of the body, which includes, blood vessels and serous membranes, are lined by endothelium (plural = endothelia), which is a type of epithelium.

Epithelial cells derive from all three major embryonic layers. The epithelia lining the skin, parts of the mouth and nose, and the anus develop from the ectoderm. Cells lining the airways and most of the digestive system originate in the endoderm. The epithelium that lines vessels in the lymphatic and cardiovascular system derives from the mesoderm and is called an endothelium.

All epithelia share some important structural and functional features. This tissue is highly cellular, with little or no extracellular material present between cells. Adjoining cells form a specialized intercellular connection between their cell membranes called a **cell junction**. The epithelial cells exhibit polarity with differences in structure and function between the exposed or **apical** facing surface of the cell and the basal surface close to the underlying body structures. The **basal lamina**, a mixture of glycoproteins and collagen, provides an attachment site for the epithelium, separating it from underlying connective tissue. The basal lamina attaches to a **reticular lamina**, which is secreted by the underlying connective tissue, forming a **basement membrane** that helps hold it all together.

Epithelial tissues are nearly completely avascular. For instance, no blood vessels cross the basement membrane to enter the tissue, and nutrients must come by diffusion or absorption from underlying tissues or the surface. Many epithelial tissues are capable of rapidly replacing damaged and dead cells. Sloughing off of damaged or dead cells is a characteristic of surface epithelium and allows our airways and digestive tracts to rapidly replace damaged cells with new cells.

Generalized Functions of Epithelial Tissue

Epithelial tissues provide the body's first line of protection from physical, chemical, and biological wear and tear. The cells of an epithelium act as gatekeepers of the body controlling permeability and allowing selective transfer of materials across a physical barrier. All substances that enter the body must cross an epithelium. Some epithelia often include structural features that allow the selective transport of molecules and ions across their cell membranes.

Many epithelial cells are capable of secretion and release mucous and specific chemical compounds onto their apical surfaces. The epithelium of the small intestine releases digestive enzymes, for example. Cells lining the respiratory tract secrete mucous that traps incoming microorganisms and particles. A glandular epithelium contains many secretory cells.

The Epithelial Cell

Epithelial cells are typically characterized by the polarized distribution of organelles and membrane-bound proteins between their basal and apical surfaces. Particular structures found in some epithelial cells are an adaptation to specific functions. Certain organelles are segregated to the basal sides, whereas other organelles and extensions, such as cilia, when present, are on the apical surface.

Cilia are microscopic extensions of the apical cell membrane that are supported by microtubules. They beat in unison and move fluids as well as trapped particles. Ciliated epithelium lines the ventricles of the brain where it helps circulate the cerebrospinal fluid. The ciliated epithelium of your airway forms a mucociliary escalator that sweeps particles of dust and pathogens trapped in the secreted mucous toward the throat. It is called an escalator because it continuously pushes mucous with trapped particles upward. In contrast, nasal cilia sweep the mucous blanket down towards your throat. In both cases, the transported materials are usually swallowed, and end up in the acidic environment of your stomach.

Cell to Cell Junctions

Cells of epithelia are closely connected and are not separated by intracellular material. Three basic types of connections allow varying degrees of interaction between the cells: tight junctions, anchoring junctions, and gap junctions (Figure 4.5).

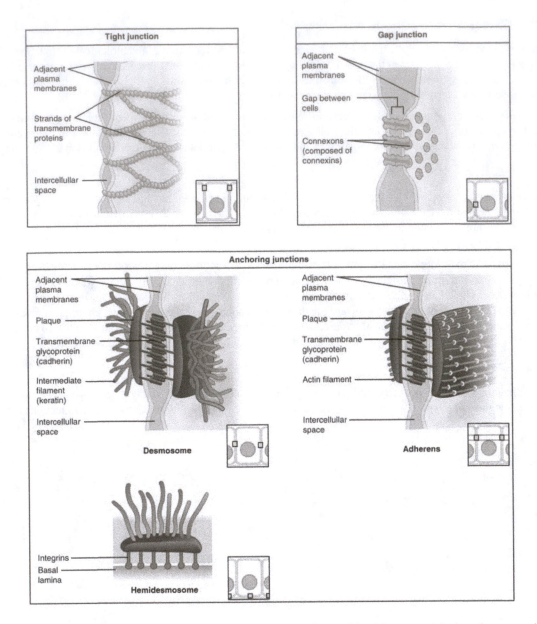

Figure 4.5 Types of Cell Junctions The three basic types of cell-to-cell junctions are tight junctions, gap junctions, and anchoring junctions.

At one end of the spectrum is the **tight junction**, which separates the cells into apical and basal compartments. When two adjacent epithelial cells form a tight junction, there is no extracellular space between them and the movement of substances through the extracellular space between the cells is blocked. This enables the epithelia to act as selective barriers. An **anchoring junction** includes several types of cell junctions that help stabilize epithelial tissues. Anchoring junctions are common on the lateral and basal surfaces of cells where they provide strong and flexible connections. There are three types of anchoring junctions: desmosomes, hemidesmosomes, and adherens. Desmosomes occur in patches on the membranes of cells. The patches are structural proteins on the inner surface of the cell's membrane. The adhesion molecule, cadherin, is embedded in these patches and projects through the cell membrane to link with the cadherin molecules of adjacent cells. These connections are especially important in holding cells together. Hemidesmosomes, which look like half a desmosome, link cells to the extracellular matrix, for example, the basal lamina. While similar in appearance to desmosomes, they include the adhesion proteins called integrins rather than cadherins. Adherens junctions use either cadherins or integrins depending on whether they are linking to other cells or matrix. The junctions are characterized by the presence of the contractile protein actin located on the cytoplasmic surface of the cell membrane. The actin can connect isolated patches or form a belt-like structure inside the cell. These junctions influence the shape and folding of the epithelial tissue.

In contrast with the tight and anchoring junctions, a **gap junction** forms an intercellular passageway between the membranes of adjacent cells to facilitate the movement of small molecules and ions between the cytoplasm of adjacent cells. These junctions allow electrical and metabolic coupling of adjacent cells, which coordinates function in large groups of cells.

Classification of Epithelial Tissues

Epithelial tissues are classified according to the shape of the cells and number of the cell layers formed (Figure 4.6). Cell shapes can be squamous (flattened and thin), cuboidal (boxy, as wide as it is tall), or columnar (rectangular, taller than it is wide). Similarly, the number of cell layers in the tissue can be one—where every cell rests on the basal lamina—which is a simple epithelium, or more than one, which is a stratified epithelium and only the basal layer of cells rests on the basal lamina. Pseudostratified (pseudo- = "false") describes tissue with a single layer of irregularly shaped cells that give the appearance of more than one layer. Transitional describes a form of specialized stratified epithelium in which the shape of the cells can vary.

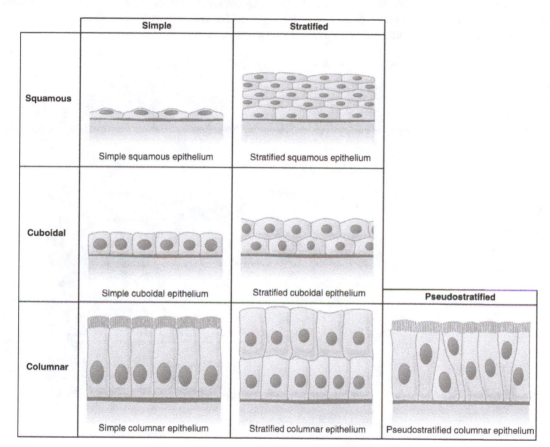

Figure 4.6 Cells of Epithelial Tissue Simple epithelial tissue is organized as a single layer of cells and stratified epithelial tissue is formed by several layers of cells.

Simple Epithelium

The shape of the cells in the single cell layer of simple epithelium reflects the functioning of those cells. The cells in **simple squamous epithelium** have the appearance of thin scales. Squamous cell nuclei tend to be flat, horizontal, and elliptical, mirroring the form of the cell. The **endothelium** is the epithelial tissue that lines vessels of the lymphatic and cardiovascular system, and it is made up of a single layer of squamous cells. Simple squamous epithelium, because of the thinness of the cell, is present where rapid passage of chemical compounds is observed. The alveoli of lungs where gases diffuse, segments of kidney tubules, and the lining of capillaries are also made of simple squamous epithelial tissue. The **mesothelium** is a simple squamous epithelium that forms the surface layer of the serous membrane that lines body cavities and internal organs. Its primary function is to provide a smooth and protective surface. Mesothelial cells are squamous epithelial cells that secrete a fluid that lubricates the mesothelium.

In **simple cuboidal epithelium**, the nucleus of the box-like cells appears round and is generally located near the center of the cell. These epithelia are active in the secretion and absorptions of molecules. Simple cuboidal epithelia are observed in the lining of the kidney tubules and in the ducts of glands.

In **simple columnar epithelium**, the nucleus of the tall column-like cells tends to be elongated and located in the basal end of the cells. Like the cuboidal epithelia, this epithelium is active in the absorption and secretion of molecules. Simple columnar epithelium forms the lining of some sections of the digestive system and parts of the female reproductive tract. Ciliated columnar epithelium is composed of simple columnar epithelial cells with cilia on their apical surfaces. These epithelial cells are found in the lining of the fallopian tubes and parts of the respiratory system, where the beating of the cilia helps remove particulate matter.

Pseudostratified columnar epithelium is a type of epithelium that appears to be stratified but instead consists of a single layer of irregularly shaped and differently sized columnar cells. In pseudostratified epithelium, nuclei of neighboring cells appear at different levels rather than clustered in the basal end. The arrangement gives the appearance of stratification; but in fact all the cells are in contact with the basal lamina, although some do not reach the apical surface. Pseudostratified columnar epithelium is found in the respiratory tract, where some of these cells have cilia.

Both simple and pseudostratified columnar epithelia are heterogeneous epithelia because they include additional types of cells interspersed among the epithelial cells. For example, a **goblet cell** is a mucous-secreting unicellular "gland" interspersed between the columnar epithelial cells of mucous membranes (Figure 4.7).

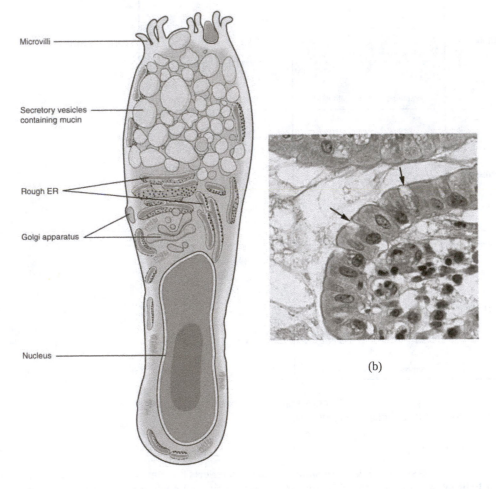

(a)

(b)

Figure 4.7 Goblet Cell (a) In the lining of the small intestine, columnar epithelium cells are interspersed with goblet cells. (b) The arrows in this micrograph point to the mucous-secreting goblet cells. LM × 1600. (Micrograph provided by the Regents of University of Michigan Medical School © 2012)

Interactive LINK

View the University of Michigan WebScope at http://virtualslides.med.umich.edu/Histology/Digestive%20System/Intestines/169_HISTO_40X.svs/view.apml (http://openstaxcollege.org/l/goblet) to explore the tissue sample in greater detail.

Stratified Epithelium

A stratified epithelium consists of several stacked layers of cells. This epithelium protects against physical and chemical wear and tear. The stratified epithelium is named by the shape of the most apical layer of cells, closest to the free space. **Stratified squamous epithelium** is the most common type of stratified epithelium in the human body. The apical cells are squamous, whereas the basal layer contains either columnar or cuboidal cells. The top layer may be covered with dead cells filled with keratin. Mammalian skin is an example of this dry, keratinized, stratified squamous epithelium. The lining of the mouth cavity is an example of an unkeratinized, stratified squamous epithelium. **Stratified cuboidal epithelium** and **stratified columnar epithelium** can also be found in certain glands and ducts, but are uncommon in the human body.

Another kind of stratified epithelium is **transitional epithelium**, so-called because of the gradual changes in the shapes of the apical cells as the bladder fills with urine. It is found only in the urinary system, specifically the ureters and urinary bladder. When the bladder is empty, this epithelium is convoluted and has cuboidal apical cells with convex, umbrella shaped, apical surfaces. As the bladder fills with urine, this epithelium loses its convolutions and the apical cells transition from cuboidal to squamous. It appears thicker and more multi-layered when the bladder is empty, and more stretched out and less stratified when the bladder is full and distended. Figure 4.8 summarizes the different categories of epithelial cell tissue cells.

Cells	Location	Function
Simple squamous epithelium 	Air sacs of lungs and the lining of the heart, blood vessels, and lymphatic vessels	Allows materials to pass through by diffusion and filtration, and secretes lubricating substance
Simple cuboidal epithelium 	In ducts and secretory portions of small glands and in kidney tubules	Secretes and absorbs
Simple columnar epithelium 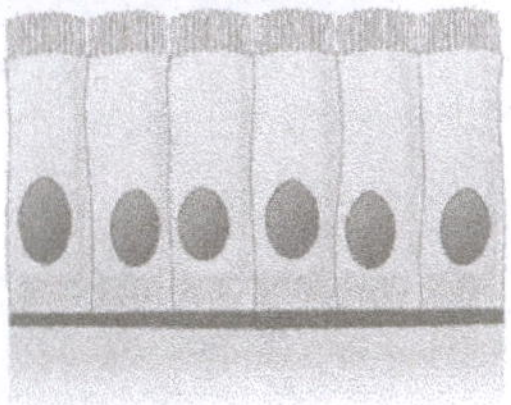	Ciliated tissues are in bronchi, uterine tubes, and uterus; smooth (nonciliated tissues) are in the digestive tract, bladder	Absorbs; it also secretes mucous and enzymes
Pseudostratified columnar epithelium 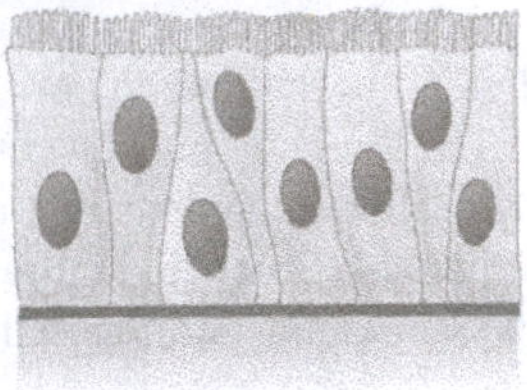	Ciliated tissue lines the trachea and much of the upper respiratory tract	Secretes mucus; ciliated tissue moves mucus
Stratified squamous epithelium 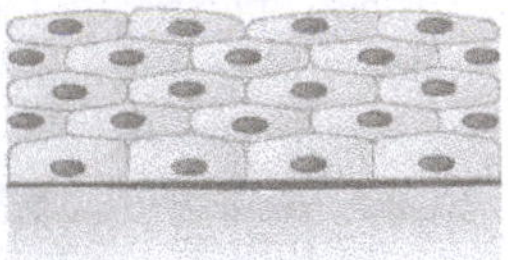	Lines the esophagus, mouth, and vagina	Protects against abrasion
Stratified cuboidal epithelium 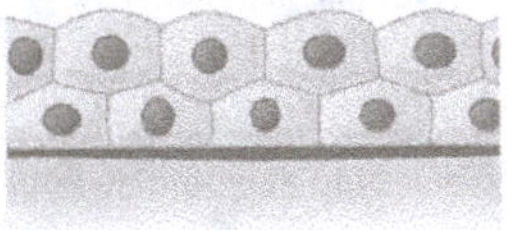	Sweat glands, salivary glands, and the mammary glands	Protective tissue
Stratified columnar epithelium 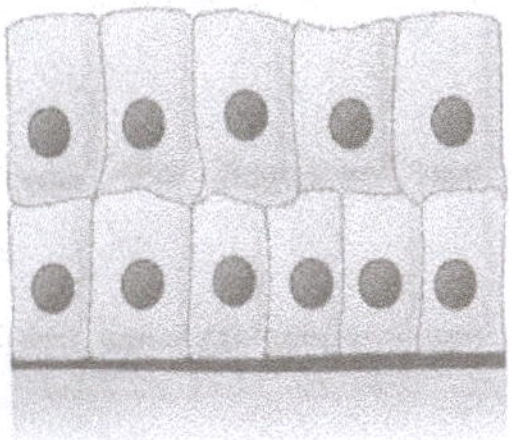	The male urethra and the ducts of some glands	Secretes and protects
Transitional epithelium 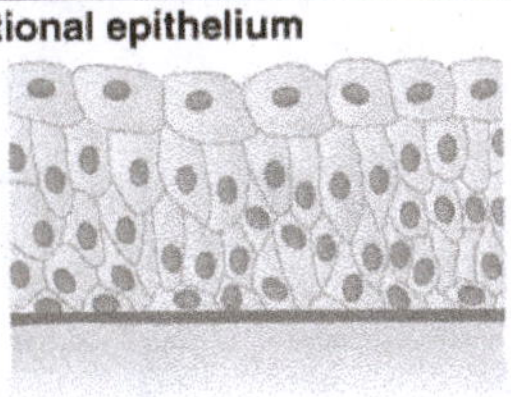	Lines the bladder, uretha, and the ureters	Allows the urinary organs to expand and stretch

Figure 4.8 Summary of Epithelial Tissue Cells

Interactive LINK

Watch this video (http://openstaxcollege.org/l/etissues) to find out more about the anatomy of epithelial tissues. Where in the body would one find non-keratinizing stratified squamous epithelium?

Glandular Epithelium

A gland is a structure made up of one or more cells modified to synthesize and secrete chemical substances. Most glands consist of groups of epithelial cells. A gland can be classified as an **endocrine gland**, a ductless gland that releases secretions directly into surrounding tissues and fluids (endo- = "inside"), or an **exocrine gland** whose secretions leave through a duct that opens directly, or indirectly, to the external environment (exo- = "outside").

Endocrine Glands

The secretions of endocrine glands are called hormones. Hormones are released into the interstitial fluid, diffused into the bloodstream, and delivered to targets, in other words, cells that have receptors to bind the hormones. The endocrine system is part of a major regulatory system coordinating the regulation and integration of body responses. A few examples of endocrine glands include the anterior pituitary, thymus, adrenal cortex, and gonads.

Exocrine Glands

Exocrine glands release their contents through a duct that leads to the epithelial surface. Mucous, sweat, saliva, and breast milk are all examples of secretions from exocrine glands. They are all discharged through tubular ducts. Secretions into the lumen of the gastrointestinal tract, technically outside of the body, are of the exocrine category.

Glandular Structure

Exocrine glands are classified as either unicellular or multicellular. The unicellular glands are scattered single cells, such as goblet cells, found in the mucous membranes of the small and large intestine.

The multicellular exocrine glands known as serous glands develop from simple epithelium to form a secretory surface that secretes directly into an inner cavity. These glands line the internal cavities of the abdomen and chest and release their secretions directly into the cavities. Other multicellular exocrine glands release their contents through a tubular duct. The duct is single in a simple gland but in compound glands is divided into one or more branches (Figure 4.9). In tubular glands, the ducts can be straight or coiled, whereas tubes that form pockets are alveolar (acinar), such as the exocrine portion of the pancreas. Combinations of tubes and pockets are known as tubuloalveolar (tubuloacinar) compound glands. In a branched gland, a duct is connected to more than one secretory group of cells.

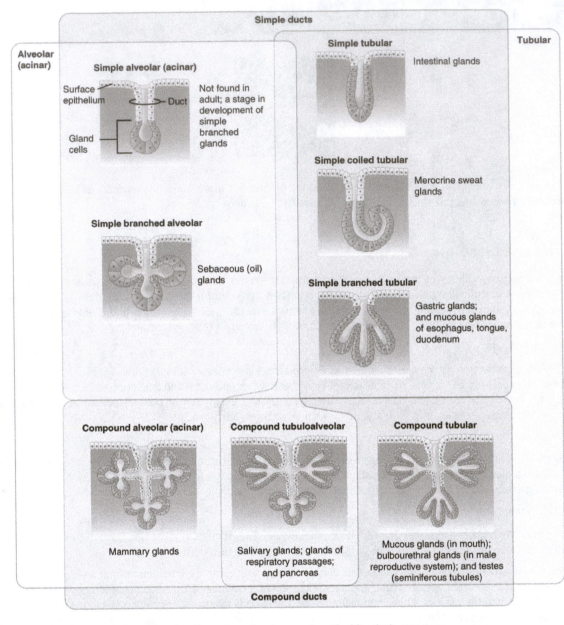

Figure 4.9 Types of Exocrine Glands Exocrine glands are classified by their structure.

Methods and Types of Secretion

Exocrine glands can be classified by their mode of secretion and the nature of the substances released, as well as by the structure of the glands and shape of ducts (Figure 4.10). **Merocrine secretion** is the most common type of exocrine secretion. The secretions are enclosed in vesicles that move to the apical surface of the cell where the contents are released by exocytosis. For example, watery mucous containing the glycoprotein mucin, a lubricant that offers some pathogen protection is a merocrine secretion. The eccrine glands that produce and secrete sweat are another example.

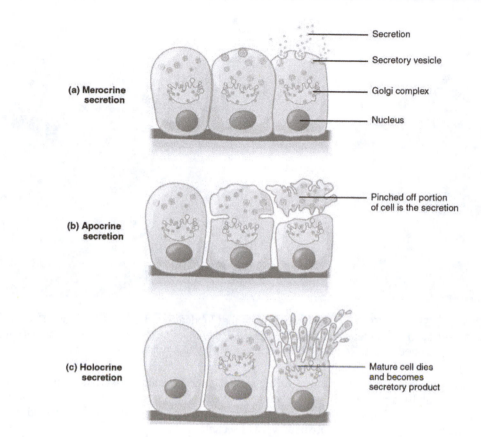

Figure 4.10 Modes of Glandular Secretion (a) In merocrine secretion, the cell remains intact. (b) In apocrine secretion, the apical portion of the cell is released, as well. (c) In holocrine secretion, the cell is destroyed as it releases its product and the cell itself becomes part of the secretion.

Apocrine secretion accumulates near the apical portion of the cell. That portion of the cell and its secretory contents pinch off from the cell and are released. Apocrine sweat glands in the axillary and genital areas release fatty secretions that local bacteria break down; this causes body odor. Both merocrine and apocrine glands continue to produce and secrete their contents with little damage caused to the cell because the nucleus and golgi regions remain intact after secretion.

In contrast, the process of **holocrine secretion** involves the rupture and destruction of the entire gland cell. The cell accumulates its secretory products and releases them only when it bursts. New gland cells differentiate from cells in the surrounding tissue to replace those lost by secretion. The sebaceous glands that produce the oils on the skin and hair are holocrine glands/cells (Figure 4.11).

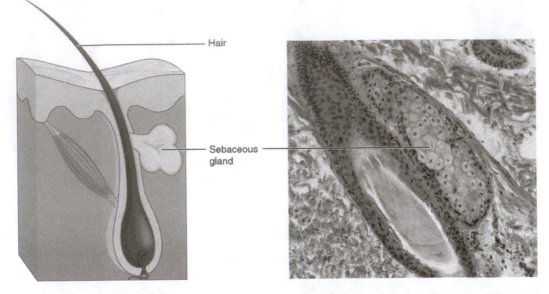

Figure 4.11 Sebaceous Glands These glands secrete oils that lubricate and protect the skin. They are holocrine glands and they are destroyed after releasing their contents. New glandular cells form to replace the cells that are lost. LM × 400. (Micrograph provided by the Regents of University of Michigan Medical School © 2012)

Glands are also named after the products they produce. The **serous gland** produces watery, blood-plasma-like secretions rich in enzymes such as alpha amylase, whereas the **mucous gland** releases watery to viscous products rich in the glycoprotein mucin. Both serous and mucous glands are common in the salivary glands of the mouth. Mixed exocrine glands contain both serous and mucous glands and release both types of secretions.

4.3 | Connective Tissue Supports and Protects

By the end of this section, you will be able to:

- Identify and distinguish between the types of connective tissue: proper, supportive, and fluid
- Explain the functions of connective tissues

As may be obvious from its name, one of the major functions of connective tissue is to connect tissues and organs. Unlike epithelial tissue, which is composed of cells closely packed with little or no extracellular space in between, connective tissue cells are dispersed in a **matrix**. The matrix usually includes a large amount of extracellular material produced by the connective tissue cells that are embedded within it. The matrix plays a major role in the functioning of this tissue. The major component of the matrix is a **ground substance** often crisscrossed by protein fibers. This ground substance is usually a fluid, but it can also be mineralized and solid, as in bones. Connective tissues come in a vast variety of forms, yet they typically have in common three characteristic components: cells, large amounts of amorphous ground substance, and protein fibers. The amount and structure of each component correlates with the function of the tissue, from the rigid ground substance in bones supporting the body to the inclusion of specialized cells; for example, a phagocytic cell that engulfs pathogens and also rids tissue of cellular debris.

Functions of Connective Tissues

Connective tissues perform many functions in the body, but most importantly, they support and connect other tissues; from the connective tissue sheath that surrounds muscle cells, to the tendons that attach muscles to bones, and to the skeleton that supports the positions of the body. Protection is another major function of connective tissue, in the form of fibrous capsules and bones that protect delicate organs and, of course, the skeletal system. Specialized cells in connective tissue defend the body from microorganisms that enter the body. Transport of fluid, nutrients, waste, and chemical messengers is ensured by specialized fluid connective tissues, such as blood and lymph. Adipose cells store surplus energy in the form of fat and contribute to the thermal insulation of the body.

Embryonic Connective Tissue

All connective tissues derive from the mesodermal layer of the embryo (see Figure 4.3). The first connective tissue to develop in the embryo is **mesenchyme**, the stem cell line from which all connective tissues are later derived. Clusters of mesenchymal cells are scattered throughout adult tissue and supply the cells needed for replacement and repair after a connective tissue injury. A second type of embryonic connective tissue forms in the umbilical cord, called **mucous connective tissue** or Wharton's jelly. This tissue is no longer present after birth, leaving only scattered mesenchymal cells throughout the body.

Classification of Connective Tissues

The three broad categories of connective tissue are classified according to the characteristics of their ground substance and the types of fibers found within the matrix (Table 4.1). **Connective tissue proper** includes **loose connective tissue** and **dense connective tissue**. Both tissues have a variety of cell types and protein fibers suspended in a viscous ground substance. Dense connective tissue is reinforced by bundles of fibers that provide tensile strength, elasticity, and protection. In loose connective tissue, the fibers are loosely organized, leaving large spaces in between. **Supportive connective tissue**—bone and cartilage—provide structure and strength to the body and protect soft tissues. A few distinct cell types and densely packed fibers in a matrix characterize these tissues. In bone, the matrix is rigid and described as calcified because of the deposited calcium salts. In **fluid connective tissue**, in other words, lymph and blood, various specialized cells circulate in a watery fluid containing salts, nutrients, and dissolved proteins.

Connective Tissue Examples

Connective tissue proper	Supportive connective tissue	Fluid connective tissue
Loose connective tissue Areolar Adipose Reticular	Cartilage Hyaline Fibrocartilage Elastic	Blood
Dense connective tissue Regular elastic Irregular elastic	Bones Compact bone Cancellous bone	Lymph

Table 4.1

Connective Tissue Proper

Fibroblasts are present in all connective tissue proper (Figure 4.12). Fibrocytes, adipocytes, and mesenchymal cells are fixed cells, which means they remain within the connective tissue. Other cells move in and out of the connective tissue in response to chemical signals. Macrophages, mast cells, lymphocytes, plasma cells, and phagocytic cells are found in connective tissue proper but are actually part of the immune system protecting the body.

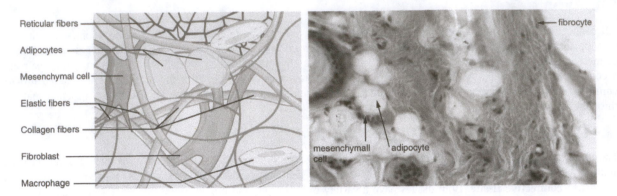

Figure 4.12 Connective Tissue Proper Fibroblasts produce this fibrous tissue. Connective tissue proper includes the fixed cells fibrocytes, adipocytes, and mesenchymal cells. LM × 400. (Micrograph provided by the Regents of University of Michigan Medical School © 2012)

Cell Types

The most abundant cell in connective tissue proper is the **fibroblast**. Polysaccharides and proteins secreted by fibroblasts combine with extra-cellular fluids to produce a viscous ground substance that, with embedded fibrous proteins, forms the extra-cellular matrix. As you might expect, a **fibrocyte**, a less active form of fibroblast, is the second most common cell type in connective tissue proper.

Adipocytes are cells that store lipids as droplets that fill most of the cytoplasm. There are two basic types of adipocytes: white and brown. The brown adipocytes store lipids as many droplets, and have high metabolic activity. In contrast, white fat adipocytes store lipids as a single large drop and are metabolically less active. Their effectiveness at storing large amounts of fat is witnessed in obese individuals. The number and type of adipocytes depends on the tissue and location, and vary among individuals in the population.

The **mesenchymal cell** is a multipotent adult stem cell. These cells can differentiate into any type of connective tissue cells needed for repair and healing of damaged tissue.

The macrophage cell is a large cell derived from a monocyte, a type of blood cell, which enters the connective tissue matrix from the blood vessels. The macrophage cells are an essential component of the immune system, which is the body's defense against potential pathogens and degraded host cells. When stimulated, macrophages release cytokines, small proteins that act as chemical messengers. Cytokines recruit other cells of the immune system to infected sites and stimulate their activities. Roaming, or free, macrophages move rapidly by amoeboid movement, engulfing infectious agents and cellular debris. In contrast, fixed macrophages are permanent residents of their tissues.

The mast cell, found in connective tissue proper, has many cytoplasmic granules. These granules contain the chemical signals histamine and heparin. When irritated or damaged, mast cells release histamine, an inflammatory mediator, which causes vasodilation and increased blood flow at a site of injury or infection, along with itching, swelling, and redness you recognize as an allergic response. Like blood cells, mast cells are derived from hematopoietic stem cells and are part of the immune system.

Connective Tissue Fibers and Ground Substance

Three main types of fibers are secreted by fibroblasts: collagen fibers, elastic fibers, and reticular fibers. **Collagen fiber** is made from fibrous protein subunits linked together to form a long and straight fiber. Collagen fibers, while flexible, have great tensile strength, resist stretching, and give ligaments and tendons their characteristic resilience and strength. These fibers hold connective tissues together, even during the movement of the body.

Elastic fiber contains the protein elastin along with lesser amounts of other proteins and glycoproteins. The main property of elastin is that after being stretched or compressed, it will return to its original shape. Elastic fibers are prominent in elastic tissues found in skin and the elastic ligaments of the vertebral column.

Reticular fiber is also formed from the same protein subunits as collagen fibers; however, these fibers remain narrow and are arrayed in a branching network. They are found throughout the body, but are most abundant in the reticular tissue of soft organs, such as liver and spleen, where they anchor and provide structural support to the **parenchyma** (the functional cells, blood vessels, and nerves of the organ).

All of these fiber types are embedded in ground substance. Secreted by fibroblasts, ground substance is made of polysaccharides, specifically hyaluronic acid, and proteins. These combine to form a proteoglycan with a protein core and polysaccharide branches. The proteoglycan attracts and traps available moisture forming the clear, viscous, colorless matrix you now know as ground substance.

Loose Connective Tissue

Loose connective tissue is found between many organs where it acts both to absorb shock and bind tissues together. It allows water, salts, and various nutrients to diffuse through to adjacent or imbedded cells and tissues.

Adipose tissue consists mostly of fat storage cells, with little extracellular matrix (Figure 4.13). A large number of capillaries allow rapid storage and mobilization of lipid molecules. White adipose tissue is most abundant. It can appear yellow and owes its color to carotene and related pigments from plant food. White fat contributes mostly to lipid storage and can serve as insulation from cold temperatures and mechanical injuries. White adipose tissue can be found protecting the kidneys and cushioning the back of the eye. Brown adipose tissue is more common in infants, hence the term "baby fat." In adults, there is a reduced amount of brown fat and it is found mainly in the neck and clavicular regions of the body. The many mitochondria in the cytoplasm of brown adipose tissue help explain its efficiency at metabolizing stored fat. Brown adipose tissue is thermogenic, meaning that as it breaks down fats, it releases metabolic heat, rather than producing adenosine triphosphate (ATP), a key molecule used in metabolism.

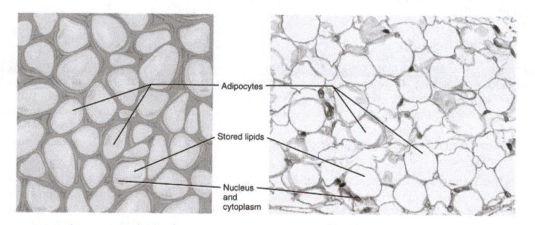

Figure 4.13 Adipose Tissue This is a loose connective tissue that consists of fat cells with little extracellular matrix. It stores fat for energy and provides insulation. LM × 800. (Micrograph provided by the Regents of University of Michigan Medical School © 2012)

Areolar tissue shows little specialization. It contains all the cell types and fibers previously described and is distributed in a random, web-like fashion. It fills the spaces between muscle fibers, surrounds blood and lymph vessels, and supports organs in the abdominal cavity. Areolar tissue underlies most epithelia and represents the connective tissue component of epithelial membranes, which are described further in a later section.

Reticular tissue is a mesh-like, supportive framework for soft organs such as lymphatic tissue, the spleen, and the liver (Figure 4.14). Reticular cells produce the reticular fibers that form the network onto which other cells attach. It derives its name from the Latin *reticulus*, which means "little net."

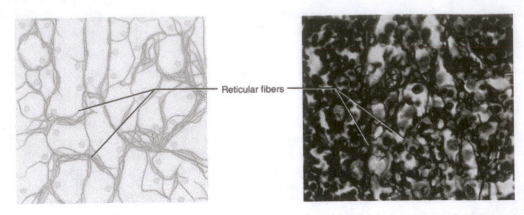

Figure 4.14 Reticular Tissue   This is a loose connective tissue made up of a network of reticular fibers that provides a supportive framework for soft organs. LM × 1600. (Micrograph provided by the Regents of University of Michigan Medical School © 2012)

Dense Connective Tissue

Dense connective tissue contains more collagen fibers than does loose connective tissue. As a consequence, it displays greater resistance to stretching. There are two major categories of dense connective tissue: regular and irregular. Dense regular connective tissue fibers are parallel to each other, enhancing tensile strength and resistance to stretching in the direction of the fiber orientations. Ligaments and tendons are made of dense regular connective tissue, but in ligaments not all fibers are parallel. Dense regular elastic tissue contains elastin fibers in addition to collagen fibers, which allows the ligament to return to its original length after stretching. The ligaments in the vocal folds and between the vertebrae in the vertebral column are elastic.

In dense irregular connective tissue, the direction of fibers is random. This arrangement gives the tissue greater strength in all directions and less strength in one particular direction. In some tissues, fibers crisscross and form a mesh. In other tissues, stretching in several directions is achieved by alternating layers where fibers run in the same orientation in each layer, and it is the layers themselves that are stacked at an angle. The dermis of the skin is an example of dense irregular connective tissue rich in collagen fibers. Dense irregular elastic tissues give arterial walls the strength and the ability to regain original shape after stretching (Figure 4.15).

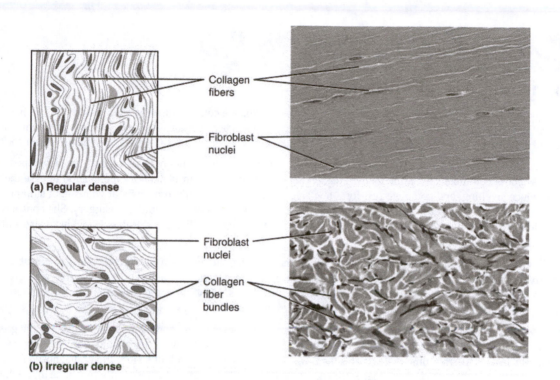

Figure 4.15 Dense Connective Tissue (a) Dense regular connective tissue consists of collagenous fibers packed into parallel bundles. (b) Dense irregular connective tissue consists of collagenous fibers interwoven into a mesh-like network. From top, LM × 1000, LM × 200. (Micrographs provided by the Regents of University of Michigan Medical School © 2012)

isorders OF THE...

Connective Tissue: Tendinitis

Your opponent stands ready as you prepare to hit the serve, but you are confident that you will smash the ball past your opponent. As you toss the ball high in the air, a burning pain shoots across your wrist and you drop the tennis racket. That dull ache in the wrist that you ignored through the summer is now an unbearable pain. The game is over for now.

After examining your swollen wrist, the doctor in the emergency room announces that you have developed wrist tendinitis. She recommends icing the tender area, taking non-steroidal anti-inflammatory medication to ease the pain and to reduce swelling, and complete rest for a few weeks. She interrupts your protests that you cannot stop playing. She issues a stern warning about the risk of aggravating the condition and the possibility of surgery. She consoles you by mentioning that well known tennis players such as Venus and Serena Williams and Rafael Nadal have also suffered from tendinitis related injuries.

What is tendinitis and how did it happen? Tendinitis is the inflammation of a tendon, the thick band of fibrous connective tissue that attaches a muscle to a bone. The condition causes pain and tenderness in the area around a joint. On rare occasions, a sudden serious injury will cause tendinitis. Most often, the condition results from repetitive motions over time that strain the tendons needed to perform the tasks.

Persons whose jobs and hobbies involve performing the same movements over and over again are often at the greatest risk of tendinitis. You hear of tennis and golfer's elbow, jumper's knee, and swimmer's shoulder. In all cases, overuse of the joint causes a microtrauma that initiates the inflammatory response. Tendinitis is routinely diagnosed through a clinical examination. In case of severe pain, X-rays can be examined to rule out the possibility of a bone injury. Severe cases of tendinitis can even tear loose a tendon. Surgical repair of a tendon is painful. Connective tissue in the tendon does not have abundant blood supply and heals slowly.

While older adults are at risk for tendinitis because the elasticity of tendon tissue decreases with age, active people of all ages can develop tendinitis. Young athletes, dancers, and computer operators; anyone who performs the same movements constantly is at risk for tendinitis. Although repetitive motions are unavoidable in many activities and may lead to tendinitis, precautions can be taken that can lessen the probability of developing tendinitis. For active individuals, stretches before exercising and cross training or changing exercises are recommended. For the passionate athlete, it may be time to take some lessons to improve technique. All of the preventive measures aim to increase the strength of the tendon and decrease the stress put on it. With proper rest and managed care, you will be back on the court to hit that slice-spin serve over the net.

Interactive LINK

Watch this animation (http://openstaxcollege.org/l/tendonitis) to learn more about tendonitis, a painful condition caused by swollen or injured tendons.

Supportive Connective Tissues

Two major forms of supportive connective tissue, cartilage and bone, allow the body to maintain its posture and protect internal organs.

Cartilage

The distinctive appearance of cartilage is due to polysaccharides called chondroitin sulfates, which bind with ground substance proteins to form proteoglycans. Embedded within the cartilage matrix are **chondrocytes**, or cartilage cells, and the space they occupy are called **lacunae** (singular = lacuna). A layer of dense irregular connective tissue, the perichondrium, encapsulates the cartilage. Cartilaginous tissue is avascular, thus all nutrients need to diffuse through the matrix to reach the chondrocytes. This is a factor contributing to the very slow healing of cartilaginous tissues.

The three main types of cartilage tissue are hyaline cartilage, fibrocartilage, and elastic cartilage (Figure 4.16). **Hyaline cartilage**, the most common type of cartilage in the body, consists of short and dispersed collagen fibers and contains large amounts of proteoglycans. Under the microscope, tissue samples appear clear. The surface of hyaline cartilage is smooth. Both strong and flexible, it is found in the rib cage and nose and covers bones where they meet to form moveable joints. It makes up a template of the embryonic skeleton before bone formation. A plate of hyaline cartilage at the ends of bone allows continued growth until adulthood. **Fibrocartilage** is tough because it has thick bundles of collagen fibers dispersed through its matrix. Menisci in the knee joint and the intervertebral discs are examples of fibrocartilage. **Elastic cartilage** contains elastic fibers as well as collagen and proteoglycans. This tissue gives rigid support as well as elasticity. Tug gently at your ear lobes, and notice that the lobes return to their initial shape. The external ear contains elastic cartilage.

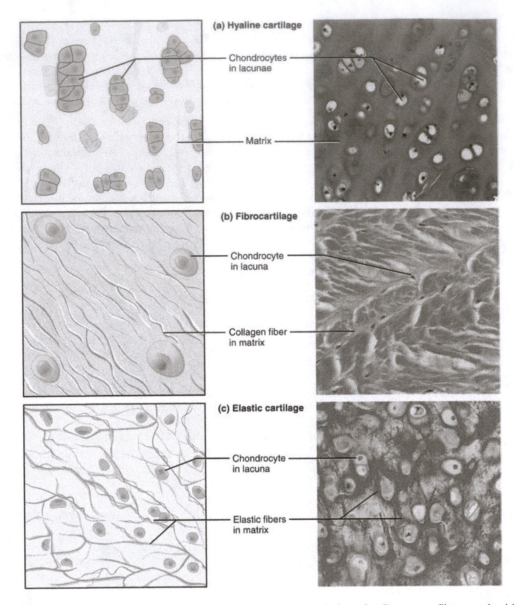

Figure 4.16 Types of Cartilage   Cartilage is a connective tissue consisting of collagenous fibers embedded in a firm matrix of chondroitin sulfates. (a) Hyaline cartilage provides support with some flexibility. The example is from dog tissue. (b) Fibrocartilage provides some compressibility and can absorb pressure. (c) Elastic cartilage provides firm but elastic support. From top, LM × 300, LM × 1200, LM × 1016. (Micrographs provided by the Regents of University of Michigan Medical School © 2012)

Bone

Bone is the hardest connective tissue. It provides protection to internal organs and supports the body. Bone's rigid extracellular matrix contains mostly collagen fibers embedded in a mineralized ground substance containing hydroxyapatite, a form of calcium phosphate. Both components of the matrix, organic and inorganic, contribute to the unusual properties of bone. Without collagen, bones would be brittle and shatter easily. Without mineral crystals, bones would flex and provide little support. Osteocytes, bone cells like chondrocytes, are located within lacunae. The histology of transverse tissue from long bone shows a typical arrangement of osteocytes in concentric circles around a central canal. Bone is a highly vascularized tissue. Unlike cartilage, bone tissue can recover from injuries in a relatively short time.

Cancellous bone looks like a sponge under the microscope and contains empty spaces between trabeculae, or arches of bone proper. It is lighter than compact bone and found in the interior of some bones and at the end of long bones. Compact bone is solid and has greater structural strength.

Fluid Connective Tissue

Blood and lymph are fluid connective tissues. Cells circulate in a liquid extracellular matrix. The formed elements circulating in blood are all derived from hematopoietic stem cells located in bone marrow (Figure 4.17). Erythrocytes, red blood cells, transport oxygen and some carbon dioxide. Leukocytes, white blood cells, are responsible for defending against potentially harmful microorganisms or molecules. Platelets are cell fragments involved in blood clotting. Some white blood cells have the ability to cross the endothelial layer that lines blood vessels and enter adjacent tissues. Nutrients, salts, and wastes are dissolved in the liquid matrix and transported through the body.

Lymph contains a liquid matrix and white blood cells. Lymphatic capillaries are extremely permeable, allowing larger molecules and excess fluid from interstitial spaces to enter the lymphatic vessels. Lymph drains into blood vessels, delivering molecules to the blood that could not otherwise directly enter the bloodstream. In this way, specialized lymphatic capillaries transport absorbed fats away from the intestine and deliver these molecules to the blood.

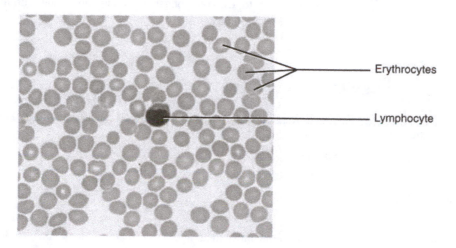

Figure 4.17 Blood: A Fluid Connective Tissue Blood is a fluid connective tissue containing erythrocytes and various types of leukocytes that circulate in a liquid extracellular matrix. LM × 1600. (Micrograph provided by the Regents of University of Michigan Medical School © 2012)

View the University of Michigan Webscope at http://virtualslides.med.umich.edu/Histology/ Cardiovascular%20System/081-3_HISTO_40X.svs/view.apml (http://openstaxcollege.org/l/cardiovascular) to explore the tissue sample in greater detail.

Interactive LINK

Visit this link (http://openstaxcollege.org/l/10quiz) to test your connective tissue knowledge with this 10-question quiz. Can you name the 10 tissue types shown in the histology slides?

4.4 | Muscle Tissue and Motion

By the end of this section, you will be able to:

- Identify the three types of muscle tissue
- Compare and contrast the functions of each muscle tissue type
- Explain how muscle tissue can enable motion

Muscle tissue is characterized by properties that allow movement. Muscle cells are excitable; they respond to a stimulus. They are contractile, meaning they can shorten and generate a pulling force. When attached between two movable objects, in other words, bones, contractions of the muscles cause the bones to move. Some muscle movement is voluntary, which means it is under conscious control. For example, a person decides to open a book and read a chapter on anatomy. Other movements are involuntary, meaning they are not under conscious control, such as the contraction of your pupil in bright light. Muscle tissue is classified into three types according to structure and function: skeletal, cardiac, and smooth (Table 4.2).

Comparison of Structure and Properties of Muscle Tissue Types

Tissue	Histology	Function	Location
Skeletal	Long cylindrical fiber, striated, many peripherally located nuclei	Voluntary movement, produces heat, protects organs	Attached to bones and around entrance points to body (e.g., mouth, anus)
Cardiac	Short, branched, striated, single central nucleus	Contracts to pump blood	Heart
Smooth	Short, spindle-shaped, no evident striation, single nucleus in each fiber	Involuntary movement, moves food, involuntary control of respiration, moves secretions, regulates flow of blood in arteries by contraction	Walls of major organs and passageways

Table 4.2

Skeletal muscle is attached to bones and its contraction makes possible locomotion, facial expressions, posture, and other voluntary movements of the body. Forty percent of your body mass is made up of skeletal muscle. Skeletal muscles generate heat as a byproduct of their contraction and thus participate in thermal homeostasis. Shivering is an involuntary contraction of skeletal muscles in response to perceived lower than normal body temperature. The muscle cell, or **myocyte**, develops from myoblasts derived from the mesoderm. Myocytes and their numbers remain relatively constant throughout life. Skeletal muscle tissue is arranged in bundles surrounded by connective tissue. Under the light microscope, muscle cells appear striated with many nuclei squeezed along the membranes. The **striation** is due to the regular alternation of the contractile proteins actin and myosin, along with the structural proteins that couple the contractile proteins to connective tissues. The cells are multinucleated as a result of the fusion of the many myoblasts that fuse to form each long muscle fiber.

Cardiac muscle forms the contractile walls of the heart. The cells of cardiac muscle, known as cardiomyocytes, also appear striated under the microscope. Unlike skeletal muscle fibers, cardiomyocytes are single cells typically with a single centrally located nucleus. A principal characteristic of cardiomyocytes is that they contract on their own intrinsic rhythms without any external stimulation. Cardiomyocyte attach to one another with specialized cell junctions called intercalated discs. Intercalated discs have both anchoring junctions and gap junctions. Attached cells form long, branching cardiac muscle fibers that are, essentially, a mechanical and electrochemical syncytium allowing the cells to synchronize their actions. The cardiac muscle pumps blood through the body and is under involuntary control. The attachment junctions hold adjacent cells together across the dynamic pressures changes of the cardiac cycle.

Smooth muscle tissue contraction is responsible for involuntary movements in the internal organs. It forms the contractile component of the digestive, urinary, and reproductive systems as well as the airways and arteries. Each cell is spindle shaped with a single nucleus and no visible striations (**Figure 4.18**).

(a)

(b)

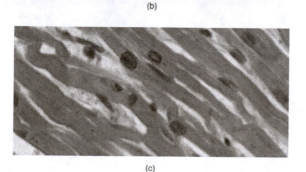

(c)

Figure 4.18 Muscle Tissue (a) Skeletal muscle cells have prominent striation and nuclei on their periphery. (b) Smooth muscle cells have a single nucleus and no visible striations. (c) Cardiac muscle cells appear striated and have a single nucleus. From top, LM × 1600, LM × 1600, LM × 1600. (Micrographs provided by the Regents of University of Michigan Medical School © 2012)

Watch this **video (http://openstaxcollege.org/l/musctissue)** to learn more about muscle tissue. In looking through a microscope how could you distinguish skeletal muscle tissue from smooth muscle?

4.5 | Nervous Tissue Mediates Perception and Response

By the end of this section, you will be able to:

- Identify the classes of cells that make up nervous tissue
- Discuss how nervous tissue mediates perception and response

Nervous tissue is characterized as being excitable and capable of sending and receiving electrochemical signals that provide the body with information. Two main classes of cells make up nervous tissue: the **neuron** and **neuroglia** (Figure 4.19). Neurons propagate information via electrochemical impulses, called action potentials, which are biochemically linked to the release of chemical signals. Neuroglia play an essential role in supporting neurons and modulating their information propagation.

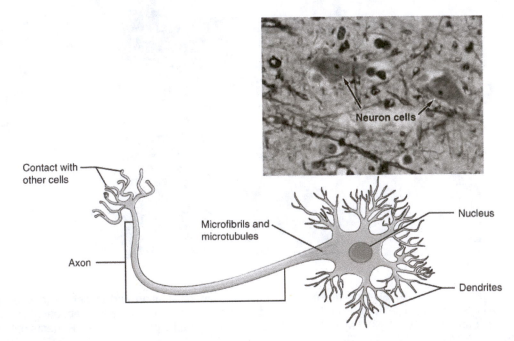

Figure 4.19 The Neuron The cell body of a neuron, also called the soma, contains the nucleus and mitochondria. The dendrites transfer the nerve impulse to the soma. The axon carries the action potential away to another excitable cell. LM × 1600. (Micrograph provided by the Regents of University of Michigan Medical School © 2012)

Interactive LINK

Follow this link (http://openstaxcollege.org/l/nobel) to learn more about nervous tissue. What are the main parts of a nerve cell?

Neurons display distinctive morphology, well suited to their role as conducting cells, with three main parts. The cell body includes most of the cytoplasm, the organelles, and the nucleus. Dendrites branch off the cell body and appear as thin extensions. A long "tail," the axon, extends from the neuron body and can be wrapped in an insulating layer known as **myelin**, which is formed by accessory cells. The synapse is the gap between nerve cells, or between a nerve cell and its target, for example, a muscle or a gland, across which the impulse is transmitted by chemical compounds known as neurotransmitters. Neurons categorized as multipolar neurons have several dendrites and a single prominent axon. Bipolar neurons possess a single dendrite and axon with the cell body, while unipolar neurons have only a single process extending out from the cell body, which divides into a functional dendrite and into a functional axon. When a neuron is sufficiently stimulated, it generates an action potential that propagates down the axon towards the synapse. If enough neurotransmitters are released at the synapse to stimulate the next neuron or target, a response is generated.

The second class of neural cells comprises the neuroglia or glial cells, which have been characterized as having a simple support role. The word "glia" comes from the Greek word for glue. Recent research is shedding light on the more complex role of neuroglia in the function of the brain and nervous system. **Astrocyte** cells, named for their distinctive star shape, are abundant in the central nervous system. The astrocytes have many functions, including regulation of ion concentration in the intercellular space, uptake and/or breakdown of some neurotransmitters, and formation of the blood-brain barrier, the membrane that separates the circulatory system from the brain. Microglia protect the nervous system against infection but are not nervous tissue because they are related to macrophages. **Oligodendrocyte** cells produce myelin in the central nervous system (brain and spinal cord) while the **Schwann cell** produces myelin in the peripheral nervous system (Figure 4.20).

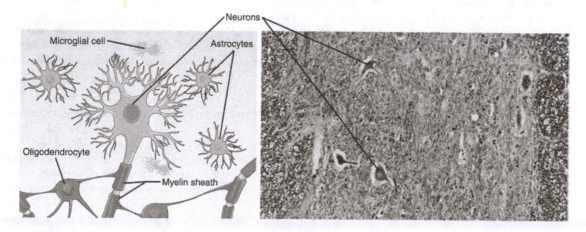

Figure 4.20 Nervous Tissue Nervous tissue is made up of neurons and neuroglia. The cells of nervous tissue are specialized to transmit and receive impulses. LM × 872. (Micrograph provided by the Regents of University of Michigan Medical School © 2012)

4.6 | Tissue Injury and Aging

By the end of this section, you will be able to:

- Identify the cardinal signs of inflammation
- List the body's response to tissue injury
- Explain the process of tissue repair
- Discuss the progressive impact of aging on tissue
- Describe cancerous mutations' effect on tissue

Tissues of all types are vulnerable to injury and, inevitably, aging. In the former case, understanding how tissues respond to damage can guide strategies to aid repair. In the latter case, understanding the impact of aging can help in the search for ways to diminish its effects.

Tissue Injury and Repair

Inflammation is the standard, initial response of the body to injury. Whether biological, chemical, physical, or radiation burns, all injuries lead to the same sequence of physiological events. Inflammation limits the extent of injury, partially or fully eliminates the cause of injury, and initiates repair and regeneration of damaged tissue. **Necrosis**, or accidental cell death, causes inflammation. **Apoptosis** is programmed cell death, a normal step-by-step process that destroys cells no longer needed by the body. By mechanisms still under investigation, apoptosis does not initiate the inflammatory response. Acute inflammation resolves over time by the healing of tissue. If inflammation persists, it becomes chronic and leads to diseased conditions. Arthritis and tuberculosis are examples of chronic inflammation. The suffix "-itis" denotes inflammation of a specific organ or type, for example, peritonitis is the inflammation of the peritoneum, and meningitis refers to the inflammation of the meninges, the tough membranes that surround the central nervous system

The four cardinal signs of inflammation—redness, swelling, pain, and local heat—were first recorded in antiquity. Cornelius Celsus is credited with documenting these signs during the days of the Roman Empire, as early as the first century AD. A fifth sign, loss of function, may also accompany inflammation.

Upon tissue injury, damaged cells release inflammatory chemical signals that evoke local **vasodilation**, the widening of the blood vessels. Increased blood flow results in apparent redness and heat. In response to injury, mast cells present in tissue degranulate, releasing the potent vasodilator **histamine**. Increased blood flow and inflammatory mediators recruit white blood cells to the site of inflammation. The endothelium lining the local blood vessel becomes "leaky" under the influence of histamine and other inflammatory mediators allowing neutrophils, macrophages, and fluid to move from the blood into the interstitial tissue spaces. The excess liquid in tissue causes swelling, more properly called edema. The swollen tissues squeezing pain receptors cause the sensation of pain. Prostaglandins released from injured cells also activate pain neurons. Non-steroidal anti-inflammatory drugs (NSAIDs) reduce pain because they inhibit the synthesis of prostaglandins. High levels of NSAIDs reduce inflammation. Antihistamines decrease allergies by blocking histamine receptors and as a result the histamine response.

After containment of an injury, the tissue repair phase starts with removal of toxins and waste products. **Clotting** (coagulation) reduces blood loss from damaged blood vessels and forms a network of fibrin proteins that trap blood cells and bind the edges of the wound together. A scab forms when the clot dries, reducing the risk of infection. Sometimes a mixture of dead leukocytes and fluid called pus accumulates in the wound. As healing progresses, fibroblasts from the surrounding connective tissues replace the collagen and extracellular material lost by the injury. Angiogenesis, the growth of new blood vessels, results in vascularization of the new tissue known as granulation tissue. The clot retracts pulling the edges of the wound together, and it slowly dissolves as the tissue is repaired. When a large amount of granulation tissue forms and capillaries disappear, a pale scar is often visible in the healed area. A **primary union** describes the healing of a wound where the edges are close together. When there is a gaping wound, it takes longer to refill the area with cells and collagen. The process called **secondary union** occurs as the edges of the wound are pulled together by what is called **wound contraction**. When a wound is more than one quarter of an inch deep, sutures (stitches) are recommended to promote a primary union and avoid the formation of a disfiguring scar. Regeneration is the addition of new cells of the same type as the ones that were injured (**Figure 4.21**).

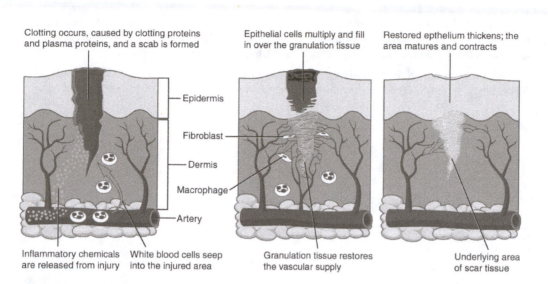

Clotting occurs, caused by clotting proteins and plasma proteins, and a scab is formed

Epithelial cells multiply and fill in over the granulation tissue

Restored epthelium thickens; the area matures and contracts

Epidermis

Fibroblast

Dermis

Macrophage

Artery

Inflammatory chemicals are released from injury

White blood cells seep into the injured area

Granulation tissue restores the vascular supply

Underlying area of scar tissue

Figure 4.21 Tissue Healing During wound repair, collagen fibers are laid down randomly by fibroblasts that move into repair the area.

Watch this video (http://openstaxcollege.org/l/healinghand) to see a hand heal. Over what period of time do you think these images were taken?

Tissue and Aging

According to poet Ralph Waldo Emerson, "The surest poison is time." In fact, biology confirms that many functions of the body decline with age. All the cells, tissues, and organs are affected by senescence, with noticeable variability between individuals owing to different genetic makeup and lifestyles. The outward signs of aging are easily recognizable. The skin and other tissues become thinner and drier, reducing their elasticity, contributing to wrinkles and high blood pressure. Hair turns gray because follicles produce less melanin, the brown pigment of hair and the iris of the eye. The face looks flabby because elastic and collagen fibers decrease in connective tissue and muscle tone is lost. Glasses and hearing aids may become parts of life as the senses slowly deteriorate, all due to reduced elasticity. Overall height decreases as the bones lose calcium and other minerals. With age, fluid decreases in the fibrous cartilage disks intercalated between the vertebrae in the spine. Joints lose cartilage and stiffen. Many tissues, including those in muscles, lose mass through a process called **atrophy**. Lumps and rigidity become more widespread. As a consequence, the passageways, blood vessels, and airways become more rigid. The brain and spinal cord lose mass. Nerves do not transmit impulses with the same speed and frequency as in the past. Some loss of thought clarity and memory can accompany aging. More severe problems are not necessarily associated with the aging process and may be symptoms of underlying illness.

As exterior signs of aging increase, so do the interior signs, which are not as noticeable. The incidence of heart diseases, respiratory syndromes, and type 2 diabetes increases with age, though these are not necessarily age-dependent effects. Wound healing is slower in the elderly, accompanied by a higher frequency of infection as the capacity of the immune system to fend off pathogen declines.

Aging is also apparent at the cellular level because all cells experience changes with aging. Telomeres, regions of the chromosomes necessary for cell division, shorten each time cells divide. As they do, cells are less able to divide and regenerate. Because of alterations in cell membranes, transport of oxygen and nutrients into the cell and removal of carbon dioxide and waste products from the cell are not as efficient in the elderly. Cells may begin to function abnormally, which may lead to diseases associated with aging, including arthritis, memory issues, and some cancers.

The progressive impact of aging on the body varies considerably among individuals, but Studies indicate, however, that exercise and healthy lifestyle choices can slow down the deterioration of the body that comes with old age.

Homeostatic IMBALANCES

Tissues and Cancer

Cancer is a generic term for many diseases in which cells escape regulatory signals. Uncontrolled growth, invasion into adjacent tissues, and colonization of other organs, if not treated early enough, are its hallmarks. Health suffers when tumors "rob" blood supply from the "normal" organs.

A mutation is defined as a permanent change in the DNA of a cell. Epigenetic modifications, changes that do not affect the code of the DNA but alter how the DNA is decoded, are also known to generate abnormal cells. Alterations in the genetic material may be caused by environmental agents, infectious agents, or errors in the replication of DNA that accumulate with age. Many mutations do not cause any noticeable change in the functions of a cell. However, if the modification affects key proteins that have an impact on the cell's ability to proliferate in an orderly fashion, the cell starts to divide abnormally. As changes in cells accumulate, they lose their ability to form regular tissues. A tumor, a mass of cells displaying abnormal architecture, forms in the tissue. Many tumors are benign, meaning they do not metastasize nor cause disease. A tumor becomes malignant, or cancerous, when it breaches the confines of its tissue, promotes angiogenesis, attracts the growth of capillaries, and metastasizes to other organs (Figure 4.22). The specific names of cancers reflect the tissue of origin. Cancers derived from epithelial cells are referred to as carcinomas. Cancer in myeloid tissue or blood cells form myelomas. Leukemias are cancers of white blood cells, whereas sarcomas derive from connective tissue. Cells in tumors differ both in structure and function. Some cells, called cancer stem cells, appear to be a subtype of cell responsible for uncontrolled growth. Recent research shows that contrary to what was previously assumed, tumors are not disorganized masses of cells, but have their own structures.

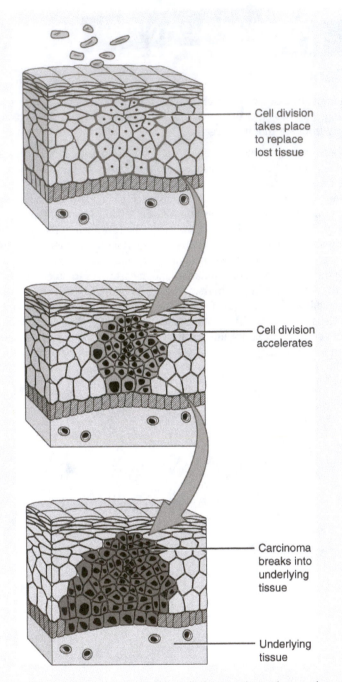

Cell division takes place to replace lost tissue

Cell division accelerates

Carcinoma breaks into underlying tissue

Underlying tissue

Figure 4.22 Development of Cancer Note the change in cell size, nucleus size, and organization in the tissue.

Interactive LINK

Watch this video (http://openstaxcollege.org/l/tumor) to learn more about tumors. What is a tumor?

Cancer treatments vary depending on the disease's type and stage. Traditional approaches, including surgery, radiation, chemotherapy, and hormonal therapy, aim to remove or kill rapidly dividing cancer cells, but these strategies have their limitations. Depending on a tumor's location, for example, cancer surgeons may be unable to remove it. Radiation and chemotherapy are difficult, and it is often impossible to target only the cancer cells. The treatments inevitably destroy healthy tissue as well. To address this, researchers are working on pharmaceuticals that can target specific proteins implicated in cancer-associated molecular pathways.

KEY TERMS

adipocytes lipid storage cells

adipose tissue specialized areolar tissue rich in stored fat

anchoring junction mechanically attaches adjacent cells to each other or to the basement membrane

apical that part of a cell or tissue which, in general, faces an open space

apocrine secretion release of a substance along with the apical portion of the cell

apoptosis programmed cell death

areolar tissue (also, loose connective tissue) a type of connective tissue proper that shows little specialization with cells dispersed in the matrix

astrocyte star-shaped cell in the central nervous system that regulates ions and uptake and/or breakdown of some neurotransmitters and contributes to the formation of the blood-brain barrier

atrophy loss of mass and function

basal lamina thin extracellular layer that lies underneath epithelial cells and separates them from other tissues

basement membrane in epithelial tissue, a thin layer of fibrous material that anchors the epithelial tissue to the underlying connective tissue; made up of the basal lamina and reticular lamina

cardiac muscle heart muscle, under involuntary control, composed of striated cells that attach to form fibers, each cell contains a single nucleus, contracts autonomously

cell junction point of cell-to-cell contact that connects one cell to another in a tissue

chondrocytes cells of the cartilage

clotting also called coagulation; complex process by which blood components form a plug to stop bleeding

collagen fiber flexible fibrous proteins that give connective tissue tensile strength

connective tissue type of tissue that serves to hold in place, connect, and integrate the body's organs and systems

connective tissue membrane connective tissue that encapsulates organs and lines movable joints

connective tissue proper connective tissue containing a viscous matrix, fibers, and cells.

cutaneous membrane skin; epithelial tissue made up of a stratified squamous epithelial cells that cover the outside of the body

dense connective tissue connective tissue proper that contains many fibers that provide both elasticity and protection

ectoderm outermost embryonic germ layer from which the epidermis and the nervous tissue derive

elastic cartilage type of cartilage, with elastin as the major protein, characterized by rigid support as well as elasticity

elastic fiber fibrous protein within connective tissue that contains a high percentage of the protein elastin that allows the fibers to stretch and return to original size

endocrine gland groups of cells that release chemical signals into the intercellular fluid to be picked up and transported to their target organs by blood

endoderm innermost embryonic germ layer from which most of the digestive system and lower respiratory system derive

endothelium tissue that lines vessels of the lymphatic and cardiovascular system, made up of a simple squamous epithelium

epithelial membrane epithelium attached to a layer of connective tissue

epithelial tissue type of tissue that serves primarily as a covering or lining of body parts, protecting the body; it also functions in absorption, transport, and secretion

exocrine gland group of epithelial cells that secrete substances through ducts that open to the skin or to internal body surfaces that lead to the exterior of the body

fibroblast most abundant cell type in connective tissue, secretes protein fibers and matrix into the extracellular space

fibrocartilage tough form of cartilage, made of thick bundles of collagen fibers embedded in chondroitin sulfate ground substance

fibrocyte less active form of fibroblast

fluid connective tissue specialized cells that circulate in a watery fluid containing salts, nutrients, and dissolved proteins

gap junction allows cytoplasmic communications to occur between cells

goblet cell unicellular gland found in columnar epithelium that secretes mucous

ground substance fluid or semi-fluid portion of the matrix

histamine chemical compound released by mast cells in response to injury that causes vasodilation and endothelium permeability

histology microscopic study of tissue architecture, organization, and function

holocrine secretion release of a substance caused by the rupture of a gland cell, which becomes part of the secretion

hyaline cartilage most common type of cartilage, smooth and made of short collagen fibers embedded in a chondroitin sulfate ground substance

inflammation response of tissue to injury

lacunae (singular = lacuna) small spaces in bone or cartilage tissue that cells occupy

lamina propria areolar connective tissue underlying a mucous membrane

loose connective tissue (also, areolar tissue) type of connective tissue proper that shows little specialization with cells dispersed in the matrix

matrix extracellular material which is produced by the cells embedded in it, containing ground substance and fibers

merocrine secretion release of a substance from a gland via exocytosis

mesenchymal cell adult stem cell from which most connective tissue cells are derived

mesenchyme embryonic tissue from which connective tissue cells derive

mesoderm middle embryonic germ layer from which connective tissue, muscle tissue, and some epithelial tissue derive

mesothelium simple squamous epithelial tissue which covers the major body cavities and is the epithelial portion of serous membranes

mucous connective tissue specialized loose connective tissue present in the umbilical cord

mucous gland group of cells that secrete mucous, a thick, slippery substance that keeps tissues moist and acts as a lubricant

mucous membrane tissue membrane that is covered by protective mucous and lines tissue exposed to the outside environment

muscle tissue type of tissue that is capable of contracting and generating tension in response to stimulation; produces movement.

myelin layer of lipid inside some neuroglial cells that wraps around the axons of some neurons

myocyte muscle cells

necrosis accidental death of cells and tissues

nervous tissue type of tissue that is capable of sending and receiving impulses through electrochemical signals.

neuroglia supportive neural cells

neuron excitable neural cell that transfer nerve impulses

oligodendrocyte neuroglial cell that produces myelin in the brain

parenchyma functional cells of a gland or organ, in contrast with the supportive or connective tissue of a gland or organ

primary union condition of a wound where the wound edges are close enough to be brought together and fastened if necessary, allowing quicker and more thorough healing

pseudostratified columnar epithelium tissue that consists of a single layer of irregularly shaped and sized cells that give the appearance of multiple layers; found in ducts of certain glands and the upper respiratory tract

reticular fiber fine fibrous protein, made of collagen subunits, which cross-link to form supporting "nets" within connective tissue

reticular lamina matrix containing collagen and elastin secreted by connective tissue; a component of the basement membrane

reticular tissue type of loose connective tissue that provides a supportive framework to soft organs, such as lymphatic tissue, spleen, and the liver

Schwann cell neuroglial cell that produces myelin in the peripheral nervous system

secondary union wound healing facilitated by wound contraction

serous gland group of cells within the serous membrane that secrete a lubricating substance onto the surface

serous membrane type of tissue membrane that lines body cavities and lubricates them with serous fluid

simple columnar epithelium tissue that consists of a single layer of column-like cells; promotes secretion and absorption in tissues and organs

simple cuboidal epithelium tissue that consists of a single layer of cube-shaped cells; promotes secretion and absorption in ducts and tubules

simple squamous epithelium tissue that consists of a single layer of flat scale-like cells; promotes diffusion and filtration across surface

skeletal muscle usually attached to bone, under voluntary control, each cell is a fiber that is multinucleated and striated

smooth muscle under involuntary control, moves internal organs, cells contain a single nucleus, are spindle-shaped, and do not appear striated; each cell is a fiber

stratified columnar epithelium tissue that consists of two or more layers of column-like cells, contains glands and is found in some ducts

stratified cuboidal epithelium tissue that consists of two or more layers of cube-shaped cells, found in some ducts

stratified squamous epithelium tissue that consists of multiple layers of cells with the most apical being flat scale-like cells; protects surfaces from abrasion

striation alignment of parallel actin and myosin filaments which form a banded pattern

supportive connective tissue type of connective tissue that provides strength to the body and protects soft tissue

synovial membrane connective tissue membrane that lines the cavities of freely movable joints, producing synovial fluid for lubrication

tight junction forms an impermeable barrier between cells

tissue group of cells that are similar in form and perform related functions

tissue membrane thin layer or sheet of cells that covers the outside of the body, organs, and internal cavities

totipotent embryonic cells that have the ability to differentiate into any type of cell and organ in the body

transitional epithelium form of stratified epithelium found in the urinary tract, characterized by an apical layer of cells that change shape in response to the presence of urine

vasodilation widening of blood vessels

wound contraction process whereby the borders of a wound are physically drawn together

CHAPTER REVIEW

4.1 Types of Tissues

The human body contains more than 200 types of cells that can all be classified into four types of tissues: epithelial, connective, muscle, and nervous. Epithelial tissues act as coverings controlling the movement of materials across the surface. Connective tissue integrates the various parts of the body and provides support and protection to organs. Muscle tissue allows the body to move. Nervous tissues propagate information.

The study of the shape and arrangement of cells in tissue is called histology. All cells and tissues in the body derive from three germ layers in the embryo: the ectoderm, mesoderm, and endoderm.

Different types of tissues form membranes that enclose organs, provide a friction-free interaction between organs, and keep organs together. Synovial membranes are connective tissue membranes that protect and line the joints. Epithelial membranes are formed from epithelial tissue attached to a layer of connective tissue. There are three types of epithelial membranes: mucous, which contain glands; serous, which secrete fluid; and cutaneous which makes up the skin.

4.2 Epithelial Tissue

In epithelial tissue, cells are closely packed with little or no extracellular matrix except for the basal lamina that separates the epithelium from underlying tissue. The main functions of epithelia are protection from the environment, coverage, secretion and excretion, absorption, and filtration. Cells are bound together by tight junctions that form an impermeable barrier. They can also be connected by gap junctions, which allow free exchange of soluble molecules between cells, and anchoring junctions, which attach cell to cell or cell to matrix. The different types of epithelial tissues are characterized by their cellular shapes and arrangements: squamous, cuboidal, or columnar epithelia. Single cell layers form simple epithelia, whereas stacked cells form stratified epithelia. Very few capillaries penetrate these tissues.

Glands are secretory tissues and organs that are derived from epithelial tissues. Exocrine glands release their products through ducts. Endocrine glands secrete hormones directly into the interstitial fluid and blood stream. Glands are classified both according to the type of secretion and by their structure. Merocrine glands secrete products as they are synthesized. Apocrine glands release secretions by pinching off the apical portion of the cell, whereas holocrine gland cells store their secretions until they rupture and release their contents. In this case, the cell becomes part of the secretion.

4.3 Connective Tissue Supports and Protects

Connective tissue is a heterogeneous tissue with many cell shapes and tissue architecture. Structurally, all connective tissues contain cells that are embedded in an extracellular matrix stabilized by proteins. The chemical nature and physical layout of the extracellular matrix and proteins vary enormously among tissues, reflecting the variety of functions that connective tissue fulfills in the body. Connective tissues separate and cushion organs, protecting them from shifting or traumatic injury. Connect tissues provide support and assist movement, store and transport energy molecules, protect against infections, and contribute to temperature homeostasis.

Many different cells contribute to the formation of connective tissues. They originate in the mesodermal germ layer and differentiate from mesenchyme and hematopoietic tissue in the bone marrow. Fibroblasts are the most abundant and secrete many protein fibers, adipocytes specialize in fat storage, hematopoietic cells from the bone marrow give rise to all the blood cells, chondrocytes form cartilage, and osteocytes form bone. The extracellular matrix contains fluid, proteins, polysaccharide derivatives, and, in the case of bone, mineral crystals. Protein fibers fall into three major groups: collagen fibers that are thick, strong, flexible, and resist stretch; reticular fibers that are thin and form a supportive mesh; and elastin fibers that are thin and elastic.

The major types of connective tissue are connective tissue proper, supportive tissue, and fluid tissue. Loose connective tissue proper includes adipose tissue, areolar tissue, and reticular tissue. These serve to hold organs and other tissues in place and, in the case of adipose tissue, isolate and store energy reserves. The matrix is the most abundant feature for loose tissue although adipose tissue does not have much extracellular matrix. Dense connective tissue proper is richer in fibers and may be regular, with fibers oriented in parallel as in ligaments and tendons, or irregular, with fibers oriented in several directions. Organ capsules (collagenous type) and walls of arteries (elastic type) contain dense irregular connective tissue. Cartilage and bone are supportive tissue. Cartilage contains chondrocytes and is somewhat flexible. Hyaline cartilage is smooth and clear, covers joints, and is found in the growing portion of bones. Fibrocartilage is tough because of extra collagen fibers and forms, among other things, the intervertebral discs. Elastic cartilage can stretch and recoil to its original shape because of its high content of elastic fibers. The matrix contains very few blood vessels. Bones are made of a rigid, mineralized matrix containing calcium salts, crystals, and osteocytes lodged in lacunae. Bone tissue is highly vascularized. Cancellous bone is spongy and less solid than compact bone. Fluid tissue, for example blood and lymph, is characterized by a liquid matrix and no supporting fibers.

4.4 Muscle Tissue and Motion

The three types of muscle cells are skeletal, cardiac, and smooth. Their morphologies match their specific functions in the body. Skeletal muscle is voluntary and responds to conscious stimuli. The cells are striated and multinucleated appearing as long, unbranched cylinders. Cardiac muscle is involuntary and found only in the heart. Each cell is striated with a single nucleus and they attach to one another to form long fibers. Cells are attached to one another at intercalated disks. The cells are interconnected physically and electrochemically to act as a syncytium. Cardiac muscle cells contract autonomously and involuntarily. Smooth muscle is involuntary. Each cell is a spindle-shaped fiber and contains a single nucleus. No striations are evident because the actin and myosin filaments do not align in the cytoplasm.

4.5 Nervous Tissue Mediates Perception and Response

The most prominent cell of the nervous tissue, the neuron, is characterized mainly by its ability to receive stimuli and respond by generating an electrical signal, known as an action potential, which can travel rapidly over great distances in the body. A typical neuron displays a distinctive morphology: a large cell body branches out into short extensions called dendrites, which receive chemical signals from other neurons, and a long tail called an axon, which relays signals away from the cell to other neurons, muscles, or glands. Many axons are wrapped by a myelin sheath, a lipid derivative that acts as an insulator and speeds up the transmission of the action potential. Other cells in the nervous tissue, the neuroglia, include the astrocytes, microglia, oligodendrocytes, and Schwann cells.

4.6 Tissue Injury and Aging

Inflammation is the classic response of the body to injury and follows a common sequence of events. The area is red, feels warm to the touch, swells, and is painful. Injured cells, mast cells, and resident macrophages release chemical signals that cause vasodilation and fluid leakage in the surrounding tissue. The repair phase includes blood clotting, followed by regeneration of tissue as fibroblasts deposit collagen. Some tissues regenerate more readily than others. Epithelial and connective tissues replace damaged or dead cells from a supply of adult stem cells. Muscle and nervous tissues undergo either slow regeneration or do not repair at all.

Age affects all the tissues and organs of the body. Damaged cells do not regenerate as rapidly as in younger people. Perception of sensation and effectiveness of response are lost in the nervous system. Muscles atrophy, and bones lose mass and become brittle. Collagen decreases in some connective tissue, and joints stiffen.

INTERACTIVE LINK QUESTIONS

1. View this slideshow (http://openstaxcollege.org/l/stemcells) to learn more about stem cells. How do somatic stem cells differ from embryonic stem cells?

2. Watch this video (http://openstaxcollege.org/l/etissues) to find out more about the anatomy of epithelial tissues. Where in the body would one find non-keratinizing stratified squamous epithelium?

3. Visit this link (http://openstaxcollege.org/l/10quiz) to test your connective tissue knowledge with this 10-question quiz. Can you name the 10 tissue types shown in the histology slides?

4. Watch this video (http://openstaxcollege.org/l/musctissue) to learn more about muscle tissue. In looking through a microscope how could you distinguish skeletal muscle tissue from smooth muscle?

5. Follow this link (http://openstaxcollege.org/l/nobel) to learn more about nervous tissue. What are the main parts of a nerve cell?

6. Watch this video (http://openstaxcollege.org/l/healinghand) to see a hand heal. Over what period of time do you think these images were taken?

7. Watch this video (http://openstaxcollege.org/l/tumor) to learn more about tumors. What is a tumor?

REVIEW QUESTIONS

8. Which of the following is not a type of tissue?
   a. muscle
   b. nervous
   c. embryonic
   d. epithelial

9. The process by which a less specialized cell matures into a more specialized cell is called _____.
   a. differentiation
   b. maturation
   c. modification
   d. specialization

10. Differentiated cells in a developing embryo derive from _____.
   a. endothelium, mesothelium, and epithelium
   b. ectoderm, mesoderm, and endoderm
   c. connective tissue, epithelial tissue, and muscle tissue
   d. epidermis, mesoderm, and endothelium

11. Which of the following lines the body cavities exposed to the external environment?
   a. mesothelium
   b. lamina propria
   c. mesenteries
   d. mucosa

12. In observing epithelial cells under a microscope, the cells are arranged in a single layer and look tall and narrow, and the nucleus is located close to the basal side of the cell. The specimen is what type of epithelial tissue?
   a. columnar
   b. stratified
   c. squamous
   d. transitional

13. Which of the following is the epithelial tissue that lines the interior of blood vessels?
   a. columnar
   b. pseudostratified
   c. simple squamous
   d. transitional

14. Which type of epithelial tissue specializes in moving particles across its surface and is found in airways and lining of the oviduct?
   a. transitional
   b. stratified columnar
   c. pseudostratified ciliated columnar
   d. stratified squamous

15. The _____ exocrine gland stores its secretion until the glandular cell ruptures, whereas the _____ gland releases its apical region and reforms.
   a. holocrine; apocrine
   b. eccrine; endocrine
   c. apocrine; holocrine
   d. eccrine; apocrine

16. Connective tissue is made of which three essential components?
   a. cells, ground substance, and carbohydrate fibers
   b. cells, ground substance, and protein fibers
   c. collagen, ground substance, and protein fibers
   d. matrix, ground substance, and fluid

17. Under the microscope, a tissue specimen shows cells located in spaces scattered in a transparent background. This is probably _____.
   a. loose connective tissue
   b. a tendon
   c. bone
   d. hyaline cartilage

18. Which connective tissue specializes in storage of fat?
   a. tendon
   b. adipose tissue
   c. reticular tissue
   d. dense connective tissue

19. Ligaments connect bones together and withstand a lot of stress. What type of connective tissue should you expect ligaments to contain?
    a. areolar tissue
    b. adipose tissue
    c. dense regular connective tissue
    d. dense irregular connective tissue

20. In adults, new connective tissue cells originate from the _____.
    a. mesoderm
    b. mesenchyme
    c. ectoderm
    d. endoderm

21. In bone, the main cells are _____.
    a. fibroblasts
    b. chondrocytes
    c. lymphocytes
    d. osteocytes

22. Striations, cylindrical cells, and multiple nuclei are observed in _____.
    a. skeletal muscle only
    b. cardiac muscle only
    c. smooth muscle only
    d. skeletal and cardiac muscles

23. The cells of muscles, myocytes, develop from _____.
    a. myoblasts
    b. endoderm
    c. fibrocytes
    d. chondrocytes

24. Skeletal muscle is composed of very hard working cells. Which organelles do you expect to find in abundance in skeletal muscle cell?
    a. nuclei
    b. striations
    c. golgi bodies
    d. mitochondria

25. The cells responsible for the transmission of the nerve impulse are _____.
    a. neurons
    b. oligodendrocytes
    c. astrocytes
    d. microglia

26. The nerve impulse travels down a(n) _____, away from the cell body.
    a. dendrite
    b. axon
    c. microglia
    d. collagen fiber

27. Which of the following central nervous system cells regulate ions, regulate the uptake and/or breakdown of some neurotransmitters, and contribute to the formation of the blood-brain barrier?
    a. microglia
    b. neuroglia
    c. oligodendrocytes
    d. astrocytes

28. Which of the following processes is not a cardinal sign of inflammation?
    a. redness
    b. heat
    c. fever
    d. swelling

29. When a mast cell reacts to an irritation, which of the following chemicals does it release?
    a. collagen
    b. histamine
    c. hyaluronic acid
    d. meylin

30. Atrophy refers to _____.
    a. loss of elasticity
    b. loss of mass
    c. loss of rigidity
    d. loss of permeability

31. Individuals can slow the rate of aging by modifying all of these lifestyle aspects except for _____.
    a. diet
    b. exercise
    c. genetic factors
    d. stress

CRITICAL THINKING QUESTIONS

32. Identify the four types of tissue in the body, and describe the major functions of each tissue.

33. The zygote is described as totipotent because it ultimately gives rise to all the cells in your body including the highly specialized cells of your nervous system. Describe this transition, discussing the steps and processes that lead to these specialized cells.

34. What is the function of synovial membranes?

35. The structure of a tissue usually is optimized for its function. Describe how the structure of individual cells and tissue arrangement of the intestine lining matches its main function, to absorb nutrients.

36. One of the main functions of connective tissue is to integrate organs and organ systems in the body. Discuss how blood fulfills this role.

37. Why does an injury to cartilage, especially hyaline cartilage, heal much more slowly than a bone fracture?

38. You are watching cells in a dish spontaneously contract. They are all contracting at different rates; some fast, some slow. After a while, several cells link up and they begin contracting in synchrony. Discuss what is going on and what type of cells you are looking at.

39. Why does skeletal muscle look striated?

40. Which morphological adaptations of neurons make them suitable for the transmission of nerve impulse?

41. What are the functions of astrocytes?

42. Why is it important to watch for increased redness, swelling and pain after a cut or abrasion has been cleaned and bandaged?

43. Aspirin is a non-steroidal anti-inflammatory drug (NSAID) that inhibits the formation of blood clots and is taken regularly by individuals with a heart condition. Steroids such as cortisol are used to control some autoimmune diseases and severe arthritis by down-regulating the inflammatory response. After reading the role of inflammation in the body's response to infection, can you predict an undesirable consequence of taking anti-inflammatory drugs on a regular basis?

44. As an individual ages, a constellation of symptoms begins the decline to the point where an individual's functioning is compromised. Identify and discuss two factors that have a role in factors leading to the compromised situation.

45. Discuss changes that occur in cells as a person ages.

5 | THE INTEGUMENTARY SYSTEM

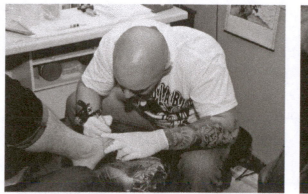
(a)

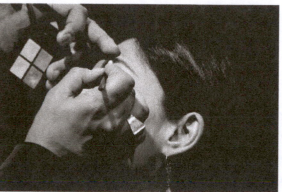
(b)

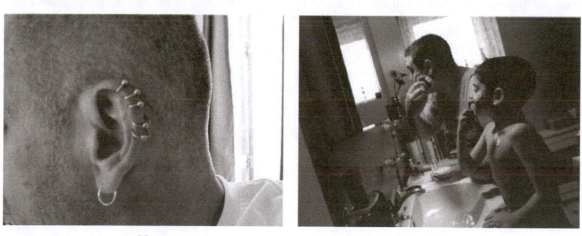
(c)   (d)

Figure 5.1 Your skin is a vital part of your life and appearance (a–d). Some people choose to embellish it with tattoos (a), makeup (b), and even piercings (c). (credit a: Steve Teo; credit b: "spaceodissey"/flickr; credit c: Mark/flickr; credit d: Lisa Schaffer)

Introduction

Chapter Objectives

After studying the chapter, you will be able to:

- Describe the integumentary system and the role it plays in homeostasis
- Describe the layers of the skin and the functions of each layer
- Describe the accessory structures of the skin and the functions of each
- Describe the changes that occur in the integumentary system during the aging process
- Discuss several common diseases, disorders, and injuries that affect the integumentary system
- Explain treatments for some common diseases, disorders, and injuries of the integumentary system

What do you think when you look at your skin in the mirror? Do you think about covering it with makeup, adding a tattoo, or maybe a body piercing? Or do you think about the fact that the skin belongs to one of the body's most essential and dynamic systems: the integumentary system? The integumentary system refers to the skin and its accessory structures, and it is responsible for much more than simply lending to your outward appearance. In the adult human body, the skin makes up about 16 percent of body weight and covers an area of 1.5 to 2 m^2. In fact, the skin and accessory structures are the largest organ system in the human body. As such, the skin protects your inner organs and it is in need of daily care and protection to maintain its health. This chapter will introduce the structure and functions of the integumentary system, as well as some of the diseases, disorders, and injuries that can affect this system.

5.1 | Layers of the Skin

By the end of this section, you will be able to:

- Identify the components of the integumentary system
- Describe the layers of the skin and the functions of each layer
- Identify and describe the hypodermis and deep fascia
- Describe the role of keratinocytes and their life cycle
- Describe the role of melanocytes in skin pigmentation

Although you may not typically think of the skin as an organ, it is in fact made of tissues that work together as a single structure to perform unique and critical functions. The skin and its accessory structures make up the **integumentary system**, which provides the body with overall protection. The skin is made of multiple layers of cells and tissues, which are held to underlying structures by connective tissue (Figure 5.2). The deeper layer of skin is well vascularized (has numerous blood vessels). It also has numerous sensory, and autonomic and sympathetic nerve fibers ensuring communication to and from the brain.

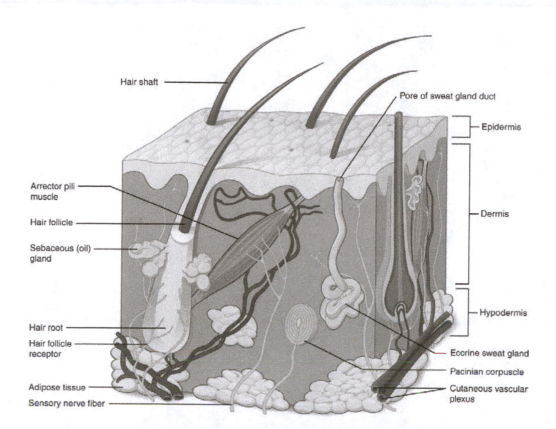

Figure 5.2 Layers of Skin The skin is composed of two main layers: the epidermis, made of closely packed epithelial cells, and the dermis, made of dense, irregular connective tissue that houses blood vessels, hair follicles, sweat glands, and other structures. Beneath the dermis lies the hypodermis, which is composed mainly of loose connective and fatty tissues.

The skin consists of two main layers and a closely associated layer. View this animation (http://openstaxcollege.org/l/layers) to learn more about layers of the skin. What are the basic functions of each of these layers?

The Epidermis

The **epidermis** is composed of keratinized, stratified squamous epithelium. It is made of four or five layers of epithelial cells, depending on its location in the body. It does not have any blood vessels within it (i.e., it is avascular). Skin that has four layers of cells is referred to as "thin skin." From deep to superficial, these layers are the stratum basale, stratum spinosum, stratum granulosum, and stratum corneum. Most of the skin can be classified as thin skin. "Thick skin" is found only on the palms of the hands and the soles of the feet. It has a fifth layer, called the stratum lucidum, located between the stratum corneum and the stratum granulosum (**Figure 5.3**).

(a)

(b)

Figure 5.3 Thin Skin versus Thick Skin These slides show cross-sections of the epidermis and dermis of (a) thin and (b) thick skin. Note the significant difference in the thickness of the epithelial layer of the thick skin. From top, LM × 40, LM × 40. (Micrographs provided by the Regents of University of Michigan Medical School © 2012)

The cells in all of the layers except the stratum basale are called keratinocytes. A **keratinocyte** is a cell that manufactures and stores the protein keratin. **Keratin** is an intracellular fibrous protein that gives hair, nails, and skin their hardness and water-resistant properties. The keratinocytes in the stratum corneum are dead and regularly slough away, being replaced by cells from the deeper layers (Figure 5.4).

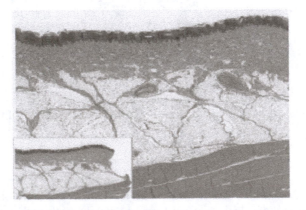

Figure 5.4 Epidermis The epidermis is epithelium composed of multiple layers of cells. The basal layer consists of cuboidal cells, whereas the outer layers are squamous, keratinized cells, so the whole epithelium is often described as being keratinized stratified squamous epithelium. LM × 40. (Micrograph provided by the Regents of University of Michigan Medical School © 2012)

Interactive LINK

View the University of Michigan WebScope at **http://virtualslides.med_umich.edu/Histology/Basic%20Tissues/Epithelium%20and%20CT/106_HISTO_40X.svs/view.apml?** **(http://openstaxcollege.org/l/Epidermis)** to explore the tissue sample in greater detail. If you zoom on the cells at the outermost layer of this section of skin, what do you notice about the cells?

Stratum Basale

The **stratum basale** (also called the stratum germinativum) is the deepest epidermal layer and attaches the epidermis to the basal lamina, below which lie the layers of the dermis. The cells in the stratum basale bond to the dermis via intertwining collagen fibers, referred to as the basement membrane. A finger-like projection, or fold, known as the **dermal papilla** (plural = dermal papillae) is found in the superficial portion of the dermis. Dermal papillae increase the strength of the connection between the epidermis and dermis; the greater the folding, the stronger the connections made (Figure 5.5).

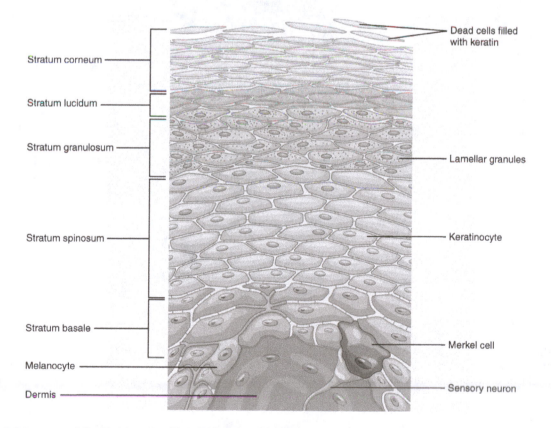

Figure 5.5 Layers of the Epidermis The epidermis of thick skin has five layers: stratum basale, stratum spinosum, stratum granulosum, stratum lucidum, and stratum corneum.

The stratum basale is a single layer of cells primarily made of basal cells. A **basal cell** is a cuboidal-shaped stem cell that is a precursor of the keratinocytes of the epidermis. All of the keratinocytes are produced from this single layer of cells, which are constantly going through mitosis to produce new cells. As new cells are formed, the existing cells are pushed superficially away from the stratum basale. Two other cell types are found dispersed among the basal cells in the stratum basale. The first is a **Merkel cell**, which functions as a receptor and is responsible for stimulating sensory nerves that the brain perceives as touch. These cells are especially abundant on the surfaces of the hands and feet. The second is a **melanocyte**, a cell that produces the pigment melanin. **Melanin** gives hair and skin its color, and also helps protect the living cells of the epidermis from ultraviolet (UV) radiation damage.

In a growing fetus, fingerprints form where the cells of the stratum basale meet the papillae of the underlying dermal layer (papillary layer), resulting in the formation of the ridges on your fingers that you recognize as fingerprints. Fingerprints are unique to each individual and are used for forensic analyses because the patterns do not change with the growth and aging processes.

Stratum Spinosum

As the name suggests, the **stratum spinosum** is spiny in appearance due to the protruding cell processes that join the cells via a structure called a **desmosome**. The desmosomes interlock with each other and strengthen the bond between the cells. It is interesting to note that the "spiny" nature of this layer is an artifact of the staining process. Unstained epidermis samples do not exhibit this characteristic appearance. The stratum spinosum is composed of eight to 10 layers of keratinocytes, formed as a result of cell division in the stratum basale (**Figure 5.6**). Interspersed among the keratinocytes of this layer is a type of dendritic cell called the **Langerhans cell**, which functions as a macrophage by engulfing bacteria, foreign particles, and damaged cells that occur in this layer.

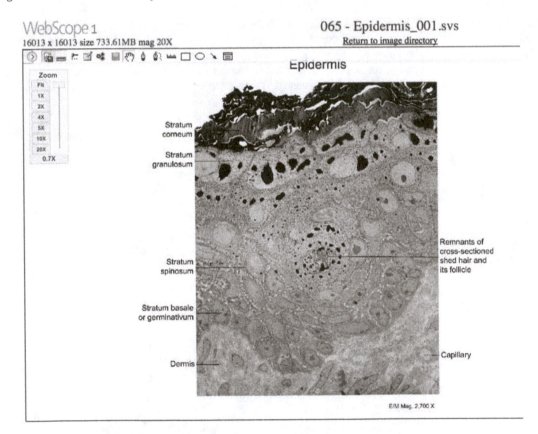

Figure 5.6 Cells of the Epidermis The cells in the different layers of the epidermis originate from basal cells located in the stratum basale, yet the cells of each layer are distinctively different. EM × 2700. (Micrograph provided by the Regents of University of Michigan Medical School © 2012)

Interactive LINK

View the University of Michigan WebScope at http://virtualslides.med.umich.edu/Histology/EMsmallCharts/ 3%20Image%20Scope%20finals/065%20-%20Epidermis_001.svs/view.apml (http://openstaxcollege.org/l/ basal) to explore the tissue sample in greater detail. If you zoom on the cells at the outermost layer of this section of skin, what do you notice about the cells?

The keratinocytes in the stratum spinosum begin the synthesis of keratin and release a water-repelling glycolipid that helps prevent water loss from the body, making the skin relatively waterproof. As new keratinocytes are produced atop the stratum basale, the keratinocytes of the stratum spinosum are pushed into the stratum granulosum.

Stratum Granulosum

The **stratum granulosum** has a grainy appearance due to further changes to the keratinocytes as they are pushed from the stratum spinosum. The cells (three to five layers deep) become flatter, their cell membranes thicken, and they generate large amounts of the proteins keratin, which is fibrous, and **keratohyalin**, which accumulates as lamellar granules within the cells (see Figure 5.5). These two proteins make up the bulk of the keratinocyte mass in the stratum granulosum and give the layer its grainy appearance. The nuclei and other cell organelles disintegrate as the cells die, leaving behind the keratin, keratohyalin, and cell membranes that will form the stratum lucidum, the stratum corneum, and the accessory structures of hair and nails.

Stratum Lucidum

The **stratum lucidum** is a smooth, seemingly translucent layer of the epidermis located just above the stratum granulosum and below the stratum corneum. This thin layer of cells is found only in the thick skin of the palms, soles, and digits. The keratinocytes that compose the stratum lucidum are dead and flattened (see Figure 5.5). These cells are densely packed with **eleiden**, a clear protein rich in lipids, derived from keratohyalin, which gives these cells their transparent (i.e., lucid) appearance and provides a barrier to water.

Stratum Corneum

The **stratum corneum** is the most superficial layer of the epidermis and is the layer exposed to the outside environment (see Figure 5.5). The increased keratinization (also called cornification) of the cells in this layer gives it its name. There are usually 15 to 30 layers of cells in the stratum corneum. This dry, dead layer helps prevent the penetration of microbes and the dehydration of underlying tissues, and provides a mechanical protection against abrasion for the more delicate, underlying layers. Cells in this layer are shed periodically and are replaced by cells pushed up from the stratum granulosum (or stratum lucidum in the case of the palms and soles of feet). The entire layer is replaced during a period of about 4 weeks. Cosmetic procedures, such as microdermabrasion, help remove some of the dry, upper layer and aim to keep the skin looking "fresh" and healthy.

Dermis

The **dermis** might be considered the "core" of the integumentary system (derma- = "skin"), as distinct from the epidermis (epi- = "upon" or "over") and hypodermis (hypo- = "below"). It contains blood and lymph vessels, nerves, and other structures, such as hair follicles and sweat glands. The dermis is made of two layers of connective tissue that compose an interconnected mesh of elastin and collagenous fibers, produced by fibroblasts (Figure 5.7).

Figure 5.7 Layers of the Dermis   This stained slide shows the two components of the dermis—the papillary layer and the reticular layer. Both are made of connective tissue with fibers of collagen extending from one to the other, making the border between the two somewhat indistinct. The dermal papillae extending into the epidermis belong to the papillary layer, whereas the dense collagen fiber bundles below belong to the reticular layer. LM × 10. (credit: modification of work by "kilbad"/Wikimedia Commons)

Papillary Layer

The **papillary layer** is made of loose, areolar connective tissue, which means the collagen and elastin fibers of this layer form a loose mesh. This superficial layer of the dermis projects into the stratum basale of the epidermis to form finger-like dermal papillae (see Figure 5.7). Within the papillary layer are fibroblasts, a small number of fat cells (adipocytes), and an abundance of small blood vessels. In addition, the papillary layer contains phagocytes, defensive cells that help fight bacteria or other infections that have breached the skin. This layer also contains lymphatic capillaries, nerve fibers, and touch receptors called the Meissner corpuscles.

Reticular Layer

Underlying the papillary layer is the much thicker **reticular layer**, composed of dense, irregular connective tissue. This layer is well vascularized and has a rich sensory and sympathetic nerve supply. The reticular layer appears reticulated (net-like) due to a tight meshwork of fibers. **Elastin fibers** provide some elasticity to the skin, enabling movement. Collagen fibers provide structure and tensile strength, with strands of collagen extending into both the papillary layer and the hypodermis. In addition, collagen binds water to keep the skin hydrated. Collagen injections and Retin-A creams help restore skin turgor by either introducing collagen externally or stimulating blood flow and repair of the dermis, respectively.

Hypodermis

The **hypodermis** (also called the subcutaneous layer or superficial fascia) is a layer directly below the dermis and serves to connect the skin to the underlying fascia (fibrous tissue) of the bones and muscles. It is not strictly a part of the skin, although the border between the hypodermis and dermis can be difficult to distinguish. The hypodermis consists of well-vascularized, loose, areolar connective tissue and adipose tissue, which functions as a mode of fat storage and provides insulation and cushioning for the integument.

Everyday CONNECTION

Lipid Storage

The hypodermis is home to most of the fat that concerns people when they are trying to keep their weight under control. Adipose tissue present in the hypodermis consists of fat-storing cells called adipocytes. This stored fat can serve as an energy reserve, insulate the body to prevent heat loss, and act as a cushion to protect underlying structures from trauma.

Where the fat is deposited and accumulates within the hypodermis depends on hormones (testosterone, estrogen, insulin, glucagon, leptin, and others), as well as genetic factors. Fat distribution changes as our bodies mature and age. Men tend to accumulate fat in different areas (neck, arms, lower back, and abdomen) than do women (breasts, hips, thighs, and buttocks). The body mass index (BMI) is often used as a measure of fat, although this measure is, in fact, derived from a mathematical formula that compares body weight (mass) to height. Therefore, its accuracy as a health indicator can be called into question in individuals who are extremely physically fit.

In many animals, there is a pattern of storing excess calories as fat to be used in times when food is not readily available. In much of the developed world, insufficient exercise coupled with the ready availability and consumption of high-calorie foods have resulted in unwanted accumulations of adipose tissue in many people. Although periodic accumulation of excess fat may have provided an evolutionary advantage to our ancestors, who experienced unpredictable bouts of famine, it is now becoming chronic and considered a major health threat. Recent studies indicate that a distressing percentage of our population is overweight and/or clinically obese. Not only is this a problem for the individuals affected, but it also has a severe impact on our healthcare system. Changes in lifestyle, specifically in diet and exercise, are the best ways to control body fat accumulation, especially when it reaches levels that increase the risk of heart disease and diabetes.

Pigmentation

The color of skin is influenced by a number of pigments, including melanin, carotene, and hemoglobin. Recall that melanin is produced by cells called melanocytes, which are found scattered throughout the stratum basale of the epidermis. The melanin is transferred into the keratinocytes via a cellular vesicle called a **melanosome** (Figure 5.8).

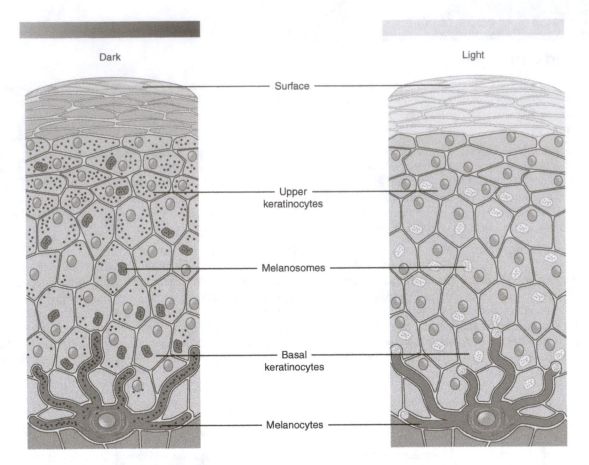

Figure 5.8 Skin Pigmentation The relative coloration of the skin depends of the amount of melanin produced by melanocytes in the stratum basale and taken up by keratinocytes.

Melanin occurs in two primary forms. Eumelanin exists as black and brown, whereas pheomelanin provides a red color. Dark-skinned individuals produce more melanin than those with pale skin. Exposure to the UV rays of the sun or a tanning salon causes melanin to be manufactured and built up in keratinocytes, as sun exposure stimulates keratinocytes to secrete chemicals that stimulate melanocytes. The accumulation of melanin in keratinocytes results in the darkening of the skin, or a tan. This increased melanin accumulation protects the DNA of epidermal cells from UV ray damage and the breakdown of folic acid, a nutrient necessary for our health and well-being. In contrast, too much melanin can interfere with the production of vitamin D, an important nutrient involved in calcium absorption. Thus, the amount of melanin present in our skin is dependent on a balance between available sunlight and folic acid destruction, and protection from UV radiation and vitamin D production.

It requires about 10 days after initial sun exposure for melanin synthesis to peak, which is why pale-skinned individuals tend to suffer sunburns of the epidermis initially. Dark-skinned individuals can also get sunburns, but are more protected than are pale-skinned individuals. Melanosomes are temporary structures that are eventually destroyed by fusion with lysosomes; this fact, along with melanin-filled keratinocytes in the stratum corneum sloughing off, makes tanning impermanent.

Too much sun exposure can eventually lead to wrinkling due to the destruction of the cellular structure of the skin, and in severe cases, can cause sufficient DNA damage to result in skin cancer. When there is an irregular accumulation of melanocytes in the skin, freckles appear. Moles are larger masses of melanocytes, and although most are benign, they should be monitored for changes that might indicate the presence of cancer (**Figure 5.9**).

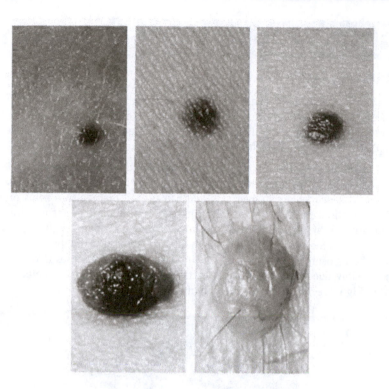

Figure 5.9 Moles   Moles range from benign accumulations of melanocytes to melanomas. These structures populate the landscape of our skin. (credit: the National Cancer Institute)

Disorders OF THE...

Integumentary System

The first thing a clinician sees is the skin, and so the examination of the skin should be part of any thorough physical examination. Most skin disorders are relatively benign, but a few, including melanomas, can be fatal if untreated. A couple of the more noticeable disorders, albinism and vitiligo, affect the appearance of the skin and its accessory organs. Although neither is fatal, it would be hard to claim that they are benign, at least to the individuals so afflicted.

Albinism is a genetic disorder that affects (completely or partially) the coloring of skin, hair, and eyes. The defect is primarily due to the inability of melanocytes to produce melanin. Individuals with albinism tend to appear white or very pale due to the lack of melanin in their skin and hair. Recall that melanin helps protect the skin from the harmful effects of UV radiation. Individuals with albinism tend to need more protection from UV radiation, as they are more prone to sunburns and skin cancer. They also tend to be more sensitive to light and have vision problems due to the lack of pigmentation on the retinal wall. Treatment of this disorder usually involves addressing the symptoms, such as limiting UV light exposure to the skin and eyes. In **vitiligo**, the melanocytes in certain areas lose their ability to produce melanin, possibly due to an autoimmune reaction. This leads to a loss of color in patches (Figure 5.10). Neither albinism nor vitiligo directly affects the lifespan of an individual.

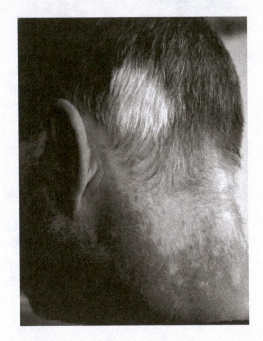

Figure 5.10 Vitiligo Individuals with vitiligo experience depigmentation that results in lighter colored patches of skin. The condition is especially noticeable on darker skin. (credit: Klaus D. Peter)

Other changes in the appearance of skin coloration can be indicative of diseases associated with other body systems. Liver disease or liver cancer can cause the accumulation of bile and the yellow pigment bilirubin, leading to the skin appearing yellow or jaundiced (*jaune* is the French word for "yellow"). Tumors of the pituitary gland can result in the secretion of large amounts of melanocyte-stimulating hormone (MSH), which results in a darkening of the skin. Similarly, Addison's disease can stimulate the release of excess amounts of adrenocorticotropic hormone (ACTH), which can give the skin a deep bronze color. A sudden drop in oxygenation can affect skin color, causing the skin to initially turn ashen (white). With a prolonged reduction in oxygen levels, dark red deoxyhemoglobin becomes dominant in the blood, making the skin appear blue, a condition referred to as cyanosis (*kyanos* is the Greek word for "blue"). This happens when the oxygen supply is restricted, as when someone is experiencing difficulty in breathing because of asthma or a heart attack. However, in these cases the effect on skin color has nothing do with the skin's pigmentation.

Interactive LINK

This ABC video follows the story of a pair of fraternal African-American twins, one of whom is albino. Watch this video (http://openstaxcollege.org/l/albino) to learn about the challenges these children and their family face. Which ethnicities do you think are exempt from the possibility of albinism?

5.2 | Accessory Structures of the Skin

By the end of this section, you will be able to:

- Identify the accessory structures of the skin
- Describe the structure and function of hair and nails
- Describe the structure and function of sweat glands and sebaceous glands

Accessory structures of the skin include hair, nails, sweat glands, and sebaceous glands. These structures embryologically originate from the epidermis and can extend down through the dermis into the hypodermis.

Hair

Hair is a keratinous filament growing out of the epidermis. It is primarily made of dead, keratinized cells. Strands of hair originate in an epidermal penetration of the dermis called the **hair follicle**. The **hair shaft** is the part of the hair not anchored to the follicle, and much of this is exposed at the skin's surface. The rest of the hair, which is anchored in the follicle, lies below the surface of the skin and is referred to as the **hair root**. The hair root ends deep in the dermis at the **hair bulb**, and includes a layer of mitotically active basal cells called the **hair matrix**. The hair bulb surrounds the **hair papilla**, which is made of connective tissue and contains blood capillaries and nerve endings from the dermis (Figure 5.11).

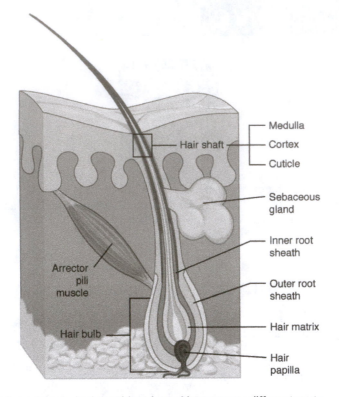

Medulla
Cortex
Cuticle

Sebaceous gland

Inner root sheath

Outer root sheath

Hair matrix

Hair papilla

Hair shaft

Arrector pili muscle

Hair bulb

Figure 5.11 Hair Hair follicles originate in the epidermis and have many different parts.

Just as the basal layer of the epidermis forms the layers of epidermis that get pushed to the surface as the dead skin on the surface sheds, the basal cells of the hair bulb divide and push cells outward in the hair root and shaft as the hair grows. The **medulla** forms the central core of the hair, which is surrounded by the **cortex**, a layer of compressed, keratinized cells that is covered by an outer layer of very hard, keratinized cells known as the **cuticle**. These layers are depicted in a longitudinal cross-section of the hair follicle (Figure 5.12), although not all hair has a medullary layer. Hair texture (straight, curly) is determined by the shape and structure of the cortex, and to the extent that it is present, the medulla. The shape and structure of these layers are, in turn, determined by the shape of the hair follicle. Hair growth begins with the production of keratinocytes by the basal cells of the hair bulb. As new cells are deposited at the hair bulb, the hair shaft is pushed through the follicle toward the surface. Keratinization is completed as the cells are pushed to the skin surface to form the shaft of hair that is externally visible. The external hair is completely dead and composed entirely of keratin. For this reason, our hair does not have sensation. Furthermore, you can cut your hair or shave without damaging the hair structure because the cut is superficial. Most chemical hair removers also act superficially; however, electrolysis and yanking both attempt to destroy the hair bulb so hair cannot grow.

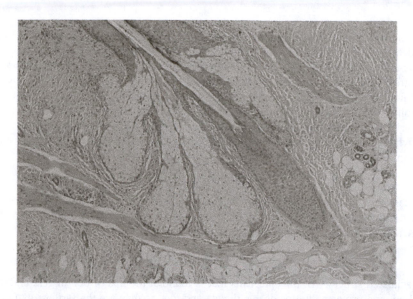

Figure 5.12 Hair Follicle The slide shows a cross-section of a hair follicle. Basal cells of the hair matrix in the center differentiate into cells of the inner root sheath. Basal cells at the base of the hair root form the outer root sheath. LM × 4. (credit: modification of work by "kilbad"/Wikimedia Commons)

The wall of the hair follicle is made of three concentric layers of cells. The cells of the **internal root sheath** surround the root of the growing hair and extend just up to the hair shaft. They are derived from the basal cells of the hair matrix. The **external root sheath**, which is an extension of the epidermis, encloses the hair root. It is made of basal cells at the base of the hair root and tends to be more keratinous in the upper regions. The **glassy membrane** is a thick, clear connective tissue sheath covering the hair root, connecting it to the tissue of the dermis.

The hair follicle is made of multiple layers of cells that form from basal cells in the hair matrix and the hair root. Cells of the hair matrix divide and differentiate to form the layers of the hair. Watch this video (http://openstaxcollege.org/l/follicle) to learn more about hair follicles.

Hair serves a variety of functions, including protection, sensory input, thermoregulation, and communication. For example, hair on the head protects the skull from the sun. The hair in the nose and ears, and around the eyes (eyelashes) defends the body by trapping and excluding dust particles that may contain allergens and microbes. Hair of the eyebrows prevents sweat and other particles from dripping into and bothering the eyes. Hair also has a sensory function due to sensory innervation by a hair root plexus surrounding the base of each hair follicle. Hair is extremely sensitive to air movement or other disturbances in the environment, much more so than the skin surface. This feature is also useful for the detection of the presence of insects or other potentially damaging substances on the skin surface. Each hair root is connected to a smooth muscle called the **arrector pili** that contracts in response to nerve signals from the sympathetic nervous system, making the external hair shaft "stand up." The primary purpose for this is to trap a layer of air to add insulation. This is visible in humans as goose bumps and even more obvious in animals, such as when a frightened cat raises its fur. Of course, this is much more obvious in organisms with a heavier coat than most humans, such as dogs and cats.

Hair Growth

Hair grows and is eventually shed and replaced by new hair. This occurs in three phases. The first is the **anagen** phase, during which cells divide rapidly at the root of the hair, pushing the hair shaft up and out. The length of this phase is measured in years, typically from 2 to 7 years. The **catagen** phase lasts only 2 to 3 weeks, and marks a transition from the hair follicle's active growth. Finally, during the **telogen** phase, the hair follicle is at rest and no new growth occurs. At the end of this phase, which lasts about 2 to 4 months, another anagen phase begins. The basal cells in the hair matrix then produce a new hair follicle, which pushes the old hair out as the growth cycle repeats itself. Hair typically grows at the rate of 0.3 mm per day during the anagen phase. On average, 50 hairs are lost and replaced per day. Hair loss occurs if there is more hair shed than what is replaced and can happen due to hormonal or dietary changes. Hair loss can also result from the aging process, or the influence of hormones.

Hair Color

Similar to the skin, hair gets its color from the pigment melanin, produced by melanocytes in the hair papilla. Different hair color results from differences in the type of melanin, which is genetically determined. As a person ages, the melanin production decreases, and hair tends to lose its color and becomes gray and/or white.

Nails

The nail bed is a specialized structure of the epidermis that is found at the tips of our fingers and toes. The **nail body** is formed on the **nail bed**, and protects the tips of our fingers and toes as they are the farthest extremities and the parts of the body that experience the maximum mechanical stress (**Figure 5.13**). In addition, the nail body forms a back-support for picking up small objects with the fingers. The nail body is composed of densely packed dead keratinocytes. The epidermis in this part of the body has evolved a specialized structure upon which nails can form. The nail body forms at the **nail root**, which has a matrix of proliferating cells from the stratum basale that enables the nail to grow continuously. The lateral **nail fold** overlaps the nail on the sides, helping to anchor the nail body. The nail fold that meets the proximal end of the nail body forms the **nail cuticle**, also called the **eponychium**. The nail bed is rich in blood vessels, making it appear pink, except at the base, where a thick layer of epithelium over the nail matrix forms a crescent-shaped region called the **lunula** (the "little moon"). The area beneath the free edge of the nail, furthest from the cuticle, is called the **hyponychium**. It consists of a thickened layer of stratum corneum.

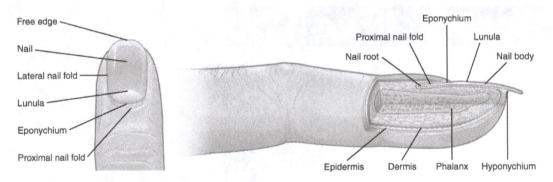

Figure 5.13 Nails The nail is an accessory structure of the integumentary system.

Nails are accessory structures of the integumentary system. Visit this link (http://openstaxcollege.org/l/nails) to learn more about the origin and growth of fingernails.

Sweat Glands

When the body becomes warm, **sudoriferous glands** produce sweat to cool the body. Sweat glands develop from epidermal projections into the dermis and are classified as merocrine glands; that is, the secretions are excreted by exocytosis through a duct without affecting the cells of the gland. There are two types of sweat glands, each secreting slightly different products.

An **eccrine sweat gland** is type of gland that produces a hypotonic sweat for thermoregulation. These glands are found all over the skin's surface, but are especially abundant on the palms of the hand, the soles of the feet, and the forehead (Figure 5.14). They are coiled glands lying deep in the dermis, with the duct rising up to a pore on the skin surface, where the sweat is released. This type of sweat, released by exocytosis, is hypotonic and composed mostly of water, with some salt, antibodies, traces of metabolic waste, and dermicidin, an antimicrobial peptide. Eccrine glands are a primary component of thermoregulation in humans and thus help to maintain homeostasis.

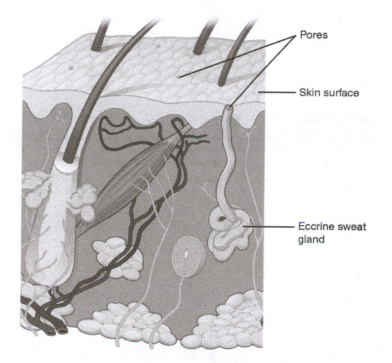

Figure 5.14 Eccrine Gland   Eccrine glands are coiled glands in the dermis that release sweat that is mostly water.

An **apocrine sweat gland** is usually associated with hair follicles in densely hairy areas, such as armpits and genital regions. Apocrine sweat glands are larger than eccrine sweat glands and lie deeper in the dermis, sometimes even reaching the hypodermis, with the duct normally emptying into the hair follicle. In addition to water and salts, apocrine sweat includes organic compounds that make the sweat thicker and subject to bacterial decomposition and subsequent smell. The release of this sweat is under both nervous and hormonal control, and plays a role in the poorly understood human pheromone response. Most commercial antiperspirants use an aluminum-based compound as their primary active ingredient to stop sweat. When the antiperspirant enters the sweat gland duct, the aluminum-based compounds precipitate due to a change in pH and form a physical block in the duct, which prevents sweat from coming out of the pore.

Interactive LINK

Sweating regulates body temperature. The composition of the sweat determines whether body odor is a byproduct of sweating. Visit this link (http://openstaxcollege.org/l/sweating) to learn more about sweating and body odor.

Sebaceous Glands

A **sebaceous gland** is a type of oil gland that is found all over the body and helps to lubricate and waterproof the skin and hair. Most sebaceous glands are associated with hair follicles. They generate and excrete **sebum**, a mixture of lipids, onto the skin surface, thereby naturally lubricating the dry and dead layer of keratinized cells of the stratum corneum, keeping it pliable. The fatty acids of sebum also have antibacterial properties, and prevent water loss from the skin in low-humidity environments. The secretion of sebum is stimulated by hormones, many of which do not become active until puberty. Thus, sebaceous glands are relatively inactive during childhood.

5.3 | Functions of the Integumentary System

By the end of this section, you will be able to:

- Describe the different functions of the skin and the structures that enable them
- Explain how the skin helps maintain body temperature

The skin and accessory structures perform a variety of essential functions, such as protecting the body from invasion by microorganisms, chemicals, and other environmental factors; preventing dehydration; acting as a sensory organ; modulating body temperature and electrolyte balance; and synthesizing vitamin D. The underlying hypodermis has important roles in storing fats, forming a "cushion" over underlying structures, and providing insulation from cold temperatures.

Protection

The skin protects the rest of the body from the basic elements of nature such as wind, water, and UV sunlight. It acts as a protective barrier against water loss, due to the presence of layers of keratin and glycolipids in the stratum corneum. It also is the first line of defense against abrasive activity due to contact with grit, microbes, or harmful chemicals. Sweat excreted from sweat glands deters microbes from over-colonizing the skin surface by generating dermicidin, which has antibiotic properties.

Everyday CONNECTION

Tattoos and Piercings

The word "armor" evokes several images. You might think of a Roman centurion or a medieval knight in a suit of armor. The skin, in its own way, functions as a form of armor—body armor. It provides a barrier between your vital, life-sustaining organs and the influence of outside elements that could potentially damage them.

For any form of armor, a breach in the protective barrier poses a danger. The skin can be breached when a child skins a knee or an adult has blood drawn—one is accidental and the other medically necessary. However, you also breach this barrier when you choose to "accessorize" your skin with a tattoo or body piercing. Because the needles involved in producing body art and piercings must penetrate the skin, there are dangers associated with the practice. These include allergic reactions; skin infections; blood-borne diseases, such as tetanus, hepatitis C, and hepatitis D; and the growth of scar tissue. Despite the risk, the practice of piercing the skin for decorative purposes has become increasingly popular. According to the American Academy of Dermatology, 24 percent of people from ages 18 to 50 have a tattoo.

Interactive LINK

Tattooing has a long history, dating back thousands of years ago. The dyes used in tattooing typically derive from metals. A person with tattoos should be cautious when having a magnetic resonance imaging (MRI) scan because an MRI machine uses powerful magnets to create images of the soft tissues of the body, which could react with the metals contained in the tattoo dyes. Watch this **video (http://openstaxcollege.org/l/tattoo)** to learn more about tattooing.

Sensory Function

The fact that you can feel an ant crawling on your skin, allowing you to flick it off before it bites, is because the skin, and especially the hairs projecting from hair follicles in the skin, can sense changes in the environment. The hair root plexus surrounding the base of the hair follicle senses a disturbance, and then transmits the information to the central nervous system (brain and spinal cord), which can then respond by activating the skeletal muscles of your eyes to see the ant and the skeletal muscles of the body to act against the ant.

The skin acts as a sense organ because the epidermis, dermis, and the hypodermis contain specialized sensory nerve structures that detect touch, surface temperature, and pain. These receptors are more concentrated on the tips of the fingers, which are most sensitive to touch, especially the **Meissner corpuscle** (tactile corpuscle) (Figure 5.15), which responds to light touch, and the **Pacinian corpuscle** (lamellated corpuscle), which responds to vibration. Merkel cells, seen scattered in the stratum basale, are also touch receptors. In addition to these specialized receptors, there are sensory nerves connected to each hair follicle, pain and temperature receptors scattered throughout the skin, and motor nerves innervate the arrector pili muscles and glands. This rich innervation helps us sense our environment and react accordingly.

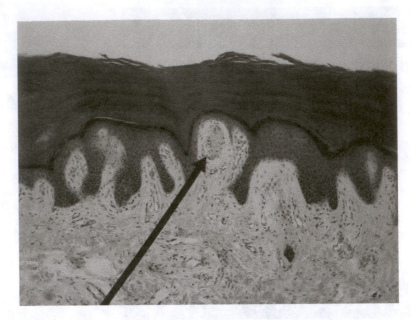

Figure 5.15 Light Micrograph of a Meissner Corpuscle In this micrograph of a skin cross-section, you can see a Meissner corpuscle (arrow), a type of touch receptor located in a dermal papilla adjacent to the basement membrane and stratum basale of the overlying epidermis. LM × 100. (credit: "Wbensmith"/Wikimedia Commons)

Thermoregulation

The integumentary system helps regulate body temperature through its tight association with the sympathetic nervous system, the division of the nervous system involved in our fight-or-flight responses. The sympathetic nervous system is continuously monitoring body temperature and initiating appropriate motor responses. Recall that sweat glands, accessory structures to the skin, secrete water, salt, and other substances to cool the body when it becomes warm. Even when the body does not appear to be noticeably sweating, approximately 500 mL of sweat (insensible perspiration) are secreted a day. If the body becomes excessively warm due to high temperatures, vigorous activity (**Figure 5.16ac**), or a combination of the two, sweat glands will be stimulated by the sympathetic nervous system to produce large amounts of sweat, as much as 0.7 to 1.5 L per hour for an active person. When the sweat evaporates from the skin surface, the body is cooled as body heat is dissipated.

In addition to sweating, arterioles in the dermis dilate so that excess heat carried by the blood can dissipate through the skin and into the surrounding environment (**Figure 5.16b**). This accounts for the skin redness that many people experience when exercising.

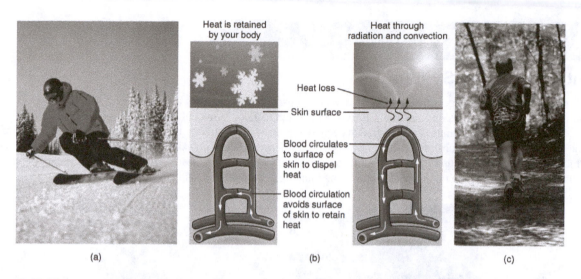

Figure 5.16 Thermoregulation During strenuous physical activities, such as skiing (a) or running (c), the dermal blood vessels dilate and sweat secretion increases (b). These mechanisms prevent the body from overheating. In contrast, the dermal blood vessels constrict to minimize heat loss in response to low temperatures (b). (credit a: "Trysil"/flickr; credit c: Ralph Daily)

When body temperatures drop, the arterioles constrict to minimize heat loss, particularly in the ends of the digits and tip of the nose. This reduced circulation can result in the skin taking on a whitish hue. Although the temperature of the skin drops as a result, passive heat loss is prevented, and internal organs and structures remain warm. If the temperature of the skin drops too much (such as environmental temperatures below freezing), the conservation of body core heat can result in the skin actually freezing, a condition called frostbite.

Integumentary System

All systems in the body accumulate subtle and some not-so-subtle changes as a person ages. Among these changes are reductions in cell division, metabolic activity, blood circulation, hormonal levels, and muscle strength (Figure 5.17). In the skin, these changes are reflected in decreased mitosis in the stratum basale, leading to a thinner epidermis. The dermis, which is responsible for the elasticity and resilience of the skin, exhibits a reduced ability to regenerate, which leads to slower wound healing. The hypodermis, with its fat stores, loses structure due to the reduction and redistribution of fat, which in turn contributes to the thinning and sagging of skin.

Figure 5.17 Aging Generally, skin, especially on the face and hands, starts to display the first noticeable signs of aging, as it loses its elasticity over time. (credit: Janet Ramsden)

The accessory structures also have lowered activity, generating thinner hair and nails, and reduced amounts of sebum and sweat. A reduced sweating ability can cause some elderly to be intolerant to extreme heat. Other cells in the skin, such as melanocytes and dendritic cells, also become less active, leading to a paler skin tone and lowered immunity. Wrinkling of the skin occurs due to breakdown of its structure, which results from decreased collagen and elastin production in the dermis, weakening of muscles lying under the skin, and the inability of the skin to retain adequate moisture.

Many anti-aging products can be found in stores today. In general, these products try to rehydrate the skin and thereby fill out the wrinkles, and some stimulate skin growth using hormones and growth factors. Additionally, invasive techniques include collagen injections to plump the tissue and injections of BOTOX® (the name brand of the botulinum neurotoxin) that paralyze the muscles that crease the skin and cause wrinkling.

Vitamin D Synthesis

The epidermal layer of human skin synthesizes **vitamin D** when exposed to UV radiation. In the presence of sunlight, a form of vitamin D_3 called cholecalciferol is synthesized from a derivative of the steroid cholesterol in the skin. The liver converts cholecalciferol to calcidiol, which is then converted to calcitriol (the active chemical form of the vitamin) in the kidneys. Vitamin D is essential for normal absorption of calcium and phosphorous, which are required for healthy bones. The absence of sun exposure can lead to a lack of vitamin D in the body, leading to a condition called **rickets**, a painful condition in children where the bones are misshapen due to a lack of calcium, causing bowleggedness. Elderly individuals who suffer from vitamin D deficiency can develop a condition called osteomalacia, a softening of the bones. In present day society, vitamin D is added as a supplement to many foods, including milk and orange juice, compensating for the need for sun exposure.

In addition to its essential role in bone health, vitamin D is essential for general immunity against bacterial, viral, and fungal infections. Recent studies are also finding a link between insufficient vitamin D and cancer.

5.4 | Diseases, Disorders, and Injuries of the Integumentary System

By the end of this section, you will be able to:

- Describe several different diseases and disorders of the skin
- Describe the effect of injury to the skin and the process of healing

The integumentary system is susceptible to a variety of diseases, disorders, and injuries. These range from annoying but relatively benign bacterial or fungal infections that are categorized as disorders, to skin cancer and severe burns, which can be fatal. In this section, you will learn several of the most common skin conditions.

Diseases

One of the most talked about diseases is skin cancer. Cancer is a broad term that describes diseases caused by abnormal cells in the body dividing uncontrollably. Most cancers are identified by the organ or tissue in which the cancer originates. One common form of cancer is skin cancer. The Skin Cancer Foundation reports that one in five Americans will experience some type of skin cancer in their lifetime. The degradation of the ozone layer in the atmosphere and the resulting increase in exposure to UV radiation has contributed to its rise. Overexposure to UV radiation damages DNA, which can lead to the formation of cancerous lesions. Although melanin offers some protection against DNA damage from the sun, often it is not enough. The fact that cancers can also occur on areas of the body that are normally not exposed to UV radiation suggests that there are additional factors that can lead to cancerous lesions.

In general, cancers result from an accumulation of DNA mutations. These mutations can result in cell populations that do not die when they should and uncontrolled cell proliferation that leads to tumors. Although many tumors are benign (harmless), some produce cells that can mobilize and establish tumors in other organs of the body; this process is referred to as **metastasis**. Cancers are characterized by their ability to metastasize.

Basal Cell Carcinoma

Basal cell carcinoma is a form of cancer that affects the mitotically active stem cells in the stratum basale of the epidermis. It is the most common of all cancers that occur in the United States and is frequently found on the head, neck, arms, and back, which are areas that are most susceptible to long-term sun exposure. Although UV rays are the main culprit, exposure to other agents, such as radiation and arsenic, can also lead to this type of cancer. Wounds on the skin due to open sores, tattoos, burns, etc. may be predisposing factors as well. Basal cell carcinomas start in the stratum basale and usually spread along this boundary. At some point, they begin to grow toward the surface and become an uneven patch, bump, growth, or scar on the skin surface (Figure 5.18). Like most cancers, basal cell carcinomas respond best to treatment when caught early. Treatment options include surgery, freezing (cryosurgery), and topical ointments (Mayo Clinic 2012).

Figure 5.18 Basal Cell Carcinoma   Basal cell carcinoma can take several different forms. Similar to other forms of skin cancer, it is readily cured if caught early and treated. (credit: John Hendrix, MD)

Squamous Cell Carcinoma

Squamous cell carcinoma is a cancer that affects the keratinocytes of the stratum spinosum and presents as lesions commonly found on the scalp, ears, and hands (Figure 5.19). It is the second most common skin cancer. The American Cancer Society reports that two of 10 skin cancers are squamous cell carcinomas, and it is more aggressive than basal cell carcinoma. If not removed, these carcinomas can metastasize. Surgery and radiation are used to cure squamous cell carcinoma.

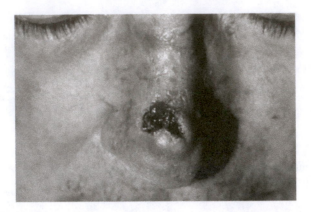

Figure 5.19 Squamous Cell Carcinoma   Squamous cell carcinoma presents here as a lesion on an individual's nose. (credit: the National Cancer Institute)

Melanoma

A **melanoma** is a cancer characterized by the uncontrolled growth of melanocytes, the pigment-producing cells in the epidermis. Typically, a melanoma develops from a mole. It is the most fatal of all skin cancers, as it is highly metastatic and can be difficult to detect before it has spread to other organs. Melanomas usually appear as asymmetrical brown and black patches with uneven borders and a raised surface (Figure 5.20). Treatment typically involves surgical excision and immunotherapy.

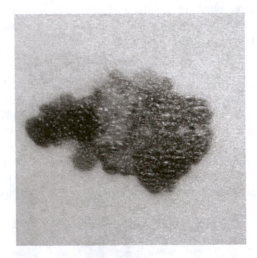

Figure 5.20 Melanoma   Melanomas typically present as large brown or black patches with uneven borders and a raised surface. (credit: the National Cancer Institute)

Doctors often give their patients the following ABCDE mnemonic to help with the diagnosis of early-stage melanoma. If you observe a mole on your body displaying these signs, consult a doctor.

- **A**symmetry – the two sides are not symmetrical
- **B**orders – the edges are irregular in shape
- **C**olor – the color is varied shades of brown or black
- **D**iameter – it is larger than 6 mm (0.24 in)
- **E**volving – its shape has changed

Some specialists cite the following additional signs for the most serious form, nodular melanoma:

- Elevated – it is raised on the skin surface
- Firm – it feels hard to the touch
- Growing – it is getting larger

Skin Disorders

Two common skin disorders are eczema and acne. Eczema is an inflammatory condition and occurs in individuals of all ages. Acne involves the clogging of pores, which can lead to infection and inflammation, and is often seen in adolescents. Other disorders, not discussed here, include seborrheic dermatitis (on the scalp), psoriasis, cold sores, impetigo, scabies, hives, and warts.

Eczema

Eczema is an allergic reaction that manifests as dry, itchy patches of skin that resemble rashes (Figure 5.21). It may be accompanied by swelling of the skin, flaking, and in severe cases, bleeding. Many who suffer from eczema have antibodies against dust mites in their blood, but the link between eczema and allergy to dust mites has not been proven. Symptoms are usually managed with moisturizers, corticosteroid creams, and immunosuppressants.

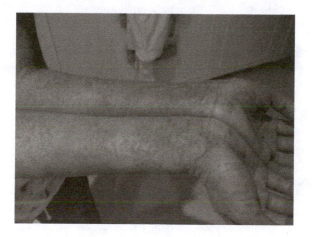

Figure 5.21 Eczema Eczema is a common skin disorder that presents as a red, flaky rash. (credit: "Jambula"/Wikimedia Commons)

Acne

Acne is a skin disturbance that typically occurs on areas of the skin that are rich in sebaceous glands (face and back). It is most common along with the onset of puberty due to associated hormonal changes, but can also occur in infants and continue into adulthood. Hormones, such as androgens, stimulate the release of sebum. An overproduction and accumulation of sebum along with keratin can block hair follicles. This plug is initially white. The sebum, when oxidized by exposure to air, turns black. Acne results from infection by acne-causing bacteria (*Propionibacterium* and *Staphylococcus*), which can lead to redness and potential scarring due to the natural wound healing process (Figure 5.22).

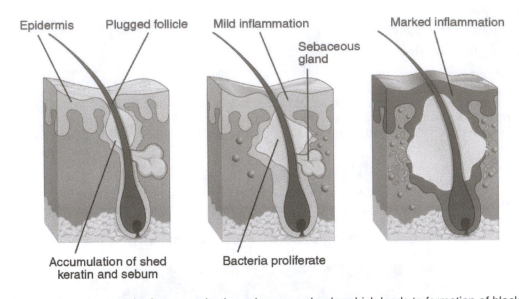

Figure 5.22 Acne Acne is a result of over-productive sebaceous glands, which leads to formation of blackheads and inflammation of the skin.

Dermatologist

Have you ever had a skin rash that did not respond to over-the-counter creams, or a mole that you were concerned about? Dermatologists help patients with these types of problems and more, on a daily basis. Dermatologists are medical doctors who specialize in diagnosing and treating skin disorders. Like all medical doctors, dermatologists earn a medical degree and then complete several years of residency training. In addition, dermatologists may then participate in a dermatology fellowship or complete additional, specialized training in a dermatology practice. If practicing in the United States, dermatologists must pass the United States Medical Licensing Exam (USMLE), become licensed in their state of practice, and be certified by the American Board of Dermatology.

Most dermatologists work in a medical office or private-practice setting. They diagnose skin conditions and rashes, prescribe oral and topical medications to treat skin conditions, and may perform simple procedures, such as mole or wart removal. In addition, they may refer patients to an oncologist if skin cancer that has metastasized is suspected. Recently, cosmetic procedures have also become a prominent part of dermatology. Botox injections, laser treatments, and collagen and dermal filler injections are popular among patients, hoping to reduce the appearance of skin aging.

Dermatology is a competitive specialty in medicine. Limited openings in dermatology residency programs mean that many medical students compete for a few select spots. Dermatology is an appealing specialty to many prospective doctors, because unlike emergency room physicians or surgeons, dermatologists generally do not have to work excessive hours or be "on-call" weekends and holidays. Moreover, the popularity of cosmetic dermatology has made it a growing field with many lucrative opportunities. It is not unusual for dermatology clinics to market themselves exclusively as cosmetic dermatology centers, and for dermatologists to specialize exclusively in these procedures.

Consider visiting a dermatologist to talk about why he or she entered the field and what the field of dermatology is like. Visit this site (http://www.Diplomaguide.com) for additional information.

Injuries

Because the skin is the part of our bodies that meets the world most directly, it is especially vulnerable to injury. Injuries include burns and wounds, as well as scars and calluses. They can be caused by sharp objects, heat, or excessive pressure or friction to the skin.

Skin injuries set off a healing process that occurs in several overlapping stages. The first step to repairing damaged skin is the formation of a blood clot that helps stop the flow of blood and scabs over with time. Many different types of cells are involved in wound repair, especially if the surface area that needs repair is extensive. Before the basal stem cells of the stratum basale can recreate the epidermis, fibroblasts mobilize and divide rapidly to repair the damaged tissue by collagen deposition, forming granulation tissue. Blood capillaries follow the fibroblasts and help increase blood circulation and oxygen supply to the area. Immune cells, such as macrophages, roam the area and engulf any foreign matter to reduce the chance of infection.

Burns

A burn results when the skin is damaged by intense heat, radiation, electricity, or chemicals. The damage results in the death of skin cells, which can lead to a massive loss of fluid. Dehydration, electrolyte imbalance, and renal and circulatory failure follow, which can be fatal. Burn patients are treated with intravenous fluids to offset dehydration, as well as intravenous nutrients that enable the body to repair tissues and replace lost proteins. Another serious threat to the lives of burn patients is infection. Burned skin is extremely susceptible to bacteria and other pathogens, due to the loss of protection by intact layers of skin.

Burns are sometimes measured in terms of the size of the total surface area affected. This is referred to as the "rule of nines," which associates specific anatomical areas with a percentage that is a factor of nine (Figure 5.23). Burns are also classified by the degree of their severity. A **first-degree burn** is a superficial burn that affects only the epidermis. Although the skin may be painful and swollen, these burns typically heal on their own within a few days. Mild sunburn fits into the category of a first-degree burn. A **second-degree burn** goes deeper and affects both the epidermis and a portion of the dermis. These burns result in swelling and a painful blistering of the skin. It is important to keep the burn site clean and sterile to prevent infection. If this is done, the burn will heal within several weeks. A **third-degree burn** fully extends into the epidermis and dermis, destroying the tissue and affecting the nerve endings and sensory function. These are serious burns that may appear white, red, or black; they require medical attention and will heal slowly without it. A **fourth-degree burn** is even more severe, affecting the underlying muscle and bone. Oddly, third and fourth-degree burns are usually not as painful because the nerve endings themselves are damaged. Full-thickness burns cannot be repaired by the body, because the local tissues used for repair are damaged and require excision (debridement), or amputation in severe cases, followed by grafting of the skin from an unaffected part of the body, or from skin grown in tissue culture for grafting purposes.

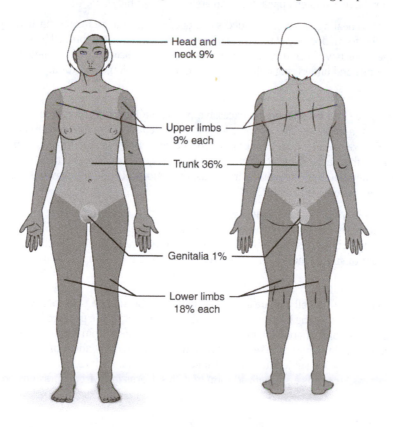

Figure 5.23 Calculating the Size of a Burn The size of a burn will guide decisions made about the need for specialized treatment. Specific parts of the body are associated with a percentage of body area.

Interactive LINK

Skin grafts are required when the damage from trauma or infection cannot be closed with sutures or staples. Watch this video (http://openstaxcollege.org/l/skingraft) to learn more about skin grafting procedures.

Scars and Keloids

Most cuts or wounds, with the exception of ones that only scratch the surface (the epidermis), lead to scar formation. A **scar** is collagen-rich skin formed after the process of wound healing that differs from normal skin. Scarring occurs in cases in which there is repair of skin damage, but the skin fails to regenerate the original skin structure. Fibroblasts generate scar tissue in the form of collagen, and the bulk of repair is due to the basket-weave pattern generated by collagen fibers and does not result in regeneration of the typical cellular structure of skin. Instead, the tissue is fibrous in nature and does not allow for the regeneration of accessory structures, such as hair follicles, sweat glands, or sebaceous glands.

Sometimes, there is an overproduction of scar tissue, because the process of collagen formation does not stop when the wound is healed; this results in the formation of a raised or hypertrophic scar called a **keloid**. In contrast, scars that result from acne and chickenpox have a sunken appearance and are called atrophic scars.

Scarring of skin after wound healing is a natural process and does not need to be treated further. Application of mineral oil and lotions may reduce the formation of scar tissue. However, modern cosmetic procedures, such as dermabrasion, laser treatments, and filler injections have been invented as remedies for severe scarring. All of these procedures try to reorganize the structure of the epidermis and underlying collagen tissue to make it look more natural.

Bedsores and Stretch Marks

Skin and its underlying tissue can be affected by excessive pressure. One example of this is called a **bedsore**. Bedsores, also called decubitis ulcers, are caused by constant, long-term, unrelieved pressure on certain body parts that are bony, reducing blood flow to the area and leading to necrosis (tissue death). Bedsores are most common in elderly patients who have debilitating conditions that cause them to be immobile. Most hospitals and long-term care facilities have the practice of turning the patients every few hours to prevent the incidence of bedsores. If left untreated by removal of necrotized tissue, bedsores can be fatal if they become infected.

The skin can also be affected by pressure associated with rapid growth. A **stretch mark** results when the dermis is stretched beyond its limits of elasticity, as the skin stretches to accommodate the excess pressure. Stretch marks usually accompany rapid weight gain during puberty and pregnancy. They initially have a reddish hue, but lighten over time. Other than for cosmetic reasons, treatment of stretch marks is not required. They occur most commonly over the hips and abdomen.

Calluses

When you wear shoes that do not fit well and are a constant source of abrasion on your toes, you tend to form a **callus** at the point of contact. This occurs because the basal stem cells in the stratum basale are triggered to divide more often to increase the thickness of the skin at the point of abrasion to protect the rest of the body from further damage. This is an example of a minor or local injury, and the skin manages to react and treat the problem independent of the rest of the body. Calluses can also form on your fingers if they are subject to constant mechanical stress, such as long periods of writing, playing string instruments, or video games. A **corn** is a specialized form of callus. Corns form from abrasions on the skin that result from an elliptical-type motion.

KEY TERMS

acne skin condition due to infected sebaceous glands

albinism genetic disorder that affects the skin, in which there is no melanin production

anagen active phase of the hair growth cycle

apocrine sweat gland type of sweat gland that is associated with hair follicles in the armpits and genital regions

arrector pili smooth muscle that is activated in response to external stimuli that pull on hair follicles and make the hair "stand up"

basal cell type of stem cell found in the stratum basale and in the hair matrix that continually undergoes cell division, producing the keratinocytes of the epidermis

basal cell carcinoma cancer that originates from basal cells in the epidermis of the skin

bedsore sore on the skin that develops when regions of the body start necrotizing due to constant pressure and lack of blood supply; also called decubitis ulcers

callus thickened area of skin that arises due to constant abrasion

catagen transitional phase marking the end of the anagen phase of the hair growth cycle

corn type of callus that is named for its shape and the elliptical motion of the abrasive force

cortex in hair, the second or middle layer of keratinocytes originating from the hair matrix, as seen in a cross-section of the hair bulb

cuticle in hair, the outermost layer of keratinocytes originating from the hair matrix, as seen in a cross-section of the hair bulb

dermal papilla (plural = dermal papillae) extension of the papillary layer of the dermis that increases surface contact between the epidermis and dermis

dermis layer of skin between the epidermis and hypodermis, composed mainly of connective tissue and containing blood vessels, hair follicles, sweat glands, and other structures

desmosome structure that forms an impermeable junction between cells

eccrine sweat gland type of sweat gland that is common throughout the skin surface; it produces a hypotonic sweat for thermoregulation

eczema skin condition due to an allergic reaction, which resembles a rash

elastin fibers fibers made of the protein elastin that increase the elasticity of the dermis

eleiden clear protein-bound lipid found in the stratum lucidum that is derived from keratohyalin and helps to prevent water loss

epidermis outermost tissue layer of the skin

eponychium nail fold that meets the proximal end of the nail body, also called the cuticle

external root sheath outer layer of the hair follicle that is an extension of the epidermis, which encloses the hair root

first-degree burn superficial burn that injures only the epidermis

fourth-degree burn burn in which full thickness of the skin and underlying muscle and bone is damaged

glassy membrane layer of connective tissue that surrounds the base of the hair follicle, connecting it to the dermis

hair keratinous filament growing out of the epidermis

hair bulb structure at the base of the hair root that surrounds the dermal papilla

hair follicle cavity or sac from which hair originates

hair matrix layer of basal cells from which a strand of hair grows

hair papilla mass of connective tissue, blood capillaries, and nerve endings at the base of the hair follicle

hair root part of hair that is below the epidermis anchored to the follicle

hair shaft part of hair that is above the epidermis but is not anchored to the follicle

hypodermis connective tissue connecting the integument to the underlying bone and muscle

hyponychium thickened layer of stratum corneum that lies below the free edge of the nail

integumentary system skin and its accessory structures

internal root sheath innermost layer of keratinocytes in the hair follicle that surround the hair root up to the hair shaft

keloid type of scar that has layers raised above the skin surface

keratin type of structural protein that gives skin, hair, and nails its hard, water-resistant properties

keratinocyte cell that produces keratin and is the most predominant type of cell found in the epidermis

keratohyalin granulated protein found in the stratum granulosum

Langerhans cell specialized dendritic cell found in the stratum spinosum that functions as a macrophage

lunula basal part of the nail body that consists of a crescent-shaped layer of thick epithelium

medulla in hair, the innermost layer of keratinocytes originating from the hair matrix

Meissner corpuscle (also, tactile corpuscle) receptor in the skin that responds to light touch

melanin pigment that determines the color of hair and skin

melanocyte cell found in the stratum basale of the epidermis that produces the pigment melanin

melanoma type of skin cancer that originates from the melanocytes of the skin

melanosome intercellular vesicle that transfers melanin from melanocytes into keratinocytes of the epidermis

Merkel cell receptor cell in the stratum basale of the epidermis that responds to the sense of touch

metastasis spread of cancer cells from a source to other parts of the body

nail bed layer of epidermis upon which the nail body forms

nail body main keratinous plate that forms the nail

nail cuticle fold of epithelium that extends over the nail bed, also called the eponychium

nail fold fold of epithelium at that extend over the sides of the nail body, holding it in place

nail root part of the nail that is lodged deep in the epidermis from which the nail grows

Pacinian corpuscle (also, lamellated corpuscle) receptor in the skin that responds to vibration

papillary layer superficial layer of the dermis, made of loose, areolar connective tissue

reticular layer deeper layer of the dermis; it has a reticulated appearance due to the presence of abundant collagen and elastin fibers

rickets disease in children caused by vitamin D deficiency, which leads to the weakening of bones

scar collagen-rich skin formed after the process of wound healing that is different from normal skin

sebaceous gland type of oil gland found in the dermis all over the body and helps to lubricate and waterproof the skin and hair by secreting sebum

sebum oily substance that is composed of a mixture of lipids that lubricates the skin and hair

second-degree burn partial-thickness burn that injures the epidermis and a portion of the dermis

squamous cell carcinoma type of skin cancer that originates from the stratum spinosum of the epidermis

stratum basale deepest layer of the epidermis, made of epidermal stem cells

stratum corneum most superficial layer of the epidermis

stratum granulosum layer of the epidermis superficial to the stratum spinosum

stratum lucidum layer of the epidermis between the stratum granulosum and stratum corneum, found only in thick skin covering the palms, soles of the feet, and digits

stratum spinosum layer of the epidermis superficial to the stratum basale, characterized by the presence of desmosomes

stretch mark mark formed on the skin due to a sudden growth spurt and expansion of the dermis beyond its elastic limits

sudoriferous gland sweat gland

telogen resting phase of the hair growth cycle initiated with catagen and terminated by the beginning of a new anagen phase of hair growth

third-degree burn burn that penetrates and destroys the full thickness of the skin (epidermis and dermis)

vitamin D compound that aids absorption of calcium and phosphates in the intestine to improve bone health

vitiligo skin condition in which melanocytes in certain areas lose the ability to produce melanin, possibly due an autoimmune reaction that leads to loss of color in patches

CHAPTER REVIEW

5.1 Layers of the Skin

The skin is composed of two major layers: a superficial epidermis and a deeper dermis. The epidermis consists of several layers beginning with the innermost (deepest) stratum basale (germinatum), followed by the stratum spinosum, stratum granulosum, stratum lucidum (when present), and ending with the outermost layer, the stratum corneum. The topmost layer, the stratum corneum, consists of dead cells that shed periodically and is progressively replaced by cells formed from the basal layer. The stratum basale also contains melanocytes, cells that produce melanin, the pigment primarily responsible for giving skin its color. Melanin is transferred to keratinocytes in the stratum spinosum to protect cells from UV rays.

The dermis connects the epidermis to the hypodermis, and provides strength and elasticity due to the presence of collagen and elastin fibers. It has only two layers: the papillary layer with papillae that extend into the epidermis and the lower, reticular layer composed of loose connective tissue. The hypodermis, deep to the dermis of skin, is the connective tissue that connects the dermis to underlying structures; it also harbors adipose tissue for fat storage and protection.

5.2 Accessory Structures of the Skin

Accessory structures of the skin include hair, nails, sweat glands, and sebaceous glands. Hair is made of dead keratinized cells, and gets its color from melanin pigments. Nails, also made of dead keratinized cells, protect the extremities of our fingers and toes from mechanical damage. Sweat glands and sebaceous glands produce sweat and sebum, respectively. Each of these fluids has a role to play in maintaining homeostasis. Sweat cools the body surface when it gets overheated and helps excrete small amounts of metabolic waste. Sebum acts as a natural moisturizer and keeps the dead, flaky, outer keratin layer healthy.

5.3 Functions of the Integumentary System

The skin plays important roles in protection, sensing stimuli, thermoregulation, and vitamin D synthesis. It is the first layer of defense to prevent dehydration, infection, and injury to the rest of the body. Sweat glands in the skin allow the skin surface to cool when the body gets overheated. Thermoregulation is also accomplished by the dilation or constriction of heat-carrying blood vessels in the skin. Immune cells present among the skin layers patrol the areas to keep them free of foreign materials. Fat stores in the hypodermis aid in both thermoregulation and protection. Finally, the skin plays a role in the synthesis of vitamin D, which is necessary for our well-being but not easily available in natural foods.

5.4 Diseases, Disorders, and Injuries of the Integumentary System

Skin cancer is a result of damage to the DNA of skin cells, often due to excessive exposure to UV radiation. Basal cell carcinoma and squamous cell carcinoma are highly curable, and arise from cells in the stratum basale and stratum spinosum, respectively. Melanoma is the most dangerous form of skin cancer, affecting melanocytes, which can spread/metastasize to other organs. Burns are an injury to the skin that occur as a result of exposure to extreme heat, radiation, or chemicals. First-degree and second-degree burns usually heal quickly, but third-degree burns can be fatal because they penetrate the full thickness of the skin. Scars occur when there is repair of skin damage. Fibroblasts generate scar tissue in the form of collagen, which forms a basket-weave pattern that looks different from normal skin.

Bedsores and stretch marks are the result of excessive pressure on the skin and underlying tissue. Bedsores are characterized by necrosis of tissue due to immobility, whereas stretch marks result from rapid growth. Eczema is an allergic reaction that manifests as a rash, and acne results from clogged sebaceous glands. Eczema and acne are usually long-term skin conditions that may be treated successfully in mild cases. Calluses and corns are the result of abrasive pressure on the skin.

INTERACTIVE LINK QUESTIONS

1. The skin consists of two layers and a closely associated layer. View this animation (http://openstaxcollege.org/l/layers) to learn more about layers of the skin. What are the basic functions of each of these layers?

2. Figure 5.4 If you zoom on the cells at the outermost layer of this section of skin, what do you notice about the cells?

3. Figure 5.6 If you zoom on the cells of the stratum spinosum, what is distinctive about them?

4. This ABC video follows the story of a pair of fraternal African-American twins, one of whom is albino. Watch this video (http://openstaxcollege.org/l/albino) to learn about the challenges these children and their family face. Which ethnicities do you think are exempt from the possibility of albinism?

REVIEW QUESTIONS

5. The papillary layer of the dermis is most closely associated with which layer of the epidermis?
   a. stratum spinosum
   b. stratum corneum
   c. stratum granulosum
   d. stratum basale

6. Langerhans cells are commonly found in the _____.

   a. stratum spinosum
   b. stratum corneum
   c. stratum granulosum
   d. stratum basale

7. The papillary and reticular layers of the dermis are composed mainly of _____.
   a. melanocytes
   b. keratinocytes
   c. connective tissue
   d. adipose tissue

8. Collagen lends _____ to the skin.
   a. elasticity
   b. structure
   c. color
   d. UV protection

9. Which of the following is not a function of the hypodermis?
   a. protects underlying organs
   b. helps maintain body temperature
   c. source of blood vessels in the epidermis
   d. a site to long-term energy storage

10. In response to stimuli from the sympathetic nervous system, the arrector pili _____.
  a. are glands on the skin surface
  b. can lead to excessive sweating
  c. are responsible for goose bumps
  d. secrete sebum

11. The hair matrix contains _____.
  a. the hair follicle
  b. the hair shaft
  c. the glassy membrane
  d. a layer of basal cells

12. Eccrine sweat glands _____.
  a. are present on hair
  b. are present in the skin throughout the body and produce watery sweat
  c. produce sebum
  d. act as a moisturizer

13. Sebaceous glands _____.
  a. are a type of sweat gland
  b. are associated with hair follicles
  c. may function in response to touch
  d. release a watery solution of salt and metabolic waste

14. Similar to the hair, nails grow continuously throughout our lives. Which of the following is furthest from the nail growth center?
  a. nail bed
  b. hyponychium
  c. nail root
  d. eponychium

15. In humans, exposure of the skin to sunlight is required for _____.
  a. vitamin D synthesis
  b. arteriole constriction
  c. folate production
  d. thermoregulation

16. One of the functions of the integumentary system is protection. Which of the following does not directly contribute to that function?
  a. stratum lucidum
  b. desmosomes
  c. folic acid synthesis
  d. Merkel cells

17. An individual using a sharp knife notices a small amount of blood where he just cut himself. Which of the following layers of skin did he have to cut into in order to bleed?
  a. stratum corneum
  b. stratum basale
  c. papillary dermis
  d. stratum granulosum

18. As you are walking down the beach, you see a dead, dry, shriveled-up fish. Which layer of your epidermis keeps you from drying out?
  a. stratum corneum
  b. stratum basale
  c. stratum spinosum
  d. stratum granulosum

19. If you cut yourself and bacteria enter the wound, which of the following cells would help get rid of the bacteria?

  a. Merkel cells
  b. keratinocytes
  c. Langerhans cells
  d. melanocytes

20. In general, skin cancers _____.
  a. are easily treatable and not a major health concern
  b. occur due to poor hygiene
  c. can be reduced by limiting exposure to the sun
  d. affect only the epidermis

21. Bedsores _____.
  a. can be treated with topical moisturizers
  b. can result from deep massages
  c. are preventable by eliminating pressure points
  d. are caused by dry skin

22. An individual has spent too much time sun bathing. Not only is his skin painful to touch, but small blisters have appeared in the affected area. This indicates that he has damaged which layers of his skin?
  a. epidermis only
  b. hypodermis only
  c. epidermis and hypodermis
  d. epidermis and dermis

23. After a skin injury, the body initiates a wound-healing response. The first step of this response is the formation of a blood clot to stop bleeding. Which of the following would be the next response?
  a. increased production of melanin by melanocytes
  b. increased production of connective tissue
  c. an increase in Pacinian corpuscles around the wound
  d. an increased activity in the stratum lucidum

24. Squamous cell carcinomas are the second most common of the skin cancers and are capable of metastasizing if not treated. This cancer affects which cells?
  a. basal cells of the stratum basale
  b. melanocytes of the stratum basale
  c. keratinocytes of the stratum spinosum
  d. Langerhans cells of the stratum lucidum

CRITICAL THINKING QUESTIONS

25. What determines the color of skin, and what is the process that darkens skin when it is exposed to UV light?

26. Cells of the epidermis derive from stem cells of the stratum basale. Describe how the cells change as they become integrated into the different layers of the epidermis.

27. Explain the differences between eccrine and apocrine sweat glands.

28. Describe the structure and composition of nails.

29. Why do people sweat excessively when exercising outside on a hot day?

30. Explain your skin's response to a drop in body core temperature.

31. Why do teenagers often experience acne?

32. Why do scars look different from surrounding skin?

6 | BONE TISSUE AND THE SKELETAL SYSTEM

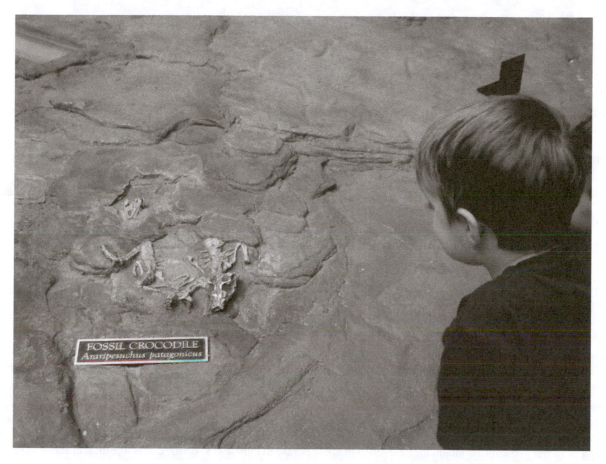

Figure 6.1 Child Looking at Bones Bone is a living tissue. Unlike the bones of a fossil made inert by a process of mineralization, a child's bones will continue to grow and develop while contributing to the support and function of other body systems. (credit: James Emery)

Introduction

Chapter Objectives
After studying this chapter, you will be able to: • List and describe the functions of bones • Describe the classes of bones • Discuss the process of bone formation and development • Explain how bone repairs itself after a fracture • Discuss the effect of exercise, nutrition, and hormones on bone tissue • Describe how an imbalance of calcium can affect bone tissue

Bones make good fossils. While the soft tissue of a once living organism will decay and fall away over time, bone tissue will, under the right conditions, undergo a process of mineralization, effectively turning the bone to stone. A well-preserved fossil skeleton can give us a good sense of the size and shape of an organism, just as your skeleton helps to define your size and shape. Unlike a fossil skeleton, however, your skeleton is a structure of living tissue that grows, repairs, and renews itself. The bones within it are dynamic and complex organs that serve a number of important functions, including some necessary to maintain homeostasis.

6.1 | The Functions of the Skeletal System

By the end of this section, you will be able to:
- Define bone, cartilage, and the skeletal system
- List and describe the functions of the skeletal system

Bone, or **osseous tissue**, is a hard, dense connective tissue that forms most of the adult skeleton, the support structure of the body. In the areas of the skeleton where bones move (for example, the ribcage and joints), **cartilage**, a semi-rigid form of connective tissue, provides flexibility and smooth surfaces for movement. The **skeletal system** is the body system composed of bones and cartilage and performs the following critical functions for the human body:

- supports the body
- facilitates movement
- protects internal organs
- produces blood cells
- stores and releases minerals and fat

Support, Movement, and Protection

The most apparent functions of the skeletal system are the gross functions—those visible by observation. Simply by looking at a person, you can see how the bones support, facilitate movement, and protect the human body.

Just as the steel beams of a building provide a scaffold to support its weight, the bones and cartilage of your skeletal system compose the scaffold that supports the rest of your body. Without the skeletal system, you would be a limp mass of organs, muscle, and skin.

Bones also facilitate movement by serving as points of attachment for your muscles. While some bones only serve as a support for the muscles, others also transmit the forces produced when your muscles contract. From a mechanical point of view, bones act as levers and joints serve as fulcrums (**Figure 6.2**). Unless a muscle spans a joint and contracts, a bone is not going to move. For information on the interaction of the skeletal and muscular systems, that is, the musculoskeletal system, seek additional content.

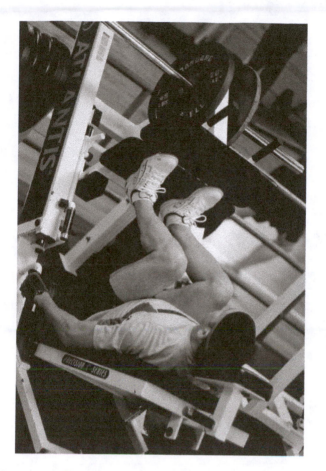

Figure 6.2 Bones Support Movement Bones act as levers when muscles span a joint and contract. (credit: Benjamin J. DeLong)

Bones also protect internal organs from injury by covering or surrounding them. For example, your ribs protect your lungs and heart, the bones of your vertebral column (spine) protect your spinal cord, and the bones of your cranium (skull) protect your brain (Figure 6.3).

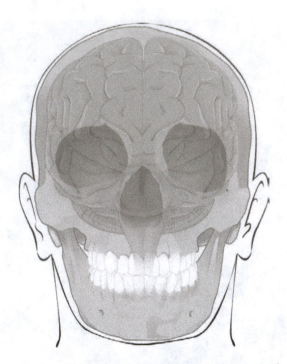

Figure 6.3 Bones Protect Brain   The cranium completely surrounds and protects the brain from non-traumatic injury.

Caeer CONNECTION

Orthopedist

An **orthopedist** is a doctor who specializes in diagnosing and treating disorders and injuries related to the musculoskeletal system. Some orthopedic problems can be treated with medications, exercises, braces, and other devices, but others may be best treated with surgery (**Figure 6.4**).

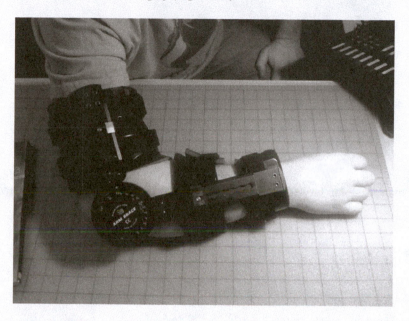

Figure 6.4 Arm Brace An orthopedist will sometimes prescribe the use of a brace that reinforces the underlying bone structure it is being used to support. (credit: Juhan Sonin)

While the origin of the word "orthopedics" (ortho- = "straight"; paed- = "child"), literally means "straightening of the child," orthopedists can have patients who range from pediatric to geriatric. In recent years, orthopedists have even performed prenatal surgery to correct spina bifida, a congenital defect in which the neural canal in the spine of the fetus fails to close completely during embryologic development.

Orthopedists commonly treat bone and joint injuries but they also treat other bone conditions including curvature of the spine. Lateral curvatures (scoliosis) can be severe enough to slip under the shoulder blade (scapula) forcing it up as a hump. Spinal curvatures can also be excessive dorsoventrally (kyphosis) causing a hunch back and thoracic compression. These curvatures often appear in preteens as the result of poor posture, abnormal growth, or indeterminate causes. Mostly, they are readily treated by orthopedists. As people age, accumulated spinal column injuries and diseases like osteoporosis can also lead to curvatures of the spine, hence the stooping you sometimes see in the elderly.

Some orthopedists sub-specialize in sports medicine, which addresses both simple injuries, such as a sprained ankle, and complex injuries, such as a torn rotator cuff in the shoulder. Treatment can range from exercise to surgery.

Mineral Storage, Energy Storage, and Hematopoiesis

On a metabolic level, bone tissue performs several critical functions. For one, the bone matrix acts as a reservoir for a number of minerals important to the functioning of the body, especially calcium, and phosphorus. These minerals, incorporated into bone tissue, can be released back into the bloodstream to maintain levels needed to support physiological processes. Calcium ions, for example, are essential for muscle contractions and controlling the flow of other ions involved in the transmission of nerve impulses.

Bone also serves as a site for fat storage and blood cell production. The softer connective tissue that fills the interior of most bone is referred to as bone marrow (**Figure 6.5**). There are two types of bone marrow: yellow marrow and red marrow. **Yellow marrow** contains adipose tissue; the triglycerides stored in the adipocytes of the tissue can serve as a source of energy. **Red marrow** is where **hematopoiesis**—the production of blood cells—takes place. Red blood cells, white blood cells, and platelets are all produced in the red marrow.

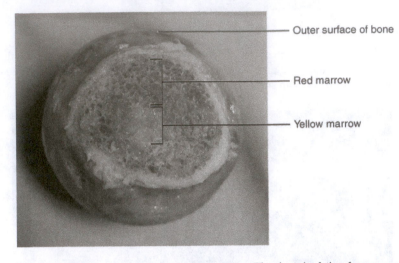

Figure 6.5 Head of Femur Showing Red and Yellow Marrow The head of the femur contains both yellow and red marrow. Yellow marrow stores fat. Red marrow is responsible for hematopoiesis. (credit: modification of work by "stevenfruitsmaak"/Wikimedia Commons)

6.2 | Bone Classification

By the end of this section, you will be able to:

- Classify bones according to their shapes
- Describe the function of each category of bones

The 206 bones that compose the adult skeleton are divided into five categories based on their shapes (Figure 6.6). Their shapes and their functions are related such that each categorical shape of bone has a distinct function.

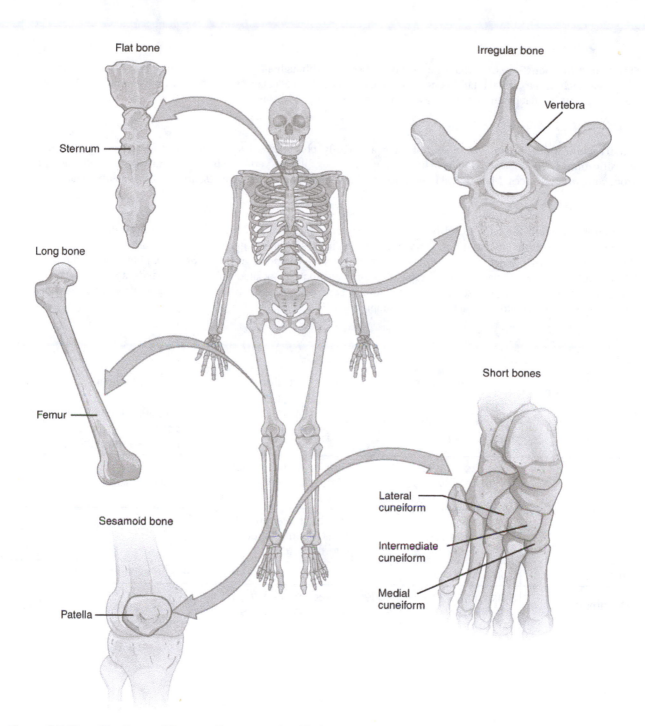

Figure 6.6 Classifications of Bones Bones are classified according to their shape.

Long Bones

A **long bone** is one that is cylindrical in shape, being longer than it is wide. Keep in mind, however, that the term describes the shape of a bone, not its size. Long bones are found in the arms (humerus, ulna, radius) and legs (femur, tibia, fibula), as well as in the fingers (metacarpals, phalanges) and toes (metatarsals, phalanges). Long bones function as levers; they move when muscles contract.

Short Bones

A **short bone** is one that is cube-like in shape, being approximately equal in length, width, and thickness. The only short bones in the human skeleton are in the carpals of the wrists and the tarsals of the ankles. Short bones provide stability and support as well as some limited motion.

Flat Bones

The term " **flat bone**" is somewhat of a misnomer because, although a flat bone is typically thin, it is also often curved. Examples include the cranial (skull) bones, the scapulae (shoulder blades), the sternum (breastbone), and the ribs. Flat bones serve as points of attachment for muscles and often protect internal organs.

Irregular Bones

An **irregular bone** is one that does not have any easily characterized shape and therefore does not fit any other classification. These bones tend to have more complex shapes, like the vertebrae that support the spinal cord and protect it from compressive forces. Many facial bones, particularly the ones containing sinuses, are classified as irregular bones.

Sesamoid Bones

A **sesamoid bone** is a small, round bone that, as the name suggests, is shaped like a sesame seed. These bones form in tendons (the sheaths of tissue that connect bones to muscles) where a great deal of pressure is generated in a joint. The sesamoid bones protect tendons by helping them overcome compressive forces. Sesamoid bones vary in number and placement from person to person but are typically found in tendons associated with the feet, hands, and knees. The patellae (singular = patella) are the only sesamoid bones found in common with every person. Table 6.1 reviews bone classifications with their associated features, functions, and examples.

Bone Classifications

Bone classification	Features	Function(s)	Examples
Long	Cylinder-like shape, longer than it is wide	Leverage	Femur, tibia, fibula, metatarsals, humerus, ulna, radius, metacarpals, phalanges
Short	Cube-like shape, approximately equal in length, width, and thickness	Provide stability, support, while allowing for some motion	Carpals, tarsals
Flat	Thin and curved	Points of attachment for muscles; protectors of internal organs	Sternum, ribs, scapulae, cranial bones
Irregular	Complex shape	Protect internal organs	Vertebrae, facial bones
Sesamoid	Small and round; embedded in tendons	Protect tendons from compressive forces	Patellae

Table 6.1

6.3 | Bone Structure

By the end of this section, you will be able to:

- Identify the anatomical features of a bone
- Define and list examples of bone markings
- Describe the histology of bone tissue
- Compare and contrast compact and spongy bone
- Identify the structures that compose compact and spongy bone
- Describe how bones are nourished and innervated

Bone tissue (osseous tissue) differs greatly from other tissues in the body. Bone is hard and many of its functions depend on that characteristic hardness. Later discussions in this chapter will show that bone is also dynamic in that its shape adjusts to accommodate stresses. This section will examine the gross anatomy of bone first and then move on to its histology.

Gross Anatomy of Bone

The structure of a long bone allows for the best visualization of all of the parts of a bone (Figure 6.7). A long bone has two parts: the **diaphysis** and the **epiphysis**. The diaphysis is the tubular shaft that runs between the proximal and distal ends of the bone. The hollow region in the diaphysis is called the **medullary cavity**, which is filled with yellow marrow. The walls of the diaphysis are composed of dense and hard **compact bone**.

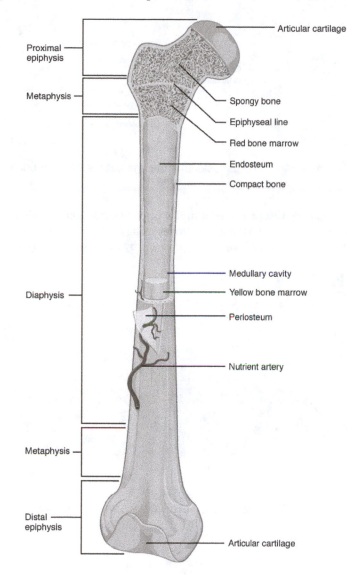

Figure 6.7 Anatomy of a Long Bone   A typical long bone shows the gross anatomical characteristics of bone.

The wider section at each end of the bone is called the epiphysis (plural = epiphyses), which is filled with spongy bone. Red marrow fills the spaces in the spongy bone. Each epiphysis meets the diaphysis at the metaphysis, the narrow area that contains the **epiphyseal plate** (growth plate), a layer of hyaline (transparent) cartilage in a growing bone. When the bone stops growing in early adulthood (approximately 18–21 years), the cartilage is replaced by osseous tissue and the epiphyseal plate becomes an epiphyseal line.

The medullary cavity has a delicate membranous lining called the **endosteum** (end- = "inside"; oste- = "bone"), where bone growth, repair, and remodeling occur. The outer surface of the bone is covered with a fibrous membrane called the **periosteum** (peri- = "around" or "surrounding"). The periosteum contains blood vessels, nerves, and lymphatic vessels that nourish compact bone. Tendons and ligaments also attach to bones at the periosteum. The periosteum covers the entire outer surface except where the epiphyses meet other bones to form joints (Figure 6.8). In this region, the epiphyses are covered with **articular cartilage**, a thin layer of cartilage that reduces friction and acts as a shock absorber.

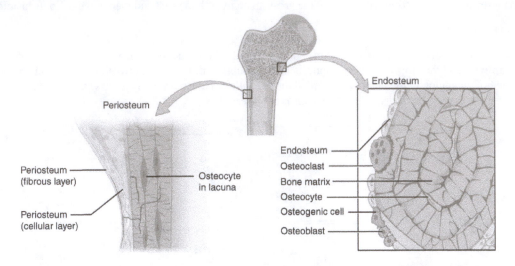

Figure 6.8 Periosteum and Endosteum The periosteum forms the outer surface of bone, and the endosteum lines the medullary cavity.

Flat bones, like those of the cranium, consist of a layer of **diploë** (spongy bone), lined on either side by a layer of compact bone (Figure 6.9). The two layers of compact bone and the interior spongy bone work together to protect the internal organs. If the outer layer of a cranial bone fractures, the brain is still protected by the intact inner layer.

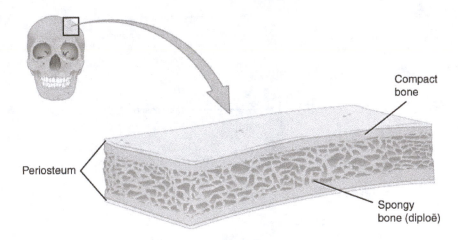

Figure 6.9 Anatomy of a Flat Bone This cross-section of a flat bone shows the spongy bone (diploë) lined on either side by a layer of compact bone.

Bone Markings

The surface features of bones vary considerably, depending on the function and location in the body. Table 6.2 describes the bone markings, which are illustrated in (Figure 6.10). There are three general classes of bone markings: (1) articulations, (2) projections, and (3) holes. As the name implies, an **articulation** is where two bone surfaces come together (articulus = "joint"). These surfaces tend to conform to one another, such as one being rounded and the other cupped, to facilitate the function of the articulation. A **projection** is an area of a bone that projects above the surface of the bone. These are the attachment points for tendons and ligaments. In general, their size and shape is an indication of the forces exerted through the attachment to the bone. A **hole** is an opening or groove in the bone that allows blood vessels and nerves to enter the bone. As with the other markings, their size and shape reflect the size of the vessels and nerves that penetrate the bone at these points.

Bone Markings

Marking	Description	Example
Articulations	Where two bones meet	Knee joint
Head	Prominent rounded surface	Head of femur
Facet	Flat surface	Vertebrae
Condyle	Rounded surface	Occipital condyles
Projections	Raised markings	Spinous process of the vertebrae
Protuberance	Protruding	Chin
Process	Prominence feature	Transverse process of vertebra
Spine	Sharp process	Ischial spine
Tubercle	Small, rounded process	Tubercle of humerus
Tuberosity	Rough surface	Deltoid tuberosity
Line	Slight, elongated ridge	Temporal lines of the parietal bones
Crest	Ridge	Iliac crest
Holes	Holes and depressions	Foramen (holes through which blood vessels can pass through)
Fossa	Elongated basin	Mandibular fossa
Fovea	Small pit	Fovea capitis on the head of the femur
Sulcus	Groove	Sigmoid sulcus of the temporal bones
Canal	Passage in bone	Auditory canal
Fissure	Slit through bone	Auricular fissure
Foramen	Hole through bone	Foramen magnum in the occipital bone
Meatus	Opening into canal	External auditory meatus
Sinus	Air-filled space in bone	Nasal sinus

Table 6.2

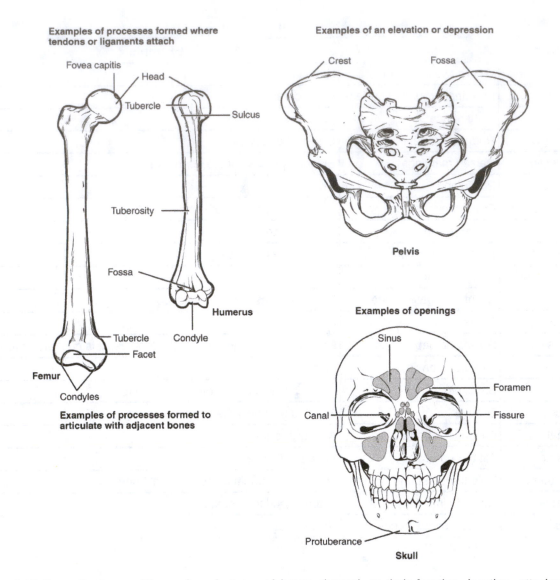

Figure 6.10 Bone Features The surface features of bones depend on their function, location, attachment of ligaments and tendons, or the penetration of blood vessels and nerves.

Bone Cells and Tissue

Bone contains a relatively small number of cells entrenched in a matrix of collagen fibers that provide a surface for inorganic salt crystals to adhere. These salt crystals form when calcium phosphate and calcium carbonate combine to create hydroxyapatite, which incorporates other inorganic salts like magnesium hydroxide, fluoride, and sulfate as it crystallizes, or calcifies, on the collagen fibers. The hydroxyapatite crystals give bones their hardness and strength, while the collagen fibers give them flexibility so that they are not brittle.

Although bone cells compose a small amount of the bone volume, they are crucial to the function of bones. Four types of cells are found within bone tissue: osteoblasts, osteocytes, osteogenic cells, and osteoclasts (**Figure 6.11**).

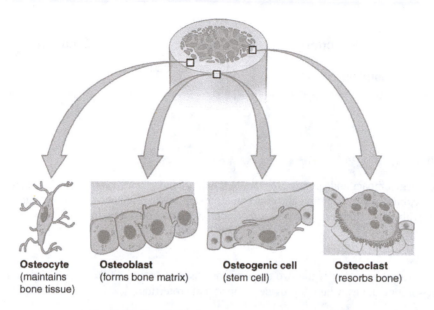

Figure 6.11 Bone Cells Four types of cells are found within bone tissue. Osteogenic cells are undifferentiated and develop into osteoblasts. When osteoblasts get trapped within the calcified matrix, their structure and function changes, and they become osteocytes. Osteoclasts develop from monocytes and macrophages and differ in appearance from other bone cells.

The **osteoblast** is the bone cell responsible for forming new bone and is found in the growing portions of bone, including the periosteum and endosteum. Osteoblasts, which do not divide, synthesize and secrete the collagen matrix and calcium salts. As the secreted matrix surrounding the osteoblast calcifies, the osteoblast become trapped within it; as a result, it changes in structure and becomes an **osteocyte**, the primary cell of mature bone and the most common type of bone cell. Each osteocyte is located in a space called a **lacuna** and is surrounded by bone tissue. Osteocytes maintain the mineral concentration of the matrix via the secretion of enzymes. Like osteoblasts, osteocytes lack mitotic activity. They can communicate with each other and receive nutrients via long cytoplasmic processes that extend through **canaliculi** (singular = canaliculus), channels within the bone matrix.

If osteoblasts and osteocytes are incapable of mitosis, then how are they replenished when old ones die? The answer lies in the properties of a third category of bone cells—the **osteogenic cell**. These osteogenic cells are undifferentiated with high mitotic activity and they are the only bone cells that divide. Immature osteogenic cells are found in the deep layers of the periosteum and the marrow. They differentiate and develop into osteoblasts.

The dynamic nature of bone means that new tissue is constantly formed, and old, injured, or unnecessary bone is dissolved for repair or for calcium release. The cell responsible for bone resorption, or breakdown, is the **osteoclast**. They are found on bone surfaces, are multinucleated, and originate from monocytes and macrophages, two types of white blood cells, not from osteogenic cells. Osteoclasts are continually breaking down old bone while osteoblasts are continually forming new bone. The ongoing balance between osteoblasts and osteoclasts is responsible for the constant but subtle reshaping of bone. Table 6.3 reviews the bone cells, their functions, and locations.

Bone Cells

Cell type	Function	Location
Osteogenic cells	Develop into osteoblasts	Deep layers of the periosteum and the marrow
Osteoblasts	Bone formation	Growing portions of bone, including periosteum and endosteum
Osteocytes	Maintain mineral concentration of matrix	Entrapped in matrix

Table 6.3

Bone Cells

Cell type	Function	Location
Osteoclasts	Bone resorption	Bone surfaces and at sites of old, injured, or unneeded bone

Table 6.3

Compact and Spongy Bone

The differences between compact and spongy bone are best explored via their histology. Most bones contain compact and spongy osseous tissue, but their distribution and concentration vary based on the bone's overall function. Compact bone is dense so that it can withstand compressive forces, while spongy (cancellous) bone has open spaces and supports shifts in weight distribution.

Compact Bone

Compact bone is the denser, stronger of the two types of bone tissue (Figure 6.12). It can be found under the periosteum and in the diaphyses of long bones, where it provides support and protection.

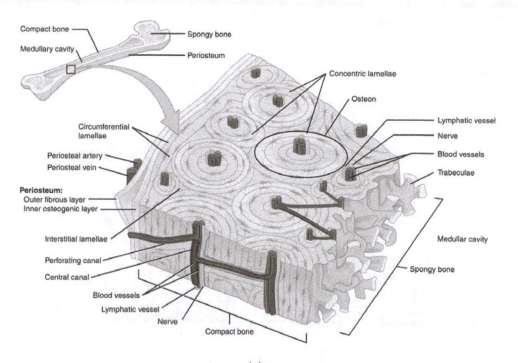

(a)

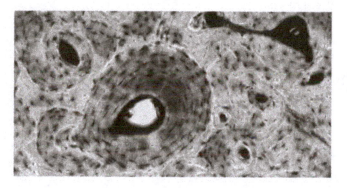

(b)

Figure 6.12 Diagram of Compact Bone (a) This cross-sectional view of compact bone shows the basic structural unit, the osteon. (b) In this micrograph of the osteon, you can clearly see the concentric lamellae and central canals. LM × 40. (Micrograph provided by the Regents of University of Michigan Medical School © 2012)

The microscopic structural unit of compact bone is called an **osteon**, or Haversian system. Each osteon is composed of concentric rings of calcified matrix called lamellae (singular = lamella). Running down the center of each osteon is the **central canal**, or Haversian canal, which contains blood vessels, nerves, and lymphatic vessels. These vessels and nerves branch off at right angles through a **perforating canal**, also known as Volkmann's canals, to extend to the periosteum and endosteum.

The osteocytes are located inside spaces called lacunae (singular = lacuna), found at the borders of adjacent lamellae. As described earlier, canaliculi connect with the canaliculi of other lacunae and eventually with the central canal. This system allows nutrients to be transported to the osteocytes and wastes to be removed from them.

Spongy (Cancellous) Bone

Like compact bone, **spongy bone**, also known as cancellous bone, contains osteocytes housed in lacunae, but they are not arranged in concentric circles. Instead, the lacunae and osteocytes are found in a lattice-like network of matrix spikes called **trabeculae** (singular = trabecula) (Figure 6.13). The trabeculae may appear to be a random network, but each trabecula forms along lines of stress to provide strength to the bone. The spaces of the trabeculated network provide balance to the dense and heavy compact bone by making bones lighter so that muscles can move them more easily. In addition, the spaces in some spongy bones contain red marrow, protected by the trabeculae, where hematopoiesis occurs.

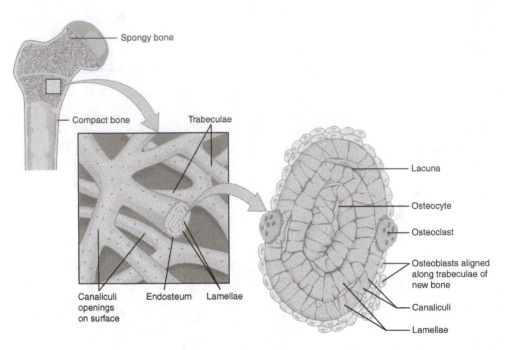

Figure 6.13 Diagram of Spongy Bone Spongy bone is composed of trabeculae that contain the osteocytes. Red marrow fills the spaces in some bones.

Ag ng AND THE...

Skeletal System: Paget's Disease

Paget's disease usually occurs in adults over age 40. It is a disorder of the bone remodeling process that begins with overactive osteoclasts. This means more bone is resorbed than is laid down. The osteoblasts try to compensate but the new bone they lay down is weak and brittle and therefore prone to fracture.

While some people with Paget's disease have no symptoms, others experience pain, bone fractures, and bone deformities (Figure 6.14). Bones of the pelvis, skull, spine, and legs are the most commonly affected. When occurring in the skull, Paget's disease can cause headaches and hearing loss.

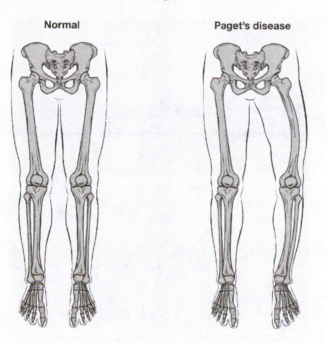

Figure 6.14 Paget's Disease Normal leg bones are relatively straight, but those affected by Paget's disease are porous and curved.

What causes the osteoclasts to become overactive? The answer is still unknown, but hereditary factors seem to play a role. Some scientists believe Paget's disease is due to an as-yet-unidentified virus.

Paget's disease is diagnosed via imaging studies and lab tests. X-rays may show bone deformities or areas of bone resorption. Bone scans are also useful. In these studies, a dye containing a radioactive ion is injected into the body. Areas of bone resorption have an affinity for the ion, so they will light up on the scan if the ions are absorbed. In addition, blood levels of an enzyme called alkaline phosphatase are typically elevated in people with Paget's disease.

Bisphosphonates, drugs that decrease the activity of osteoclasts, are often used in the treatment of Paget's disease. However, in a small percentage of cases, bisphosphonates themselves have been linked to an increased risk of fractures because the old bone that is left after bisphosphonates are administered becomes worn out and brittle. Still, most doctors feel that the benefits of bisphosphonates more than outweigh the risk; the medical professional has to weigh the benefits and risks on a case-by-case basis. Bisphosphonate treatment can reduce the overall risk of deformities or fractures, which in turn reduces the risk of surgical repair and its associated risks and complications.

Blood and Nerve Supply

The spongy bone and medullary cavity receive nourishment from arteries that pass through the compact bone. The arteries enter through the **nutrient foramen** (plural = foramina), small openings in the diaphysis (Figure 6.15). The osteocytes in spongy bone are nourished by blood vessels of the periosteum that penetrate spongy bone and blood that circulates in the marrow cavities. As the blood passes through the marrow cavities, it is collected by veins, which then pass out of the bone through the foramina.

In addition to the blood vessels, nerves follow the same paths into the bone where they tend to concentrate in the more metabolically active regions of the bone. The nerves sense pain, and it appears the nerves also play roles in regulating blood supplies and in bone growth, hence their concentrations in metabolically active sites of the bone.

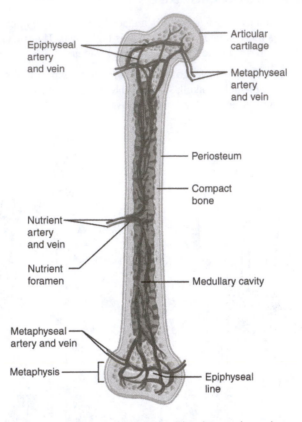

Figure 6.15 Diagram of Blood and Nerve Supply to Bone   Blood vessels and nerves enter the bone through the nutrient foramen.

Watch this **video (http://openstaxcollege.org/l/microbone)** to see the microscopic features of a bone.

6.4 | Bone Formation and Development

By the end of this section, you will be able to:

- Explain the function of cartilage
- List the steps of intramembranous ossification
- List the steps of endochondral ossification
- Explain the growth activity at the epiphyseal plate
- Compare and contrast the processes of modeling and remodeling

In the early stages of embryonic development, the embryo's skeleton consists of fibrous membranes and hyaline cartilage. By the sixth or seventh week of embryonic life, the actual process of bone development, **ossification** (osteogenesis), begins. There are two osteogenic pathways—intramembranous ossification and endochondral ossification—but bone is the same regardless of the pathway that produces it.

Cartilage Templates

Bone is a replacement tissue; that is, it uses a model tissue on which to lay down its mineral matrix. For skeletal development, the most common template is cartilage. During fetal development, a framework is laid down that determines where bones will form. This framework is a flexible, semi-solid matrix produced by chondroblasts and consists of hyaluronic acid, chondroitin sulfate, collagen fibers, and water. As the matrix surrounds and isolates chondroblasts, they are called chondrocytes. Unlike most connective tissues, cartilage is avascular, meaning that it has no blood vessels supplying nutrients and removing metabolic wastes. All of these functions are carried on by diffusion through the matrix. This is why damaged cartilage does not repair itself as readily as most tissues do.

Throughout fetal development and into childhood growth and development, bone forms on the cartilaginous matrix. By the time a fetus is born, most of the cartilage has been replaced with bone. Some additional cartilage will be replaced throughout childhood, and some cartilage remains in the adult skeleton.

Intramembranous Ossification

During **intramembranous ossification**, compact and spongy bone develops directly from sheets of mesenchymal (undifferentiated) connective tissue. The flat bones of the face, most of the cranial bones, and the clavicles (collarbones) are formed via intramembranous ossification.

The process begins when mesenchymal cells in the embryonic skeleton gather together and begin to differentiate into specialized cells (Figure 6.16**a**). Some of these cells will differentiate into capillaries, while others will become osteogenic cells and then osteoblasts. Although they will ultimately be spread out by the formation of bone tissue, early osteoblasts appear in a cluster called an **ossification center**.

The osteoblasts secrete **osteoid**, uncalcified matrix, which calcifies (hardens) within a few days as mineral salts are deposited on it, thereby entrapping the osteoblasts within. Once entrapped, the osteoblasts become osteocytes (Figure 6.16**b**). As osteoblasts transform into osteocytes, osteogenic cells in the surrounding connective tissue differentiate into new osteoblasts.

Osteoid (unmineralized bone matrix) secreted around the capillaries results in a trabecular matrix, while osteoblasts on the surface of the spongy bone become the periosteum (Figure 6.16**c**). The periosteum then creates a protective layer of compact bone superficial to the trabecular bone. The trabecular bone crowds nearby blood vessels, which eventually condense into red marrow (Figure 6.16**d**).

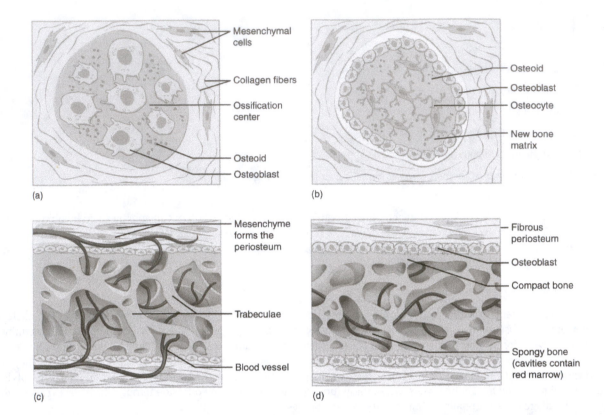

Figure 6.16 Intramembranous Ossification Intramembranous ossification follows four steps. (a) Mesenchymal cells group into clusters, and ossification centers form. (b) Secreted osteoid traps osteoblasts, which then become osteocytes. (c) Trabecular matrix and periosteum form. (d) Compact bone develops superficial to the trabecular bone, and crowded blood vessels condense into red marrow.

Intramembranous ossification begins *in utero* during fetal development and continues on into adolescence. At birth, the skull and clavicles are not fully ossified nor are the sutures of the skull closed. This allows the skull and shoulders to deform during passage through the birth canal. The last bones to ossify via intramembranous ossification are the flat bones of the face, which reach their adult size at the end of the adolescent growth spurt.

Endochondral Ossification

In **endochondral ossification**, bone develops by *replacing* hyaline cartilage. Cartilage does not become bone. Instead, cartilage serves as a template to be completely replaced by new bone. Endochondral ossification takes much longer than intramembranous ossification. Bones at the base of the skull and long bones form via endochondral ossification.

In a long bone, for example, at about 6 to 8 weeks after conception, some of the mesenchymal cells differentiate into chondrocytes (cartilage cells) that form the cartilaginous skeletal precursor of the bones (**Figure 6.17a**). Soon after, the **perichondrium**, a membrane that covers the cartilage, appears **Figure 6.17b**).

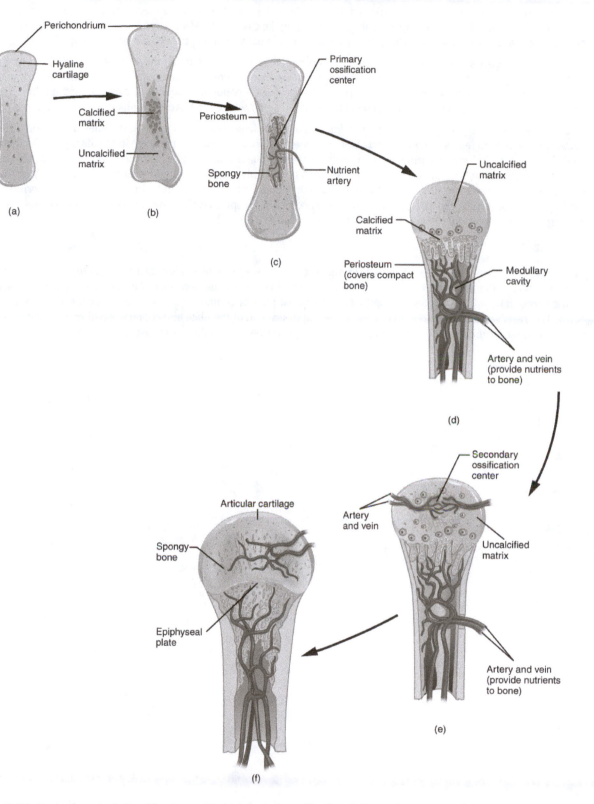

Figure 6.17 Endochondral Ossification Endochondral ossification follows five steps. (a) Mesenchymal cells differentiate into chondrocytes. (b) The cartilage model of the future bony skeleton and the perichondrium form. (c) Capillaries penetrate cartilage. Perichondrium transforms into periosteum. Periosteal collar develops. Primary ossification center develops. (d) Cartilage and chondrocytes continue to grow at ends of the bone. (e) Secondary ossification centers develop. (f) Cartilage remains at epiphyseal (growth) plate and at joint surface as articular cartilage.

As more matrix is produced, the chondrocytes in the center of the cartilaginous model grow in size. As the matrix calcifies, nutrients can no longer reach the chondrocytes. This results in their death and the disintegration of the surrounding cartilage. Blood vessels invade the resulting spaces, not only enlarging the cavities but also carrying osteogenic cells with them, many of which will become osteoblasts. These enlarging spaces eventually combine to become the medullary cavity.

As the cartilage grows, capillaries penetrate it. This penetration initiates the transformation of the perichondrium into the bone-producing periosteum. Here, the osteoblasts form a periosteal collar of compact bone around the cartilage of the diaphysis. By the second or third month of fetal life, bone cell development and ossification ramps up and creates the **primary ossification center**, a region deep in the periosteal collar where ossification begins (Figure 6.17c).

While these deep changes are occurring, chondrocytes and cartilage continue to grow at the ends of the bone (the future epiphyses), which increases the bone's length at the same time bone is replacing cartilage in the diaphyses. By the time the fetal skeleton is fully formed, cartilage only remains at the joint surface as articular cartilage and between the diaphysis and epiphysis as the epiphyseal plate, the latter of which is responsible for the longitudinal growth of bones. After birth, this same sequence of events (matrix mineralization, death of chondrocytes, invasion of blood vessels from the periosteum, and seeding with osteogenic cells that become osteoblasts) occurs in the epiphyseal regions, and each of these centers of activity is referred to as a **secondary ossification center** (Figure 6.17e).

How Bones Grow in Length

The epiphyseal plate is the area of growth in a long bone. It is a layer of hyaline cartilage where ossification occurs in immature bones. On the epiphyseal side of the epiphyseal plate, cartilage is formed. On the diaphyseal side, cartilage is ossified, and the diaphysis grows in length. The epiphyseal plate is composed of four zones of cells and activity (Figure 6.18). The **reserve zone** is the region closest to the epiphyseal end of the plate and contains small chondrocytes within the matrix. These chondrocytes do not participate in bone growth but secure the epiphyseal plate to the osseous tissue of the epiphysis.

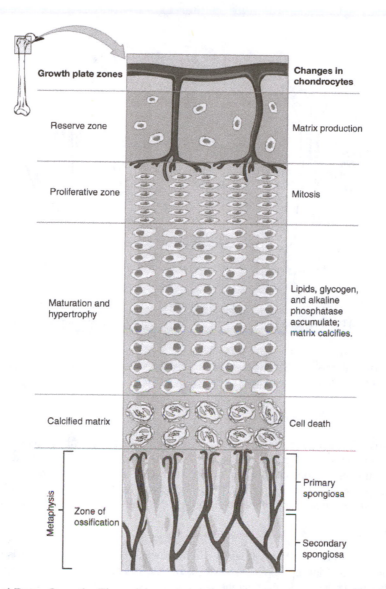

Figure 6.18 Longitudinal Bone Growth The epiphyseal plate is responsible for longitudinal bone growth.

The **proliferative zone** is the next layer toward the diaphysis and contains stacks of slightly larger chondrocytes. It makes new chondrocytes (via mitosis) to replace those that die at the diaphyseal end of the plate. Chondrocytes in the next layer, the **zone of maturation and hypertrophy**, are older and larger than those in the proliferative zone. The more mature cells are situated closer to the diaphyseal end of the plate. The longitudinal growth of bone is a result of cellular division in the proliferative zone and the maturation of cells in the zone of maturation and hypertrophy.

Most of the chondrocytes in the **zone of calcified matrix**, the zone closest to the diaphysis, are dead because the matrix around them has calcified. Capillaries and osteoblasts from the diaphysis penetrate this zone, and the osteoblasts secrete bone tissue on the remaining calcified cartilage. Thus, the zone of calcified matrix connects the epiphyseal plate to the diaphysis. A bone grows in length when osseous tissue is added to the diaphysis.

Bones continue to grow in length until early adulthood. The rate of growth is controlled by hormones, which will be discussed later. When the chondrocytes in the epiphyseal plate cease their proliferation and bone replaces the cartilage, longitudinal growth stops. All that remains of the epiphyseal plate is the **epiphyseal line** (Figure 6.19).

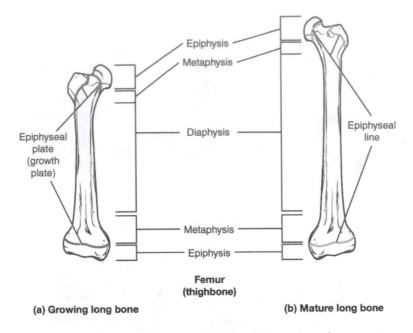

Figure 6.19 Progression from Epiphyseal Plate to Epiphyseal Line As a bone matures, the epiphyseal plate progresses to an epiphyseal line. (a) Epiphyseal plates are visible in a growing bone. (b) Epiphyseal lines are the remnants of epiphyseal plates in a mature bone.

How Bones Grow in Diameter

While bones are increasing in length, they are also increasing in diameter; growth in diameter can continue even after longitudinal growth ceases. This is called appositional growth. Osteoclasts resorb old bone that lines the medullary cavity, while osteoblasts, via intramembranous ossification, produce new bone tissue beneath the periosteum. The erosion of old bone along the medullary cavity and the deposition of new bone beneath the periosteum not only increase the diameter of the diaphysis but also increase the diameter of the medullary cavity. This process is called **modeling**.

Bone Remodeling

The process in which matrix is resorbed on one surface of a bone and deposited on another is known as bone modeling. Modeling primarily takes place during a bone's growth. However, in adult life, bone undergoes **remodeling**, in which resorption of old or damaged bone takes place on the same surface where osteoblasts lay new bone to replace that which is resorbed. Injury, exercise, and other activities lead to remodeling. Those influences are discussed later in the chapter, but even without injury or exercise, about 5 to 10 percent of the skeleton is remodeled annually just by destroying old bone and renewing it with fresh bone.

Diseases OF THE...

Skeletal System

Osteogenesis imperfecta (OI) is a genetic disease in which bones do not form properly and therefore are fragile and break easily. It is also called brittle bone disease. The disease is present from birth and affects a person throughout life.

The genetic mutation that causes OI affects the body's production of collagen, one of the critical components of bone matrix. The severity of the disease can range from mild to severe. Those with the most severe forms of the disease sustain many more fractures than those with a mild form. Frequent and multiple fractures typically lead to bone deformities and short stature. Bowing of the long bones and curvature of the spine are also common in people afflicted with OI. Curvature of the spine makes breathing difficult because the lungs are compressed.

Because collagen is such an important structural protein in many parts of the body, people with OI may also experience fragile skin, weak muscles, loose joints, easy bruising, frequent nosebleeds, brittle teeth, blue sclera, and hearing loss. There is no known cure for OI. Treatment focuses on helping the person retain as much independence as possible while minimizing fractures and maximizing mobility. Toward that end, safe exercises, like swimming, in which the body is less likely to experience collisions or compressive forces, are recommended. Braces to support legs, ankles, knees, and wrists are used as needed. Canes, walkers, or wheelchairs can also help compensate for weaknesses.

When bones do break, casts, splints, or wraps are used. In some cases, metal rods may be surgically implanted into the long bones of the arms and legs. Research is currently being conducted on using bisphosphonates to treat OI. Smoking and being overweight are especially risky in people with OI, since smoking is known to weaken bones, and extra body weight puts additional stress on the bones.

Interactive LINK

Watch this **video (http://openstaxcollege.org/l/bonegrows)** to see how a bone grows.

6.5 | Fractures: Bone Repair

By the end of this section, you will be able to:

- Differentiate among the different types of fractures
- Describe the steps involved in bone repair

A **fracture** is a broken bone. It will heal whether or not a physician resets it in its anatomical position. If the bone is not reset correctly, the healing process will keep the bone in its deformed position.

When a broken bone is manipulated and set into its natural position without surgery, the procedure is called a **closed reduction. Open reduction** requires surgery to expose the fracture and reset the bone. While some fractures can be minor, others are quite severe and result in grave complications. For example, a fractured diaphysis of the femur has the potential to release fat globules into the bloodstream. These can become lodged in the capillary beds of the lungs, leading to respiratory distress and if not treated quickly, death.

Types of Fractures

Fractures are classified by their complexity, location, and other features (Figure 6.20). Table 6.4 outlines common types of fractures. Some fractures may be described using more than one term because it may have the features of more than one type (e.g., an open transverse fracture).

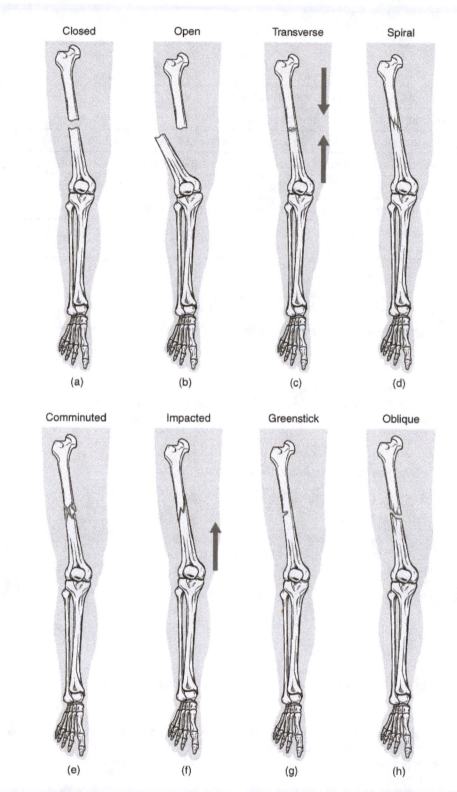

Figure 6.20 Types of Fractures Compare healthy bone with different types of fractures: (a) closed fracture, (b) open fracture, (c) transverse fracture, (d) spiral fracture, (e) comminuted fracture, (f) impacted fracture, (g) greenstick fracture, and (h) oblique fracture.

Types of Fractures

Type of fracture	Description
Transverse	Occurs straight across the long axis of the bone
Oblique	Occurs at an angle that is not 90 degrees
Spiral	Bone segments are pulled apart as a result of a twisting motion
Comminuted	Several breaks result in many small pieces between two large segments
Impacted	One fragment is driven into the other, usually as a result of compression
Greenstick	A partial fracture in which only one side of the bone is broken
Open (or compound)	A fracture in which at least one end of the broken bone tears through the skin; carries a high risk of infection
Closed (or simple)	A fracture in which the skin remains intact

Table 6.4

Bone Repair

When a bone breaks, blood flows from any vessel torn by the fracture. These vessels could be in the periosteum, osteons, and/or medullary cavity. The blood begins to clot, and about six to eight hours after the fracture, the clotting blood has formed a **fracture hematoma** (Figure 6.21a). The disruption of blood flow to the bone results in the death of bone cells around the fracture.

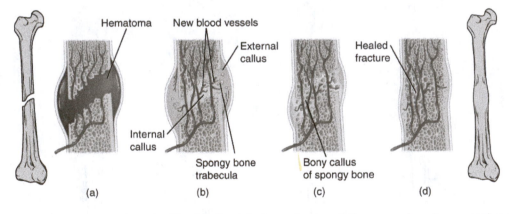

Figure 6.21 Stages in Fracture Repair   The healing of a bone fracture follows a series of progressive steps: (a) A fracture hematoma forms. (b) Internal and external calli form. (c) Cartilage of the calli is replaced by trabecular bone. (d) Remodeling occurs.

Within about 48 hours after the fracture, chondrocytes from the endosteum have created an **internal callus** (plural = calli) by secreting a fibrocartilaginous matrix between the two ends of the broken bone, while the periosteal chondrocytes and osteoblasts create an **external callus** of hyaline cartilage and bone, respectively, around the outside of the break (Figure 6.21b). This stabilizes the fracture.

Over the next several weeks, osteoclasts resorb the dead bone; osteogenic cells become active, divide, and differentiate into osteoblasts. The cartilage in the calli is replaced by trabecular bone via endochondral ossification (Figure 6.21c).

Eventually, the internal and external calli unite, compact bone replaces spongy bone at the outer margins of the fracture, and healing is complete. A slight swelling may remain on the outer surface of the bone, but quite often, that region undergoes remodeling (Figure 6.21d), and no external evidence of the fracture remains.

Interactive LINK

Visit this website (http://openstaxcollege.org/l/fracturequiz) to review different types of fractures and then take a short self-assessment quiz.

6.6 | Exercise, Nutrition, Hormones, and Bone Tissue

By the end of this section, you will be able to:

- Describe the effect exercise has on bone tissue
- List the nutrients that affect bone health
- Discuss the role those nutrients play in bone health
- Describe the effects of hormones on bone tissue

All of the organ systems of your body are interdependent, and the skeletal system is no exception. The food you take in via your digestive system and the hormones secreted by your endocrine system affect your bones. Even using your muscles to engage in exercise has an impact on your bones.

Exercise and Bone Tissue

During long space missions, astronauts can lose approximately 1 to 2 percent of their bone mass per month. This loss of bone mass is thought to be caused by the lack of mechanical stress on astronauts' bones due to the low gravitational forces in space. Lack of mechanical stress causes bones to lose mineral salts and collagen fibers, and thus strength. Similarly, mechanical stress stimulates the deposition of mineral salts and collagen fibers. The internal and external structure of a bone will change as stress increases or decreases so that the bone is an ideal size and weight for the amount of activity it endures. That is why people who exercise regularly have thicker bones than people who are more sedentary. It is also why a broken bone in a cast atrophies while its contralateral mate maintains its concentration of mineral salts and collagen fibers. The bones undergo remodeling as a result of forces (or lack of forces) placed on them.

Numerous, controlled studies have demonstrated that people who exercise regularly have greater bone density than those who are more sedentary. Any type of exercise will stimulate the deposition of more bone tissue, but resistance training has a greater effect than cardiovascular activities. Resistance training is especially important to slow down the eventual bone loss due to aging and for preventing osteoporosis.

Nutrition and Bone Tissue

The vitamins and minerals contained in all of the food we consume are important for all of our organ systems. However, there are certain nutrients that affect bone health.

Calcium and Vitamin D

You already know that calcium is a critical component of bone, especially in the form of calcium phosphate and calcium carbonate. Since the body cannot make calcium, it must be obtained from the diet. However, calcium cannot be absorbed from the small intestine without vitamin D. Therefore, intake of vitamin D is also critical to bone health. In addition to vitamin D's role in calcium absorption, it also plays a role, though not as clearly understood, in bone remodeling.

Milk and other dairy foods are not the only sources of calcium. This important nutrient is also found in green leafy vegetables, broccoli, and intact salmon and canned sardines with their soft bones. Nuts, beans, seeds, and shellfish provide calcium in smaller quantities.

Except for fatty fish like salmon and tuna, or fortified milk or cereal, vitamin D is not found naturally in many foods. The action of sunlight on the skin triggers the body to produce its own vitamin D (Figure 6.22), but many people, especially those of darker complexion and those living in northern latitudes where the sun's rays are not as strong, are deficient in vitamin D. In cases of deficiency, a doctor can prescribe a vitamin D supplement.

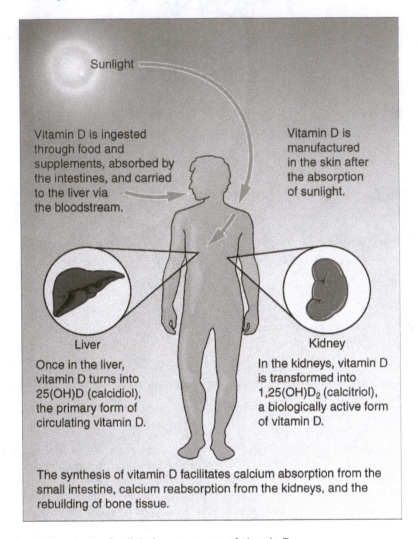

Figure 6.22 Synthesis of Vitamin D Sunlight is one source of vitamin D.

Other Nutrients

Vitamin K also supports bone mineralization and may have a synergistic role with vitamin D in the regulation of bone growth. Green leafy vegetables are a good source of vitamin K.

The minerals magnesium and fluoride may also play a role in supporting bone health. While magnesium is only found in trace amounts in the human body, more than 60 percent of it is in the skeleton, suggesting it plays a role in the structure of bone. Fluoride can displace the hydroxyl group in bone's hydroxyapatite crystals and form fluorapatite. Similar to its effect on dental enamel, fluorapatite helps stabilize and strengthen bone mineral. Fluoride can also enter spaces within hydroxyapatite crystals, thus increasing their density.

Omega-3 fatty acids have long been known to reduce inflammation in various parts of the body. Inflammation can interfere with the function of osteoblasts, so consuming omega-3 fatty acids, in the diet or in supplements, may also help enhance production of new osseous tissue. Table 6.5 summarizes the role of nutrients in bone health.

Nutrients and Bone Health

Nutrient	Role in bone health
Calcium	Needed to make calcium phosphate and calcium carbonate, which form the hydroxyapatite crystals that give bone its hardness
Vitamin D	Needed for calcium absorption
Vitamin K	Supports bone mineralization; may have synergistic effect with vitamin D
Magnesium	Structural component of bone
Fluoride	Structural component of bone
Omega-3 fatty acids	Reduces inflammation that may interfere with osteoblast function

Table 6.5

Hormones and Bone Tissue

The endocrine system produces and secretes hormones, many of which interact with the skeletal system. These hormones are involved in controlling bone growth, maintaining bone once it is formed, and remodeling it.

Hormones That Influence Osteoblasts and/or Maintain the Matrix

Several hormones are necessary for controlling bone growth and maintaining the bone matrix. The pituitary gland secretes growth hormone (GH), which, as its name implies, controls bone growth in several ways. It triggers chondrocyte proliferation in epiphyseal plates, resulting in the increasing length of long bones. GH also increases calcium retention, which enhances mineralization, and stimulates osteoblastic activity, which improves bone density.

GH is not alone in stimulating bone growth and maintaining osseous tissue. Thyroxine, a hormone secreted by the thyroid gland promotes osteoblastic activity and the synthesis of bone matrix. During puberty, the sex hormones (estrogen in girls, testosterone in boys) also come into play. They too promote osteoblastic activity and production of bone matrix, and in addition, are responsible for the growth spurt that often occurs during adolescence. They also promote the conversion of the epiphyseal plate to the epiphyseal line (i.e., cartilage to its bony remnant), thus bringing an end to the longitudinal growth of bones. Additionally, calcitriol, the active form of vitamin D, is produced by the kidneys and stimulates the absorption of calcium and phosphate from the digestive tract.

Aging AND THE...

Skeletal System

Osteoporosis is a disease characterized by a decrease in bone mass that occurs when the rate of bone resorption exceeds the rate of bone formation, a common occurrence as the body ages. Notice how this is different from Paget's disease. In Paget's disease, new bone is formed in an attempt to keep up with the resorption by the overactive osteoclasts, but that new bone is produced haphazardly. In fact, when a physician is evaluating a patient with thinning bone, he or she will test for osteoporosis and Paget's disease (as well as other diseases). Osteoporosis does not have the elevated blood levels of alkaline phosphatase found in Paget's disease.

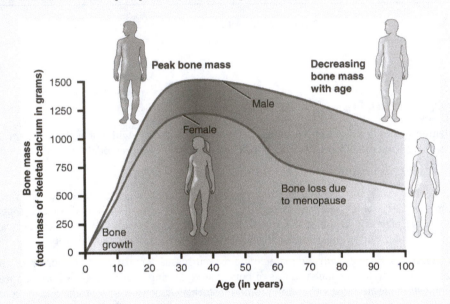

Figure 6.23 Graph Showing Relationship Between Age and Bone Mass Bone density peaks at about 30 years of age. Women lose bone mass more rapidly than men.

While osteoporosis can involve any bone, it most commonly affects the proximal ends of the femur, vertebrae, and wrist. As a result of the loss of bone density, the osseous tissue may not provide adequate support for everyday functions, and something as simple as a sneeze can cause a vertebral fracture. When an elderly person falls and breaks a hip (really, the femur), it is very likely the femur that broke first, which resulted in the fall. Histologically, osteoporosis is characterized by a reduction in the thickness of compact bone and the number and size of trabeculae in cancellous bone.

Figure 6.23 shows that women lose bone mass more quickly than men starting at about 50 years of age. This occurs because 50 is the approximate age at which women go through menopause. Not only do their menstrual periods lessen and eventually cease, but their ovaries reduce in size and then cease the production of estrogen, a hormone that promotes osteoblastic activity and production of bone matrix. Thus, osteoporosis is more common in women than in men, but men can develop it, too. Anyone with a family history of osteoporosis has a greater risk of developing the disease, so the best treatment is prevention, which should start with a childhood diet that includes adequate intake of calcium and vitamin D and a lifestyle that includes weight-bearing exercise. These actions, as discussed above, are important in building bone mass. Promoting proper nutrition and weight-bearing exercise early in life can maximize bone mass before the age of 30, thus reducing the risk of osteoporosis.

For many elderly people, a hip fracture can be life threatening. The fracture itself may not be serious, but the immobility that comes during the healing process can lead to the formation of blood clots that can lodge in the capillaries of the lungs, resulting in respiratory failure; pneumonia due to the lack of poor air exchange that accompanies immobility; pressure sores (bed sores) that allow pathogens to enter the body and cause infections; and urinary tract infections from catheterization.

Current treatments for managing osteoporosis include bisphosphonates (the same medications often used in Paget's disease), calcitonin, and estrogen (for women only). Minimizing the risk of falls, for example, by removing tripping hazards, is also an important step in managing the potential outcomes from the disease.

Hormones That Influence Osteoclasts

Bone modeling and remodeling require osteoclasts to resorb unneeded, damaged, or old bone, and osteoblasts to lay down new bone. Two hormones that affect the osteoclasts are parathyroid hormone (PTH) and calcitonin.

PTH stimulates osteoclast proliferation and activity. As a result, calcium is released from the bones into the circulation, thus increasing the calcium ion concentration in the blood. PTH also promotes the reabsorption of calcium by the kidney tubules, which can affect calcium homeostasis (see below).

The small intestine is also affected by PTH, albeit indirectly. Because another function of PTH is to stimulate the synthesis of vitamin D, and because vitamin D promotes intestinal absorption of calcium, PTH indirectly increases calcium uptake by the small intestine. Calcitonin, a hormone secreted by the thyroid gland, has some effects that counteract those of PTH. Calcitonin inhibits osteoclast activity and stimulates calcium uptake by the bones, thus reducing the concentration of calcium ions in the blood. As evidenced by their opposing functions in maintaining calcium homeostasis, PTH and calcitonin are generally *not* secreted at the same time. Table 6.6 summarizes the hormones that influence the skeletal system.

Hormones That Affect the Skeletal System

Hormone	Role
Growth hormone	Increases length of long bones, enhances mineralization, and improves bone density
Thyroxine	Stimulates bone growth and promotes synthesis of bone matrix
Sex hormones	Promote osteoblastic activity and production of bone matrix; responsible for adolescent growth spurt; promote conversion of epiphyseal plate to epiphyseal line
Calcitriol	Stimulates absorption of calcium and phosphate from digestive tract
Parathyroid hormone	Stimulates osteoclast proliferation and resorption of bone by osteoclasts; promotes reabsorption of calcium by kidney tubules; indirectly increases calcium absorption by small intestine
Calcitonin	Inhibits osteoclast activity and stimulates calcium uptake by bones

Table 6.6

6.7 | Calcium Homeostasis: Interactions of the Skeletal System and Other Organ Systems

By the end of this section, you will be able to:

- Describe the effect of too much or too little calcium on the body
- Explain the process of calcium homeostasis

Calcium is not only the most abundant mineral in bone, it is also the most abundant mineral in the human body. Calcium ions are needed not only for bone mineralization but for tooth health, regulation of the heart rate and strength of contraction, blood coagulation, contraction of smooth and skeletal muscle cells, and regulation of nerve impulse conduction. The normal level of calcium in the blood is about 10 mg/dL. When the body cannot maintain this level, a person will experience hypo- or hypercalcemia.

Hypocalcemia, a condition characterized by abnormally low levels of calcium, can have an adverse effect on a number of different body systems including circulation, muscles, nerves, and bone. Without adequate calcium, blood has difficulty coagulating, the heart may skip beats or stop beating altogether, muscles may have difficulty contracting, nerves may have difficulty functioning, and bones may become brittle. The causes of hypocalcemia can range from hormonal imbalances to an improper diet. Treatments vary according to the cause, but prognoses are generally good.

Conversely, in **hypercalcemia**, a condition characterized by abnormally high levels of calcium, the nervous system is underactive, which results in lethargy, sluggish reflexes, constipation and loss of appetite, confusion, and in severe cases, coma.

Obviously, calcium homeostasis is critical. The skeletal, endocrine, and digestive systems play a role in this, but the kidneys do, too. These body systems work together to maintain a normal calcium level in the blood (Figure 6.24).

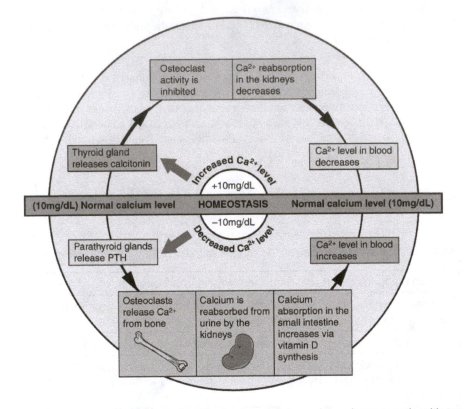

Figure 6.24 Pathways in Calcium Homeostasis The body regulates calcium homeostasis with two pathways; one is signaled to turn on when blood calcium levels drop below normal and one is the pathway that is signaled to turn on when blood calcium levels are elevated.

Calcium is a chemical element that cannot be produced by any biological processes. The only way it can enter the body is through the diet. The bones act as a storage site for calcium: The body deposits calcium in the bones when blood levels get too high, and it releases calcium when blood levels drop too low. This process is regulated by PTH, vitamin D, and calcitonin.

Cells of the parathyroid gland have plasma membrane receptors for calcium. When calcium is not binding to these receptors, the cells release PTH, which stimulates osteoclast proliferation and resorption of bone by osteoclasts. This demineralization process releases calcium into the blood. PTH promotes reabsorption of calcium from the urine by the kidneys, so that the calcium returns to the blood. Finally, PTH stimulates the synthesis of vitamin D, which in turn, stimulates calcium absorption from any digested food in the small intestine.

When all these processes return blood calcium levels to normal, there is enough calcium to bind with the receptors on the surface of the cells of the parathyroid glands, and this cycle of events is turned off (Figure 6.24).

When blood levels of calcium get too high, the thyroid gland is stimulated to release calcitonin (Figure 6.24), which inhibits osteoclast activity and stimulates calcium uptake by the bones, but also decreases reabsorption of calcium by the kidneys. All of these actions lower blood levels of calcium. When blood calcium levels return to normal, the thyroid gland stops secreting calcitonin.

KEY TERMS

articular cartilage thin layer of cartilage covering an epiphysis; reduces friction and acts as a shock absorber

articulation where two bone surfaces meet

bone hard, dense connective tissue that forms the structural elements of the skeleton

canaliculi (singular = canaliculus) channels within the bone matrix that house one of an osteocyte's many cytoplasmic extensions that it uses to communicate and receive nutrients

cartilage semi-rigid connective tissue found on the skeleton in areas where flexibility and smooth surfaces support movement

central canal longitudinal channel in the center of each osteon; contains blood vessels, nerves, and lymphatic vessels; also known as the Haversian canal

closed reduction manual manipulation of a broken bone to set it into its natural position without surgery

compact bone dense osseous tissue that can withstand compressive forces

diaphysis tubular shaft that runs between the proximal and distal ends of a long bone

diploë layer of spongy bone, that is sandwiched between two the layers of compact bone found in flat bones

endochondral ossification process in which bone forms by replacing hyaline cartilage

endosteum delicate membranous lining of a bone's medullary cavity

epiphyseal line completely ossified remnant of the epiphyseal plate

epiphyseal plate (also, growth plate) sheet of hyaline cartilage in the metaphysis of an immature bone; replaced by bone tissue as the organ grows in length

epiphysis wide section at each end of a long bone; filled with spongy bone and red marrow

external callus collar of hyaline cartilage and bone that forms around the outside of a fracture

flat bone thin and curved bone; serves as a point of attachment for muscles and protects internal organs

fracture broken bone

fracture hematoma blood clot that forms at the site of a broken bone

hematopoiesis production of blood cells, which occurs in the red marrow of the bones

hole opening or depression in a bone

hypercalcemia condition characterized by abnormally high levels of calcium

hypocalcemia condition characterized by abnormally low levels of calcium

internal callus fibrocartilaginous matrix, in the endosteal region, between the two ends of a broken bone

intramembranous ossification process by which bone forms directly from mesenchymal tissue

irregular bone bone of complex shape; protects internal organs from compressive forces

lacunae (singular = lacuna) spaces in a bone that house an osteocyte

long bone cylinder-shaped bone that is longer than it is wide; functions as a lever

medullary cavity hollow region of the diaphysis; filled with yellow marrow

modeling process, during bone growth, by which bone is resorbed on one surface of a bone and deposited on another

nutrient foramen small opening in the middle of the external surface of the diaphysis, through which an artery enters the bone to provide nourishment

open reduction surgical exposure of a bone to reset a fracture

orthopedist doctor who specializes in diagnosing and treating musculoskeletal disorders and injuries

osseous tissue bone tissue; a hard, dense connective tissue that forms the structural elements of the skeleton

ossification (also, osteogenesis) bone formation

ossification center cluster of osteoblasts found in the early stages of intramembranous ossification

osteoblast cell responsible for forming new bone

osteoclast cell responsible for resorbing bone

osteocyte primary cell in mature bone; responsible for maintaining the matrix

osteogenic cell undifferentiated cell with high mitotic activity; the only bone cells that divide; they differentiate and develop into osteoblasts

osteoid uncalcified bone matrix secreted by osteoblasts

osteon (also, Haversian system) basic structural unit of compact bone; made of concentric layers of calcified matrix

osteoporosis disease characterized by a decrease in bone mass; occurs when the rate of bone resorption exceeds the rate of bone formation, a common occurrence as the body ages

perforating canal (also, Volkmann's canal) channel that branches off from the central canal and houses vessels and nerves that extend to the periosteum and endosteum

perichondrium membrane that covers cartilage

periosteum fibrous membrane covering the outer surface of bone and continuous with ligaments

primary ossification center region, deep in the periosteal collar, where bone development starts during endochondral ossification

projection bone markings where part of the surface sticks out above the rest of the surface, where tendons and ligaments attach

proliferative zone region of the epiphyseal plate that makes new chondrocytes to replace those that die at the diaphyseal end of the plate and contributes to longitudinal growth of the epiphyseal plate

red marrow connective tissue in the interior cavity of a bone where hematopoiesis takes place

remodeling process by which osteoclasts resorb old or damaged bone at the same time as and on the same surface where osteoblasts form new bone to replace that which is resorbed

reserve zone region of the epiphyseal plate that anchors the plate to the osseous tissue of the epiphysis

secondary ossification center region of bone development in the epiphyses

sesamoid bone small, round bone embedded in a tendon; protects the tendon from compressive forces

short bone cube-shaped bone that is approximately equal in length, width, and thickness; provides limited motion

skeletal system organ system composed of bones and cartilage that provides for movement, support, and protection

spongy bone (also, cancellous bone) trabeculated osseous tissue that supports shifts in weight distribution

trabeculae (singular = trabecula) spikes or sections of the lattice-like matrix in spongy bone

yellow marrow connective tissue in the interior cavity of a bone where fat is stored

zone of calcified matrix region of the epiphyseal plate closest to the diaphyseal end; functions to connect the epiphyseal plate to the diaphysis

zone of maturation and hypertrophy region of the epiphyseal plate where chondrocytes from the proliferative zone grow and mature and contribute to the longitudinal growth of the epiphyseal plate

CHAPTER REVIEW

6.1 The Functions of the Skeletal System

The major functions of the bones are body support, facilitation of movement, protection of internal organs, storage of minerals and fat, and hematopoiesis. Together, the muscular system and skeletal system are known as the musculoskeletal system.

6.2 Bone Classification

Bones can be classified according to their shapes. Long bones, such as the femur, are longer than they are wide. Short bones, such as the carpals, are approximately equal in length, width, and thickness. Flat bones are thin, but are often curved, such as the ribs. Irregular bones such as those of the face have no characteristic shape. Sesamoid bones, such as the patellae, are small and round, and are located in tendons.

6.3 Bone Structure

A hollow medullary cavity filled with yellow marrow runs the length of the diaphysis of a long bone. The walls of the diaphysis are compact bone. The epiphyses, which are wider sections at each end of a long bone, are filled with spongy bone and red marrow. The epiphyseal plate, a layer of hyaline cartilage, is replaced by osseous tissue as the organ grows in length. The medullary cavity has a delicate membranous lining called the endosteum. The outer surface of bone, except in regions covered with articular cartilage, is covered with a fibrous membrane called the periosteum. Flat bones consist of two layers of compact bone surrounding a layer of spongy bone. Bone markings depend on the function and location of bones. Articulations are places where two bones meet. Projections stick out from the surface of the bone and provide attachment points for tendons and ligaments. Holes are openings or depressions in the bones.

Bone matrix consists of collagen fibers and organic ground substance, primarily hydroxyapatite formed from calcium salts. Osteogenic cells develop into osteoblasts. Osteoblasts are cells that make new bone. They become osteocytes, the cells of mature bone, when they get trapped in the matrix. Osteoclasts engage in bone resorption. Compact bone is dense and composed of osteons, while spongy bone is less dense and made up of trabeculae. Blood vessels and nerves enter the bone through the nutrient foramina to nourish and innervate bones.

6.4 Bone Formation and Development

All bone formation is a replacement process. Embryos develop a cartilaginous skeleton and various membranes. During development, these are replaced by bone during the ossification process. In intramembranous ossification, bone develops directly from sheets of mesenchymal connective tissue. In endochondral ossification, bone develops by replacing hyaline cartilage. Activity in the epiphyseal plate enables bones to grow in length. Modeling allows bones to grow in diameter. Remodeling occurs as bone is resorbed and replaced by new bone. Osteogenesis imperfecta is a genetic disease in which collagen production is altered, resulting in fragile, brittle bones.

6.5 Fractures: Bone Repair

Fractured bones may be repaired by closed reduction or open reduction. Fractures are classified by their complexity, location, and other features. Common types of fractures are transverse, oblique, spiral, comminuted, impacted, greenstick, open (or compound), and closed (or simple). Healing of fractures begins with the formation of a hematoma, followed by internal and external calli. Osteoclasts resorb dead bone, while osteoblasts create new bone that replaces the cartilage in the calli. The calli eventually unite, remodeling occurs, and healing is complete.

6.6 Exercise, Nutrition, Hormones, and Bone Tissue

Mechanical stress stimulates the deposition of mineral salts and collagen fibers within bones. Calcium, the predominant mineral in bone, cannot be absorbed from the small intestine if vitamin D is lacking. Vitamin K supports bone mineralization and may have a synergistic role with vitamin D. Magnesium and fluoride, as structural elements, play a supporting role in bone health. Omega-3 fatty acids reduce inflammation and may promote production of new osseous tissue. Growth hormone increases the length of long bones, enhances mineralization, and improves bone density. Thyroxine stimulates bone growth and promotes the synthesis of bone matrix. The sex hormones (estrogen in women; testosterone in men) promote osteoblastic activity and the production of bone matrix, are responsible for the adolescent growth spurt, and promote closure of the epiphyseal plates. Osteoporosis is a disease characterized by decreased bone mass that is common in aging adults. Calcitriol stimulates the digestive tract to absorb calcium and phosphate. Parathyroid hormone (PTH) stimulates osteoclast proliferation and resorption of bone by osteoclasts. Vitamin D plays a synergistic role with PTH in stimulating the osteoclasts. Additional functions of PTH include promoting reabsorption of calcium by kidney tubules and indirectly increasing calcium absorption from the small intestine. Calcitonin inhibits osteoclast activity and stimulates calcium uptake by bones.

6.7 Calcium Homeostasis: Interactions of the Skeletal System and Other Organ Systems

Calcium homeostasis, i.e., maintaining a blood calcium level of about 10 mg/dL, is critical for normal body functions. Hypocalcemia can result in problems with blood coagulation, muscle contraction, nerve functioning, and bone strength. Hypercalcemia can result in lethargy, sluggish reflexes, constipation and loss of appetite, confusion, and coma. Calcium homeostasis is controlled by PTH, vitamin D, and calcitonin and the interactions of the skeletal, endocrine, digestive, and urinary systems.

REVIEW QUESTIONS

1. Which function of the skeletal system would be especially important if you were in a car accident?

   a. storage of minerals
   b. protection of internal organs
   c. facilitation of movement
   d. fat storage

2. Bone tissue can be described as _____.
   a. dead calcified tissue
   b. cartilage
   c. the skeletal system
   d. dense, hard connective tissue

3. Without red marrow, bones would not be able to _____.
   a. store phosphate
   b. store calcium
   c. make blood cells
   d. move like levers

4. Yellow marrow has been identified as _____.

   a. an area of fat storage
   b. a point of attachment for muscles
   c. the hard portion of bone
   d. the cause of kyphosis

5. Which of the following can be found in areas of movement?
   a. hematopoiesis
   b. cartilage
   c. yellow marrow
   d. red marrow

6. The skeletal system is made of _____.
   a. muscles and tendons
   b. bones and cartilage
   c. vitreous humor
   d. minerals and fat

7. Most of the bones of the arms and hands are long bones; however, the bones in the wrist are categorized as _____.
   a. flat bones
   b. short bones
   c. sesamoid bones
   d. irregular bones

8. Sesamoid bones are found embedded in _____.

   a. joints
   b. muscles
   c. ligaments
   d. tendons

9. Bones that surround the spinal cord are classified as _____ bones.
   a. irregular
   b. sesamoid
   c. flat
   d. short

10. Which category of bone is among the most numerous in the skeleton?
   a. long bone
   b. sesamoid bone
   c. short bone
   d. flat bone

11. Long bones enable body movement by acting as a _____.
   a. counterweight
   b. resistive force
   c. lever
   d. fulcrum

12. Which of the following occurs in the spongy bone of the epiphysis?
   a. bone growth
   b. bone remodeling
   c. hematopoiesis
   d. shock absorption

13. The diaphysis contains _____.
   a. the metaphysis
   b. fat stores
   c. spongy bone
   d. compact bone

14. The fibrous membrane covering the outer surface of the bone is the _____.
   a. periosteum
   b. epiphysis
   c. endosteum
   d. diaphysis

15. Which of the following are incapable of undergoing mitosis?
   a. osteoblasts and osteoclasts
   b. osteocytes and osteoclasts
   c. osteoblasts and osteocytes
   d. osteogenic cells and osteoclasts

16. Which cells do not originate from osteogenic cells?
   a. osteoblasts
   b. osteoclasts
   c. osteocytes
   d. osteoprogenitor cells

17. Which of the following are found in compact bone and cancellous bone?
   a. Haversian systems
   b. Haversian canals
   c. lamellae
   d. lacunae

18. Which of the following are *only* found in cancellous bone?
   a. canaliculi
   b. Volkmann's canals
   c. trabeculae
   d. calcium salts

19. The area of a bone where the nutrient foramen passes forms what kind of bone marking?
   a. a hole
   b. a facet
   c. a canal
   d. a fissure

20. Why is cartilage slow to heal?
   a. because it eventually develops into bone
   b. because it is semi-solid and flexible
   c. because it does not have a blood supply
   d. because endochondral ossification replaces all cartilage with bone

21. Why are osteocytes spread out in bone tissue?
   a. They develop from mesenchymal cells.
   b. They are surrounded by osteoid.
   c. They travel through the capillaries.
   d. Formation of osteoid spreads out the osteoblasts that formed the ossification centers.

22. In endochondral ossification, what happens to the chondrocytes?
   a. They develop into osteocytes.
   b. They die in the calcified matrix that surrounds them and form the medullary cavity.
   c. They grow and form the periosteum.
   d. They group together to form the primary ossification center.

23. Which of the following bones is (are) formed by intramembranous ossification?
   a. the metatarsals
   b. the femur
   c. the ribs
   d. the flat bones of the cranium

24. Bones grow in length due to activity in the _____.
   a. epiphyseal plate
   b. perichondrium
   c. periosteum
   d. medullary cavity

25. Bones grow in diameter due to bone formation _____.
   a. in the medullary cavity
   b. beneath the periosteum
   c. in the epiphyseal plate
   d. within the metaphysis

26. Which of the following represents the correct sequence of zones in the epiphyseal plate?
   a. proliferation, reserved, maturation, calcification
   b. maturation, proliferation, reserved, calcification
   c. calcification, maturation, proliferation, reserved
   d. calcification, reserved, proliferation, maturation

27. A fracture can be both _____.
   a. open and closed
   b. open and transverse
   c. transverse and greenstick
   d. greenstick and comminuted

28. How can a fractured diaphysis release fat globules into the bloodstream?
    a. The bone pierces fat stores in the skin.
    b. The yellow marrow in the diaphysis is exposed and damaged.
    c. The injury triggers the body to release fat from healthy bones.
    d. The red marrow in the fractured bone releases fat to heal the fracture.

29. In a compound fracture, _____.
    a. the break occurs at an angle to the bone
    b. the broken bone does not tear the skin
    c. one fragment of broken bone is compressed into the other
    d. broken bone pierces the skin

30. The internal and external calli are replaced by _____.
    a. hyaline cartilage
    b. trabecular bone
    c. osteogenic cells
    d. osteoclasts

31. The first type of bone to form during fracture repair is _____ bone.
    a. compact
    b. lamellar
    c. spongy
    d. dense

32. Wolff's law, which describes the effect of mechanical forces in bone modeling/remodeling, would predict that _____
    a. a right-handed pitcher will have thicker bones in his right arm compared to his left.
    b. a right-handed cyclist will have thicker bones in her right leg compared to her left.
    c. a broken bone will heal thicker than it was before the fracture.
    d. a bed-ridden patient will have thicker bones than an athlete.

33. Calcium cannot be absorbed from the small intestine if _____ is lacking.
    a. vitamin D
    b. vitamin K
    c. calcitonin
    d. fluoride

34. Which one of the following foods is best for bone health?
    a. carrots
    b. liver
    c. leafy green vegetables
    d. oranges

35. Which of the following hormones are responsible for the adolescent growth spurt?
    a. estrogen and testosterone
    b. calcitonin and calcitriol
    c. growth hormone and parathyroid hormone
    d. thyroxine and progesterone

36. With respect to their direct effects on osseous tissue, which pair of hormones has actions that oppose each other?
    a. estrogen and testosterone
    b. calcitonin and calcitriol
    c. estrogen and progesterone
    d. calcitonin and parathyroid hormone

37. When calcium levels are too high or too low, which body system is primarily affected?
    a. skeletal system
    b. endocrine system
    c. digestive system
    d. nervous system

38. All of the following play a role in calcium homeostasis except
    a. thyroxine
    b. calcitonin
    c. parathyroid hormone
    d. vitamin D

39. Which of the following is most likely to be released when blood calcium levels are elevated?
    a. thyroxine
    b. calcitonin
    c. parathyroid hormone
    d. vitamin D

CRITICAL THINKING QUESTIONS

40. The skeletal system is composed of bone and cartilage and has many functions. Choose three of these functions and discuss what features of the skeletal system allow it to accomplish these functions.

41. What are the structural and functional differences between a tarsal and a metatarsal?

42. What are the structural and functional differences between the femur and the patella?

43. If the articular cartilage at the end of one of your long bones were to degenerate, what symptoms do you think you would experience? Why?

44. In what ways is the structural makeup of compact and spongy bone well suited to their respective functions?

45. In what ways do intramembranous and endochondral ossification differ?

46. Considering how a long bone develops, what are the similarities and differences between a primary and a secondary ossification center?

47. What is the difference between closed reduction and open reduction? In what type of fracture would closed reduction most likely occur? In what type of fracture would open reduction most likely occur?

48. In terms of origin and composition, what are the differences between an internal callus and an external callus?

49. If you were a dietician who had a young female patient with a family history of osteoporosis, what foods would you suggest she include in her diet? Why?

50. During the early years of space exploration our astronauts, who had been floating in space, would return to earth showing significant bone loss dependent on how long they were in space. Discuss how this might happen and what could be done to alleviate this condition.

51. An individual with very low levels of vitamin D presents themselves to you complaining of seemingly fragile bones. Explain how these might be connected.

52. Describe the effects caused when the parathyroid gland fails to respond to calcium bound to its receptors.

7 | AXIAL SKELETON

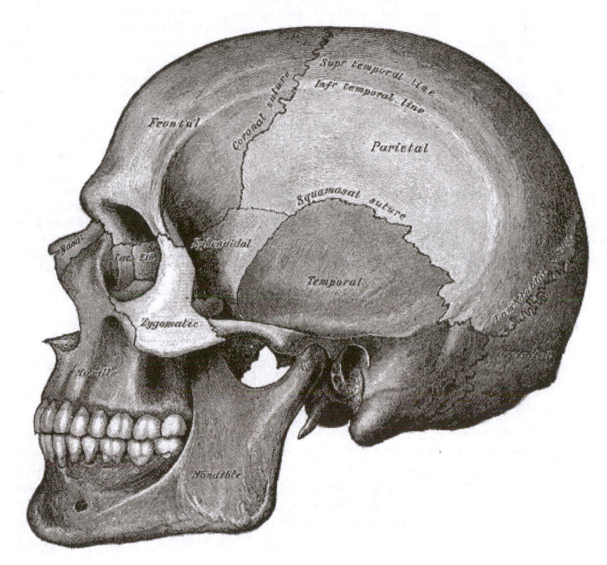

Figure 7.1 Lateral View of the Human Skull

Introduction

Chapter Objectives

After studying this chapter, you will be able to:

- Describe the functions of the skeletal system and define its two major subdivisions
- Identify the bones and bony structures of the skull, the cranial suture lines, the cranial fossae, and the openings in the skull
- Discuss the vertebral column and regional variations in its bony components and curvatures
- Describe the components of the thoracic cage
- Discuss the embryonic development of the axial skeleton

The skeletal system forms the rigid internal framework of the body. It consists of the bones, cartilages, and ligaments. Bones support the weight of the body, allow for body movements, and protect internal organs. Cartilage provides flexible strength and support for body structures such as the thoracic cage, the external ear, and the trachea and larynx. At joints of the body, cartilage can also unite adjacent bones or provide cushioning between them. Ligaments are the strong connective tissue bands that hold the bones at a moveable joint together and serve to prevent excessive movements of the joint that would result in injury. Providing movement of the skeleton are the muscles of the body, which are firmly attached to the skeleton via connective tissue structures called tendons. As muscles contract, they pull on the bones to produce movements of the body. Thus, without a skeleton, you would not be able to stand, run, or even feed yourself!

Each bone of the body serves a particular function, and therefore bones vary in size, shape, and strength based on these functions. For example, the bones of the lower back and lower limb are thick and strong to support your body weight. Similarly, the size of a bony landmark that serves as a muscle attachment site on an individual bone is related to the strength of this muscle. Muscles can apply very strong pulling forces to the bones of the skeleton. To resist these forces, bones have enlarged bony landmarks at sites where powerful muscles attach. This means that not only the size of a bone, but also its shape, is related to its function. For this reason, the identification of bony landmarks is important during your study of the skeletal system.

Bones are also dynamic organs that can modify their strength and thickness in response to changes in muscle strength or body weight. Thus, muscle attachment sites on bones will thicken if you begin a workout program that increases muscle strength. Similarly, the walls of weight-bearing bones will thicken if you gain body weight or begin pounding the pavement as part of a new running regimen. In contrast, a reduction in muscle strength or body weight will cause bones to become thinner. This may happen during a prolonged hospital stay, following limb immobilization in a cast, or going into the weightlessness of outer space. Even a change in diet, such as eating only soft food due to the loss of teeth, will result in a noticeable decrease in the size and thickness of the jaw bones.

7.1 | Divisions of the Skeletal System

By the end of this section, you will be able to:

- Discuss the functions of the skeletal system
- Distinguish between the axial skeleton and appendicular skeleton
- Define the axial skeleton and its components
- Define the appendicular skeleton and its components

The skeletal system includes all of the bones, cartilages, and ligaments of the body that support and give shape to the body and body structures. The **skeleton** consists of the bones of the body. For adults, there are 206 bones in the skeleton. Younger individuals have higher numbers of bones because some bones fuse together during childhood and adolescence to form an adult bone. The primary functions of the skeleton are to provide a rigid, internal structure that can support the weight of the body against the force of gravity, and to provide a structure upon which muscles can act to produce movements of the body. The lower portion of the skeleton is specialized for stability during walking or running. In contrast, the upper skeleton has greater mobility and ranges of motion, features that allow you to lift and carry objects or turn your head and trunk.

In addition to providing for support and movements of the body, the skeleton has protective and storage functions. It protects the internal organs, including the brain, spinal cord, heart, lungs, and pelvic organs. The bones of the skeleton serve as the primary storage site for important minerals such as calcium and phosphate. The bone marrow found within bones stores fat and houses the blood-cell producing tissue of the body.

The skeleton is subdivided into two major divisions—the axial and appendicular.

The Axial Skeleton

The skeleton is subdivided into two major divisions—the axial and appendicular. The **axial skeleton** forms the vertical, central axis of the body and includes all bones of the head, neck, chest, and back (**Figure 7.2**). It serves to protect the brain, spinal cord, heart, and lungs. It also serves as the attachment site for muscles that move the head, neck, and back, and for muscles that act across the shoulder and hip joints to move their corresponding limbs.

The axial skeleton of the adult consists of 80 bones, including the **skull**, the **vertebral column**, and the **thoracic cage**. The skull is formed by 22 bones. Also associated with the head are an additional seven bones, including the **hyoid bone** and the **ear ossicles** (three small bones found in each middle ear). The vertebral column consists of 24 bones, each called a **vertebra**, plus the **sacrum** and **coccyx**. The thoracic cage includes the 12 pairs of **ribs**, and the **sternum**, the flattened bone of the anterior chest.

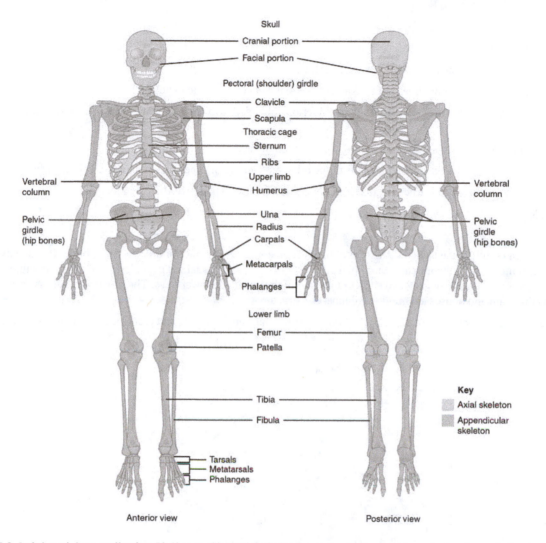

Figure 7.2 Axial and Appendicular Skeleton The axial skeleton supports the head, neck, back, and chest and thus forms the vertical axis of the body. It consists of the skull, vertebral column (including the sacrum and coccyx), and the thoracic cage, formed by the ribs and sternum. The appendicular skeleton is made up of all bones of the upper and lower limbs.

The Appendicular Skeleton

The **appendicular skeleton** includes all bones of the upper and lower limbs, plus the bones that attach each limb to the axial skeleton. There are 126 bones in the appendicular skeleton of an adult. The bones of the appendicular skeleton are covered in a separate chapter.

7.2 | The Skull

By the end of this section, you will be able to:

- List and identify the bones of the brain case and face
- Locate the major suture lines of the skull and name the bones associated with each
- Locate and define the boundaries of the anterior, middle, and posterior cranial fossae, the temporal fossa, and infratemporal fossa
- Define the paranasal sinuses and identify the location of each
- Name the bones that make up the walls of the orbit and identify the openings associated with the orbit
- Identify the bones and structures that form the nasal septum and nasal conchae, and locate the hyoid bone
- Identify the bony openings of the skull

The **cranium** (skull) is the skeletal structure of the head that supports the face and protects the brain. It is subdivided into the **facial bones** and the **brain case**, or cranial vault (Figure 7.3). The facial bones underlie the facial structures, form the nasal cavity, enclose the eyeballs, and support the teeth of the upper and lower jaws. The rounded brain case surrounds and protects the brain and houses the middle and inner ear structures.

In the adult, the skull consists of 22 individual bones, 21 of which are immobile and united into a single unit. The 22nd bone is the **mandible** (lower jaw), which is the only moveable bone of the skull.

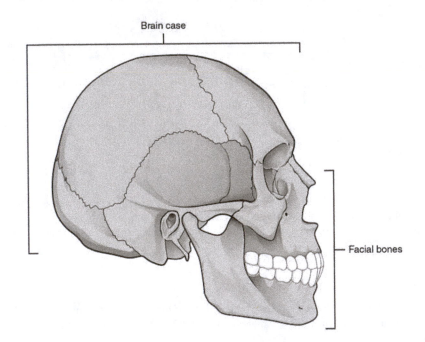

Figure 7.3 Parts of the Skull   The skull consists of the rounded brain case that houses the brain and the facial bones that form the upper and lower jaws, nose, orbits, and other facial structures.

Watch this **video (http://openstaxcollege.org/l/skull1)** to view a rotating and exploded skull, with color-coded bones. Which bone (yellow) is centrally located and joins with most of the other bones of the skull?

Anterior View of Skull

The anterior skull consists of the facial bones and provides the bony support for the eyes and structures of the face. This view of the skull is dominated by the openings of the orbits and the nasal cavity. Also seen are the upper and lower jaws, with their respective teeth (**Figure 7.4**).

The **orbit** is the bony socket that houses the eyeball and muscles that move the eyeball or open the upper eyelid. The upper margin of the anterior orbit is the **supraorbital margin**. Located near the midpoint of the supraorbital margin is a small opening called the **supraorbital foramen**. This provides for passage of a sensory nerve to the skin of the forehead. Below the orbit is the **infraorbital foramen**, which is the point of emergence for a sensory nerve that supplies the anterior face below the orbit.

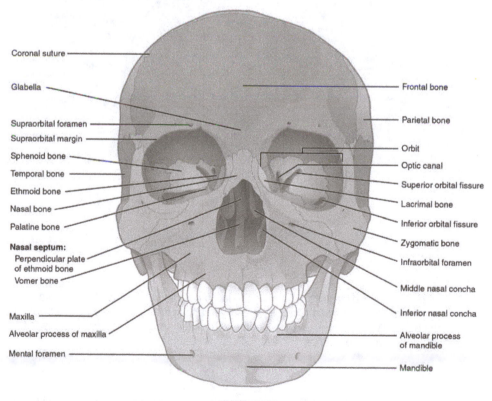

Figure 7.4 Anterior View of Skull An anterior view of the skull shows the bones that form the forehead, orbits (eye sockets), nasal cavity, nasal septum, and upper and lower jaws.

Inside the nasal area of the skull, the **nasal cavity** is divided into halves by the **nasal septum**. The upper portion of the nasal septum is formed by the **perpendicular plate of the ethmoid bone** and the lower portion is the **vomer bone**. Each side of the nasal cavity is triangular in shape, with a broad inferior space that narrows superiorly. When looking into the nasal cavity from the front of the skull, two bony plates are seen projecting from each lateral wall. The larger of these is the **inferior nasal concha**, an independent bone of the skull. Located just above the inferior concha is the **middle nasal concha**, which is part of the ethmoid bone. A third bony plate, also part of the ethmoid bone, is the **superior nasal concha**. It is much smaller and out of sight, above the middle concha. The superior nasal concha is located just lateral to the perpendicular plate, in the upper nasal cavity.

Lateral View of Skull

A view of the lateral skull is dominated by the large, rounded brain case above and the upper and lower jaws with their teeth below (**Figure 7.5**). Separating these areas is the bridge of bone called the zygomatic arch. The **zygomatic arch** is the bony arch on the side of skull that spans from the area of the cheek to just above the ear canal. It is formed by the junction of two bony processes: a short anterior component, the **temporal process of the zygomatic bone** (the cheekbone) and a longer posterior portion, the **zygomatic process of the temporal bone**, extending forward from the temporal bone. Thus the temporal process (anteriorly) and the zygomatic process (posteriorly) join together, like the two ends of a drawbridge, to form the zygomatic arch. One of the major muscles that pulls the mandible upward during biting and chewing arises from the zygomatic arch.

On the lateral side of the brain case, above the level of the zygomatic arch, is a shallow space called the **temporal fossa**. Below the level of the zygomatic arch and deep to the vertical portion of the mandible is another space called the **infratemporal fossa**. Both the temporal fossa and infratemporal fossa contain muscles that act on the mandible during chewing.

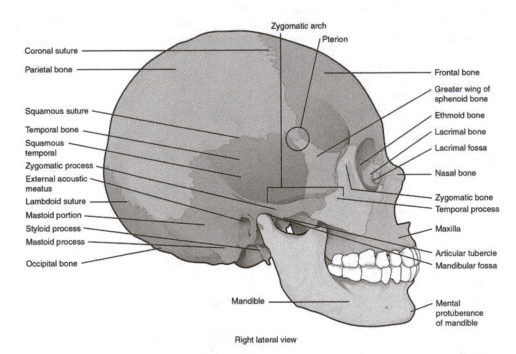

Right lateral view

Figure 7.5 Lateral View of Skull The lateral skull shows the large rounded brain case, zygomatic arch, and the upper and lower jaws. The zygomatic arch is formed jointly by the zygomatic process of the temporal bone and the temporal process of the zygomatic bone. The shallow space above the zygomatic arch is the temporal fossa. The space inferior to the zygomatic arch and deep to the posterior mandible is the infratemporal fossa.

Bones of the Brain Case

The brain case contains and protects the brain. The interior space that is almost completely occupied by the brain is called the **cranial cavity**. This cavity is bounded superiorly by the rounded top of the skull, which is called the **calvaria** (skullcap), and the lateral and posterior sides of the skull. The bones that form the top and sides of the brain case are usually referred to as the "flat" bones of the skull.

The floor of the brain case is referred to as the base of the skull. This is a complex area that varies in depth and has numerous openings for the passage of cranial nerves, blood vessels, and the spinal cord. Inside the skull, the base is subdivided into three large spaces, called the **anterior cranial fossa**, **middle cranial fossa**, and **posterior cranial fossa** (fossa = "trench or ditch") (**Figure 7.6**). From anterior to posterior, the fossae increase in depth. The shape and depth of each fossa corresponds to the shape and size of the brain region that each houses. The boundaries and openings of the cranial fossae (singular = fossa) will be described in a later section.

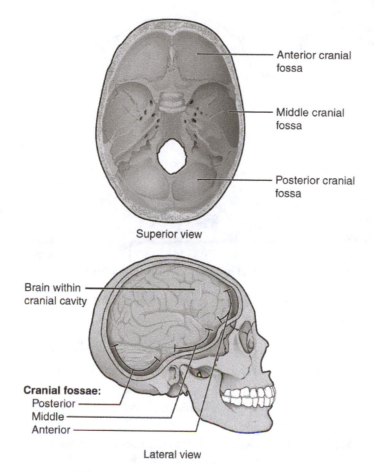

Figure 7.6 Cranial Fossae   The bones of the brain case surround and protect the brain, which occupies the cranial cavity. The base of the brain case, which forms the floor of cranial cavity, is subdivided into the shallow anterior cranial fossa, the middle cranial fossa, and the deep posterior cranial fossa.

The brain case consists of eight bones. These include the paired parietal and temporal bones, plus the unpaired frontal, occipital, sphenoid, and ethmoid bones.

Parietal Bone

The **parietal bone** forms most of the upper lateral side of the skull (see **Figure 7.5**). These are paired bones, with the right and left parietal bones joining together at the top of the skull. Each parietal bone is also bounded anteriorly by the frontal bone, inferiorly by the temporal bone, and posteriorly by the occipital bone.

Temporal Bone

The **temporal bone** forms the lower lateral side of the skull (see **Figure 7.5**). Common wisdom has it that the temporal bone (temporal = "time") is so named because this area of the head (the temple) is where hair typically first turns gray, indicating the passage of time.

The temporal bone is subdivided into several regions (**Figure 7.7**). The flattened, upper portion is the squamous portion of the temporal bone. Below this area and projecting anteriorly is the zygomatic process of the temporal bone, which forms the posterior portion of the zygomatic arch. Posteriorly is the mastoid portion of the temporal bone. Projecting inferiorly from this region is a large prominence, the **mastoid process**, which serves as a muscle attachment site. The mastoid process can easily be felt on the side of the head just behind your earlobe. On the interior of the skull, the petrous portion of each temporal bone forms the prominent, diagonally oriented **petrous ridge** in the floor of the cranial cavity. Located inside each petrous ridge are small cavities that house the structures of the middle and inner ears.

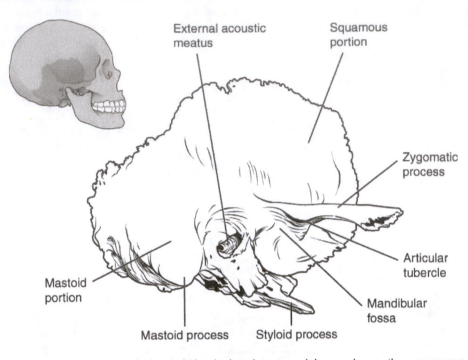

Figure 7.7 Temporal Bone A lateral view of the isolated temporal bone shows the squamous, mastoid, and zygomatic portions of the temporal bone.

Important landmarks of the temporal bone, as shown in Figure 7.8, include the following:

- **External acoustic meatus** (ear canal)—This is the large opening on the lateral side of the skull that is associated with the ear.

- **Internal acoustic meatus**—This opening is located inside the cranial cavity, on the medial side of the petrous ridge. It connects to the middle and inner ear cavities of the temporal bone.

- **Mandibular fossa**—This is the deep, oval-shaped depression located on the external base of the skull, just in front of the external acoustic meatus. The mandible (lower jaw) joins with the skull at this site as part of the temporomandibular joint, which allows for movements of the mandible during opening and closing of the mouth.

- **Articular tubercle**—The smooth ridge located immediately anterior to the mandibular fossa. Both the articular tubercle and mandibular fossa contribute to the temporomandibular joint, the joint that provides for movements between the temporal bone of the skull and the mandible.

- **Styloid process**—Posterior to the mandibular fossa on the external base of the skull is an elongated, downward bony projection called the styloid process, so named because of its resemblance to a stylus (a pen or writing tool). This structure serves as an attachment site for several small muscles and for a ligament that supports the hyoid bone of the neck. (See also Figure 7.7.)

- **Stylomastoid foramen**—This small opening is located between the styloid process and mastoid process. This is the point of exit for the cranial nerve that supplies the facial muscles.

- **Carotid canal**—The carotid canal is a zig-zag shaped tunnel that provides passage through the base of the skull for one of the major arteries that supplies the brain. Its entrance is located on the outside base of the skull, anteromedial to the styloid process. The canal then runs anteromedially within the bony base of the skull, and then turns upward to its exit in the floor of the middle cranial cavity, above the foramen lacerum.

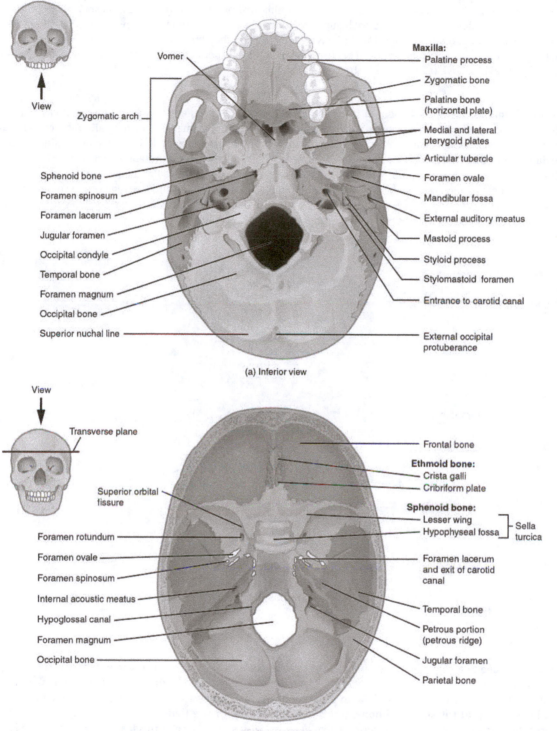

Vomer

View

Zygomatic arch

Sphenoid bone

Foramen spinosum

Foramen lacerum

Jugular foramen

Occipital condyle

Temporal bone

Foramen magnum

Occipital bone

Superior nuchal line

Maxilla:
Palatine process

Zygomatic bone

Palatine bone
(horizontal plate)

Medial and lateral
pterygoid plates

Articular tubercle

Foramen ovale

Mandibular fossa

External auditory meatus

Mastoid process

Styloid process

Stylomastoid foramen

Entrance to carotid canal

External occipital
protuberance

(a) Inferior view

View

Transverse plane

Superior orbital
fissure

Foramen rotundum

Foramen ovale

Foramen spinosum

Internal acoustic meatus

Hypoglossal canal

Foramen magnum

Occipital bone

Frontal bone

Ethmoid bone:
Crista galli
Cribriform plate

Sphenoid bone:
Lesser wing
Hypophyseal fossa ⎤ Sella
           ⎦ turcica

Foramen lacerum
and exit of carotid
canal

Temporal bone

Petrous portion
(petrous ridge)

Jugular foramen

Parietal bone

(b) Superior view

Figure 7.8 External and Internal Views of Base of Skull (a) The hard palate is formed anteriorly by the palatine processes of the maxilla bones and posteriorly by the horizontal plate of the palatine bones. (b) The complex floor of the cranial cavity is formed by the frontal, ethmoid, sphenoid, temporal, and occipital bones. The lesser wing of the sphenoid bone separates the anterior and middle cranial fossae. The petrous ridge (petrous portion of temporal bone) separates the middle and posterior cranial fossae.

Frontal Bone

The **frontal bone** is the single bone that forms the forehead. At its anterior midline, between the eyebrows, there is a slight depression called the **glabella** (see Figure 7.5). The frontal bone also forms the supraorbital margin of the orbit. Near the middle of this margin, is the supraorbital foramen, the opening that provides passage for a sensory nerve to the forehead. The frontal bone is thickened just above each supraorbital margin, forming rounded brow ridges. These are located just behind your eyebrows and vary in size among individuals, although they are generally larger in males. Inside the cranial cavity, the frontal bone extends posteriorly. This flattened region forms both the roof of the orbit below and the floor of the anterior cranial cavity above (see Figure 7.8b).

Occipital Bone

The **occipital bone** is the single bone that forms the posterior skull and posterior base of the cranial cavity (Figure 7.9; see also Figure 7.8). On its outside surface, at the posterior midline, is a small protrusion called the **external occipital protuberance**, which serves as an attachment site for a ligament of the posterior neck. Lateral to either side of this bump is a **superior nuchal line** (nuchal = "nape" or "posterior neck"). The nuchal lines represent the most superior point at which muscles of the neck attach to the skull, with only the scalp covering the skull above these lines. On the base of the skull, the occipital bone contains the large opening of the **foramen magnum**, which allows for passage of the spinal cord as it exits the skull. On either side of the foramen magnum is an oval-shaped **occipital condyle**. These condyles form joints with the first cervical vertebra and thus support the skull on top of the vertebral column.

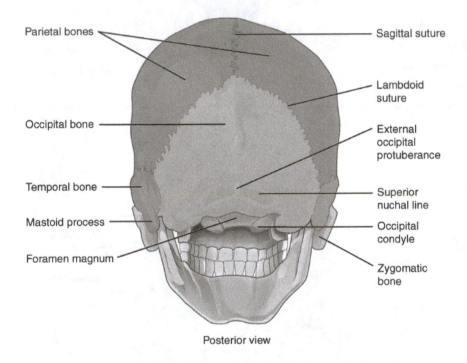

Posterior view

Figure 7.9 Posterior View of Skull This view of the posterior skull shows attachment sites for muscles and joints that support the skull.

Sphenoid Bone

The **sphenoid bone** is a single, complex bone of the central skull (Figure 7.10). It serves as a "keystone" bone, because it joins with almost every other bone of the skull. The sphenoid forms much of the base of the central skull (see Figure 7.8) and also extends laterally to contribute to the sides of the skull (see Figure 7.5). Inside the cranial cavity, the right and left **lesser wings of the sphenoid bone**, which resemble the wings of a flying bird, form the lip of a prominent ridge that marks the boundary between the anterior and middle cranial fossae. The **sella turcica** ("Turkish saddle") is located at the midline of the middle cranial fossa. This bony region of the sphenoid bone is named for its resemblance to the horse saddles used by the Ottoman Turks, with a high back and a tall front. The rounded depression in the floor of the sella turcica is the **hypophyseal (pituitary) fossa**, which houses the pea-sized pituitary (hypophyseal) gland. The **greater wings of the sphenoid bone** extend laterally to either side away from the sella turcica, where they form the anterior floor of the middle cranial fossa. The greater wing is best seen on the outside of the lateral skull, where it forms a rectangular area immediately anterior to the squamous portion of the temporal bone.

On the inferior aspect of the skull, each half of the sphenoid bone forms two thin, vertically oriented bony plates. These are the **medial pterygoid plate** and **lateral pterygoid plate** (pterygoid = "wing-shaped"). The right and left medial pterygoid plates form the posterior, lateral walls of the nasal cavity. The somewhat larger lateral pterygoid plates serve as attachment sites for chewing muscles that fill the infratemporal space and act on the mandible.

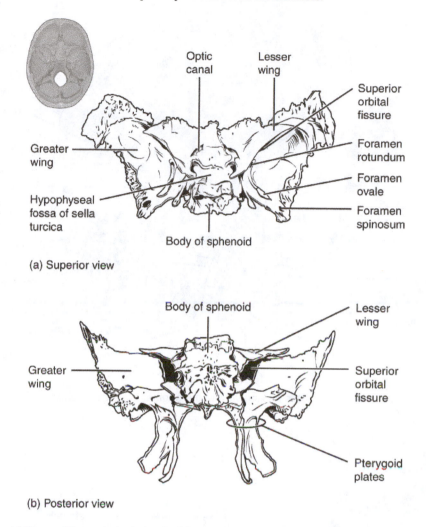

Optic canal

Lesser wing

Superior orbital fissure

Foramen rotundum

Foramen ovale

Foramen spinosum

Greater wing

Hypophyseal fossa of sella turcica

Body of sphenoid

(a) Superior view

Body of sphenoid

Lesser wing

Greater wing

Superior orbital fissure

Pterygoid plates

(b) Posterior view

Figure 7.10 Sphenoid Bone   Shown in isolation in (a) superior and (b) posterior views, the sphenoid bone is a single midline bone that forms the anterior walls and floor of the middle cranial fossa. It has a pair of lesser wings and a pair of greater wings. The sella turcica surrounds the hypophyseal fossa. Projecting downward are the medial and lateral pterygoid plates. The sphenoid has multiple openings for the passage of nerves and blood vessels, including the optic canal, superior orbital fissure, foramen rotundum, foramen ovale, and foramen spinosum.

Ethmoid Bone

The **ethmoid bone** is a single, midline bone that forms the roof and lateral walls of the upper nasal cavity, the upper portion of the nasal septum, and contributes to the medial wall of the orbit (Figure 7.11 and Figure 7.12). On the interior of the skull, the ethmoid also forms a portion of the floor of the anterior cranial cavity (see Figure 7.8b).

Within the nasal cavity, the perpendicular plate of the ethmoid bone forms the upper portion of the nasal septum. The ethmoid bone also forms the lateral walls of the upper nasal cavity. Extending from each lateral wall are the superior nasal concha and middle nasal concha, which are thin, curved projections that extend into the nasal cavity (Figure 7.13).

In the cranial cavity, the ethmoid bone forms a small area at the midline in the floor of the anterior cranial fossa. This region also forms the narrow roof of the underlying nasal cavity. This portion of the ethmoid bone consists of two parts, the crista galli and cribriform plates. The **crista galli** ("rooster's comb or crest") is a small upward bony projection located at the midline. It functions as an anterior attachment point for one of the covering layers of the brain. To either side of the crista galli is the **cribriform plate** (cribrum = "sieve"), a small, flattened area with numerous small openings termed olfactory foramina. Small nerve branches from the olfactory areas of the nasal cavity pass through these openings to enter the brain.

The lateral portions of the ethmoid bone are located between the orbit and upper nasal cavity, and thus form the lateral nasal cavity wall and a portion of the medial orbit wall. Located inside this portion of the ethmoid bone are several small, air-filled spaces that are part of the paranasal sinus system of the skull.

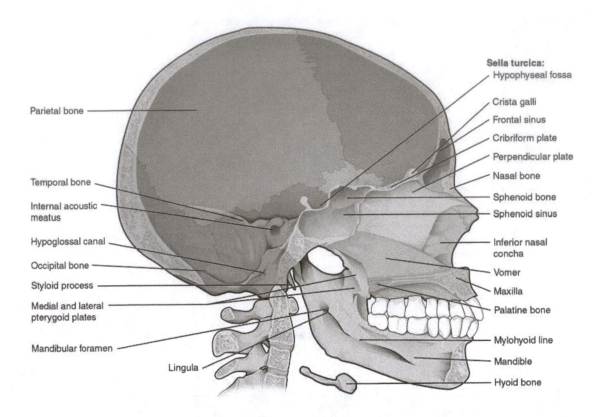

Figure 7.11 Sagittal Section of Skull This midline view of the sagittally sectioned skull shows the nasal septum.

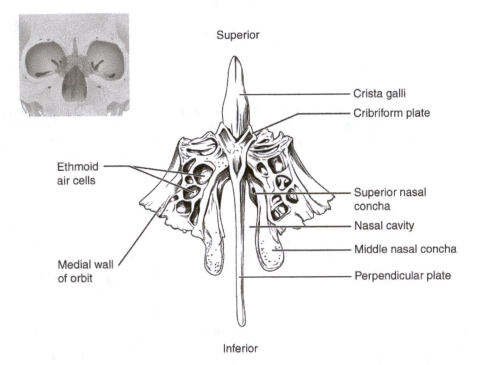

Figure 7.12 Ethmoid Bone The unpaired ethmoid bone is located at the midline within the central skull. It has an upward projection, the crista galli, and a downward projection, the perpendicular plate, which forms the upper nasal septum. The cribriform plates form both the roof of the nasal cavity and a portion of the anterior cranial fossa floor. The lateral sides of the ethmoid bone form the lateral walls of the upper nasal cavity, part of the medial orbit wall, and give rise to the superior and middle nasal conchae. The ethmoid bone also contains the ethmoid air cells.

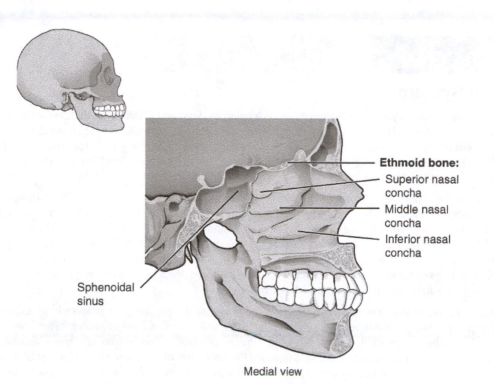

Medial view

Figure 7.13 Lateral Wall of Nasal Cavity The three nasal conchae are curved bones that project from the lateral walls of the nasal cavity. The superior nasal concha and middle nasal concha are parts of the ethmoid bone. The inferior nasal concha is an independent bone of the skull.

Sutures of the Skull

A **suture** is an immobile joint between adjacent bones of the skull. The narrow gap between the bones is filled with dense, fibrous connective tissue that unites the bones. The long sutures located between the bones of the brain case are not straight, but instead follow irregular, tightly twisting paths. These twisting lines serve to tightly interlock the adjacent bones, thus adding strength to the skull for brain protection.

The two suture lines seen on the top of the skull are the coronal and sagittal sutures. The **coronal suture** runs from side to side across the skull, within the coronal plane of section (see Figure 7.5). It joins the frontal bone to the right and left parietal bones. The **sagittal suture** extends posteriorly from the coronal suture, running along the midline at the top of the skull in the sagittal plane of section (see Figure 7.9). It unites the right and left parietal bones. On the posterior skull, the sagittal suture terminates by joining the lambdoid suture. The **lambdoid suture** extends downward and laterally to either side away from its junction with the sagittal suture. The lambdoid suture joins the occipital bone to the right and left parietal and temporal bones. This suture is named for its upside-down "V" shape, which resembles the capital letter version of the Greek letter lambda (Λ). The **squamous suture** is located on the lateral skull. It unites the squamous portion of the temporal bone with the parietal bone (see Figure 7.5). At the intersection of four bones is the **pterion**, a small, capital-H-shaped suture line region that unites the frontal bone, parietal bone, squamous portion of the temporal bone, and greater wing of the sphenoid bone. It is the weakest part of the skull. The pterion is located approximately two finger widths above the zygomatic arch and a thumb's width posterior to the upward portion of the zygomatic bone.

isorders OF THE...

Skeletal System

Head and traumatic brain injuries are major causes of immediate death and disability, with bleeding and infections as possible additional complications. According to the Centers for Disease Control and Prevention (2010), approximately 30 percent of all injury-related deaths in the United States are caused by head injuries. The majority of head injuries involve falls. They are most common among young children (ages 0–4 years), adolescents (15–19 years), and the elderly (over 65 years). Additional causes vary, but prominent among these are automobile and motorcycle accidents.

Strong blows to the brain-case portion of the skull can produce fractures. These may result in bleeding inside the skull with subsequent injury to the brain. The most common is a linear skull fracture, in which fracture lines radiate from the point of impact. Other fracture types include a comminuted fracture, in which the bone is broken into several pieces at the point of impact, or a depressed fracture, in which the fractured bone is pushed inward. In a contrecoup (counterblow) fracture, the bone at the point of impact is not broken, but instead a fracture occurs on the opposite side of the skull. Fractures of the occipital bone at the base of the skull can occur in this manner, producing a basilar fracture that can damage the artery that passes through the carotid canal.

A blow to the lateral side of the head may fracture the bones of the pterion. The pterion is an important clinical landmark because located immediately deep to it on the inside of the skull is a major branch of an artery that supplies the skull and covering layers of the brain. A strong blow to this region can fracture the bones around the pterion. If the underlying artery is damaged, bleeding can cause the formation of a hematoma (collection of blood) between the brain and interior of the skull. As blood accumulates, it will put pressure on the brain. Symptoms associated with a hematoma may not be apparent immediately following the injury, but if untreated, blood accumulation will exert increasing pressure on the brain and can result in death within a few hours.

View this animation (http://openstaxcollege.org/l/headblow) to see how a blow to the head may produce a contrecoup (counterblow) fracture of the basilar portion of the occipital bone on the base of the skull. Why may a basilar fracture be life threatening?

Facial Bones of the Skull

The facial bones of the skull form the upper and lower jaws, the nose, nasal cavity and nasal septum, and the orbit. The facial bones include 14 bones, with six paired bones and two unpaired bones. The paired bones are the maxilla, palatine, zygomatic, nasal, lacrimal, and inferior nasal conchae bones. The unpaired bones are the vomer and mandible bones. Although classified with the brain-case bones, the ethmoid bone also contributes to the nasal septum and the walls of the nasal cavity and orbit.

Maxillary Bone

The **maxillary bone**, often referred to simply as the maxilla (plural = maxillae), is one of a pair that together form the upper jaw, much of the hard palate, the medial floor of the orbit, and the lateral base of the nose (see Figure 7.4). The curved, inferior margin of the maxillary bone that forms the upper jaw and contains the upper teeth is the **alveolar process of the maxilla** (Figure 7.14). Each tooth is anchored into a deep socket called an alveolus. On the anterior maxilla, just below the orbit, is the infraorbital foramen. This is the point of exit for a sensory nerve that supplies the nose, upper lip, and anterior cheek. On the inferior skull, the **palatine process** from each maxillary bone can be seen joining together at the midline to form the anterior three-quarters of the hard palate (see Figure 7.8a). The **hard palate** is the bony plate that forms the roof of the mouth and floor of the nasal cavity, separating the oral and nasal cavities.

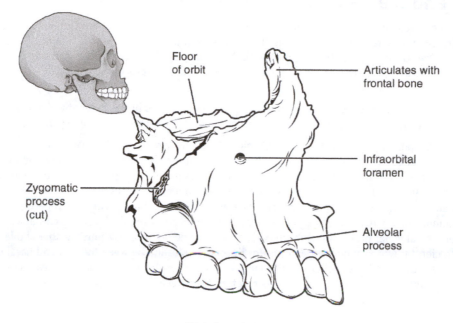

Right lateral view

Figure 7.14 Maxillary Bone The maxillary bone forms the upper jaw and supports the upper teeth. Each maxilla also forms the lateral floor of each orbit and the majority of the hard palate.

Palatine Bone

The **palatine bone** is one of a pair of irregularly shaped bones that contribute small areas to the lateral walls of the nasal cavity and the medial wall of each orbit. The largest region of each of the palatine bone is the **horizontal plate**. The plates from the right and left palatine bones join together at the midline to form the posterior quarter of the hard palate (see Figure 7.8a). Thus, the palatine bones are best seen in an inferior view of the skull and hard palate.

Homeostatic IMBALANCES

Cleft Lip and Cleft Palate

During embryonic development, the right and left maxilla bones come together at the midline to form the upper jaw. At the same time, the muscle and skin overlying these bones join together to form the upper lip. Inside the mouth, the palatine processes of the maxilla bones, along with the horizontal plates of the right and left palatine bones, join together to form the hard palate. If an error occurs in these developmental processes, a birth defect of cleft lip or cleft palate may result.

Cleft lip is a common development defect that affects approximately 1:1000 births, most of which are male. This defect involves a partial or complete failure of the right and left portions of the upper lip to fuse together, leaving a cleft (gap).

A more severe developmental defect is cleft palate, which affects the hard palate. The hard palate is the bony structure that separates the nasal cavity from the oral cavity. It is formed during embryonic development by the midline fusion of the horizontal plates from the right and left palatine bones and the palatine processes of the maxilla bones. Cleft palate affects approximately 1:2500 births and is more common in females. It results from a failure of the two halves of the hard palate to completely come together and fuse at the midline, thus leaving a gap between them. This gap allows for communication between the nasal and oral cavities. In severe cases, the bony gap continues into the anterior upper jaw where the alveolar processes of the maxilla bones also do not properly join together above the front teeth. If this occurs, a cleft lip will also be seen. Because of the communication between the oral and nasal cavities, a cleft palate makes it very difficult for an infant to generate the suckling needed for nursing, thus leaving the infant at risk for malnutrition. Surgical repair is required to correct cleft palate defects.

Zygomatic Bone

The **zygomatic bone** is also known as the cheekbone. Each of the paired zygomatic bones forms much of the lateral wall of the orbit and the lateral-inferior margins of the anterior orbital opening (see Figure 7.4). The short temporal process of the zygomatic bone projects posteriorly, where it forms the anterior portion of the zygomatic arch (see Figure 7.5).

Nasal Bone

The **nasal bone** is one of two small bones that articulate (join) with each other to form the bony base (bridge) of the nose. They also support the cartilages that form the lateral walls of the nose (see Figure 7.11). These are the bones that are damaged when the nose is broken.

Lacrimal Bone

Each **lacrimal bone** is a small, rectangular bone that forms the anterior, medial wall of the orbit (see Figure 7.4 and Figure 7.5). The anterior portion of the lacrimal bone forms a shallow depression called the **lacrimal fossa**, and extending inferiorly from this is the **nasolacrimal canal**. The lacrimal fluid (tears of the eye), which serves to maintain the moist surface of the eye, drains at the medial corner of the eye into the nasolacrimal canal. This duct then extends downward to open into the nasal cavity, behind the inferior nasal concha. In the nasal cavity, the lacrimal fluid normally drains posteriorly, but with an increased flow of tears due to crying or eye irritation, some fluid will also drain anteriorly, thus causing a runny nose.

Inferior Nasal Conchae

The right and left inferior nasal conchae form a curved bony plate that projects into the nasal cavity space from the lower lateral wall (see Figure 7.13). The inferior concha is the largest of the nasal conchae and can easily be seen when looking into the anterior opening of the nasal cavity.

Vomer Bone

The unpaired vomer bone, often referred to simply as the vomer, is triangular-shaped and forms the posterior-inferior part of the nasal septum (see Figure 7.11). The vomer is best seen when looking from behind into the posterior openings of the nasal cavity (see Figure 7.8a). In this view, the vomer is seen to form the entire height of the nasal septum. A much smaller portion of the vomer can also be seen when looking into the anterior opening of the nasal cavity.

Mandible

The **mandible** forms the lower jaw and is the only moveable bone of the skull. At the time of birth, the mandible consists of paired right and left bones, but these fuse together during the first year to form the single U-shaped mandible of the adult skull. Each side of the mandible consists of a horizontal body and posteriorly, a vertically oriented **ramus of the mandible** (ramus = "branch"). The outside margin of the mandible, where the body and ramus come together is called the **angle of the mandible** (Figure 7.15).

The ramus on each side of the mandible has two upward-going bony projections. The more anterior projection is the flattened **coronoid process of the mandible**, which provides attachment for one of the biting muscles. The posterior projection is the **condylar process of the mandible**, which is topped by the oval-shaped **condyle**. The condyle of the mandible articulates (joins) with the mandibular fossa and articular tubercle of the temporal bone. Together these articulations form the temporomandibular joint, which allows for opening and closing of the mouth (see Figure 7.5). The broad U-shaped curve located between the coronoid and condylar processes is the **mandibular notch**.

Important landmarks for the mandible include the following:

- **Alveolar process of the mandible**—This is the upper border of the mandibular body and serves to anchor the lower teeth.

- **Mental protuberance**—The forward projection from the inferior margin of the anterior mandible that forms the chin (mental = "chin").

- **Mental foramen**—The opening located on each side of the anterior-lateral mandible, which is the exit site for a sensory nerve that supplies the chin.

- **Mylohyoid line**—This bony ridge extends along the inner aspect of the mandibular body (see Figure 7.11). The muscle that forms the floor of the oral cavity attaches to the mylohyoid lines on both sides of the mandible.

- **Mandibular foramen**—This opening is located on the medial side of the ramus of the mandible. The opening leads into a tunnel that runs down the length of the mandibular body. The sensory nerve and blood vessels that supply the lower teeth enter the mandibular foramen and then follow this tunnel. Thus, to numb the lower teeth prior to dental work, the dentist must inject anesthesia into the lateral wall of the oral cavity at a point prior to where this sensory nerve enters the mandibular foramen.

- **Lingula**—This small flap of bone is named for its shape (lingula = "little tongue"). It is located immediately next to the mandibular foramen, on the medial side of the ramus. A ligament that anchors the mandible during opening and closing of the mouth extends down from the base of the skull and attaches to the lingula.

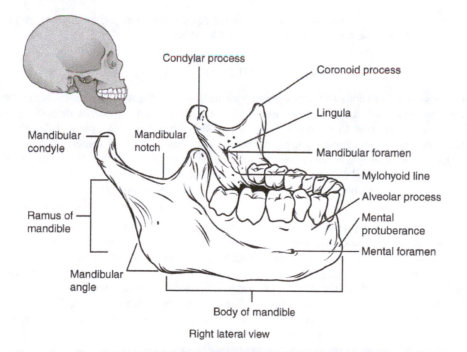

Figure 7.15 Isolated Mandible   The mandible is the only moveable bone of the skull.

The Orbit

The orbit is the bony socket that houses the eyeball and contains the muscles that move the eyeball or open the upper eyelid. Each orbit is cone-shaped, with a narrow posterior region that widens toward the large anterior opening. To help protect the eye, the bony margins of the anterior opening are thickened and somewhat constricted. The medial walls of the two orbits are parallel to each other but each lateral wall diverges away from the midline at a 45° angle. This divergence provides greater lateral peripheral vision.

The walls of each orbit include contributions from seven skull bones (Figure 7.16). The frontal bone forms the roof and the zygomatic bone forms the lateral wall and lateral floor. The medial floor is primarily formed by the maxilla, with a small contribution from the palatine bone. The ethmoid bone and lacrimal bone make up much of the medial wall and the sphenoid bone forms the posterior orbit.

At the posterior apex of the orbit is the opening of the **optic canal**, which allows for passage of the optic nerve from the retina to the brain. Lateral to this is the elongated and irregularly shaped superior orbital fissure, which provides passage for the artery that supplies the eyeball, sensory nerves, and the nerves that supply the muscles involved in eye movements.

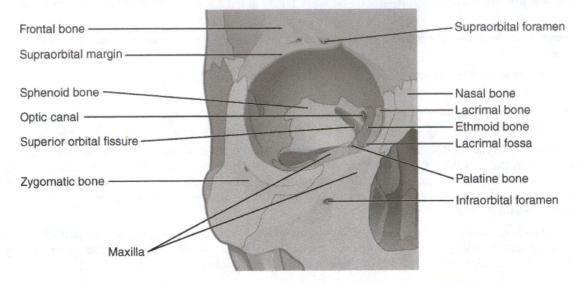

Figure 7.16 Bones of the Orbit Seven skull bones contribute to the walls of the orbit. Opening into the posterior orbit from the cranial cavity are the optic canal and superior orbital fissure.

The Nasal Septum and Nasal Conchae

The **nasal septum** consists of both bone and cartilage components (Figure 7.17; see also Figure 7.11). The upper portion of the septum is formed by the perpendicular plate of the ethmoid bone. The lower and posterior parts of the septum are formed by the triangular-shaped vomer bone. In an anterior view of the skull, the perpendicular plate of the ethmoid bone is easily seen inside the nasal opening as the upper nasal septum, but only a small portion of the vomer is seen as the inferior septum. A better view of the vomer bone is seen when looking into the posterior nasal cavity with an inferior view of the skull, where the vomer forms the full height of the nasal septum. The anterior nasal septum is formed by the **septal cartilage**, a flexible plate that fills in the gap between the perpendicular plate of the ethmoid and vomer bones. This cartilage also extends outward into the nose where it separates the right and left nostrils. The septal cartilage is not found in the dry skull.

Attached to the lateral wall on each side of the nasal cavity are the superior, middle, and inferior **nasal conchae** (singular = concha), which are named for their positions (see Figure 7.13). These are bony plates that curve downward as they project into the space of the nasal cavity. They serve to swirl the incoming air, which helps to warm and moisturize it before the air moves into the delicate air sacs of the lungs. This also allows mucus, secreted by the tissue lining the nasal cavity, to trap incoming dust, pollen, bacteria, and viruses. The largest of the conchae is the inferior nasal concha, which is an independent bone of the skull. The middle concha and the superior conchae, which is the smallest, are both formed by the ethmoid bone. When looking into the anterior nasal opening of the skull, only the inferior and middle conchae can be seen. The small superior nasal concha is well hidden above and behind the middle concha.

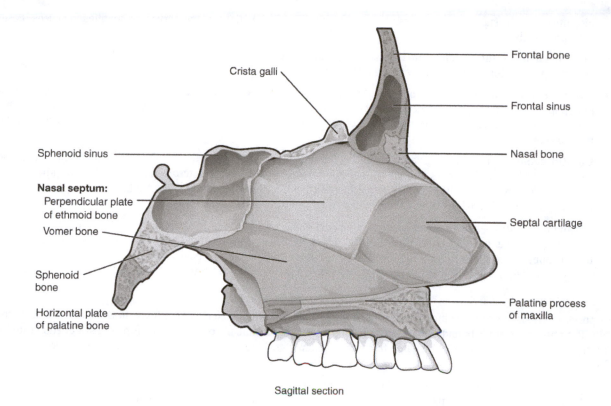

Sagittal section

Figure 7.17 Nasal Septum The nasal septum is formed by the perpendicular plate of the ethmoid bone and the vomer bone. The septal cartilage fills the gap between these bones and extends into the nose.

Cranial Fossae

Inside the skull, the floor of the cranial cavity is subdivided into three cranial fossae (spaces), which increase in depth from anterior to posterior (see Figure 7.6, Figure 7.8b, and Figure 7.11). Since the brain occupies these areas, the shape of each conforms to the shape of the brain regions that it contains. Each cranial fossa has anterior and posterior boundaries and is divided at the midline into right and left areas by a significant bony structure or opening.

Anterior Cranial Fossa

The anterior cranial fossa is the most anterior and the shallowest of the three cranial fossae. It overlies the orbits and contains the frontal lobes of the brain. Anteriorly, the anterior fossa is bounded by the frontal bone, which also forms the majority of the floor for this space. The lesser wings of the sphenoid bone form the prominent ledge that marks the boundary between the anterior and middle cranial fossae. Located in the floor of the anterior cranial fossa at the midline is a portion of the ethmoid bone, consisting of the upward projecting crista galli and to either side of this, the cribriform plates.

Middle Cranial Fossa

The middle cranial fossa is deeper and situated posterior to the anterior fossa. It extends from the lesser wings of the sphenoid bone anteriorly, to the petrous ridges (petrous portion of the temporal bones) posteriorly. The large, diagonally positioned petrous ridges give the middle cranial fossa a butterfly shape, making it narrow at the midline and broad laterally. The temporal lobes of the brain occupy this fossa. The middle cranial fossa is divided at the midline by the upward bony prominence of the sella turcica, a part of the sphenoid bone. The middle cranial fossa has several openings for the passage of blood vessels and cranial nerves (see Figure 7.8).

Openings in the middle cranial fossa are as follows:

- **Optic canal**—This opening is located at the anterior lateral corner of the sella turcica. It provides for passage of the optic nerve into the orbit.

- **Superior orbital fissure**—This large, irregular opening into the posterior orbit is located on the anterior wall of the middle cranial fossa, lateral to the optic canal and under the projecting margin of the lesser wing of the sphenoid bone. Nerves to the eyeball and associated muscles, and sensory nerves to the forehead pass through this opening.

- **Foramen rotundum**—This rounded opening (rotundum = "round") is located in the floor of the middle cranial fossa, just inferior to the superior orbital fissure. It is the exit point for a major sensory nerve that supplies the cheek, nose, and upper teeth.

- **Foramen ovale of the middle cranial fossa**—This large, oval-shaped opening in the floor of the middle cranial fossa provides passage for a major sensory nerve to the lateral head, cheek, chin, and lower teeth.

- **Foramen spinosum**—This small opening, located posterior-lateral to the foramen ovale, is the entry point for an important artery that supplies the covering layers surrounding the brain. The branching pattern of this artery forms readily visible grooves on the internal surface of the skull and these grooves can be traced back to their origin at the foramen spinosum.

- **Carotid canal**—This is the zig-zag passageway through which a major artery to the brain enters the skull. The entrance to the carotid canal is located on the inferior aspect of the skull, anteromedial to the styloid process (see Figure 7.8a). From here, the canal runs anteromedially within the bony base of the skull. Just above the foramen lacerum, the carotid canal opens into the middle cranial cavity, near the posterior-lateral base of the sella turcica.

- **Foramen lacerum**—This irregular opening is located in the base of the skull, immediately inferior to the exit of the carotid canal. This opening is an artifact of the dry skull, because in life it is completely filled with cartilage. All the openings of the skull that provide for passage of nerves or blood vessels have smooth margins; the word lacerum ("ragged" or "torn") tells us that this opening has ragged edges and thus nothing passes through it.

Posterior Cranial Fossa

The posterior cranial fossa is the most posterior and deepest portion of the cranial cavity. It contains the cerebellum of the brain. The posterior fossa is bounded anteriorly by the petrous ridges, while the occipital bone forms the floor and posterior wall. It is divided at the midline by the large foramen magnum ("great aperture"), the opening that provides for passage of the spinal cord.

Located on the medial wall of the petrous ridge in the posterior cranial fossa is the internal acoustic meatus (see Figure 7.11). This opening provides for passage of the nerve from the hearing and equilibrium organs of the inner ear, and the nerve that supplies the muscles of the face. Located at the anterior-lateral margin of the foramen magnum is the **hypoglossal canal**. These emerge on the inferior aspect of the skull at the base of the occipital condyle and provide passage for an important nerve to the tongue.

Immediately inferior to the internal acoustic meatus is the large, irregularly shaped **jugular foramen** (see Figure 7.8a). Several cranial nerves from the brain exit the skull via this opening. It is also the exit point through the base of the skull for all the venous return blood leaving the brain. The venous structures that carry blood inside the skull form large, curved grooves on the inner walls of the posterior cranial fossa, which terminate at each jugular foramen.

Paranasal Sinuses

The **paranasal sinuses** are hollow, air-filled spaces located within certain bones of the skull (Figure 7.18). All of the sinuses communicate with the nasal cavity (paranasal = "next to nasal cavity") and are lined with nasal mucosa. They serve to reduce bone mass and thus lighten the skull, and they also add resonance to the voice. This second feature is most obvious when you have a cold or sinus congestion. These produce swelling of the mucosa and excess mucus production, which can obstruct the narrow passageways between the sinuses and the nasal cavity, causing your voice to sound different to yourself and others. This blockage can also allow the sinuses to fill with fluid, with the resulting pressure producing pain and discomfort.

The paranasal sinuses are named for the skull bone that each occupies. The **frontal sinus** is located just above the eyebrows, within the frontal bone (see Figure 7.17). This irregular space may be divided at the midline into bilateral spaces, or these may be fused into a single sinus space. The frontal sinus is the most anterior of the paranasal sinuses. The largest sinus is the **maxillary sinus**. These are paired and located within the right and left maxillary bones, where they occupy the area just below the orbits. The maxillary sinuses are most commonly involved during sinus infections. Because their connection to the nasal cavity is located high on their medial wall, they are difficult to drain. The **sphenoid sinus** is a single, midline sinus. It is located within the body of the sphenoid bone, just anterior and inferior to the sella turcica, thus making it the most posterior of the paranasal sinuses. The lateral aspects of the ethmoid bone contain multiple small spaces separated by very thin bony walls. Each of these spaces is called an **ethmoid air cell**. These are located on both sides of the ethmoid bone, between the upper nasal cavity and medial orbit, just behind the superior nasal conchae.

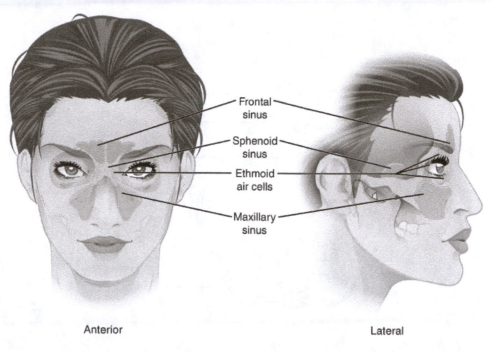

Anterior   Lateral

Figure 7.18 Paranasal Sinuses The paranasal sinuses are hollow, air-filled spaces named for the skull bone that each occupies. The most anterior is the frontal sinus, located in the frontal bone above the eyebrows. The largest are the maxillary sinuses, located in the right and left maxillary bones below the orbits. The most posterior is the sphenoid sinus, located in the body of the sphenoid bone, under the sella turcica. The ethmoid air cells are multiple small spaces located in the right and left sides of the ethmoid bone, between the medial wall of the orbit and lateral wall of the upper nasal cavity.

Hyoid Bone

The hyoid bone is an independent bone that does not contact any other bone and thus is not part of the skull (**Figure 7.19**). It is a small U-shaped bone located in the upper neck near the level of the inferior mandible, with the tips of the "U" pointing posteriorly. The hyoid serves as the base for the tongue above, and is attached to the larynx below and the pharynx posteriorly. The hyoid is held in position by a series of small muscles that attach to it either from above or below. These muscles act to move the hyoid up/down or forward/back. Movements of the hyoid are coordinated with movements of the tongue, larynx, and pharynx during swallowing and speaking.

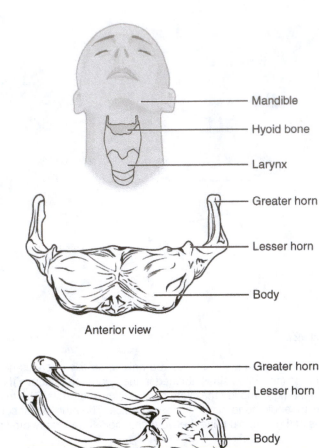

Anterior view

Right lateral view

Figure 7.19 Hyoid Bone The hyoid bone is located in the upper neck and does not join with any other bone. It provides attachments for muscles that act on the tongue, larynx, and pharynx.

7.3 | The Vertebral Column

By the end of this section, you will be able to:

- Describe each region of the vertebral column and the number of bones in each region
- Discuss the curves of the vertebral column and how these change after birth
- Describe a typical vertebra and determine the distinguishing characteristics for vertebrae in each vertebral region and features of the sacrum and the coccyx
- Define the structure of an intervertebral disc
- Determine the location of the ligaments that provide support for the vertebral column

The vertebral column is also known as the spinal column or spine (**Figure 7.20**). It consists of a sequence of vertebrae (singular = vertebra), each of which is separated and united by an **intervertebral disc**. Together, the vertebrae and intervertebral discs form the vertebral column. It is a flexible column that supports the head, neck, and body and allows for their movements. It also protects the spinal cord, which passes down the back through openings in the vertebrae.

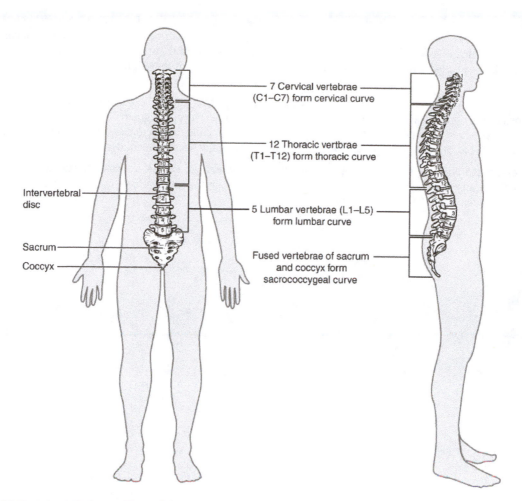

Figure 7.20 Vertebral Column The adult vertebral column consists of 24 vertebrae, plus the sacrum and coccyx. The vertebrae are divided into three regions: cervical C1–C7 vertebrae, thoracic T1–T12 vertebrae, and lumbar L1–L5 vertebrae. The vertebral column is curved, with two primary curvatures (thoracic and sacrococcygeal curves) and two secondary curvatures (cervical and lumbar curves).

Regions of the Vertebral Column

The vertebral column originally develops as a series of 33 vertebrae, but this number is eventually reduced to 24 vertebrae, plus the sacrum and coccyx. The vertebral column is subdivided into five regions, with the vertebrae in each area named for that region and numbered in descending order. In the neck, there are seven cervical vertebrae, each designated with the letter "C" followed by its number. Superiorly, the C1 vertebra articulates (forms a joint) with the occipital condyles of the skull. Inferiorly, C1 articulates with the C2 vertebra, and so on. Below these are the 12 thoracic vertebrae, designated T1–T12. The lower back contains the L1–L5 lumbar vertebrae. The single sacrum, which is also part of the pelvis, is formed by the fusion of five sacral vertebrae. Similarly, the coccyx, or tailbone, results from the fusion of four small coccygeal vertebrae. However, the sacral and coccygeal fusions do not start until age 20 and are not completed until middle age.

An interesting anatomical fact is that almost all mammals have seven cervical vertebrae, regardless of body size. This means that there are large variations in the size of cervical vertebrae, ranging from the very small cervical vertebrae of a shrew to the greatly elongated vertebrae in the neck of a giraffe. In a full-grown giraffe, each cervical vertebra is 11 inches tall.

Curvatures of the Vertebral Column

The adult vertebral column does not form a straight line, but instead has four curvatures along its length (see Figure 7.20). These curves increase the vertebral column's strength, flexibility, and ability to absorb shock. When the load on the spine is increased, by carrying a heavy backpack for example, the curvatures increase in depth (become more curved) to accommodate the extra weight. They then spring back when the weight is removed. The four adult curvatures are classified as either primary or secondary curvatures. Primary curves are retained from the original fetal curvature, while secondary curvatures develop after birth.

During fetal development, the body is flexed anteriorly into the fetal position, giving the entire vertebral column a single curvature that is concave anteriorly. In the adult, this fetal curvature is retained in two regions of the vertebral column as the **thoracic curve**, which involves the thoracic vertebrae, and the **sacrococcygeal curve**, formed by the sacrum and coccyx. Each of these is thus called a **primary curve** because they are retained from the original fetal curvature of the vertebral column.

A **secondary curve** develops gradually after birth as the child learns to sit upright, stand, and walk. Secondary curves are concave posteriorly, opposite in direction to the original fetal curvature. The **cervical curve** of the neck region develops as the infant begins to hold their head upright when sitting. Later, as the child begins to stand and then to walk, the **lumbar curve** of the lower back develops. In adults, the lumbar curve is generally deeper in females.

Disorders associated with the curvature of the spine include **kyphosis** (an excessive posterior curvature of the thoracic region), **lordosis** (an excessive anterior curvature of the lumbar region), and **scoliosis** (an abnormal, lateral curvature, accompanied by twisting of the vertebral column).

isorders OF THE...

Vertebral Column

Developmental anomalies, pathological changes, or obesity can enhance the normal vertebral column curves, resulting in the development of abnormal or excessive curvatures (Figure 7.21). Kyphosis, also referred to as humpback or hunchback, is an excessive posterior curvature of the thoracic region. This can develop when osteoporosis causes weakening and erosion of the anterior portions of the upper thoracic vertebrae, resulting in their gradual collapse (Figure 7.22). Lordosis, or swayback, is an excessive anterior curvature of the lumbar region and is most commonly associated with obesity or late pregnancy. The accumulation of body weight in the abdominal region results an anterior shift in the line of gravity that carries the weight of the body. This causes in an anterior tilt of the pelvis and a pronounced enhancement of the lumbar curve.

Scoliosis is an abnormal, lateral curvature, accompanied by twisting of the vertebral column. Compensatory curves may also develop in other areas of the vertebral column to help maintain the head positioned over the feet. Scoliosis is the most common vertebral abnormality among girls. The cause is usually unknown, but it may result from weakness of the back muscles, defects such as differential growth rates in the right and left sides of the vertebral column, or differences in the length of the lower limbs. When present, scoliosis tends to get worse during adolescent growth spurts. Although most individuals do not require treatment, a back brace may be recommended for growing children. In extreme cases, surgery may be required.

Excessive vertebral curves can be identified while an individual stands in the anatomical position. Observe the vertebral profile from the side and then from behind to check for kyphosis or lordosis. Then have the person bend forward. If scoliosis is present, an individual will have difficulty in bending directly forward, and the right and left sides of the back will not be level with each other in the bent position.

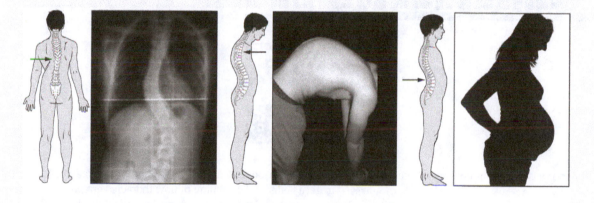

(a) Scoliosis   (b) Kyphosis   (c) Lordosis

Figure 7.21 Abnormal Curvatures of the Vertebral Column (a) Scoliosis is an abnormal lateral bending of the vertebral column. (b) An excessive curvature of the upper thoracic vertebral column is called kyphosis. (c) Lordosis is an excessive curvature in the lumbar region of the vertebral column.

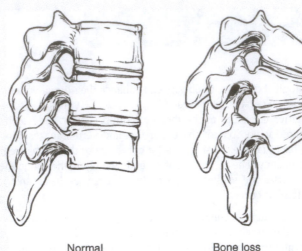

Normal
vertebrae

Bone loss
amplifies curvature

Figure 7.22 Osteoporosis Osteoporosis is an age-related disorder that causes the gradual loss of bone density and strength. When the thoracic vertebrae are affected, there can be a gradual collapse of the vertebrae. This results in kyphosis, an excessive curvature of the thoracic region.

Interactive LINK

Osteoporosis is a common age-related bone disease in which bone density and strength is decreased. Watch this video (http://openstaxcollege.org/l/osteoporosis) to get a better understanding of how thoracic vertebrae may become weakened and may fracture due to this disease. How may vertebral osteoporosis contribute to kyphosis?

General Structure of a Vertebra

Within the different regions of the vertebral column, vertebrae vary in size and shape, but they all follow a similar structural pattern. A typical vertebra will consist of a body, a vertebral arch, and seven processes (Figure 7.23).

The body is the anterior portion of each vertebra and is the part that supports the body weight. Because of this, the vertebral bodies progressively increase in size and thickness going down the vertebral column. The bodies of adjacent vertebrae are separated and strongly united by an intervertebral disc.

The **vertebral arch** forms the posterior portion of each vertebra. It consists of four parts, the right and left pedicles and the right and left laminae. Each **pedicle** forms one of the lateral sides of the vertebral arch. The pedicles are anchored to the posterior side of the vertebral body. Each **lamina** forms part of the posterior roof of the vertebral arch. The large opening between the vertebral arch and body is the **vertebral foramen**, which contains the spinal cord. In the intact vertebral column, the vertebral foramina of all of the vertebrae align to form the **vertebral (spinal) canal**, which serves as the bony protection and passageway for the spinal cord down the back. When the vertebrae are aligned together in the vertebral column, notches in the margins of the pedicles of adjacent vertebrae together form an **intervertebral foramen**, the opening through which a spinal nerve exits from the vertebral column (Figure 7.24).

Seven processes arise from the vertebral arch. Each paired **transverse process** projects laterally and arises from the junction point between the pedicle and lamina. The single **spinous process** (vertebral spine) projects posteriorly at the midline of the back. The vertebral spines can easily be felt as a series of bumps just under the skin down the middle of the back. The transverse and spinous processes serve as important muscle attachment sites. A **superior articular process** extends or faces upward, and an **inferior articular process** faces or projects downward on each side of a vertebrae. The paired superior articular processes of one vertebra join with the corresponding paired inferior articular processes from the next higher vertebra. These junctions form slightly moveable joints between the adjacent vertebrae. The shape and orientation of the articular processes vary in different regions of the vertebral column and play a major role in determining the type and range of motion available in each region.

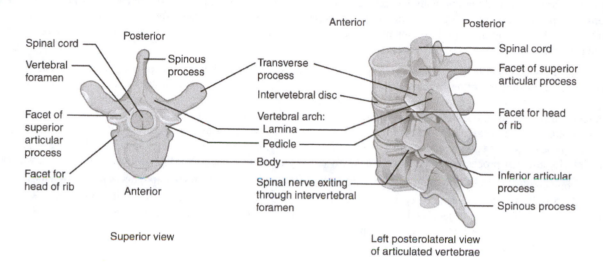

Figure 7.23 Parts of a Typical Vertebra A typical vertebra consists of a body and a vertebral arch. The arch is formed by the paired pedicles and paired laminae. Arising from the vertebral arch are the transverse, spinous, superior articular, and inferior articular processes. The vertebral foramen provides for passage of the spinal cord. Each spinal nerve exits through an intervertebral foramen, located between adjacent vertebrae. Intervertebral discs unite the bodies of adjacent vertebrae.

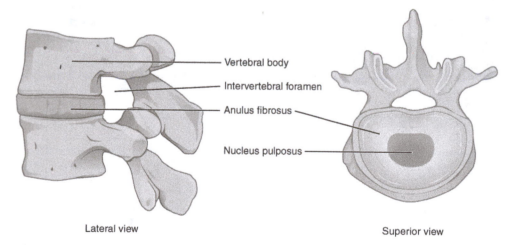

Figure 7.24 Intervertebral Disc The bodies of adjacent vertebrae are separated and united by an intervertebral disc, which provides padding and allows for movements between adjacent vertebrae. The disc consists of a fibrous outer layer called the anulus fibrosus and a gel-like center called the nucleus pulposus. The intervertebral foramen is the opening formed between adjacent vertebrae for the exit of a spinal nerve.

Regional Modifications of Vertebrae

In addition to the general characteristics of a typical vertebra described above, vertebrae also display characteristic size and structural features that vary between the different vertebral column regions. Thus, cervical vertebrae are smaller than lumbar vertebrae due to differences in the proportion of body weight that each supports. Thoracic vertebrae have sites for rib attachment, and the vertebrae that give rise to the sacrum and coccyx have fused together into single bones.

Cervical Vertebrae

Typical **cervical vertebrae**, such as C4 or C5, have several characteristic features that differentiate them from thoracic or lumbar vertebrae (Figure 7.25). Cervical vertebrae have a small body, reflecting the fact that they carry the least amount of body weight. Cervical vertebrae usually have a bifid (Y-shaped) spinous process. The spinous processes of the C3–C6 vertebrae are short, but the spine of C7 is much longer. You can find these vertebrae by running your finger down the midline of the posterior neck until you encounter the prominent C7 spine located at the base of the neck. The transverse processes of the cervical vertebrae are sharply curved (U-shaped) to allow for passage of the cervical spinal nerves. Each transverse process also has an opening called the **transverse foramen**. An important artery that supplies the brain ascends up the neck by passing through these openings. The superior and inferior articular processes of the cervical vertebrae are flattened and largely face upward or downward, respectively.

The first and second cervical vertebrae are further modified, giving each a distinctive appearance. The first cervical (C1) vertebra is also called the **atlas**, because this is the vertebra that supports the skull on top of the vertebral column (in Greek mythology, Atlas was the god who supported the heavens on his shoulders). The C1 vertebra does not have a body or spinous process. Instead, it is ring-shaped, consisting of an **anterior arch** and a **posterior arch**. The transverse processes of the atlas are longer and extend more laterally than do the transverse processes of any other cervical vertebrae. The superior articular processes face upward and are deeply curved for articulation with the occipital condyles on the base of the skull. The inferior articular processes are flat and face downward to join with the superior articular processes of the C2 vertebra.

The second cervical (C2) vertebra is called the **axis**, because it serves as the axis for rotation when turning the head toward the right or left. The axis resembles typical cervical vertebrae in most respects, but is easily distinguished by the **dens** (odontoid process), a bony projection that extends upward from the vertebral body. The dens joins with the inner aspect of the anterior arch of the atlas, where it is held in place by transverse ligament.

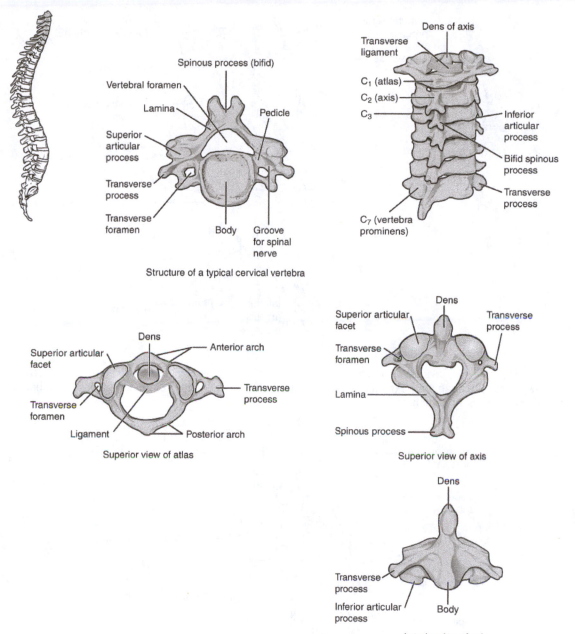

Figure 7.25 Cervical Vertebrae A typical cervical vertebra has a small body, a bifid spinous process, transverse processes that have a transverse foramen and are curved for spinal nerve passage. The atlas (C1 vertebra) does not have a body or spinous process. It consists of an anterior and a posterior arch and elongated transverse processes. The axis (C2 vertebra) has the upward projecting dens, which articulates with the anterior arch of the atlas.

Thoracic Vertebrae

The bodies of the **thoracic vertebrae** are larger than those of cervical vertebrae (Figure 7.26). The characteristic feature for a typical midthoracic vertebra is the spinous process, which is long and has a pronounced downward angle that causes it to overlap the next inferior vertebra. The superior articular processes of thoracic vertebrae face anteriorly and the inferior processes face posteriorly. These orientations are important determinants for the type and range of movements available to the thoracic region of the vertebral column.

Thoracic vertebrae have several additional articulation sites, each of which is called a **facet**, where a rib is attached. Most thoracic vertebrae have two facets located on the lateral sides of the body, each of which is called a **costal facet** (costal = "rib"). These are for articulation with the head (end) of a rib. An additional facet is located on the transverse process for articulation with the tubercle of a rib.

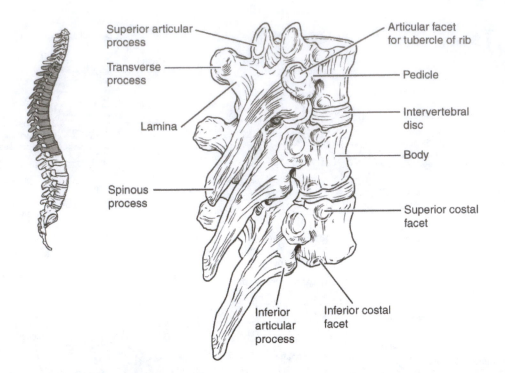

Figure 7.26 Thoracic Vertebrae A typical thoracic vertebra is distinguished by the spinous process, which is long and projects downward to overlap the next inferior vertebra. It also has articulation sites (facets) on the vertebral body and a transverse process for rib attachment.

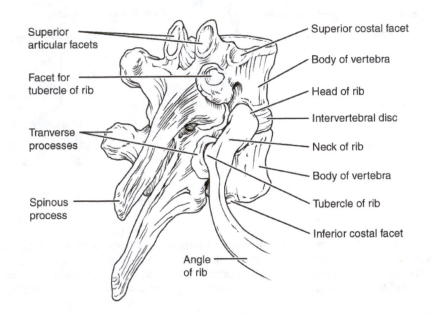

Figure 7.27 Rib Articulation in Thoracic Vertebrae Thoracic vertebrae have superior and inferior articular facets on the vertebral body for articulation with the head of a rib, and a transverse process facet for articulation with the rib tubercle.

Lumbar Vertebrae

Lumbar vertebrae carry the greatest amount of body weight and are thus characterized by the large size and thickness of the vertebral body (**Figure 7.28**). They have short transverse processes and a short, blunt spinous process that projects posteriorly. The articular processes are large, with the superior process facing backward and the inferior facing forward.

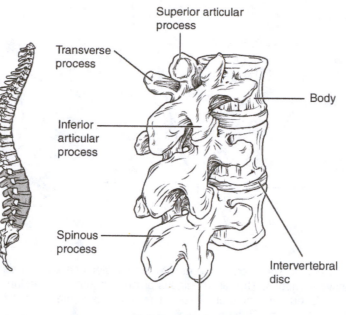

Figure 7.28 Lumbar Vertebrae Lumbar vertebrae are characterized by having a large, thick body and a short, rounded spinous process.

Sacrum and Coccyx

The sacrum is a triangular-shaped bone that is thick and wide across its superior base where it is weight bearing and then tapers down to an inferior, non-weight bearing apex (Figure 7.29). It is formed by the fusion of five sacral vertebrae, a process that does not begin until after the age of 20. On the anterior surface of the older adult sacrum, the lines of vertebral fusion can be seen as four transverse ridges. On the posterior surface, running down the midline, is the **median sacral crest**, a bumpy ridge that is the remnant of the fused spinous processes (median = "midline"; while medial = "toward, but not necessarily at, the midline"). Similarly, the fused transverse processes of the sacral vertebrae form the **lateral sacral crest**.

The **sacral promontory** is the anterior lip of the superior base of the sacrum. Lateral to this is the roughened auricular surface, which joins with the ilium portion of the hipbone to form the immobile sacroiliac joints of the pelvis. Passing inferiorly through the sacrum is a bony tunnel called the **sacral canal**, which terminates at the **sacral hiatus** near the inferior tip of the sacrum. The anterior and posterior surfaces of the sacrum have a series of paired openings called **sacral foramina** (singular = foramen) that connect to the sacral canal. Each of these openings is called a **posterior (dorsal) sacral foramen** or **anterior (ventral) sacral foramen**. These openings allow for the anterior and posterior branches of the sacral spinal nerves to exit the sacrum. The **superior articular process of the sacrum**, one of which is found on either side of the superior opening of the sacral canal, articulates with the inferior articular processes from the L5 vertebra.

The coccyx, or tailbone, is derived from the fusion of four very small coccygeal vertebrae (see Figure 7.29). It articulates with the inferior tip of the sacrum. It is not weight bearing in the standing position, but may receive some body weight when sitting.

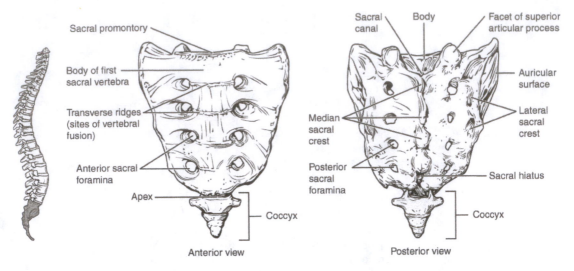

Anterior view

Posterior view

Figure 7.29 Sacrum and Coccyx The sacrum is formed from the fusion of five sacral vertebrae, whose lines of fusion are indicated by the transverse ridges. The fused spinous processes form the median sacral crest, while the lateral sacral crest arises from the fused transverse processes. The coccyx is formed by the fusion of four small coccygeal vertebrae.

Intervertebral Discs and Ligaments of the Vertebral Column

The bodies of adjacent vertebrae are strongly anchored to each other by an intervertebral disc. This structure provides padding between the bones during weight bearing, and because it can change shape, also allows for movement between the vertebrae. Although the total amount of movement available between any two adjacent vertebrae is small, when these movements are summed together along the entire length of the vertebral column, large body movements can be produced. Ligaments that extend along the length of the vertebral column also contribute to its overall support and stability.

Intervertebral Disc

An **intervertebral disc** is a fibrocartilaginous pad that fills the gap between adjacent vertebral bodies (see Figure 7.24). Each disc is anchored to the bodies of its adjacent vertebrae, thus strongly uniting these. The discs also provide padding between vertebrae during weight bearing. Because of this, intervertebral discs are thin in the cervical region and thickest in the lumbar region, which carries the most body weight. In total, the intervertebral discs account for approximately 25 percent of your body height between the top of the pelvis and the base of the skull. Intervertebral discs are also flexible and can change shape to allow for movements of the vertebral column.

Each intervertebral disc consists of two parts. The **anulus fibrosus** is the tough, fibrous outer layer of the disc. It forms a circle (anulus = "ring" or "circle") and is firmly anchored to the outer margins of the adjacent vertebral bodies. Inside is the **nucleus pulposus**, consisting of a softer, more gel-like material. It has a high water content that serves to resist compression and thus is important for weight bearing. With increasing age, the water content of the nucleus pulposus gradually declines. This causes the disc to become thinner, decreasing total body height somewhat, and reduces the flexibility and range of motion of the disc, making bending more difficult.

The gel-like nature of the nucleus pulposus also allows the intervertebral disc to change shape as one vertebra rocks side to side or forward and back in relation to its neighbors during movements of the vertebral column. Thus, bending forward causes compression of the anterior portion of the disc but expansion of the posterior disc. If the posterior anulus fibrosus is weakened due to injury or increasing age, the pressure exerted on the disc when bending forward and lifting a heavy object can cause the nucleus pulposus to protrude posteriorly through the anulus fibrosus, resulting in a herniated disc ("ruptured" or "slipped" disc) (Figure 7.30). The posterior bulging of the nucleus pulposus can cause compression of a spinal nerve at the point where it exits through the intervertebral foramen, with resulting pain and/or muscle weakness in those body regions supplied by that nerve. The most common sites for disc herniation are the L4/L5 or L5/S1 intervertebral discs, which can cause sciatica, a widespread pain that radiates from the lower back down the thigh and into the leg. Similar injuries of the C5/C6 or C6/C7 intervertebral discs, following forcible hyperflexion of the neck from a collision accident or football injury, can produce pain in the neck, shoulder, and upper limb.

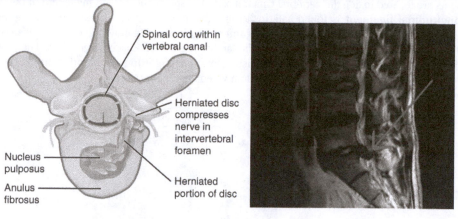

Superior view

Figure 7.30 Herniated Intervertebral Disc Weakening of the anulus fibrosus can result in herniation (protrusion) of the nucleus pulposus and compression of a spinal nerve, resulting in pain and/or muscle weakness in the body regions supplied by that nerve.

Interactive LINK

Watch this animation (http://openstaxcollege.org/l/diskslip) to see what it means to "slip" a disk. Watch this second animation (http://openstaxcollege.org/l/herndisc) to see one possible treatment for a herniated disc, removing and replacing the damaged disc with an artificial one that allows for movement between the adjacent certebrae. How could lifting a heavy object produce pain in a lower limb?

Ligaments of the Vertebral Column

Adjacent vertebrae are united by ligaments that run the length of the vertebral column along both its posterior and anterior aspects (Figure 7.31). These serve to resist excess forward or backward bending movements of the vertebral column, respectively.

The **anterior longitudinal ligament** runs down the anterior side of the entire vertebral column, uniting the vertebral bodies. It serves to resist excess backward bending of the vertebral column. Protection against this movement is particularly important in the neck, where extreme posterior bending of the head and neck can stretch or tear this ligament, resulting in a painful whiplash injury. Prior to the mandatory installation of seat headrests, whiplash injuries were common for passengers involved in a rear-end automobile collision.

The **supraspinous ligament** is located on the posterior side of the vertebral column, where it interconnects the spinous processes of the thoracic and lumbar vertebrae. This strong ligament supports the vertebral column during forward bending motions. In the posterior neck, where the cervical spinous processes are short, the supraspinous ligament expands to become the **nuchal ligament** (nuchae = "nape" or "back of the neck"). The nuchal ligament is attached to the cervical spinous processes and extends upward and posteriorly to attach to the midline base of the skull, out to the external occipital protuberance. It supports the skull and prevents it from falling forward. This ligament is much larger and stronger in four-legged animals such as cows, where the large skull hangs off the front end of the vertebral column. You can easily feel this ligament by first extending your head backward and pressing down on the posterior midline of your neck. Then tilt your head forward and you will fill the nuchal ligament popping out as it tightens to limit anterior bending of the head and neck.

Additional ligaments are located inside the vertebral canal, next to the spinal cord, along the length of the vertebral column. The **posterior longitudinal ligament** is found anterior to the spinal cord, where it is attached to the posterior sides of the vertebral bodies. Posterior to the spinal cord is the **ligamentum flavum** ("yellow ligament"). This consists of a series of short, paired ligaments, each of which interconnects the lamina regions of adjacent vertebrae. The ligamentum flavum has large numbers of elastic fibers, which have a yellowish color, allowing it to stretch and then pull back. Both of these ligaments provide important support for the vertebral column when bending forward.

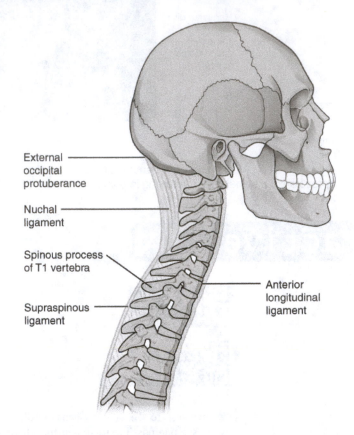

Figure 7.31 Ligaments of Vertebral Column The anterior longitudinal ligament runs the length of the vertebral column, uniting the anterior sides of the vertebral bodies. The supraspinous ligament connects the spinous processes of the thoracic and lumbar vertebrae. In the posterior neck, the supraspinous ligament enlarges to form the nuchal ligament, which attaches to the cervical spinous processes and to the base of the skull.

Use this tool (http://openstaxcollege.org/l/vertcolumn) to identify the bones, intervertebral discs, and ligaments of the vertebral column. The thickest portions of the anterior longitudinal ligament and the supraspinous ligament are found in which regions of the vertebral column?

Chiropractor

Chiropractors are health professionals who use nonsurgical techniques to help patients with musculoskeletal system problems that involve the bones, muscles, ligaments, tendons, or nervous system. They treat problems such as neck pain, back pain, joint pain, or headaches. Chiropractors focus on the patient's overall health and can also provide counseling related to lifestyle issues, such as diet, exercise, or sleep problems. If needed, they will refer the patient to other medical specialists.

Chiropractors use a drug-free, hands-on approach for patient diagnosis and treatment. They will perform a physical exam, assess the patient's posture and spine, and may perform additional diagnostic tests, including taking X-ray images. They primarily use manual techniques, such as spinal manipulation, to adjust the patient's spine or other joints. They can recommend therapeutic or rehabilitative exercises, and some also include acupuncture, massage therapy, or ultrasound as part of the treatment program. In addition to those in general practice, some chiropractors specialize in sport injuries, neurology, orthopaedics, pediatrics, nutrition, internal disorders, or diagnostic imaging.

To become a chiropractor, students must have 3–4 years of undergraduate education, attend an accredited, four-year Doctor of Chiropractic (D.C.) degree program, and pass a licensure examination to be licensed for practice in their state. With the aging of the baby-boom generation, employment for chiropractors is expected to increase.

7.4 | The Thoracic Cage

By the end of this section, you will be able to:

- Discuss the components that make up the thoracic cage
- Identify the parts of the sternum and define the sternal angle
- Discuss the parts of a rib and rib classifications

The thoracic cage (rib cage) forms the thorax (chest) portion of the body. It consists of the 12 pairs of ribs with their costal cartilages and the sternum (Figure 7.32). The ribs are anchored posteriorly to the 12 thoracic vertebrae (T1–T12). The thoracic cage protects the heart and lungs.

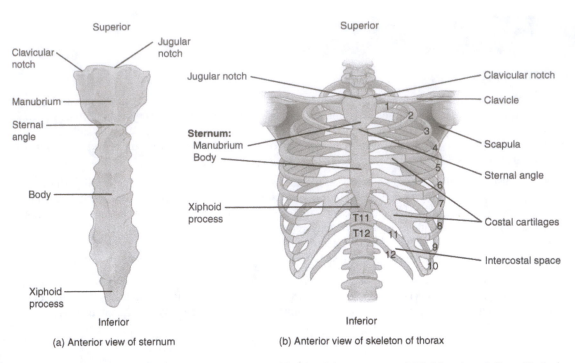

Figure 7.32 Thoracic Cage The thoracic cage is formed by the (a) sternum and (b) 12 pairs of ribs with their costal cartilages. The ribs are anchored posteriorly to the 12 thoracic vertebrae. The sternum consists of the manubrium, body, and xiphoid process. The ribs are classified as true ribs (1–7) and false ribs (8–12). The last two pairs of false ribs are also known as floating ribs (11–12).

Sternum

The sternum is the elongated bony structure that anchors the anterior thoracic cage. It consists of three parts: the manubrium, body, and xiphoid process. The **manubrium** is the wider, superior portion of the sternum. The top of the manubrium has a shallow, U-shaped border called the **jugular (suprasternal) notch**. This can be easily felt at the anterior base of the neck, between the medial ends of the clavicles. The **clavicular notch** is the shallow depression located on either side at the superior-lateral margins of the manubrium. This is the site of the sternoclavicular joint, between the sternum and clavicle. The first ribs also attach to the manubrium.

The elongated, central portion of the sternum is the body. The manubrium and body join together at the **sternal angle**, so called because the junction between these two components is not flat, but forms a slight bend. The second rib attaches to the sternum at the sternal angle. Since the first rib is hidden behind the clavicle, the second rib is the highest rib that can be identified by palpation. Thus, the sternal angle and second rib are important landmarks for the identification and counting of the lower ribs. Ribs 3–7 attach to the sternal body.

The inferior tip of the sternum is the **xiphoid process**. This small structure is cartilaginous early in life, but gradually becomes ossified starting during middle age.

Ribs

Each rib is a curved, flattened bone that contributes to the wall of the thorax. The ribs articulate posteriorly with the T1–T12 thoracic vertebrae, and most attach anteriorly via their costal cartilages to the sternum. There are 12 pairs of ribs. The ribs are numbered 1–12 in accordance with the thoracic vertebrae.

Parts of a Typical Rib

The posterior end of a typical rib is called the **head of the rib** (see Figure 7.27). This region articulates primarily with the costal facet located on the body of the same numbered thoracic vertebra and to a lesser degree, with the costal facet located on the body of the next higher vertebra. Lateral to the head is the narrowed **neck of the rib**. A small bump on the posterior rib surface is the **tubercle of the rib**, which articulates with the facet located on the transverse process of the same numbered vertebra. The remainder of the rib is the **body of the rib** (shaft). Just lateral to the tubercle is the **angle of the rib**, the point at which the rib has its greatest degree of curvature. The angles of the ribs form the most posterior extent of the thoracic cage. In the anatomical position, the angles align with the medial border of the scapula. A shallow **costal groove** for the passage of blood vessels and a nerve is found along the inferior margin of each rib.

Rib Classifications

The bony ribs do not extend anteriorly completely around to the sternum. Instead, each rib ends in a **costal cartilage**. These cartilages are made of hyaline cartilage and can extend for several inches. Most ribs are then attached, either directly or indirectly, to the sternum via their costal cartilage (see Figure 7.32). The ribs are classified into three groups based on their relationship to the sternum.

Ribs 1–7 are classified as **true ribs** (vertebrosternal ribs). The costal cartilage from each of these ribs attaches directly to the sternum. Ribs 8–12 are called **false ribs** (vertebrochondral ribs). The costal cartilages from these ribs do not attach directly to the sternum. For ribs 8–10, the costal cartilages are attached to the cartilage of the next higher rib. Thus, the cartilage of rib 10 attaches to the cartilage of rib 9, rib 9 then attaches to rib 8, and rib 8 is attached to rib 7. The last two false ribs (11–12) are also called **floating ribs** (vertebral ribs). These are short ribs that do not attach to the sternum at all. Instead, their small costal cartilages terminate within the musculature of the lateral abdominal wall.

7.5 | Embryonic Development of the Axial Skeleton

By the end of this section, you will be able to:

- Discuss the two types of embryonic bone development within the skull
- Describe the development of the vertebral column and thoracic cage

The axial skeleton begins to form during early embryonic development. However, growth, remodeling, and ossification (bone formation) continue for several decades after birth before the adult skeleton is fully formed. Knowledge of the developmental processes that give rise to the skeleton is important for understanding the abnormalities that may arise in skeletal structures.

Development of the Skull

During the third week of embryonic development, a rod-like structure called the **notochord** develops dorsally along the length of the embryo. The tissue overlying the notochord enlarges and forms the neural tube, which will give rise to the brain and spinal cord. By the fourth week, mesoderm tissue located on either side of the notochord thickens and separates into a repeating series of block-like tissue structures, each of which is called a **somite**. As the somites enlarge, each one will split into several parts. The most medial of these parts is called a **sclerotome**. The sclerotomes consist of an embryonic tissue called mesenchyme, which will give rise to the fibrous connective tissues, cartilages, and bones of the body.

The bones of the skull arise from mesenchyme during embryonic development in two different ways. The first mechanism produces the bones that form the top and sides of the brain case. This involves the local accumulation of mesenchymal cells at the site of the future bone. These cells then differentiate directly into bone producing cells, which form the skull bones through the process of intramembranous ossification. As the brain case bones grow in the fetal skull, they remain separated from each other by large areas of dense connective tissue, each of which is called a **fontanelle** (Figure 7.33). The fontanelles are the soft spots on an infant's head. They are important during birth because these areas allow the skull to change shape as it squeezes through the birth canal. After birth, the fontanelles allow for continued growth and expansion of the skull as the brain enlarges. The largest fontanelle is located on the anterior head, at the junction of the frontal and parietal bones. The fontanelles decrease in size and disappear by age 2. However, the skull bones remained separated from each other at the sutures, which contain dense fibrous connective tissue that unites the adjacent bones. The connective tissue of the sutures allows for continued growth of the skull bones as the brain enlarges during childhood growth.

The second mechanism for bone development in the skull produces the facial bones and floor of the brain case. This also begins with the localized accumulation of mesenchymal cells. However, these cells differentiate into cartilage cells, which produce a hyaline cartilage model of the future bone. As this cartilage model grows, it is gradually converted into bone through the process of endochondral ossification. This is a slow process and the cartilage is not completely converted to bone until the skull achieves its full adult size.

At birth, the brain case and orbits of the skull are disproportionally large compared to the bones of the jaws and lower face. This reflects the relative underdevelopment of the maxilla and mandible, which lack teeth, and the small sizes of the paranasal sinuses and nasal cavity. During early childhood, the mastoid process enlarges, the two halves of the mandible and frontal bone fuse together to form single bones, and the paranasal sinuses enlarge. The jaws also expand as the teeth begin to appear. These changes all contribute to the rapid growth and enlargement of the face during childhood.

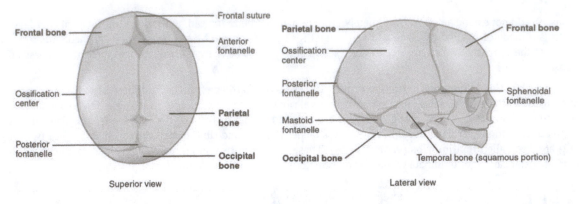

Figure 7.33 Newborn Skull The bones of the newborn skull are not fully ossified and are separated by large areas called fontanelles, which are filled with fibrous connective tissue. The fontanelles allow for continued growth of the skull after birth. At the time of birth, the facial bones are small and underdeveloped, and the mastoid process has not yet formed.

Development of the Vertebral Column and Thoracic cage

Development of the vertebrae begins with the accumulation of mesenchyme cells from each sclerotome around the notochord. These cells differentiate into a hyaline cartilage model for each vertebra, which then grow and eventually ossify into bone through the process of endochondral ossification. As the developing vertebrae grow, the notochord largely disappears. However, small areas of notochord tissue persist between the adjacent vertebrae and this contributes to the formation of each intervertebral disc.

The ribs and sternum also develop from mesenchyme. The ribs initially develop as part of the cartilage model for each vertebra, but in the thorax region, the rib portion separates from the vertebra by the eighth week. The cartilage model of the rib then ossifies, except for the anterior portion, which remains as the costal cartilage. The sternum initially forms as paired hyaline cartilage models on either side of the anterior midline, beginning during the fifth week of development. The cartilage models of the ribs become attached to the lateral sides of the developing sternum. Eventually, the two halves of the cartilaginous sternum fuse together along the midline and then ossify into bone. The manubrium and body of the sternum are converted into bone first, with the xiphoid process remaining as cartilage until late in life.

View this **video (http://openstaxcollege.org/l/skullbones)** to review the two processes that give rise to the bones of the skull and body. What are the two mechanisms by which the bones of the body are formed and which bones are formed by each mechanism?

Homeostatic IMBALANCES

Craniosynostosis

The premature closure (fusion) of a suture line is a condition called craniosynostosis. This error in the normal developmental process results in abnormal growth of the skull and deformity of the head. It is produced either by defects in the ossification process of the skull bones or failure of the brain to properly enlarge. Genetic factors are involved, but the underlying cause is unknown. It is a relatively common condition, occurring in approximately 1:2000 births, with males being more commonly affected. Primary craniosynostosis involves the early fusion of one cranial suture, whereas complex craniosynostosis results from the premature fusion of several sutures.

The early fusion of a suture in primary craniosynostosis prevents any additional enlargement of the cranial bones and skull along this line. Continued growth of the brain and skull is therefore diverted to other areas of the head, causing an abnormal enlargement of these regions. For example, the early disappearance of the anterior fontanelle and premature closure of the sagittal suture prevents growth across the top of the head. This is compensated by upward growth by the bones of the lateral skull, resulting in a long, narrow, wedge-shaped head. This condition, known as scaphocephaly, accounts for approximately 50 percent of craniosynostosis abnormalities. Although the skull is misshapen, the brain still has adequate room to grow and thus there is no accompanying abnormal neurological development.

In cases of complex craniosynostosis, several sutures close prematurely. The amount and degree of skull deformity is determined by the location and extent of the sutures involved. This results in more severe constraints on skull growth, which can alter or impede proper brain growth and development.

Cases of craniosynostosis are usually treated with surgery. A team of physicians will open the skull along the fused suture, which will then allow the skull bones to resume their growth in this area. In some cases, parts of the skull will be removed and replaced with an artificial plate. The earlier after birth that surgery is performed, the better the outcome. After treatment, most children continue to grow and develop normally and do not exhibit any neurological problems.

KEY TERMS

alveolar process of the mandible upper border of mandibular body that contains the lower teeth

alveolar process of the maxilla curved, inferior margin of the maxilla that supports and anchors the upper teeth

angle of the mandible rounded corner located at outside margin of the body and ramus junction

angle of the rib portion of rib with greatest curvature; together, the rib angles form the most posterior extent of the thoracic cage

anterior (ventral) sacral foramen one of the series of paired openings located on the anterior (ventral) side of the sacrum

anterior arch anterior portion of the ring-like C1 (atlas) vertebra

anterior cranial fossa shallowest and most anterior cranial fossa of the cranial base that extends from the frontal bone to the lesser wing of the sphenoid bone

anterior longitudinal ligament ligament that runs the length of the vertebral column, uniting the anterior aspects of the vertebral bodies

anulus fibrosus tough, fibrous outer portion of an intervertebral disc, which is strongly anchored to the bodies of the adjacent vertebrae

appendicular skeleton all bones of the upper and lower limbs, plus the girdle bones that attach each limb to the axial skeleton

articular tubercle smooth ridge located on the inferior skull, immediately anterior to the mandibular fossa

atlas first cervical (C1) vertebra

axial skeleton central, vertical axis of the body, including the skull, vertebral column, and thoracic cage

axis second cervical (C2) vertebra

body of the rib shaft portion of a rib

brain case portion of the skull that contains and protects the brain, consisting of the eight bones that form the cranial base and rounded upper skull

calvaria (also, skullcap) rounded top of the skull

carotid canal zig-zag tunnel providing passage through the base of the skull for the internal carotid artery to the brain; begins anteromedial to the styloid process and terminates in the middle cranial cavity, near the posterior-lateral base of the sella turcica

cervical curve posteriorly concave curvature of the cervical vertebral column region; a secondary curve of the vertebral column

cervical vertebrae seven vertebrae numbered as C1–C7 that are located in the neck region of the vertebral column

clavicular notch paired notches located on the superior-lateral sides of the sternal manubrium, for articulation with the clavicle

coccyx small bone located at inferior end of the adult vertebral column that is formed by the fusion of four coccygeal vertebrae; also referred to as the "tailbone"

condylar process of the mandible thickened upward projection from posterior margin of mandibular ramus

condyle oval-shaped process located at the top of the condylar process of the mandible

coronal suture joint that unites the frontal bone to the right and left parietal bones across the top of the skull

coronoid process of the mandible flattened upward projection from the anterior margin of the mandibular ramus

costal cartilage hyaline cartilage structure attached to the anterior end of each rib that provides for either direct or indirect attachment of most ribs to the sternum

costal facet site on the lateral sides of a thoracic vertebra for articulation with the head of a rib

costal groove shallow groove along the inferior margin of a rib that provides passage for blood vessels and a nerve

cranial cavity interior space of the skull that houses the brain

cranium skull

cribriform plate small, flattened areas with numerous small openings, located to either side of the midline in the floor of the anterior cranial fossa; formed by the ethmoid bone

crista galli small upward projection located at the midline in the floor of the anterior cranial fossa; formed by the ethmoid bone

dens bony projection (odontoid process) that extends upward from the body of the C2 (axis) vertebra

ear ossicles three small bones located in the middle ear cavity that serve to transmit sound vibrations to the inner ear

ethmoid air cell one of several small, air-filled spaces located within the lateral sides of the ethmoid bone, between the orbit and upper nasal cavity

ethmoid bone unpaired bone that forms the roof and upper, lateral walls of the nasal cavity, portions of the floor of the anterior cranial fossa and medial wall of orbit, and the upper portion of the nasal septum

external acoustic meatus ear canal opening located on the lateral side of the skull

external occipital protuberance small bump located at the midline on the posterior skull

facet small, flattened area on a bone for an articulation (joint) with another bone, or for muscle attachment

facial bones fourteen bones that support the facial structures and form the upper and lower jaws and the hard palate

false ribs vertebrochondral ribs 8–12 whose costal cartilage either attaches indirectly to the sternum via the costal cartilage of the next higher rib or does not attach to the sternum at all

floating ribs vertebral ribs 11–12 that do not attach to the sternum or to the costal cartilage of another rib

fontanelle expanded area of fibrous connective tissue that separates the brain case bones of the skull prior to birth and during the first year after birth

foramen lacerum irregular opening in the base of the skull, located inferior to the exit of carotid canal

foramen magnum large opening in the occipital bone of the skull through which the spinal cord emerges and the vertebral arteries enter the cranium

foramen ovale of the middle cranial fossa oval-shaped opening in the floor of the middle cranial fossa

foramen rotundum round opening in the floor of the middle cranial fossa, located between the superior orbital fissure and foramen ovale

foramen spinosum small opening in the floor of the middle cranial fossa, located lateral to the foramen ovale

frontal bone unpaired bone that forms forehead, roof of orbit, and floor of anterior cranial fossa

frontal sinus air-filled space within the frontal bone; most anterior of the paranasal sinuses

glabella slight depression of frontal bone, located at the midline between the eyebrows

greater wings of sphenoid bone lateral projections of the sphenoid bone that form the anterior wall of the middle cranial fossa and an area of the lateral skull

hard palate bony structure that forms the roof of the mouth and floor of the nasal cavity, formed by the palatine process of the maxillary bones and the horizontal plate of the palatine bones

head of the rib posterior end of a rib that articulates with the bodies of thoracic vertebrae

horizontal plate medial extension from the palatine bone that forms the posterior quarter of the hard palate

hyoid bone small, U-shaped bone located in upper neck that does not contact any other bone

hypoglossal canal paired openings that pass anteriorly from the anterior-lateral margins of the foramen magnum deep to the occipital condyles

hypophyseal (pituitary) fossa shallow depression on top of the sella turcica that houses the pituitary (hypophyseal) gland

inferior articular process bony process that extends downward from the vertebral arch of a vertebra that articulates with the superior articular process of the next lower vertebra

inferior nasal concha one of the paired bones that project from the lateral walls of the nasal cavity to form the largest and most inferior of the nasal conchae

infraorbital foramen opening located on anterior skull, below the orbit

infratemporal fossa space on lateral side of skull, below the level of the zygomatic arch and deep (medial) to the ramus of the mandible

internal acoustic meatus opening into petrous ridge, located on the lateral wall of the posterior cranial fossa

intervertebral disc structure located between the bodies of adjacent vertebrae that strongly joins the vertebrae; provides padding, weight bearing ability, and enables vertebral column movements

intervertebral foramen opening located between adjacent vertebrae for exit of a spinal nerve

jugular (suprasternal) notch shallow notch located on superior surface of sternal manubrium

jugular foramen irregularly shaped opening located in the lateral floor of the posterior cranial cavity

kyphosis (also, humpback or hunchback) excessive posterior curvature of the thoracic vertebral column region

lacrimal bone paired bones that contribute to the anterior-medial wall of each orbit

lacrimal fossa shallow depression in the anterior-medial wall of the orbit, formed by the lacrimal bone that gives rise to the nasolacrimal canal

lambdoid suture inverted V-shaped joint that unites the occipital bone to the right and left parietal bones on the posterior skull

lamina portion of the vertebral arch on each vertebra that extends between the transverse and spinous process

lateral pterygoid plate paired, flattened bony projections of the sphenoid bone located on the inferior skull, lateral to the medial pterygoid plate

lateral sacral crest paired irregular ridges running down the lateral sides of the posterior sacrum that was formed by the fusion of the transverse processes from the five sacral vertebrae

lesser wings of the sphenoid bone lateral extensions of the sphenoid bone that form the bony lip separating the anterior and middle cranial fossae

ligamentum flavum series of short ligaments that unite the lamina of adjacent vertebrae

lingula small flap of bone located on the inner (medial) surface of mandibular ramus, next to the mandibular foramen

lordosis (also, swayback) excessive anterior curvature of the lumbar vertebral column region

lumbar curve posteriorly concave curvature of the lumbar vertebral column region; a secondary curve of the vertebral column

lumbar vertebrae five vertebrae numbered as L1–L5 that are located in lumbar region (lower back) of the vertebral column

mandible unpaired bone that forms the lower jaw bone; the only moveable bone of the skull

mandibular foramen opening located on the inner (medial) surface of the mandibular ramus

mandibular fossa oval depression located on the inferior surface of the skull

mandibular notch large U-shaped notch located between the condylar process and coronoid process of the mandible

manubrium expanded, superior portion of the sternum

mastoid process large bony prominence on the inferior, lateral skull, just behind the earlobe

maxillary bone (also, maxilla) paired bones that form the upper jaw and anterior portion of the hard palate

maxillary sinus air-filled space located with each maxillary bone; largest of the paranasal sinuses

medial pterygoid plate paired, flattened bony projections of the sphenoid bone located on the inferior skull medial to the lateral pterygoid plate; form the posterior portion of the nasal cavity lateral wall

median sacral crest irregular ridge running down the midline of the posterior sacrum that was formed from the fusion of the spinous processes of the five sacral vertebrae

mental foramen opening located on the anterior-lateral side of the mandibular body

mental protuberance inferior margin of anterior mandible that forms the chin

middle cranial fossa centrally located cranial fossa that extends from the lesser wings of the sphenoid bone to the petrous ridge

middle nasal concha nasal concha formed by the ethmoid bone that is located between the superior and inferior conchae

mylohyoid line bony ridge located along the inner (medial) surface of the mandibular body

nasal bone paired bones that form the base of the nose

nasal cavity opening through skull for passage of air

nasal conchae curved bony plates that project from the lateral walls of the nasal cavity; include the superior and middle nasal conchae, which are parts of the ethmoid bone, and the independent inferior nasal conchae bone

nasal septum flat, midline structure that divides the nasal cavity into halves, formed by the perpendicular plate of the ethmoid bone, vomer bone, and septal cartilage

nasolacrimal canal passage for drainage of tears that extends downward from the medial-anterior orbit to the nasal cavity, terminating behind the inferior nasal conchae

neck of the rib narrowed region of a rib, next to the rib head

notochord rod-like structure along dorsal side of the early embryo; largely disappears during later development but does contribute to formation of the intervertebral discs

nuchal ligament expanded portion of the supraspinous ligament within the posterior neck; interconnects the spinous processes of the cervical vertebrae and attaches to the base of the skull

nucleus pulposus gel-like central region of an intervertebral disc; provides for padding, weight-bearing, and movement between adjacent vertebrae

occipital bone unpaired bone that forms the posterior portions of the brain case and base of the skull

occipital condyle paired, oval-shaped bony knobs located on the inferior skull, to either side of the foramen magnum

optic canal opening spanning between middle cranial fossa and posterior orbit

orbit bony socket that contains the eyeball and associated muscles

palatine bone paired bones that form the posterior quarter of the hard palate and a small area in floor of the orbit

palatine process medial projection from the maxilla bone that forms the anterior three quarters of the hard palate

paranasal sinuses cavities within the skull that are connected to the conchae that serve to warm and humidify incoming air, produce mucus, and lighten the weight of the skull; consist of frontal, maxillary, sphenoidal, and ethmoidal sinuses

parietal bone paired bones that form the upper, lateral sides of the skull

pedicle portion of the vertebral arch that extends from the vertebral body to the transverse process

perpendicular plate of the ethmoid bone downward, midline extension of the ethmoid bone that forms the superior portion of the nasal septum

petrous ridge petrous portion of the temporal bone that forms a large, triangular ridge in the floor of the cranial cavity, separating the middle and posterior cranial fossae; houses the middle and inner ear structures

posterior (dorsal) sacral foramen one of the series of paired openings located on the posterior (dorsal) side of the sacrum

posterior arch posterior portion of the ring-like C1 (atlas) vertebra

posterior cranial fossa deepest and most posterior cranial fossa; extends from the petrous ridge to the occipital bone

posterior longitudinal ligament ligament that runs the length of the vertebral column, uniting the posterior sides of the vertebral bodies

primary curve anteriorly concave curvatures of the thoracic and sacrococcygeal regions that are retained from the original fetal curvature of the vertebral column

pterion H-shaped suture junction region that unites the frontal, parietal, temporal, and sphenoid bones on the lateral side of the skull

ramus of the mandible vertical portion of the mandible

ribs thin, curved bones of the chest wall

sacral canal bony tunnel that runs through the sacrum

sacral foramina series of paired openings for nerve exit located on both the anterior (ventral) and posterior (dorsal) aspects of the sacrum

sacral hiatus inferior opening and termination of the sacral canal

sacral promontory anterior lip of the base (superior end) of the sacrum

sacrococcygeal curve anteriorly concave curvature formed by the sacrum and coccyx; a primary curve of the vertebral column

sacrum single bone located near the inferior end of the adult vertebral column that is formed by the fusion of five sacral vertebrae; forms the posterior portion of the pelvis

sagittal suture joint that unites the right and left parietal bones at the midline along the top of the skull

sclerotome medial portion of a somite consisting of mesenchyme tissue that will give rise to bone, cartilage, and fibrous connective tissues

scoliosis abnormal lateral curvature of the vertebral column

secondary curve posteriorly concave curvatures of the cervical and lumbar regions of the vertebral column that develop after the time of birth

sella turcica elevated area of sphenoid bone located at midline of the middle cranial fossa

septal cartilage flat cartilage structure that forms the anterior portion of the nasal septum

skeleton bones of the body

skull bony structure that forms the head, face, and jaws, and protects the brain; consists of 22 bones

somite one of the paired, repeating blocks of tissue located on either side of the notochord in the early embryo

sphenoid bone unpaired bone that forms the central base of skull

sphenoid sinus air-filled space located within the sphenoid bone; most posterior of the paranasal sinuses

spinous process unpaired bony process that extends posteriorly from the vertebral arch of a vertebra

squamous suture joint that unites the parietal bone to the squamous portion of the temporal bone on the lateral side of the skull

sternal angle junction line between manubrium and body of the sternum and the site for attachment of the second rib to the sternum

sternum flattened bone located at the center of the anterior chest

styloid process downward projecting, elongated bony process located on the inferior aspect of the skull

stylomastoid foramen opening located on inferior skull, between the styloid process and mastoid process

superior articular process bony process that extends upward from the vertebral arch of a vertebra that articulates with the inferior articular process of the next higher vertebra

superior articular process of the sacrum paired processes that extend upward from the sacrum to articulate (join) with the inferior articular processes from the L5 vertebra

superior nasal concha smallest and most superiorly located of the nasal conchae; formed by the ethmoid bone

superior nuchal line paired bony lines on the posterior skull that extend laterally from the external occipital protuberance

superior orbital fissure irregularly shaped opening between the middle cranial fossa and the posterior orbit

supraorbital foramen opening located on anterior skull, at the superior margin of the orbit

supraorbital margin superior margin of the orbit

supraspinous ligament ligament that interconnects the spinous processes of the thoracic and lumbar vertebrae

suture junction line at which adjacent bones of the skull are united by fibrous connective tissue

temporal bone paired bones that form the lateral, inferior portions of the skull, with squamous, mastoid, and petrous portions

temporal fossa shallow space on the lateral side of the skull, above the level of the zygomatic arch

temporal process of the zygomatic bone short extension from the zygomatic bone that forms the anterior portion of the zygomatic arch

thoracic cage consists of 12 pairs of ribs and sternum

thoracic curve anteriorly concave curvature of the thoracic vertebral column region; a primary curve of the vertebral column

thoracic vertebrae twelve vertebrae numbered as T1–T12 that are located in the thoracic region (upper back) of the vertebral column

transverse foramen opening found only in the transverse processes of cervical vertebrae

transverse process paired bony processes that extends laterally from the vertebral arch of a vertebra

true ribs vertebrosternal ribs 1–7 that attach via their costal cartilage directly to the sternum

tubercle of the rib small bump on the posterior side of a rib for articulation with the transverse process of a thoracic vertebra

vertebra individual bone in the neck and back regions of the vertebral column

vertebral (spinal) canal bony passageway within the vertebral column for the spinal cord that is formed by the series of individual vertebral foramina

vertebral arch bony arch formed by the posterior portion of each vertebra that surrounds and protects the spinal cord

vertebral column entire sequence of bones that extend from the skull to the tailbone

vertebral foramen opening associated with each vertebra defined by the vertebral arch that provides passage for the spinal cord

vomer bone unpaired bone that forms the inferior and posterior portions of the nasal septum

xiphoid process small process that forms the inferior tip of the sternum

zygomatic arch elongated, free-standing arch on the lateral skull, formed anteriorly by the temporal process of the zygomatic bone and posteriorly by the zygomatic process of the temporal bone

zygomatic bone cheekbone; paired bones that contribute to the lateral orbit and anterior zygomatic arch

zygomatic process of the temporal bone extension from the temporal bone that forms the posterior portion of the zygomatic arch

CHAPTER REVIEW

7.1 Divisions of the Skeletal System

The skeletal system includes all of the bones, cartilages, and ligaments of the body. It serves to support the body, protect the brain and other internal organs, and provides a rigid structure upon which muscles can pull to generate body movements. It also stores fat and the tissue responsible for the production of blood cells. The skeleton is subdivided into two parts. The axial skeleton forms a vertical axis that includes the head, neck, back, and chest. It has 80 bones and consists of the skull, vertebral column, and thoracic cage. The adult vertebral column consists of 24 vertebrae plus the sacrum and coccyx. The thoracic cage is formed by 12 pairs of ribs and the sternum. The appendicular skeleton consists of 126 bones in the adult and includes all of the bones of the upper and lower limbs plus the bones that anchor each limb to the axial skeleton.

7.2 The Skull

The skull consists of the brain case and the facial bones. The brain case surrounds and protects the brain, which occupies the cranial cavity inside the skull. It consists of the rounded calvaria and a complex base. The brain case is formed by eight bones, the paired parietal and temporal bones plus the unpaired frontal, occipital, sphenoid, and ethmoid bones. The narrow gap between the bones is filled with dense, fibrous connective tissue that unites the bones. The sagittal suture joins the right and left parietal bones. The coronal suture joins the parietal bones to the frontal bone, the lamboid suture joins them to the occipital bone, and the squamous suture joins them to the temporal bone.

The facial bones support the facial structures and form the upper and lower jaws. These consist of 14 bones, with the paired maxillary, palatine, zygomatic, nasal, lacrimal, and inferior conchae bones and the unpaired vomer and mandible bones. The ethmoid bone also contributes to the formation of facial structures. The maxilla forms the upper jaw and the mandible forms the lower jaw. The maxilla also forms the larger anterior portion of the hard palate, which is completed by the smaller palatine bones that form the posterior portion of the hard palate.

The floor of the cranial cavity increases in depth from front to back and is divided into three cranial fossae. The anterior cranial fossa is located between the frontal bone and lesser wing of the sphenoid bone. A small area of the ethmoid bone, consisting of the crista galli and cribriform plates, is located at the midline of this fossa. The middle cranial fossa extends from the lesser wing of the sphenoid bone to the petrous ridge (petrous portion of temporal bone). The right and left sides are separated at the midline by the sella turcica, which surrounds the shallow hypophyseal fossa. Openings through the skull in the floor of the middle fossa include the optic canal and superior orbital fissure, which open into the posterior orbit, the foramen rotundum, foramen ovale, and foramen spinosum, and the exit of the carotid canal with its underlying foramen lacerum. The deep posterior cranial fossa extends from the petrous ridge to the occipital bone. Openings here include the large foramen magnum, plus the internal acoustic meatus, jugular foramina, and hypoglossal canals. Additional openings located on the external base of the skull include the stylomastoid foramen and the entrance to the carotid canal.

The anterior skull has the orbits that house the eyeballs and associated muscles. The walls of the orbit are formed by contributions from seven bones: the frontal, zygomatic, maxillary, palatine, ethmoid, lacrimal, and sphenoid. Located at the superior margin of the orbit is the supraorbital foramen, and below the orbit is the infraorbital foramen. The mandible has two openings, the mandibular foramen on its inner surface and the mental foramen on its external surface near the chin. The nasal conchae are bony projections from the lateral walls of the nasal cavity. The large inferior nasal concha is an independent bone, while the middle and superior conchae are parts of the ethmoid bone. The nasal septum is formed by the perpendicular plate of the ethmoid bone, the vomer bone, and the septal cartilage. The paranasal sinuses are air-filled spaces located within the frontal, maxillary, sphenoid, and ethmoid bones.

On the lateral skull, the zygomatic arch consists of two parts, the temporal process of the zygomatic bone anteriorly and the zygomatic process of the temporal bone posteriorly. The temporal fossa is the shallow space located on the lateral skull above the level of the zygomatic arch. The infratemporal fossa is located below the zygomatic arch and deep to the ramus of the mandible.

The hyoid bone is located in the upper neck and does not join with any other bone. It is held in position by muscles and serves to support the tongue above, the larynx below, and the pharynx posteriorly.

7.3 The Vertebral Column

The vertebral column forms the neck and back. The vertebral column originally develops as 33 vertebrae, but is eventually reduced to 24 vertebrae, plus the sacrum and coccyx. The vertebrae are divided into the cervical region (C1–C7 vertebrae), the thoracic region (T1–T12 vertebrae), and the lumbar region (L1–L5 vertebrae). The sacrum arises from the fusion of five sacral vertebrae and the coccyx from the fusion of four small coccygeal vertebrae. The vertebral column has four curvatures, the cervical, thoracic, lumbar, and sacrococcygeal curves. The thoracic and sacrococcygeal curves are primary curves retained from the original fetal curvature. The cervical and lumbar curves develop after birth and thus are secondary curves. The cervical curve develops as the infant begins to hold up the head, and the lumbar curve appears with standing and walking.

A typical vertebra consists of an enlarged anterior portion called the body, which provides weight-bearing support. Attached posteriorly to the body is a vertebral arch, which surrounds and defines the vertebral foramen for passage of the spinal cord. The vertebral arch consists of the pedicles, which attach to the vertebral body, and the laminae, which come together to form the roof of the arch. Arising from the vertebral arch are the laterally projecting transverse processes and the posteriorly oriented spinous process. The superior articular processes project upward, where they articulate with the downward projecting inferior articular processes of the next higher vertebrae.

A typical cervical vertebra has a small body, a bifid (Y-shaped) spinous process, and U-shaped transverse processes with a transverse foramen. In addition to these characteristics, the axis (C2 vertebra) also has the dens projecting upward from the vertebral body. The atlas (C1 vertebra) differs from the other cervical vertebrae in that it does not have a body, but instead consists of bony ring formed by the anterior and posterior arches. The atlas articulates with the dens from the axis. A typical thoracic vertebra is distinguished by its long, downward projecting spinous process. Thoracic vertebrae also have articulation facets on the body and transverse processes for attachment of the ribs. Lumbar vertebrae support the greatest amount of body weight and thus have a large, thick body. They also have a short, blunt spinous process. The sacrum is triangular in shape. The median sacral crest is formed by the fused vertebral spinous processes and the lateral sacral crest is derived from the fused transverse processes. Anterior (ventral) and posterior (dorsal) sacral foramina allow branches of the sacral spinal nerves to exit the sacrum. The auricular surfaces are articulation sites on the lateral sacrum that anchor the sacrum to the hipbones to form the pelvis. The coccyx is small and derived from the fusion of four small vertebrae.

The intervertebral discs fill in the gaps between the bodies of adjacent vertebrae. They provide strong attachments and padding between the vertebrae. The outer, fibrous layer of a disc is called the anulus fibrosus. The gel-like interior is called the nucleus pulposus. The disc can change shape to allow for movement between vertebrae. If the anulus fibrosus is weakened or damaged, the nucleus pulposus can protrude outward, resulting in a herniated disc.

The anterior longitudinal ligament runs along the full length of the anterior vertebral column, uniting the vertebral bodies. The supraspinous ligament is located posteriorly and interconnects the spinous processes of the thoracic and lumbar vertebrae. In the neck, this ligament expands to become the nuchal ligament. The nuchal ligament is attached to the cervical spinous processes and superiorly to the base of the skull, out to the external occipital protuberance. The posterior longitudinal ligament runs within the vertebral canal and unites the posterior sides of the vertebral bodies. The ligamentum flavum unites the lamina of adjacent vertebrae.

7.4 The Thoracic Cage

The thoracic cage protects the heart and lungs. It is composed of 12 pairs of ribs with their costal cartilages and the sternum. The ribs are anchored posteriorly to the 12 thoracic vertebrae. The sternum consists of the manubrium, body, and xiphoid process. The manubrium and body are joined at the sternal angle, which is also the site for attachment of the second ribs.

Ribs are flattened, curved bones and are numbered 1–12. Posteriorly, the head of the rib articulates with the costal facets located on the bodies of thoracic vertebrae and the rib tubercle articulates with the facet located on the vertebral transverse process. The angle of the ribs forms the most posterior portion of the thoracic cage. The costal groove in the inferior margin of each rib carries blood vessels and a nerve. Anteriorly, each rib ends in a costal cartilage. True ribs (1–7) attach directly to the sternum via their costal cartilage. The false ribs (8–12) either attach to the sternum indirectly or not at all. Ribs 8–10 have their costal cartilages attached to the cartilage of the next higher rib. The floating ribs (11–12) are short and do not attach to the sternum or to another rib.

7.5 Embryonic Development of the Axial Skeleton

Formation of the axial skeleton begins during early embryonic development with the appearance of the rod-like notochord along the dorsal length of the early embryo. Repeating, paired blocks of tissue called somites then appear along either side of notochord. As the somites grow, they split into parts, one of which is called a sclerotome. This consists of mesenchyme, the embryonic tissue that will become the bones, cartilages, and connective tissues of the body.

Mesenchyme in the head region will produce the bones of the skull via two different mechanisms. The bones of the brain case arise via intramembranous ossification in which embryonic mesenchyme tissue converts directly into bone. At the time of birth, these bones are separated by fontanelles, wide areas of fibrous connective tissue. As the bones grow, the fontanelles are reduced to sutures, which allow for continued growth of the skull throughout childhood. In contrast, the cranial base and facial bones are produced by the process of endochondral ossification, in which mesenchyme tissue initially produces a hyaline cartilage model of the future bone. The cartilage model allows for growth of the bone and is gradually converted into bone over a period of many years.

The vertebrae, ribs, and sternum also develop via endochondral ossification. Mesenchyme accumulates around the notochord and produces hyaline cartilage models of the vertebrae. The notochord largely disappears, but remnants of the notochord contribute to formation of the intervertebral discs. In the thorax region, a portion of the vertebral cartilage model splits off to form the ribs. These then become attached anteriorly to the developing cartilage model of the sternum. Growth of the cartilage models for the vertebrae, ribs, and sternum allow for enlargement of the thoracic cage during childhood and adolescence. The cartilage models gradually undergo ossification and are converted into bone.

INTERACTIVE LINK QUESTIONS

1. Watch this video (http://openstaxcollege.org/l/skull1) to view a rotating and exploded skull with color-coded bones. Which bone (yellow) is centrally located and joins with most of the other bones of the skull?

2. View this animation (http://openstaxcollege.org/l/headblow) to see how a blow to the head may produce a contrecoup (counterblow) fracture of the basilar portion of the occipital bone on the base of the skull. Why may a basilar fracture be life threatening?

3. Osteoporosis is a common age-related bone disease in which bone density and strength is decreased. Watch this video (http://openstaxcollege.org/l/osteoporosis) to get a better understanding of how thoracic vertebrae may become weakened and may fractured due to this disease. How may vertebral osteoporosis contribute to kyphosis?

4. Watch this animation (http://openstaxcollege.org/l/diskslip) to see what it means to "slip" a disk. Watch this second animation (http://openstaxcollege.org/l/herndisc) to see one possible treatment for a herniated disc, removing and replacing the damaged disc with an artificial one that allows for movement between the adjacent certebrae. How could lifting a heavy object produce pain in a lower limb?

5. Use this tool (http://openstaxcollege.org/l/vertcolumn) to identify the bones, intervertebral discs, and ligaments of the vertebral column. The thickest portions of the anterior longitudinal ligament and the supraspinous ligament are found in which regions of the vertebral column?

6. View this video (http://openstaxcollege.org/l/skullbones) to review the two processes that give rise to the bones of the skull and body. What are the two mechanisms by which the bones of the body are formed and which bones are formed by each mechanism?

REVIEW QUESTIONS

7. Which of the following is part of the axial skeleton?

    a. shoulder bones
    b. thigh bone
    c. foot bones
    d. vertebral column

8. Which of the following is a function of the axial skeleton?
    a. allows for movement of the wrist and hand
    b. protects nerves and blood vessels at the elbow
    c. supports trunk of body
    d. allows for movements of the ankle and foot

9. The axial skeleton _____.
    a. consists of 126 bones
    b. forms the vertical axis of the body
    c. includes all bones of the body trunk and limbs
    d. includes only the bones of the lower limbs

10. Which of the following is a bone of the brain case?

    a. parietal bone
    b. zygomatic bone
    c. maxillary bone
    d. lacrimal bone

11. The lambdoid suture joins the parietal bone to the _____.
    a. frontal bone
    b. occipital bone
    c. other parietal bone
    d. temporal bone

12. The middle cranial fossa _____.
    a. is bounded anteriorly by the petrous ridge
    b. is bounded posteriorly by the lesser wing of the sphenoid bone
    c. is divided at the midline by a small area of the ethmoid bone
    d. has the foramen rotundum, foramen ovale, and foramen spinosum

13. The paranasal sinuses are _____.
    a. air-filled spaces found within the frontal, maxilla, sphenoid, and ethmoid bones only
    b. air-filled spaces found within all bones of the skull
    c. not connected to the nasal cavity
    d. divided at the midline by the nasal septum

14. Parts of the sphenoid bone include the _____.

    a. sella turcica
    b. squamous portion
    c. glabella
    d. zygomatic process

15. The bony openings of the skull include the _____.

    a. carotid canal, which is located in the anterior cranial fossa
    b. superior orbital fissure, which is located at the superior margin of the anterior orbit
    c. mental foramen, which is located just below the orbit
    d. hypoglossal canal, which is located in the posterior cranial fossa

16. The cervical region of the vertebral column consists of _____.
    a. seven vertebrae
    b. 12 vertebrae
    c. five vertebrae
    d. a single bone derived from the fusion of five vertebrae

17. The primary curvatures of the vertebral column _____.
    a. include the lumbar curve
    b. are remnants of the original fetal curvature
    c. include the cervical curve
    d. develop after the time of birth

18. A typical vertebra has _____.
    a. a vertebral foramen that passes through the body
    b. a superior articular process that projects downward to articulate with the superior portion of the next lower vertebra
    c. lamina that spans between the transverse process and spinous process
    d. a pair of laterally projecting spinous processes

19. A typical lumbar vertebra has _____.
    a. a short, rounded spinous process
    b. a bifid spinous process
    c. articulation sites for ribs
    d. a transverse foramen

20. Which is found only in the cervical region of the vertebral column?
    a. nuchal ligament
    b. ligamentum flavum
    c. supraspinous ligament
    d. anterior longitudinal ligament

21. The sternum _____.
    a. consists of only two parts, the manubrium and xiphoid process
    b. has the sternal angle located between the manubrium and body
    c. receives direct attachments from the costal cartilages of all 12 pairs of ribs
    d. articulates directly with the thoracic vertebrae

22. The sternal angle is the _____.
    a. junction between the body and xiphoid process
    b. site for attachment of the clavicle
    c. site for attachment of the floating ribs
    d. junction between the manubrium and body

23. The tubercle of a rib _____.
    a. is for articulation with the transverse process of a thoracic vertebra
    b. is for articulation with the body of a thoracic vertebra
    c. provides for passage of blood vessels and a nerve
    d. is the area of greatest rib curvature

24. True ribs are _____.
    a. ribs 8–12
    b. attached via their costal cartilage to the next higher rib
    c. made entirely of bone, and thus do not have a costal cartilage
    d. attached via their costal cartilage directly to the sternum

25. Embryonic development of the axial skeleton involves _____.
    a. intramembranous ossification, which forms the facial bones.
    b. endochondral ossification, which forms the ribs and sternum
    c. the notochord, which produces the cartilage models for the vertebrae
    d. the formation of hyaline cartilage models, which give rise to the flat bones of the skull

26. A fontanelle _____.
    a. is the cartilage model for a vertebra that later is converted into bone
    b. gives rise to the facial bones and vertebrae
    c. is the rod-like structure that runs the length of the early embryo
    d. is the area of fibrous connective tissue found at birth between the brain case bones

CRITICAL THINKING QUESTIONS

27. Define the two divisions of the skeleton.

28. Discuss the functions of the axial skeleton.

29. Define and list the bones that form the brain case or support the facial structures.

30. Identify the major sutures of the skull, their locations, and the bones united by each.

31. Describe the anterior, middle, and posterior cranial fossae and their boundaries, and give the midline structure that divides each into right and left areas.

32. Describe the parts of the nasal septum in both the dry and living skull.

33. Describe the vertebral column and define each region.

34. Describe a typical vertebra.

35. Describe the sacrum.

36. Describe the structure and function of an intervertebral disc.

37. Define the ligaments of the vertebral column.

38. Define the parts and functions of the thoracic cage.

39. Describe the parts of the sternum.

40. Discuss the parts of a typical rib.

41. Define the classes of ribs.

42. Discuss the processes by which the brain-case bones of the skull are formed and grow during skull enlargement.

43. Discuss the process that gives rise to the base and facial bones of the skull.

44. Discuss the development of the vertebrae, ribs, and sternum.

8 | THE APPENDICULAR SKELETON

Figure 8.1 Dancer The appendicular skeleton consists of the upper and lower limb bones, the bones of the hands and feet, and the bones that anchor the limbs to the axial skeleton. (credit: Melissa Dooley/flickr)

Introduction

Chapter Objectives

After studying this chapter, you will be able to:

- Discuss the bones of the pectoral and pelvic girdles, and describe how these unite the limbs with the axial skeleton
- Describe the bones of the upper limb, including the bones of the arm, forearm, wrist, and hand
- Identify the features of the pelvis and explain how these differ between the adult male and female pelvis
- Describe the bones of the lower limb, including the bones of the thigh, leg, ankle, and foot
- Describe the embryonic formation and growth of the limb bones

Your skeleton provides the internal supporting structure of the body. The adult axial skeleton consists of 80 bones that form the head and body trunk. Attached to this are the limbs, whose 126 bones constitute the appendicular skeleton. These bones are divided into two groups: the bones that are located within the limbs themselves, and the girdle bones that attach the limbs to the axial skeleton. The bones of the shoulder region form the pectoral girdle, which anchors the upper limb to the thoracic cage of the axial skeleton. The lower limb is attached to the vertebral column by the pelvic girdle.

Because of our upright stance, different functional demands are placed upon the upper and lower limbs. Thus, the bones of the lower limbs are adapted for weight-bearing support and stability, as well as for body locomotion via walking or running. In contrast, our upper limbs are not required for these functions. Instead, our upper limbs are highly mobile and can be utilized for a wide variety of activities. The large range of upper limb movements, coupled with the ability to easily manipulate objects with our hands and opposable thumbs, has allowed humans to construct the modern world in which we live.

8.1 | The Pectoral Girdle

By the end of this section, you will be able to:

- Describe the bones that form the pectoral girdle
- List the functions of the pectoral girdle

The appendicular skeleton includes all of the limb bones, plus the bones that unite each limb with the axial skeleton (Figure 8.2). The bones that attach each upper limb to the axial skeleton form the pectoral girdle (shoulder girdle). This consists of two bones, the scapula and clavicle (Figure 8.3). The clavicle (collarbone) is an S-shaped bone located on the anterior side of the shoulder. It is attached on its medial end to the sternum of the thoracic cage, which is part of the axial skeleton. The lateral end of the clavicle articulates (joins) with the scapula just above the shoulder joint. You can easily palpate, or feel with your fingers, the entire length of your clavicle.

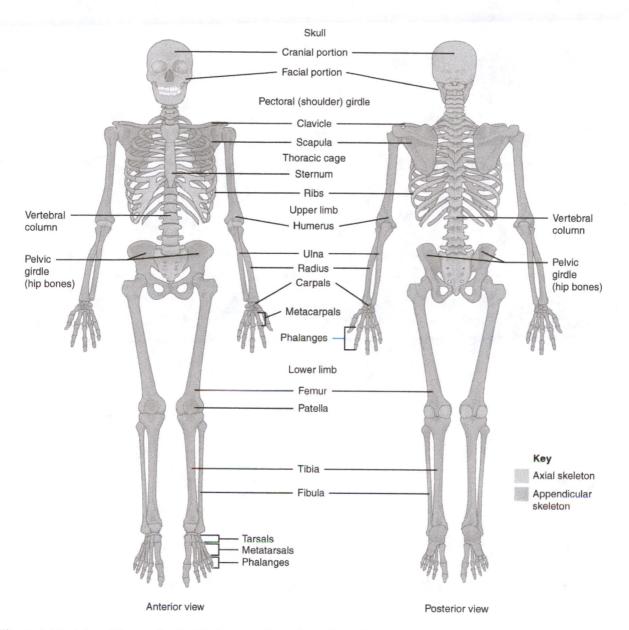

Skull
Cranial portion
Facial portion
Pectoral (shoulder) girdle
Clavicle
Scapula
Thoracic cage
Sternum
Ribs
Upper limb
Humerus
Ulna
Radius
Carpals
Metacarpals
Phalanges
Lower limb
Femur
Patella
Tibia
Fibula
Tarsals
Metatarsals
Phalanges

Vertebral column

Pelvic girdle (hip bones)

Vertebral column

Pelvic girdle (hip bones)

Key
Axial skeleton
Appendicular skeleton

Anterior view

Posterior view

Figure 8.2 Axial and Appendicular Skeletons The axial skeleton forms the central axis of the body and consists of the skull, vertebral column, and thoracic cage. The appendicular skeleton consists of the pectoral and pelvic girdles, the limb bones, and the bones of the hands and feet.

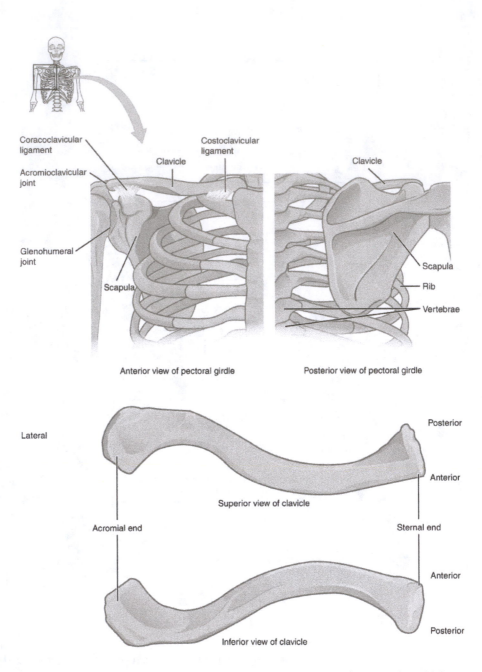

Figure 8.3 Pectoral Girdle The pectoral girdle consists of the clavicle and the scapula, which serve to attach the upper limb to the sternum of the axial skeleton.

The **scapula** (shoulder blade) lies on the posterior aspect of the shoulder. It is supported by the **clavicle**, which also articulates with the humerus (arm bone) to form the shoulder joint. The scapula is a flat, triangular-shaped bone with a prominent ridge running across its posterior surface. This ridge extends out laterally, where it forms the bony tip of the shoulder and joins with the lateral end of the clavicle. By following along the clavicle, you can palpate out to the bony tip of the shoulder, and from there, you can move back across your posterior shoulder to follow the ridge of the scapula. Move your shoulder around and feel how the clavicle and scapula move together as a unit. Both of these bones serve as important attachment sites for muscles that aid with movements of the shoulder and arm.

The right and left pectoral girdles are not joined to each other, allowing each to operate independently. In addition, the clavicle of each **pectoral girdle** is anchored to the axial skeleton by a single, highly mobile joint. This allows for the extensive mobility of the entire pectoral girdle, which in turn enhances movements of the shoulder and upper limb.

Clavicle

The clavicle is the only long bone that lies in a horizontal position in the body (see Figure 8.3). The clavicle has several important functions. First, anchored by muscles from above, it serves as a strut that extends laterally to support the scapula. This in turn holds the shoulder joint superiorly and laterally from the body trunk, allowing for maximal freedom of motion for the upper limb. The clavicle also transmits forces acting on the upper limb to the sternum and axial skeleton. Finally, it serves to protect the underlying nerves and blood vessels as they pass between the trunk of the body and the upper limb.

The clavicle has three regions: the medial end, the lateral end, and the shaft. The medial end, known as the **sternal end of the clavicle**, has a triangular shape and articulates with the manubrium portion of the sternum. This forms the **sternoclavicular joint**, which is the only bony articulation between the pectoral girdle of the upper limb and the axial skeleton. This joint allows considerable mobility, enabling the clavicle and scapula to move in upward/downward and anterior/posterior directions during shoulder movements. The sternoclavicular joint is indirectly supported by the **costoclavicular ligament** (costo- = "rib"), which spans the sternal end of the clavicle and the underlying first rib. The lateral or **acromial end of the clavicle** articulates with the acromion of the scapula, the portion of the scapula that forms the bony tip of the shoulder. There are some sex differences in the morphology of the clavicle. In women, the clavicle tends to be shorter, thinner, and less curved. In men, the clavicle is heavier and longer, and has a greater curvature and rougher surfaces where muscles attach, features that are more pronounced in manual workers.

The clavicle is the most commonly fractured bone in the body. Such breaks often occur because of the force exerted on the clavicle when a person falls onto his or her outstretched arms, or when the lateral shoulder receives a strong blow. Because the sternoclavicular joint is strong and rarely dislocated, excessive force results in the breaking of the clavicle, usually between the middle and lateral portions of the bone. If the fracture is complete, the shoulder and lateral clavicle fragment will drop due to the weight of the upper limb, causing the person to support the sagging limb with their other hand. Muscles acting across the shoulder will also pull the shoulder and lateral clavicle anteriorly and medially, causing the clavicle fragments to override. The clavicle overlies many important blood vessels and nerves for the upper limb, but fortunately, due to the anterior displacement of a broken clavicle, these structures are rarely affected when the clavicle is fractured.

Scapula

The scapula is also part of the pectoral girdle and thus plays an important role in anchoring the upper limb to the body. The scapula is located on the posterior side of the shoulder. It is surrounded by muscles on both its anterior (deep) and posterior (superficial) sides, and thus does not articulate with the ribs of the thoracic cage.

The scapula has several important landmarks (Figure 8.4). The three margins or borders of the scapula, named for their positions within the body, are the **superior border of the scapula**, the **medial border of the scapula**, and the **lateral border of the scapula**. The **suprascapular notch** is located lateral to the midpoint of the superior border. The corners of the triangular scapula, at either end of the medial border, are the **superior angle of the scapula**, located between the medial and superior borders, and the **inferior angle of the scapula**, located between the medial and lateral borders. The inferior angle is the most inferior portion of the scapula, and is particularly important because it serves as the attachment point for several powerful muscles involved in shoulder and upper limb movements. The remaining corner of the scapula, between the superior and lateral borders, is the location of the **glenoid cavity** (glenoid fossa). This shallow depression articulates with the humerus bone of the arm to form the **glenohumeral joint** (shoulder joint). The small bony bumps located immediately above and below the glenoid cavity are the **supraglenoid tubercle** and the **infraglenoid tubercle**, respectively. These provide attachments for muscles of the arm.

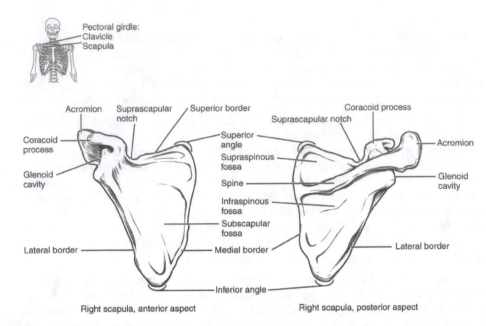

Figure 8.4 Scapula The isolated scapula is shown here from its anterior (deep) side and its posterior (superficial) side.

The scapula also has two prominent projections. Toward the lateral end of the superior border, between the suprascapular notch and glenoid cavity, is the hook-like **coracoid process** (coracoid = "shaped like a crow's beak"). This process projects anteriorly and curves laterally. At the shoulder, the coracoid process is located inferior to the lateral end of the clavicle. It is anchored to the clavicle by a strong ligament, and serves as the attachment site for muscles of the anterior chest and arm. On the posterior aspect, the **spine of the scapula** is a long and prominent ridge that runs across its upper portion. Extending laterally from the spine is a flattened and expanded region called the **acromion** or **acromial process**. The acromion forms the bony tip of the superior shoulder region and articulates with the lateral end of the clavicle, forming the **acromioclavicular joint** (see Figure 8.3). Together, the clavicle, acromion, and spine of the scapula form a V-shaped bony line that provides for the attachment of neck and back muscles that act on the shoulder, as well as muscles that pass across the shoulder joint to act on the arm.

The scapula has three depressions, each of which is called a **fossa** (plural = fossae). Two of these are found on the posterior scapula, above and below the scapular spine. Superior to the spine is the narrow **supraspinous fossa**, and inferior to the spine is the broad **infraspinous fossa**. The anterior (deep) surface of the scapula forms the broad **subscapular fossa**. All of these fossae provide large surface areas for the attachment of muscles that cross the shoulder joint to act on the humerus.

The acromioclavicular joint transmits forces from the upper limb to the clavicle. The ligaments around this joint are relatively weak. A hard fall onto the elbow or outstretched hand can stretch or tear the acromioclavicular ligaments, resulting in a moderate injury to the joint. However, the primary support for the acromioclavicular joint comes from a very strong ligament called the **coracoclavicular ligament** (see Figure 8.3). This connective tissue band anchors the coracoid process of the scapula to the inferior surface of the acromial end of the clavicle and thus provides important indirect support for the acromioclavicular joint. Following a strong blow to the lateral shoulder, such as when a hockey player is driven into the boards, a complete dislocation of the acromioclavicular joint can result. In this case, the acromion is thrust under the acromial end of the clavicle, resulting in ruptures of both the acromioclavicular and coracoclavicular ligaments. The scapula then separates from the clavicle, with the weight of the upper limb pulling the shoulder downward. This dislocation injury of the acromioclavicular joint is known as a "shoulder separation" and is common in contact sports such as hockey, football, or martial arts.

8.2 | Bones of the Upper Limb

By the end of this section, you will be able to:

- Identify the divisions of the upper limb and describe the bones in each region
- List the bones and bony landmarks that articulate at each joint of the upper limb

The upper limb is divided into three regions. These consist of the **arm**, located between the shoulder and elbow joints; the **forearm**, which is between the elbow and wrist joints; and the **hand**, which is located distal to the wrist. There are 30 bones in each upper limb (see **Figure 8.2**). The **humerus** is the single bone of the upper arm, and the **ulna** (medially) and the **radius** (laterally) are the paired bones of the forearm. The base of the hand contains eight bones, each called a **carpal bone**, and the palm of the hand is formed by five bones, each called a **metacarpal bone**. The fingers and thumb contain a total of 14 bones, each of which is a **phalanx bone of the hand**.

Humerus

The humerus is the single bone of the upper arm region (**Figure 8.5**). At its proximal end is the **head of the humerus**. This is the large, round, smooth region that faces medially. The head articulates with the glenoid cavity of the scapula to form the glenohumeral (shoulder) joint. The margin of the smooth area of the head is the **anatomical neck** of the humerus. Located on the lateral side of the proximal humerus is an expanded bony area called the **greater tubercle**. The smaller **lesser tubercle** of the humerus is found on the anterior aspect of the humerus. Both the greater and lesser tubercles serve as attachment sites for muscles that act across the shoulder joint. Passing between the greater and lesser tubercles is the narrow **intertubercular groove (sulcus)**, which is also known as the **bicipital groove** because it provides passage for a tendon of the biceps brachii muscle. The **surgical neck** is located at the base of the expanded, proximal end of the humerus, where it joins the narrow **shaft of the humerus**. The surgical neck is a common site of arm fractures. The **deltoid tuberosity** is a roughened, V-shaped region located on the lateral side in the middle of the humerus shaft. As its name indicates, it is the site of attachment for the deltoid muscle.

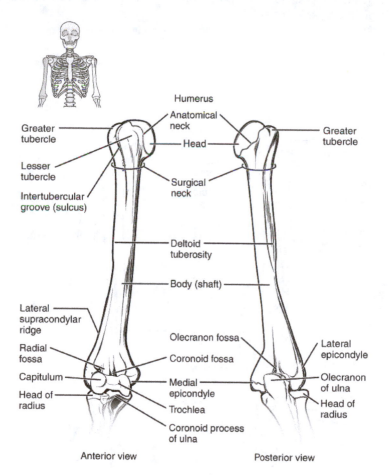

Figure 8.5 Humerus and Elbow Joint The humerus is the single bone of the upper arm region. It articulates with the radius and ulna bones of the forearm to form the elbow joint.

Distally, the humerus becomes flattened. The prominent bony projection on the medial side is the **medial epicondyle of the humerus**. The much smaller **lateral epicondyle of the humerus** is found on the lateral side of the distal humerus. The roughened ridge of bone above the lateral epicondyle is the **lateral supracondylar ridge**. All of these areas are attachment points for muscles that act on the forearm, wrist, and hand. The powerful grasping muscles of the anterior forearm arise from the medial epicondyle, which is thus larger and more robust than the lateral epicondyle that gives rise to the weaker posterior forearm muscles.

The distal end of the humerus has two articulation areas, which join the ulna and radius bones of the forearm to form the **elbow joint**. The more medial of these areas is the **trochlea**, a spindle- or pulley-shaped region (trochlea = "pulley"), which articulates with the ulna bone. Immediately lateral to the trochlea is the **capitulum** ("small head"), a knob-like structure located on the anterior surface of the distal humerus. The capitulum articulates with the radius bone of the forearm. Just above these bony areas are two small depressions. These spaces accommodate the forearm bones when the elbow is fully bent (flexed). Superior to the trochlea is the **coronoid fossa**, which receives the coronoid process of the ulna, and above the capitulum is the **radial fossa**, which receives the head of the radius when the elbow is flexed. Similarly, the posterior humerus has the **olecranon fossa**, a larger depression that receives the olecranon process of the ulna when the forearm is fully extended.

Ulna

The ulna is the medial bone of the forearm. It runs parallel to the radius, which is the lateral bone of the forearm (Figure 8.6). The proximal end of the ulna resembles a crescent wrench with its large, C-shaped **trochlear notch**. This region articulates with the trochlea of the humerus as part of the elbow joint. The inferior margin of the trochlear notch is formed by a prominent lip of bone called the **coronoid process of the ulna**. Just below this on the anterior ulna is a roughened area called the **ulnar tuberosity**. To the lateral side and slightly inferior to the trochlear notch is a small, smooth area called the **radial notch of the ulna**. This area is the site of articulation between the proximal radius and the ulna, forming the **proximal radioulnar joint**. The posterior and superior portions of the proximal ulna make up the **olecranon process**, which forms the bony tip of the elbow.

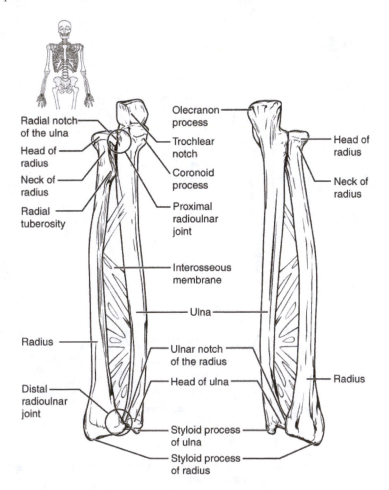

Figure 8.6 Ulna and Radius The ulna is located on the medial side of the forearm, and the radius is on the lateral side. These bones are attached to each other by an interosseous membrane.

More distal is the **shaft of the ulna**. The lateral side of the shaft forms a ridge called the **interosseous border of the ulna**. This is the line of attachment for the **interosseous membrane of the forearm**, a sheet of dense connective tissue that unites the ulna and radius bones. The small, rounded area that forms the distal end is the **head of the ulna**. Projecting from the posterior side of the ulnar head is the **styloid process of the ulna**, a short bony projection. This serves as an attachment point for a connective tissue structure that unites the distal ends of the ulna and radius.

In the anatomical position, with the elbow fully extended and the palms facing forward, the arm and forearm do not form a straight line. Instead, the forearm deviates laterally by 5–15 degrees from the line of the arm. This deviation is called the carrying angle. It allows the forearm and hand to swing freely or to carry an object without hitting the hip. The carrying angle is larger in females to accommodate their wider pelvis.

Radius

The radius runs parallel to the ulna, on the lateral (thumb) side of the forearm (see Figure 8.6). The **head of the radius** is a disc-shaped structure that forms the proximal end. The small depression on the surface of the head articulates with the capitulum of the humerus as part of the elbow joint, whereas the smooth, outer margin of the head articulates with the radial notch of the ulna at the proximal radioulnar joint. The **neck of the radius** is the narrowed region immediately below the expanded head. Inferior to this point on the medial side is the **radial tuberosity**, an oval-shaped, bony protuberance that serves as a muscle attachment point. The **shaft of the radius** is slightly curved and has a small ridge along its medial side. This ridge forms the **interosseous border of the radius**, which, like the similar border of the ulna, is the line of attachment for the interosseous membrane that unites the two forearm bones. The distal end of the radius has a smooth surface for articulation with two carpal bones to form the **radiocarpal joint** or wrist joint (Figure 8.7 and Figure 8.8). On the medial side of the distal radius is the **ulnar notch of the radius**. This shallow depression articulates with the head of the ulna, which together form the **distal radioulnar joint**. The lateral end of the radius has a pointed projection called the **styloid process of the radius**. This provides attachment for ligaments that support the lateral side of the wrist joint. Compared to the styloid process of the ulna, the styloid process of the radius projects more distally, thereby limiting the range of movement for lateral deviations of the hand at the wrist joint.

Interactive LINK

Watch this video (http://openstaxcollege.org/l/fractures) to see how fractures of the distal radius bone can affect the wrist joint. Explain the problems that may occur if a fracture of the distal radius involves the joint surface of the radiocarpal joint of the wrist.

Carpal Bones

The wrist and base of the hand are formed by a series of eight small carpal bones (see Figure 8.7). The carpal bones are arranged in two rows, forming a proximal row of four carpal bones and a distal row of four carpal bones. The bones in the proximal row, running from the lateral (thumb) side to the medial side, are the **scaphoid** ("boat-shaped"), **lunate** ("moon-shaped"), **triquetrum** ("three-cornered"), and **pisiform** ("pea-shaped") bones. The small, rounded pisiform bone articulates with the anterior surface of the triquetrum bone. The pisiform thus projects anteriorly, where it forms the bony bump that can be felt at the medial base of your hand. The distal bones (lateral to medial) are the **trapezium** ("table"), **trapezoid** ("resembles a table"), **capitate** ("head-shaped"), and **hamate** ("hooked bone") bones. The hamate bone is characterized by a prominent bony extension on its anterior side called the **hook of the hamate bone**.

A helpful mnemonic for remembering the arrangement of the carpal bones is "So Long To Pinky, Here Comes The Thumb." This mnemonic starts on the lateral side and names the proximal bones from lateral to medial (scaphoid, lunate, triquetrum, pisiform), then makes a U-turn to name the distal bones from medial to lateral (hamate, capitate, trapezoid, trapezium). Thus, it starts and finishes on the lateral side.

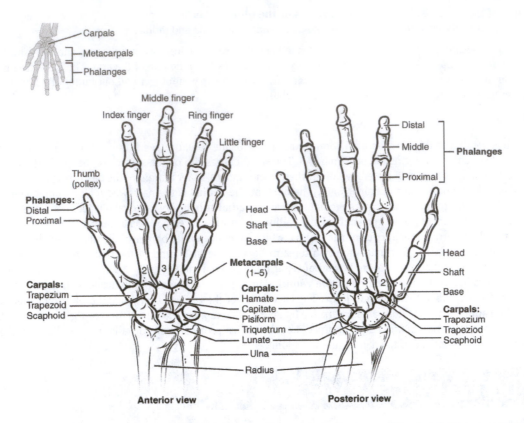

Figure 8.7 Bones of the Wrist and Hand The eight carpal bones form the base of the hand. These are arranged into proximal and distal rows of four bones each. The metacarpal bones form the palm of the hand. The thumb and fingers consist of the phalanx bones.

The carpal bones form the base of the hand. This can be seen in the radiograph (X-ray image) of the hand that shows the relationships of the hand bones to the skin creases of the hand (see Figure 8.8). Within the carpal bones, the four proximal bones are united to each other by ligaments to form a unit. Only three of these bones, the scaphoid, lunate, and triquetrum, contribute to the radiocarpal joint. The scaphoid and lunate bones articulate directly with the distal end of the radius, whereas the triquetrum bone articulates with a fibrocartilaginous pad that spans the radius and styloid process of the ulna. The distal end of the ulna thus does not directly articulate with any of the carpal bones.

The four distal carpal bones are also held together as a group by ligaments. The proximal and distal rows of carpal bones articulate with each other to form the **midcarpal joint** (see Figure 8.8). Together, the radiocarpal and midcarpal joints are responsible for all movements of the hand at the wrist. The distal carpal bones also articulate with the metacarpal bones of the hand.

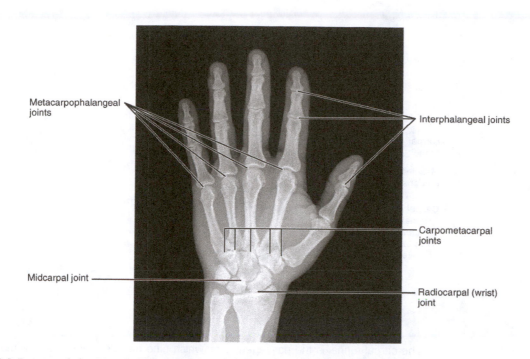

Metacarpophalangeal joints

Interphalangeal joints

Carpometacarpal joints

Midcarpal joint

Radiocarpal (wrist) joint

Figure 8.8 Bones of the Hand This radiograph shows the position of the bones within the hand. Note the carpal bones that form the base of the hand. (credit: modification of work by Trace Meek)

In the articulated hand, the carpal bones form a U-shaped grouping. A strong ligament called the **flexor retinaculum** spans the top of this U-shaped area to maintain this grouping of the carpal bones. The flexor retinaculum is attached laterally to the trapezium and scaphoid bones, and medially to the hamate and pisiform bones. Together, the carpal bones and the flexor retinaculum form a passageway called the **carpal tunnel**, with the carpal bones forming the walls and floor, and the flexor retinaculum forming the roof of this space (Figure 8.9). The tendons of nine muscles of the anterior forearm and an important nerve pass through this narrow tunnel to enter the hand. Overuse of the muscle tendons or wrist injury can produce inflammation and swelling within this space. This produces compression of the nerve, resulting in carpal tunnel syndrome, which is characterized by pain or numbness, and muscle weakness in those areas of the hand supplied by this nerve.

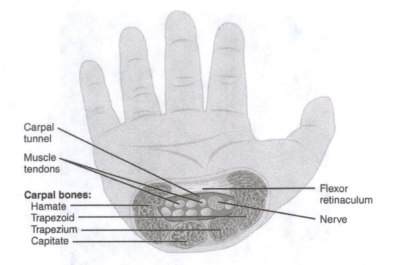

Figure 8.9 Carpal Tunnel   The carpal tunnel is the passageway by which nine muscle tendons and a major nerve enter the hand from the anterior forearm. The walls and floor of the carpal tunnel are formed by the U-shaped grouping of the carpal bones, and the roof is formed by the flexor retinaculum, a strong ligament that anteriorly unites the bones.

Metacarpal Bones

The palm of the hand contains five elongated metacarpal bones. These bones lie between the carpal bones of the wrist and the bones of the fingers and thumb (see Figure 8.7). The proximal end of each metacarpal bone articulates with one of the distal carpal bones. Each of these articulations is a **carpometacarpal joint** (see Figure 8.8). The expanded distal end of each metacarpal bone articulates at the **metacarpophalangeal joint** with the proximal phalanx bone of the thumb or one of the fingers. The distal end also forms the knuckles of the hand, at the base of the fingers. The metacarpal bones are numbered 1–5, beginning at the thumb.

The first metacarpal bone, at the base of the thumb, is separated from the other metacarpal bones. This allows it a freedom of motion that is independent of the other metacarpal bones, which is very important for thumb mobility. The remaining metacarpal bones are united together to form the palm of the hand. The second and third metacarpal bones are firmly anchored in place and are immobile. However, the fourth and fifth metacarpal bones have limited anterior-posterior mobility, a motion that is greater for the fifth bone. This mobility is important during power gripping with the hand (Figure 8.10). The anterior movement of these bones, particularly the fifth metacarpal bone, increases the strength of contact for the medial hand during gripping actions.

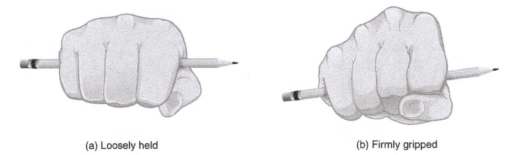

(a) Loosely held   (b) Firmly gripped

Figure 8.10 Hand During Gripping   During tight gripping—compare (b) to (a)—the fourth and, particularly, the fifth metatarsal bones are pulled anteriorly. This increases the contact between the object and the medial side of the hand, thus improving the firmness of the grip.

Phalanx Bones

The fingers and thumb contain 14 bones, each of which is called a phalanx bone (plural = phalanges), named after the ancient Greek phalanx (a rectangular block of soldiers). The thumb (**pollex**) is digit number 1 and has two phalanges, a proximal phalanx, and a distal phalanx bone (see Figure 8.7). Digits 2 (index finger) through 5 (little finger) have three phalanges each, called the proximal, middle, and distal phalanx bones. An **interphalangeal joint** is one of the articulations between adjacent phalanges of the digits (see Figure 8.8).

Visit this site (http://openstaxcollege.org/l/handbone) to explore the bones and joints of the hand. What are the three arches of the hand, and what is the importance of these during the gripping of an object?

Disorders OF THE...

Appendicular System: Fractures of Upper Limb Bones

Due to our constant use of the hands and the rest of our upper limbs, an injury to any of these areas will cause a significant loss of functional ability. Many fractures result from a hard fall onto an outstretched hand. The resulting transmission of force up the limb may result in a fracture of the humerus, radius, or scaphoid bones. These injuries are especially common in elderly people whose bones are weakened due to osteoporosis.

Falls onto the hand or elbow, or direct blows to the arm, can result in fractures of the humerus (Figure 8.11). Following a fall, fractures at the surgical neck, the region at which the expanded proximal end of the humerus joins with the shaft, can result in an impacted fracture, in which the distal portion of the humerus is driven into the proximal portion. Falls or blows to the arm can also produce transverse or spiral fractures of the humeral shaft.

In children, a fall onto the tip of the elbow frequently results in a distal humerus fracture. In these, the olecranon of the ulna is driven upward, resulting in a fracture across the distal humerus, above both epicondyles (supracondylar fracture), or a fracture between the epicondyles, thus separating one or both of the epicondyles from the body of the humerus (intercondylar fracture). With these injuries, the immediate concern is possible compression of the artery to the forearm due to swelling of the surrounding tissues. If compression occurs, the resulting ischemia (lack of oxygen) due to reduced blood flow can quickly produce irreparable damage to the forearm muscles. In addition, four major nerves for shoulder and upper limb muscles are closely associated with different regions of the humerus, and thus, humeral fractures may also damage these nerves.

Another frequent injury following a fall onto an outstretched hand is a Colles fracture ("col-lees") of the distal radius (see Figure 8.11). This involves a complete transverse fracture across the distal radius that drives the separated distal fragment of the radius posteriorly and superiorly. This injury results in a characteristic "dinner fork" bend of the forearm just above the wrist due to the posterior displacement of the hand. This is the most frequent forearm fracture and is a common injury in persons over the age of 50, particularly in older women with osteoporosis. It also commonly occurs following a high-speed fall onto the hand during activities such as snowboarding or skating.

The most commonly fractured carpal bone is the scaphoid, often resulting from a fall onto the hand. Deep pain at the lateral wrist may yield an initial diagnosis of a wrist sprain, but a radiograph taken several weeks after the injury, after tissue swelling has subsided, will reveal the fracture. Due to the poor blood supply to the scaphoid bone, healing will be slow and there is the danger of bone necrosis and subsequent degenerative joint disease of the wrist.

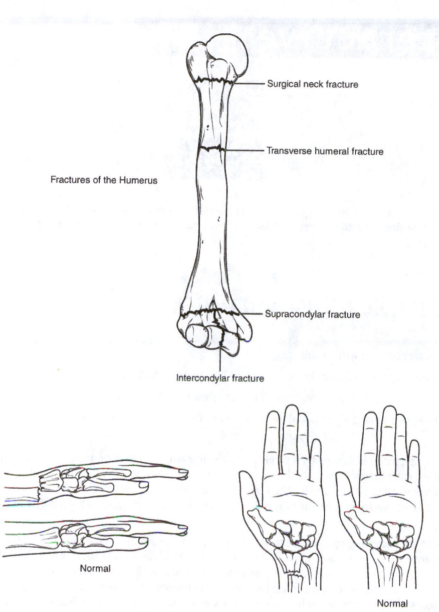

Surgical neck fracture

Transverse humeral fracture

Fractures of the Humerus

Supracondylar fracture

Intercondylar fracture

Normal

Normal

Colles Fracture of the Distal Radius

Figure 8.11 Fractures of the Humerus and Radius Falls or direct blows can result in fractures of the surgical neck or shaft of the humerus. Falls onto the elbow can fracture the distal humerus. A Colles fracture of the distal radius is the most common forearm fracture.

Interactive LINK

Watch this video (http://openstaxcollege.org/l/colles) to learn about a Colles fracture, a break of the distal radius, usually caused by falling onto an outstretched hand. When would surgery be required and how would the fracture be repaired in this case?

8.3 | The Pelvic Girdle and Pelvis

By the end of this section, you will be able to:

- Define the pelvic girdle and describe the bones and ligaments of the pelvis
- Explain the three regions of the hip bone and identify their bony landmarks
- Describe the openings of the pelvis and the boundaries of the greater and lesser pelvis

The **pelvic girdle** (hip girdle) is formed by a single bone, the **hip bone** or **coxal bone** (coxal = "hip"), which serves as the attachment point for each lower limb. Each hip bone, in turn, is firmly joined to the axial skeleton via its attachment to the sacrum of the vertebral column. The right and left hip bones also converge anteriorly to attach to each other. The bony **pelvis** is the entire structure formed by the two hip bones, the sacrum, and, attached inferiorly to the sacrum, the coccyx (Figure 8.12).

Unlike the bones of the pectoral girdle, which are highly mobile to enhance the range of upper limb movements, the bones of the pelvis are strongly united to each other to form a largely immobile, weight-bearing structure. This is important for stability because it enables the weight of the body to be easily transferred laterally from the vertebral column, through the pelvic girdle and hip joints, and into either lower limb whenever the other limb is not bearing weight. Thus, the immobility of the pelvis provides a strong foundation for the upper body as it rests on top of the mobile lower limbs.

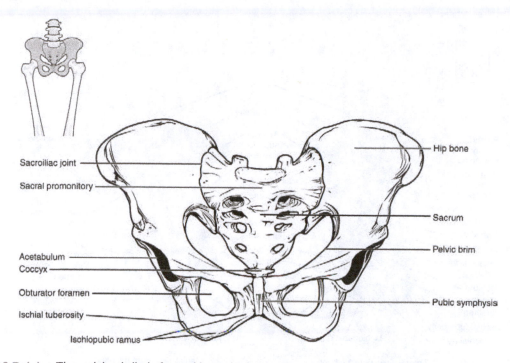

Figure 8.12 Pelvis   The pelvic girdle is formed by a single hip bone. The hip bone attaches the lower limb to the axial skeleton through its articulation with the sacrum. The right and left hip bones, plus the sacrum and the coccyx, together form the pelvis.

Hip Bone

The hip bone, or coxal bone, forms the pelvic girdle portion of the pelvis. The paired hip bones are the large, curved bones that form the lateral and anterior aspects of the pelvis. Each adult hip bone is formed by three separate bones that fuse together during the late teenage years. These bony components are the ilium, ischium, and pubis (Figure 8.13). These names are retained and used to define the three regions of the adult hip bone.

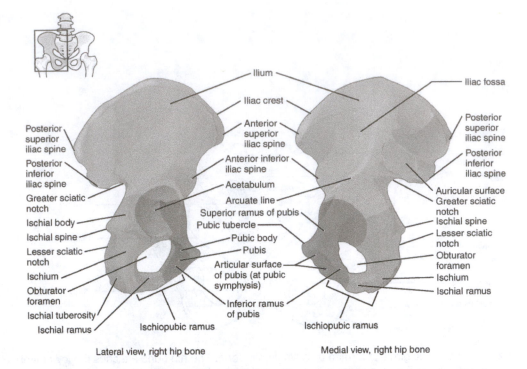

Lateral view, right hip bone   Medial view, right hip bone

Figure 8.13 The Hip Bone The adult hip bone consists of three regions. The ilium forms the large, fan-shaped superior portion, the ischium forms the posteroinferior portion, and the pubis forms the anteromedial portion.

The **ilium** is the fan-like, superior region that forms the largest part of the hip bone. It is firmly united to the sacrum at the largely immobile **sacroiliac joint** (see Figure 8.12). The **ischium** forms the posteroinferior region of each hip bone. It supports the body when sitting. The **pubis** forms the anterior portion of the hip bone. The pubis curves medially, where it joins to the pubis of the opposite hip bone at a specialized joint called the **pubic symphysis**.

Ilium

When you place your hands on your waist, you can feel the arching, superior margin of the ilium along your waistline (see Figure 8.13). This curved, superior margin of the ilium is the **iliac crest**. The rounded, anterior termination of the iliac crest is the **anterior superior iliac spine**. This important bony landmark can be felt at your anterolateral hip. Inferior to the anterior superior iliac spine is a rounded protuberance called the **anterior inferior iliac spine**. Both of these iliac spines serve as attachment points for muscles of the thigh. Posteriorly, the iliac crest curves downward to terminate as the **posterior superior iliac spine**. Muscles and ligaments surround but do not cover this bony landmark, thus sometimes producing a depression seen as a "dimple" located on the lower back. More inferiorly is the **posterior inferior iliac spine**. This is located at the inferior end of a large, roughened area called the **auricular surface of the ilium**. The auricular surface articulates with the auricular surface of the sacrum to form the sacroiliac joint. Both the posterior superior and posterior inferior iliac spines serve as attachment points for the muscles and very strong ligaments that support the sacroiliac joint.

The shallow depression located on the anteromedial (internal) surface of the upper ilium is called the **iliac fossa**. The inferior margin of this space is formed by the **arcuate line of the ilium**, the ridge formed by the pronounced change in curvature between the upper and lower portions of the ilium. The large, inverted U-shaped indentation located on the posterior margin of the lower ilium is called the **greater sciatic notch**.

Ischium

The ischium forms the posterolateral portion of the hip bone (see Figure 8.13). The large, roughened area of the inferior ischium is the **ischial tuberosity**. This serves as the attachment for the posterior thigh muscles and also carries the weight of the body when sitting. You can feel the ischial tuberosity if you wiggle your pelvis against the seat of a chair. Projecting superiorly and anteriorly from the ischial tuberosity is a narrow segment of bone called the **ischial ramus**. The slightly curved posterior margin of the ischium above the ischial tuberosity is the **lesser sciatic notch**. The bony projection separating the lesser sciatic notch and greater sciatic notch is the **ischial spine**.

Pubis

The pubis forms the anterior portion of the hip bone (see Figure 8.13). The enlarged medial portion of the pubis is the **pubic**

body. Located superiorly on the pubic body is a small bump called the **pubic tubercle**. The **superior pubic ramus** is the segment of bone that passes laterally from the pubic body to join the ilium. The narrow ridge running along the superior margin of the superior pubic ramus is the **pectineal line** of the pubis.

The pubic body is joined to the pubic body of the opposite hip bone by the pubic symphysis. Extending downward and laterally from the body is the **inferior pubic ramus**. The **pubic arch** is the bony structure formed by the pubic symphysis, and the bodies and inferior pubic rami of the adjacent pubic bones. The inferior pubic ramus extends downward to join the ischial ramus. Together, these form the single **ischiopubic ramus**, which extends from the pubic body to the ischial tuberosity. The inverted V-shape formed as the ischiopubic rami from both sides come together at the pubic symphysis is called the **subpubic angle**.

Pelvis

The pelvis consists of four bones: the right and left hip bones, the sacrum, and the coccyx (see Figure 8.12). The pelvis has several important functions. Its primary role is to support the weight of the upper body when sitting and to transfer this weight to the lower limbs when standing. It serves as an attachment point for trunk and lower limb muscles, and also protects the internal pelvic organs. When standing in the anatomical position, the pelvis is tilted anteriorly. In this position, the anterior superior iliac spines and the pubic tubercles lie in the same vertical plane, and the anterior (internal) surface of the sacrum faces forward and downward.

The three areas of each hip bone, the ilium, pubis, and ischium, converge centrally to form a deep, cup-shaped cavity called the **acetabulum**. This is located on the lateral side of the hip bone and is part of the hip joint. The large opening in the anteroinferior hip bone between the ischium and pubis is the **obturator foramen**. This space is largely filled in by a layer of connective tissue and serves for the attachment of muscles on both its internal and external surfaces.

Several ligaments unite the bones of the pelvis (Figure 8.14). The largely immobile sacroiliac joint is supported by a pair of strong ligaments that are attached between the sacrum and ilium portions of the hip bone. These are the **anterior sacroiliac ligament** on the anterior side of the joint and the **posterior sacroiliac ligament** on the posterior side. Also spanning the sacrum and hip bone are two additional ligaments. The **sacrospinous ligament** runs from the sacrum to the ischial spine, and the **sacrotuberous ligament** runs from the sacrum to the ischial tuberosity. These ligaments help to support and immobilize the sacrum as it carries the weight of the body.

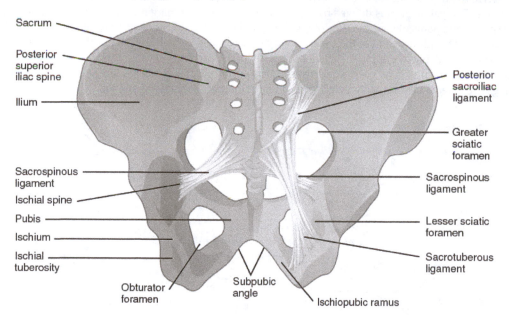

Figure 8.14 Ligaments of the Pelvis The posterior sacroiliac ligament supports the sacroiliac joint. The sacrospinous ligament spans the sacrum to the ischial spine, and the sacrotuberous ligament spans the sacrum to the ischial tuberosity. The sacrospinous and sacrotuberous ligaments contribute to the formation of the greater and lesser sciatic foramens.

Interactive LINK

Watch this video (http://openstaxcollege.org/l/3Dpelvis) for a 3-D view of the pelvis and its associated ligaments. What is the large opening in the bony pelvis, located between the ischium and pubic regions, and what two parts of the pubis contribute to the formation of this opening?

The sacrospinous and sacrotuberous ligaments also help to define two openings on the posterolateral sides of the pelvis through which muscles, nerves, and blood vessels for the lower limb exit. The superior opening is the **greater sciatic foramen**. This large opening is formed by the greater sciatic notch of the hip bone, the sacrum, and the sacrospinous ligament. The smaller, more inferior **lesser sciatic foramen** is formed by the lesser sciatic notch of the hip bone, together with the sacrospinous and sacrotuberous ligaments.

The space enclosed by the bony pelvis is divided into two regions (Figure 8.15). The broad, superior region, defined laterally by the large, fan-like portion of the upper hip bone, is called the **greater pelvis** (greater pelvic cavity; false pelvis). This broad area is occupied by portions of the small and large intestines, and because it is more closely associated with the abdominal cavity, it is sometimes referred to as the false pelvis. More inferiorly, the narrow, rounded space of the **lesser pelvis** (lesser pelvic cavity; true pelvis) contains the bladder and other pelvic organs, and thus is also known as the true pelvis. The **pelvic brim** (also known as the **pelvic inlet**) forms the superior margin of the lesser pelvis, separating it from the greater pelvis. The pelvic brim is defined by a line formed by the upper margin of the pubic symphysis anteriorly, and the pectineal line of the pubis, the arcuate line of the ilium, and the sacral promontory (the anterior margin of the superior sacrum) posteriorly. The inferior limit of the lesser pelvic cavity is called the **pelvic outlet**. This large opening is defined by the inferior margin of the pubic symphysis anteriorly, and the ischiopubic ramus, the ischial tuberosity, the sacrotuberous ligament, and the inferior tip of the coccyx posteriorly. Because of the anterior tilt of the pelvis, the lesser pelvis is also angled, giving it an anterosuperior (pelvic inlet) to posteroinferior (pelvic outlet) orientation.

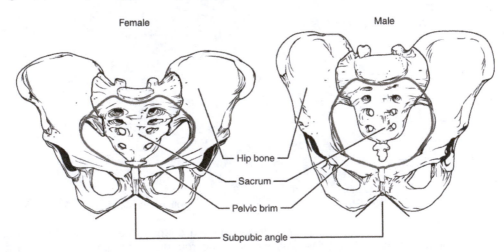

Figure 8.15 Male and Female Pelvis The female pelvis is adapted for childbirth and is broader, with a larger subpubic angle, a rounder pelvic brim, and a wider and more shallow lesser pelvic cavity than the male pelvis.

Comparison of the Female and Male Pelvis

The differences between the adult female and male pelvis relate to function and body size. In general, the bones of the male pelvis are thicker and heavier, adapted for support of the male's heavier physical build and stronger muscles. The greater sciatic notch of the male hip bone is narrower and deeper than the broader notch of females. Because the female pelvis is adapted for childbirth, it is wider than the male pelvis, as evidenced by the distance between the anterior superior iliac spines (see Figure 8.15). The ischial tuberosities of females are also farther apart, which increases the size of the pelvic outlet. Because of this increased pelvic width, the subpubic angle is larger in females (greater than 80 degrees) than it is in males (less than 70 degrees). The female sacrum is wider, shorter, and less curved, and the sacral promontory projects less into the pelvic cavity, thus giving the female pelvic inlet (pelvic brim) a more rounded or oval shape compared to males. The lesser pelvic cavity of females is also wider and more shallow than the narrower, deeper, and tapering lesser pelvis of males. Because of the obvious differences between female and male hip bones, this is the one bone of the body that allows for the most accurate sex determination. Table 8.1 provides an overview of the general differences between the female and male pelvis.

Overview of Differences between the Female and Male Pelvis

	Female pelvis	Male pelvis
Pelvic weight	Bones of the pelvis are lighter and thinner	Bones of the pelvis are thicker and heavier
Pelvic inlet shape	Pelvic inlet has a round or oval shape	Pelvic inlet is heart-shaped
Lesser pelvic cavity shape	Lesser pelvic cavity is shorter and wider	Lesser pelvic cavity is longer and narrower
Subpubic angle	Subpubic angle is greater than 80 degrees	Subpubic angle is less than 70 degrees
Pelvic outlet shape	Pelvic outlet is rounded and larger	Pelvic outlet is smaller

Table 8.1

Career CONNECTION

Forensic Pathology and Forensic Anthropology

A forensic pathologist (also known as a medical examiner) is a medically trained physician who has been specifically trained in pathology to examine the bodies of the deceased to determine the cause of death. A forensic pathologist applies his or her understanding of disease as well as toxins, blood and DNA analysis, firearms and ballistics, and other factors to assess the cause and manner of death. At times, a forensic pathologist will be called to testify under oath in situations that involve a possible crime. Forensic pathology is a field that has received much media attention on television shows or following a high-profile death.

While forensic pathologists are responsible for determining whether the cause of someone's death was natural, a suicide, accidental, or a homicide, there are times when uncovering the cause of death is more complex, and other skills are needed. Forensic anthropology brings the tools and knowledge of physical anthropology and human osteology (the study of the skeleton) to the task of investigating a death. A forensic anthropologist assists medical and legal professionals in identifying human remains. The science behind forensic anthropology involves the study of archaeological excavation; the examination of hair; an understanding of plants, insects, and footprints; the ability to determine how much time has elapsed since the person died; the analysis of past medical history and toxicology; the ability to determine whether there are any postmortem injuries or alterations of the skeleton; and the identification of the decedent (deceased person) using skeletal and dental evidence.

Due to the extensive knowledge and understanding of excavation techniques, a forensic anthropologist is an integral and invaluable team member to have on-site when investigating a crime scene, especially when the recovery of human skeletal remains is involved. When remains are bought to a forensic anthropologist for examination, he or she must first determine whether the remains are in fact human. Once the remains have been identified as belonging to a person and not to an animal, the next step is to approximate the individual's age, sex, race, and height. The forensic anthropologist does not determine the cause of death, but rather provides information to the forensic pathologist, who will use all of the data collected to make a final determination regarding the cause of death.

8.4 | Bones of the Lower Limb

By the end of this section, you will be able to:

- Identify the divisions of the lower limb and describe the bones of each region
- Describe the bones and bony landmarks that articulate at each joint of the lower limb

Like the upper limb, the lower limb is divided into three regions. The **thigh** is that portion of the lower limb located between the hip joint and knee joint. The **leg** is specifically the region between the knee joint and the ankle joint. Distal to the ankle is the **foot**. The lower limb contains 30 bones. These are the femur, patella, tibia, fibula, tarsal bones, metatarsal bones, and phalanges (see Figure 8.2). The **femur** is the single bone of the thigh. The **patella** is the kneecap and articulates with the distal femur. The **tibia** is the larger, weight-bearing bone located on the medial side of the leg, and the **fibula** is the thin bone of the lateral leg. The bones of the foot are divided into three groups. The posterior portion of the foot is formed by a group of seven bones, each of which is known as a **tarsal bone**, whereas the mid-foot contains five elongated bones, each of which is a **metatarsal bone**. The toes contain 14 small bones, each of which is a **phalanx bone of the foot**.

Femur

The femur, or thigh bone, is the single bone of the thigh region (Figure 8.16). It is the longest and strongest bone of the body, and accounts for approximately one-quarter of a person's total height. The rounded, proximal end is the **head of the femur**, which articulates with the acetabulum of the hip bone to form the **hip joint**. The **fovea capitis** is a minor indentation on the medial side of the femoral head that serves as the site of attachment for the **ligament of the head of the femur**. This ligament spans the femur and acetabulum, but is weak and provides little support for the hip joint. It does, however, carry an important artery that supplies the head of the femur.

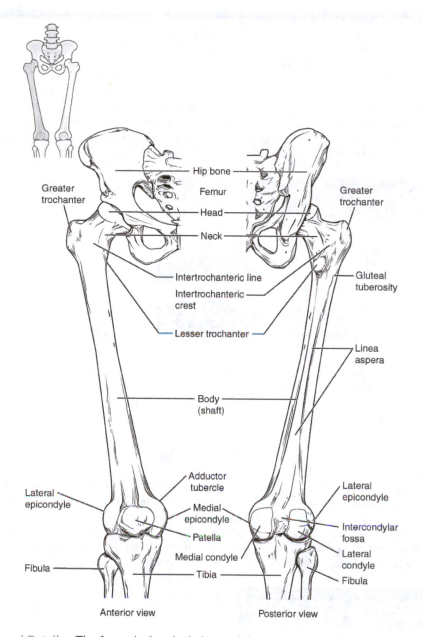

Figure 8.16 Femur and Patella The femur is the single bone of the thigh region. It articulates superiorly with the hip bone at the hip joint, and inferiorly with the tibia at the knee joint. The patella only articulates with the distal end of the femur.

The narrowed region below the head is the **neck of the femur**. This is a common area for fractures of the femur. The **greater trochanter** is the large, upward, bony projection located above the base of the neck. Multiple muscles that act across the hip joint attach to the greater trochanter, which, because of its projection from the femur, gives additional leverage to these muscles. The greater trochanter can be felt just under the skin on the lateral side of your upper thigh. The **lesser trochanter** is a small, bony prominence that lies on the medial aspect of the femur, just below the neck. A single, powerful muscle attaches to the lesser trochanter. Running between the greater and lesser trochanters on the anterior side of the femur is the roughened **intertrochanteric line**. The trochanters are also connected on the posterior side of the femur by the larger **intertrochanteric crest**.

The elongated **shaft of the femur** has a slight anterior bowing or curvature. At its proximal end, the posterior shaft has the **gluteal tuberosity**, a roughened area extending inferiorly from the greater trochanter. More inferiorly, the gluteal tuberosity becomes continuous with the **linea aspera** ("rough line"). This is the roughened ridge that passes distally along the posterior side of the mid-femur. Multiple muscles of the hip and thigh regions make long, thin attachments to the femur along the linea aspera.

The distal end of the femur has medial and lateral bony expansions. On the lateral side, the smooth portion that covers the distal and posterior aspects of the lateral expansion is the **lateral condyle of the femur**. The roughened area on the outer, lateral side of the condyle is the **lateral epicondyle of the femur**. Similarly, the smooth region of the distal and posterior medial femur is the **medial condyle of the femur**, and the irregular outer, medial side of this is the **medial epicondyle of the femur**. The lateral and medial condyles articulate with the tibia to form the knee joint. The epicondyles provide attachment for muscles and supporting ligaments of the knee. The **adductor tubercle** is a small bump located at the superior margin of the medial epicondyle. Posteriorly, the medial and lateral condyles are separated by a deep depression called the **intercondylar fossa**. Anteriorly, the smooth surfaces of the condyles join together to form a wide groove called the **patellar surface**, which provides for articulation with the patella bone. The combination of the medial and lateral condyles with the patellar surface gives the distal end of the femur a horseshoe (U) shape.

Watch this **video (http://openstaxcollege.org/l/midfemur)** to view how a fracture of the mid-femur is surgically repaired. How are the two portions of the broken femur stabilized during surgical repair of a fractured femur?

Patella

The patella (kneecap) is largest sesamoid bone of the body (see **Figure 8.16**). A sesamoid bone is a bone that is incorporated into the tendon of a muscle where that tendon crosses a joint. The sesamoid bone articulates with the underlying bones to prevent damage to the muscle tendon due to rubbing against the bones during movements of the joint. The patella is found in the tendon of the quadriceps femoris muscle, the large muscle of the anterior thigh that passes across the anterior knee to attach to the tibia. The patella articulates with the patellar surface of the femur and thus prevents rubbing of the muscle tendon against the distal femur. The patella also lifts the tendon away from the knee joint, which increases the leverage power of the quadriceps femoris muscle as it acts across the knee. The patella does not articulate with the tibia.

Visit this **site (http://openstaxcollege.org/l/kneesurgery)** to perform a virtual knee replacement surgery. The prosthetic knee components must be properly aligned to function properly. How is this alignment ensured?

Homeostatic IMBALANCES

Runner's Knee

Runner's knee, also known as patellofemoral syndrome, is the most common overuse injury among runners. It is most frequent in adolescents and young adults, and is more common in females. It often results from excessive running, particularly downhill, but may also occur in athletes who do a lot of knee bending, such as jumpers, skiers, cyclists, weight lifters, and soccer players. It is felt as a dull, aching pain around the front of the knee and deep to the patella. The pain may be felt when walking or running, going up or down stairs, kneeling or squatting, or after sitting with the knee bent for an extended period.

Patellofemoral syndrome may be initiated by a variety of causes, including individual variations in the shape and movement of the patella, a direct blow to the patella, or flat feet or improper shoes that cause excessive turning in or out of the feet or leg. These factors may cause in an imbalance in the muscle pull that acts on the patella, resulting in an abnormal tracking of the patella that allows it to deviate too far toward the lateral side of the patellar surface on the distal femur.

Because the hips are wider than the knee region, the femur has a diagonal orientation within the thigh, in contrast to the vertically oriented tibia of the leg (Figure 8.17). The Q-angle is a measure of how far the femur is angled laterally away from vertical. The Q-angle is normally 10–15 degrees, with females typically having a larger Q-angle due to their wider pelvis. During extension of the knee, the quadriceps femoris muscle pulls the patella both superiorly and laterally, with the lateral pull greater in women due to their large Q-angle. This makes women more vulnerable to developing patellofemoral syndrome than men. Normally, the large lip on the lateral side of the patellar surface of the femur compensates for the lateral pull on the patella, and thus helps to maintain its proper tracking.

However, if the pull produced by the medial and lateral sides of the quadriceps femoris muscle is not properly balanced, abnormal tracking of the patella toward the lateral side may occur. With continued use, this produces pain and could result in damage to the articulating surfaces of the patella and femur, and the possible future development of arthritis. Treatment generally involves stopping the activity that produces knee pain for a period of time, followed by a gradual resumption of activity. Proper strengthening of the quadriceps femoris muscle to correct for imbalances is also important to help prevent reoccurrence.

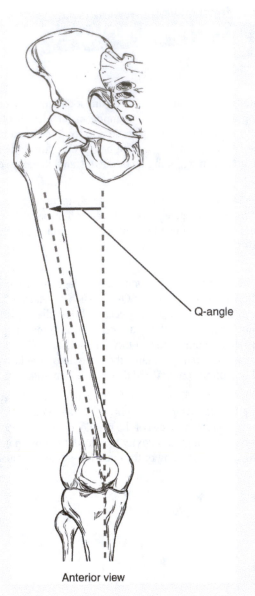

Anterior view

Figure 8.17 The Q-Angle The Q-angle is a measure of the amount of lateral deviation of the femur from the vertical line of the tibia. Adult females have a larger Q-angle due to their wider pelvis than adult males.

Tibia

The tibia (shin bone) is the medial bone of the leg and is larger than the fibula, with which it is paired (Figure 8.18). The tibia is the main weight-bearing bone of the lower leg and the second longest bone of the body, after the femur. The medial side of the tibia is located immediately under the skin, allowing it to be easily palpated down the entire length of the medial leg.

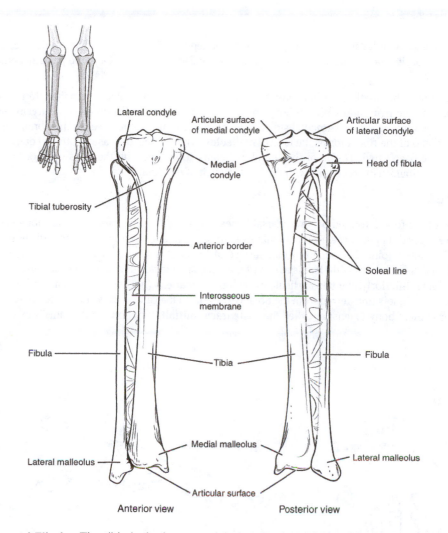

Figure 8.18 Tibia and Fibula The tibia is the larger, weight-bearing bone located on the medial side of the leg. The fibula is the slender bone of the lateral side of the leg and does not bear weight.

The proximal end of the tibia is greatly expanded. The two sides of this expansion form the **medial condyle of the tibia** and the **lateral condyle of the tibia**. The tibia does not have epicondyles. The top surface of each condyle is smooth and flattened. These areas articulate with the medial and lateral condyles of the femur to form the **knee joint**. Between the articulating surfaces of the tibial condyles is the **intercondylar eminence**, an irregular, elevated area that serves as the inferior attachment point for two supporting ligaments of the knee.

The **tibial tuberosity** is an elevated area on the anterior side of the tibia, near its proximal end. It is the final site of attachment for the muscle tendon associated with the patella. More inferiorly, the **shaft of the tibia** becomes triangular in shape. The anterior apex of

MH this triangle forms the **anterior border of the tibia**, which begins at the tibial tuberosity and runs inferiorly along the length of the tibia. Both the anterior border and the medial side of the triangular shaft are located immediately under the skin and can be easily palpated along the entire length of the tibia. A small ridge running down the lateral side of the tibial shaft is the **interosseous border of the tibia**. This is for the attachment of the **interosseous membrane of the leg**, the sheet of dense connective tissue that unites the tibia and fibula bones. Located on the posterior side of the tibia is the **soleal line**, a diagonally running, roughened ridge that begins below the base of the lateral condyle, and runs down and medially across the proximal third of the posterior tibia. Muscles of the posterior leg attach to this line.

The large expansion found on the medial side of the distal tibia is the **medial malleolus** ("little hammer"). This forms the large bony bump found on the medial side of the ankle region. Both the smooth surface on the inside of the medial malleolus and the smooth area at the distal end of the tibia articulate with the talus bone of the foot as part of the ankle joint. On the lateral side of the distal tibia is a wide groove called the **fibular notch**. This area articulates with the distal end of the fibula, forming the **distal tibiofibular joint**.

Fibula

The fibula is the slender bone located on the lateral side of the leg (see Figure 8.18). The fibula does not bear weight. It serves primarily for muscle attachments and thus is largely surrounded by muscles. Only the proximal and distal ends of the fibula can be palpated.

The **head of the fibula** is the small, knob-like, proximal end of the fibula. It articulates with the inferior aspect of the lateral tibial condyle, forming the **proximal tibiofibular joint**. The thin **shaft of the fibula** has the **interosseous border of the fibula**, a narrow ridge running down its medial side for the attachment of the interosseous membrane that spans the fibula and tibia. The distal end of the fibula forms the **lateral malleolus**, which forms the easily palpated bony bump on the lateral side of the ankle. The deep (medial) side of the lateral malleolus articulates with the talus bone of the foot as part of the ankle joint. The distal fibula also articulates with the fibular notch of the tibia.

Tarsal Bones

The posterior half of the foot is formed by seven tarsal bones (Figure 8.19). The most superior bone is the **talus**. This has a relatively square-shaped, upper surface that articulates with the tibia and fibula to form the **ankle joint**. Three areas of articulation form the ankle joint: The superomedial surface of the talus bone articulates with the medial malleolus of the tibia, the top of the talus articulates with the distal end of the tibia, and the lateral side of the talus articulates with the lateral malleolus of the fibula. Inferiorly, the talus articulates with the **calcaneus** (heel bone), the largest bone of the foot, which forms the heel. Body weight is transferred from the tibia to the talus to the calcaneus, which rests on the ground. The medial calcaneus has a prominent bony extension called the **sustentaculum tali** ("support for the talus") that supports the medial side of the talus bone.

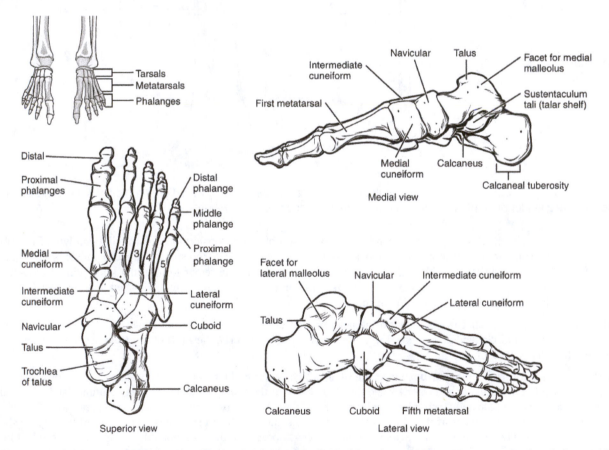

Figure 8.19 Bones of the Foot   The bones of the foot are divided into three groups. The posterior foot is formed by the seven tarsal bones. The mid-foot has the five metatarsal bones. The toes contain the phalanges.

The **cuboid** bone articulates with the anterior end of the calcaneus bone. The cuboid has a deep groove running across its inferior surface, which provides passage for a muscle tendon. The talus bone articulates anteriorly with the **navicular** bone, which in turn articulates anteriorly with the three cuneiform ("wedge-shaped") bones. These bones are the **medial cuneiform**, the **intermediate cuneiform**, and the **lateral cuneiform**. Each of these bones has a broad superior surface and a narrow inferior surface, which together produce the transverse (medial-lateral) curvature of the foot. The navicular and lateral cuneiform bones also articulate with the medial side of the cuboid bone.

Use this tutorial (http://openstaxcollege.org/l/footbones) to review the bones of the foot. Which tarsal bones are in the proximal, intermediate, and distal groups?

Metatarsal Bones

The anterior half of the foot is formed by the five metatarsal bones, which are located between the tarsal bones of the posterior foot and the phalanges of the toes (see Figure 8.19). These elongated bones are numbered 1–5, starting with the medial side of the foot. The first metatarsal bone is shorter and thicker than the others. The second metatarsal is the longest. The **base of the metatarsal bone** is the proximal end of each metatarsal bone. These articulate with the cuboid or cuneiform bones. The base of the fifth metatarsal has a large, lateral expansion that provides for muscle attachments. This expanded base of the fifth metatarsal can be felt as a bony bump at the midpoint along the lateral border of the foot. The expanded distal end of each metatarsal is the **head of the metatarsal bone**. Each metatarsal bone articulates with the proximal phalanx of a toe to form a **metatarsophalangeal joint**. The heads of the metatarsal bones also rest on the ground and form the ball (anterior end) of the foot.

Phalanges

The toes contain a total of 14 phalanx bones (phalanges), arranged in a similar manner as the phalanges of the fingers (see Figure 8.19). The toes are numbered 1–5, starting with the big toe (**hallux**). The big toe has two phalanx bones, the proximal and distal phalanges. The remaining toes all have proximal, middle, and distal phalanges. A joint between adjacent phalanx bones is called an interphalangeal joint.

View this link (http://openstaxcollege.org/l/bunion) to learn about a bunion, a localized swelling on the medial side of the foot, next to the first metatarsophalangeal joint, at the base of the big toe. What is a bunion and what type of shoe is most likely to cause this to develop?

Arches of the Foot

When the foot comes into contact with the ground during walking, running, or jumping activities, the impact of the body weight puts a tremendous amount of pressure and force on the foot. During running, the force applied to each foot as it contacts the ground can be up to 2.5 times your body weight. The bones, joints, ligaments, and muscles of the foot absorb this force, thus greatly reducing the amount of shock that is passed superiorly into the lower limb and body. The arches of the foot play an important role in this shock-absorbing ability. When weight is applied to the foot, these arches will flatten somewhat, thus absorbing energy. When the weight is removed, the arch rebounds, giving "spring" to the step. The arches also serve to distribute body weight side to side and to either end of the foot.

The foot has a transverse arch, a medial longitudinal arch, and a lateral longitudinal arch (see Figure 8.19). The transverse arch forms the medial-lateral curvature of the mid-foot. It is formed by the wedge shapes of the cuneiform bones and bases (proximal ends) of the first to fourth metatarsal bones. This arch helps to distribute body weight from side to side within the foot, thus allowing the foot to accommodate uneven terrain.

The longitudinal arches run down the length of the foot. The lateral longitudinal arch is relatively flat, whereas the medial longitudinal arch is larger (taller). The longitudinal arches are formed by the tarsal bones posteriorly and the metatarsal bones anteriorly. These arches are supported at either end, where they contact the ground. Posteriorly, this support is provided by the calcaneus bone and anteriorly by the heads (distal ends) of the metatarsal bones. The talus bone, which receives the weight of the body, is located at the top of the longitudinal arches. Body weight is then conveyed from the talus to the ground by the anterior and posterior ends of these arches. Strong ligaments unite the adjacent foot bones to prevent disruption of the arches during weight bearing. On the bottom of the foot, additional ligaments tie together the anterior and posterior ends of the arches. These ligaments have elasticity, which allows them to stretch somewhat during weight bearing, thus allowing the longitudinal arches to spread. The stretching of these ligaments stores energy within the foot, rather than passing these forces into the leg. Contraction of the foot muscles also plays an important role in this energy absorption. When the weight is removed, the elastic ligaments recoil and pull the ends of the arches closer together. This recovery of the arches releases the stored energy and improves the energy efficiency of walking.

Stretching of the ligaments that support the longitudinal arches can lead to pain. This can occur in overweight individuals, with people who have jobs that involve standing for long periods of time (such as a waitress), or walking or running long distances. If stretching of the ligaments is prolonged, excessive, or repeated, it can result in a gradual lengthening of the supporting ligaments, with subsequent depression or collapse of the longitudinal arches, particularly on the medial side of the foot. This condition is called pes planus ("flat foot" or "fallen arches").

8.5 | Development of the Appendicular Skeleton

By the end of this section, you will be able to:

- Describe the growth and development of the embryonic limb buds
- Discuss the appearance of primary and secondary ossification centers

Embryologically, the appendicular skeleton arises from mesenchyme, a type of embryonic tissue that can differentiate into many types of tissues, including bone or muscle tissue. Mesenchyme gives rise to the bones of the upper and lower limbs, as well as to the pectoral and pelvic girdles. Development of the limbs begins near the end of the fourth embryonic week, with the upper limbs appearing first. Thereafter, the development of the upper and lower limbs follows similar patterns, with the lower limbs lagging behind the upper limbs by a few days.

Limb Growth

Each upper and lower limb initially develops as a small bulge called a **limb bud**, which appears on the lateral side of the early embryo. The upper limb bud appears near the end of the fourth week of development, with the lower limb bud appearing shortly after (Figure 8.20).

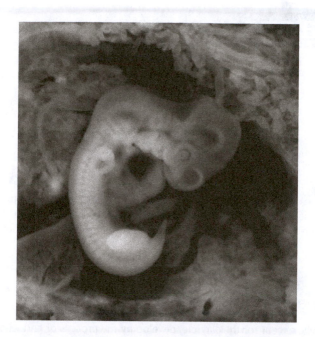

Figure 8.20 Embryo at Seven Weeks Limb buds are visible in an embryo at the end of the seventh week of development (embryo derived from an ectopic pregnancy). (credit: Ed Uthman/flickr)

Initially, the limb buds consist of a core of mesenchyme covered by a layer of ectoderm. The ectoderm at the end of the limb bud thickens to form a narrow crest called the **apical ectodermal ridge**. This ridge stimulates the underlying mesenchyme to rapidly proliferate, producing the outgrowth of the developing limb. As the limb bud elongates, cells located farther from the apical ectodermal ridge slow their rates of cell division and begin to differentiate. In this way, the limb develops along a proximal-to-distal axis.

During the sixth week of development, the distal ends of the upper and lower limb buds expand and flatten into a paddle shape. This region will become the hand or foot. The wrist or ankle areas then appear as a constriction that develops at the base of the paddle. Shortly after this, a second constriction on the limb bud appears at the future site of the elbow or knee. Within the paddle, areas of tissue undergo cell death, producing separations between the growing fingers and toes. Also during the sixth week of development, mesenchyme within the limb buds begins to differentiate into hyaline cartilage that will form models of the future limb bones.

The early outgrowth of the upper and lower limb buds initially has the limbs positioned so that the regions that will become the palm of the hand or the bottom of the foot are facing medially toward the body, with the future thumb or big toe both oriented toward the head. During the seventh week of development, the upper limb rotates laterally by 90 degrees, so that the palm of the hand faces anteriorly and the thumb points laterally. In contrast, the lower limb undergoes a 90-degree medial rotation, thus bringing the big toe to the medial side of the foot.

Interactive LINK

Watch this **animation (http://openstaxcollege.org/l/limbbuds)** to follow the development and growth of the upper and lower limb buds. On what days of embryonic development do these events occur: (a) first appearance of the upper limb bud (limb ridge); (b) the flattening of the distal limb to form the handplate or footplate; and (c) the beginning of limb rotation?

Ossification of Appendicular Bones

All of the girdle and limb bones, except for the clavicle, develop by the process of endochondral ossification. This process begins as the mesenchyme within the limb bud differentiates into hyaline cartilage to form cartilage models for future bones. By the twelfth week, a primary ossification center will have appeared in the diaphysis (shaft) region of the long bones, initiating the process that converts the cartilage model into bone. A secondary ossification center will appear in each epiphysis (expanded end) of these bones at a later time, usually after birth. The primary and secondary ossification centers are separated by the epiphyseal plate, a layer of growing hyaline cartilage. This plate is located between the diaphysis and each epiphysis. It continues to grow and is responsible for the lengthening of the bone. The epiphyseal plate is retained for many years, until the bone reaches its final, adult size, at which time the epiphyseal plate disappears and the epiphysis fuses to the diaphysis. (Seek additional content on ossification in the chapter on bone tissue.)

Small bones, such as the phalanges, will develop only one secondary ossification center and will thus have only a single epiphyseal plate. Large bones, such as the femur, will develop several secondary ossification centers, with an epiphyseal plate associated with each secondary center. Thus, ossification of the femur begins at the end of the seventh week with the appearance of the primary ossification center in the diaphysis, which rapidly expands to ossify the shaft of the bone prior to birth. Secondary ossification centers develop at later times. Ossification of the distal end of the femur, to form the condyles and epicondyles, begins shortly before birth. Secondary ossification centers also appear in the femoral head late in the first year after birth, in the greater trochanter during the fourth year, and in the lesser trochanter between the ages of 9 and 10 years. Once these areas have ossified, their fusion to the diaphysis and the disappearance of each epiphyseal plate follow a reversed sequence. Thus, the lesser trochanter is the first to fuse, doing so at the onset of puberty (around 11 years of age), followed by the greater trochanter approximately 1 year later. The femoral head fuses between the ages of 14–17 years, whereas the distal condyles of the femur are the last to fuse, between the ages of 16–19 years. Knowledge of the age at which different epiphyseal plates disappear is important when interpreting radiographs taken of children. Since the cartilage of an epiphyseal plate is less dense than bone, the plate will appear dark in a radiograph image. Thus, a normal epiphyseal plate may be mistaken for a bone fracture.

The clavicle is the one appendicular skeleton bone that does not develop via endochondral ossification. Instead, the clavicle develops through the process of intramembranous ossification. During this process, mesenchymal cells differentiate directly into bone-producing cells, which produce the clavicle directly, without first making a cartilage model. Because of this early production of bone, the clavicle is the first bone of the body to begin ossification, with ossification centers appearing during the fifth week of development. However, ossification of the clavicle is not complete until age 25.

⌕isorders OF THE...

Appendicular System: Congenital Clubfoot

Clubfoot, also known as talipes, is a congenital (present at birth) disorder of unknown cause and is the most common deformity of the lower limb. It affects the foot and ankle, causing the foot to be twisted inward at a sharp angle, like the head of a golf club (Figure 8.21). Clubfoot has a frequency of about 1 out of every 1,000 births, and is twice as likely to occur in a male child as in a female child. In 50 percent of cases, both feet are affected.

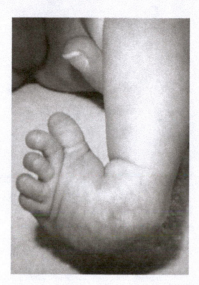

Figure 8.21 Clubfoot Clubfoot is a common deformity of the ankle and foot that is present at birth. Most cases are corrected without surgery, and affected individuals will grow up to lead normal, active lives. (credit: James W. Hanson)

At birth, children with a clubfoot have the heel turned inward and the anterior foot twisted so that the lateral side of the foot is facing inferiorly, commonly due to ligaments or leg muscles attached to the foot that are shortened or abnormally tight. These pull the foot into an abnormal position, resulting in bone deformities. Other symptoms may include bending of the ankle that lifts the heel of the foot and an extremely high foot arch. Due to the limited range of motion in the affected foot, it is difficult to place the foot into the correct position. Additionally, the affected foot may be shorter than normal, and the calf muscles are usually underdeveloped on the affected side. Despite the appearance, this is not a painful condition for newborns. However, it must be treated early to avoid future pain and impaired walking ability.

Although the cause of clubfoot is idiopathic (unknown), evidence indicates that fetal position within the uterus is not a contributing factor. Genetic factors are involved, because clubfoot tends to run within families. Cigarette smoking during pregnancy has been linked to the development of clubfoot, particularly in families with a history of clubfoot.

Previously, clubfoot required extensive surgery. Today, 90 percent of cases are successfully treated without surgery using new corrective casting techniques. The best chance for a full recovery requires that clubfoot treatment begin during the first 2 weeks after birth. Corrective casting gently stretches the foot, which is followed by the application of a holding cast to keep the foot in the proper position. This stretching and casting is repeated weekly for several weeks. In severe cases, surgery may also be required, after which the foot typically remains in a cast for 6 to 8 weeks. After the cast is removed following either surgical or nonsurgical treatment, the child will be required to wear a brace part-time (at night) for up to 4 years. In addition, special exercises will be prescribed, and the child must also wear special shoes. Close monitoring by the parents and adherence to postoperative instructions are imperative in minimizing the risk of relapse.

Despite these difficulties, treatment for clubfoot is usually successful, and the child will grow up to lead a normal, active life. Numerous examples of individuals born with a clubfoot who went on to successful careers include Dudley Moore (comedian and actor), Damon Wayans (comedian and actor), Troy Aikman (three-time Super Bowl-winning quarterback), Kristi Yamaguchi (Olympic gold medalist in figure skating), Mia Hamm (two-time Olympic gold medalist in soccer), and Charles Woodson (Heisman trophy and Super Bowl winner).

KEY TERMS

acetabulum large, cup-shaped cavity located on the lateral side of the hip bone; formed by the junction of the ilium, pubis, and ischium portions of the hip bone

acromial end of the clavicle lateral end of the clavicle that articulates with the acromion of the scapula

acromial process acromion of the scapula

acromioclavicular joint articulation between the acromion of the scapula and the acromial end of the clavicle

acromion flattened bony process that extends laterally from the scapular spine to form the bony tip of the shoulder

adductor tubercle small, bony bump located on the superior aspect of the medial epicondyle of the femur

anatomical neck line on the humerus located around the outside margin of the humeral head

ankle joint joint that separates the leg and foot portions of the lower limb; formed by the articulations between the talus bone of the foot inferiorly, and the distal end of the tibia, medial malleolus of the tibia, and lateral malleolus of the fibula superiorly

anterior border of the tibia narrow, anterior margin of the tibia that extends inferiorly from the tibial tuberosity

anterior inferior iliac spine small, bony projection located on the anterior margin of the ilium, below the anterior superior iliac spine

anterior sacroiliac ligament strong ligament between the sacrum and the ilium portions of the hip bone that supports the anterior side of the sacroiliac joint

anterior superior iliac spine rounded, anterior end of the iliac crest

apical ectodermal ridge enlarged ridge of ectoderm at the distal end of a limb bud that stimulates growth and elongation of the limb

arcuate line of the ilium smooth ridge located at the inferior margin of the iliac fossa; forms the lateral portion of the pelvic brim

arm region of the upper limb located between the shoulder and elbow joints; contains the humerus bone

auricular surface of the ilium roughened area located on the posterior, medial side of the ilium of the hip bone; articulates with the auricular surface of the sacrum to form the sacroiliac joint

base of the metatarsal bone expanded, proximal end of each metatarsal bone

bicipital groove intertubercular groove; narrow groove located between the greater and lesser tubercles of the humerus

calcaneus heel bone; posterior, inferior tarsal bone that forms the heel of the foot

capitate from the lateral side, the third of the four distal carpal bones; articulates with the scaphoid and lunate proximally, the trapezoid laterally, the hamate medially, and primarily with the third metacarpal distally

capitulum knob-like bony structure located anteriorly on the lateral, distal end of the humerus

carpal bone one of the eight small bones that form the wrist and base of the hand; these are grouped as a proximal row consisting of (from lateral to medial) the scaphoid, lunate, triquetrum, and pisiform bones, and a distal row containing (from lateral to medial) the trapezium, trapezoid, capitate, and hamate bones

carpal tunnel passageway between the anterior forearm and hand formed by the carpal bones and flexor retinaculum

carpometacarpal joint articulation between one of the carpal bones in the distal row and a metacarpal bone of the hand

clavicle collarbone; elongated bone that articulates with the manubrium of the sternum medially and the acromion of the scapula laterally

coracoclavicular ligament strong band of connective tissue that anchors the coracoid process of the scapula to the lateral clavicle; provides important indirect support for the acromioclavicular joint

coracoid process short, hook-like process that projects anteriorly and laterally from the superior margin of the scapula

coronoid fossa depression on the anterior surface of the humerus above the trochlea; this space receives the coronoid process of the ulna when the elbow is maximally flexed

coronoid process of the ulna projecting bony lip located on the anterior, proximal ulna; forms the inferior margin of the trochlear notch

costoclavicular ligament band of connective tissue that unites the medial clavicle with the first rib

coxal bone hip bone

cuboid tarsal bone that articulates posteriorly with the calcaneus bone, medially with the lateral cuneiform bone, and anteriorly with the fourth and fifth metatarsal bones

deltoid tuberosity roughened, V-shaped region located laterally on the mid-shaft of the humerus

distal radioulnar joint articulation between the head of the ulna and the ulnar notch of the radius

distal tibiofibular joint articulation between the distal fibula and the fibular notch of the tibia

elbow joint joint located between the upper arm and forearm regions of the upper limb; formed by the articulations between the trochlea of the humerus and the trochlear notch of the ulna, and the capitulum of the humerus and the head of the radius

femur thigh bone; the single bone of the thigh

fibula thin, non-weight-bearing bone found on the lateral side of the leg

fibular notch wide groove on the lateral side of the distal tibia for articulation with the fibula at the distal tibiofibular joint

flexor retinaculum strong band of connective tissue at the anterior wrist that spans the top of the U-shaped grouping of the carpal bones to form the roof of the carpal tunnel

foot portion of the lower limb located distal to the ankle joint

forearm region of the upper limb located between the elbow and wrist joints; contains the radius and ulna bones

fossa (plural = fossae) shallow depression on the surface of a bone

fovea capitis minor indentation on the head of the femur that serves as the site of attachment for the ligament to the head of the femur

glenohumeral joint shoulder joint; formed by the articulation between the glenoid cavity of the scapula and the head of the humerus

glenoid cavity (also, glenoid fossa) shallow depression located on the lateral scapula, between the superior and lateral borders

gluteal tuberosity roughened area on the posterior side of the proximal femur, extending inferiorly from the base of the greater trochanter

greater pelvis (also, greater pelvic cavity or false pelvis) broad space above the pelvic brim defined laterally by the fan-like portion of the upper ilium

greater sciatic foramen pelvic opening formed by the greater sciatic notch of the hip bone, the sacrum, and the sacrospinous ligament

greater sciatic notch large, U-shaped indentation located on the posterior margin of the ilium, superior to the ischial spine

greater trochanter large, bony expansion of the femur that projects superiorly from the base of the femoral neck

greater tubercle enlarged prominence located on the lateral side of the proximal humerus

hallux big toe; digit 1 of the foot

hamate from the lateral side, the fourth of the four distal carpal bones; articulates with the lunate and triquetrum proximally, the fourth and fifth metacarpals distally, and the capitate laterally

hand region of the upper limb distal to the wrist joint

head of the femur rounded, proximal end of the femur that articulates with the acetabulum of the hip bone to form the hip joint

head of the fibula small, knob-like, proximal end of the fibula; articulates with the inferior aspect of the lateral condyle of the tibia

head of the humerus smooth, rounded region on the medial side of the proximal humerus; articulates with the glenoid fossa of the scapula to form the glenohumeral (shoulder) joint

head of the metatarsal bone expanded, distal end of each metatarsal bone

head of the radius disc-shaped structure that forms the proximal end of the radius; articulates with the capitulum of the humerus as part of the elbow joint, and with the radial notch of the ulna as part of the proximal radioulnar joint

head of the ulna small, rounded distal end of the ulna; articulates with the ulnar notch of the distal radius, forming the distal radioulnar joint

hip bone coxal bone; single bone that forms the pelvic girdle; consists of three areas, the ilium, ischium, and pubis

hip joint joint located at the proximal end of the lower limb; formed by the articulation between the acetabulum of the hip bone and the head of the femur

hook of the hamate bone bony extension located on the anterior side of the hamate carpal bone

humerus single bone of the upper arm

iliac crest curved, superior margin of the ilium

iliac fossa shallow depression found on the anterior and medial surfaces of the upper ilium

ilium superior portion of the hip bone

inferior angle of the scapula inferior corner of the scapula located where the medial and lateral borders meet

inferior pubic ramus narrow segment of bone that passes inferiorly and laterally from the pubic body; joins with the ischial ramus to form the ischiopubic ramus

infraglenoid tubercle small bump or roughened area located on the lateral border of the scapula, near the inferior margin of the glenoid cavity

infraspinous fossa broad depression located on the posterior scapula, inferior to the spine

intercondylar eminence irregular elevation on the superior end of the tibia, between the articulating surfaces of the medial and lateral condyles

intercondylar fossa deep depression on the posterior side of the distal femur that separates the medial and lateral condyles

intermediate cuneiform middle of the three cuneiform tarsal bones; articulates posteriorly with the navicular bone, medially with the medial cuneiform bone, laterally with the lateral cuneiform bone, and anteriorly with the second metatarsal bone

interosseous border of the fibula small ridge running down the medial side of the fibular shaft; for attachment of the interosseous membrane between the fibula and tibia

interosseous border of the radius narrow ridge located on the medial side of the radial shaft; for attachment of the interosseous membrane between the ulna and radius bones

interosseous border of the tibia small ridge running down the lateral side of the tibial shaft; for attachment of the interosseous membrane between the tibia and fibula

interosseous border of the ulna narrow ridge located on the lateral side of the ulnar shaft; for attachment of the interosseous membrane between the ulna and radius

interosseous membrane of the forearm sheet of dense connective tissue that unites the radius and ulna bones

interosseous membrane of the leg sheet of dense connective tissue that unites the shafts of the tibia and fibula bones

interphalangeal joint articulation between adjacent phalanx bones of the hand or foot digits

intertrochanteric crest short, prominent ridge running between the greater and lesser trochanters on the posterior side of the proximal femur

intertrochanteric line small ridge running between the greater and lesser trochanters on the anterior side of the proximal femur

intertubercular groove (sulcus) bicipital groove; narrow groove located between the greater and lesser tubercles of the humerus

ischial ramus bony extension projecting anteriorly and superiorly from the ischial tuberosity; joins with the inferior pubic ramus to form the ischiopubic ramus

ischial spine pointed, bony projection from the posterior margin of the ischium that separates the greater sciatic notch and lesser sciatic notch

ischial tuberosity large, roughened protuberance that forms the posteroinferior portion of the hip bone; weight-bearing region of the pelvis when sitting

ischiopubic ramus narrow extension of bone that connects the ischial tuberosity to the pubic body; formed by the junction of the ischial ramus and inferior pubic ramus

ischium posteroinferior portion of the hip bone

knee joint joint that separates the thigh and leg portions of the lower limb; formed by the articulations between the medial and lateral condyles of the femur, and the medial and lateral condyles of the tibia

lateral border of the scapula diagonally oriented lateral margin of the scapula

lateral condyle of the femur smooth, articulating surface that forms the distal and posterior sides of the lateral expansion of the distal femur

lateral condyle of the tibia lateral, expanded region of the proximal tibia that includes the smooth surface that articulates with the lateral condyle of the femur as part of the knee joint

lateral cuneiform most lateral of the three cuneiform tarsal bones; articulates posteriorly with the navicular bone, medially with the intermediate cuneiform bone, laterally with the cuboid bone, and anteriorly with the third metatarsal bone

lateral epicondyle of the femur roughened area of the femur located on the lateral side of the lateral condyle

lateral epicondyle of the humerus small projection located on the lateral side of the distal humerus

lateral malleolus expanded distal end of the fibula

lateral supracondylar ridge narrow, bony ridge located along the lateral side of the distal humerus, superior to the lateral epicondyle

leg portion of the lower limb located between the knee and ankle joints

lesser pelvis (also, lesser pelvic cavity or true pelvis) narrow space located within the pelvis, defined superiorly by the pelvic brim (pelvic inlet) and inferiorly by the pelvic outlet

lesser sciatic foramen pelvic opening formed by the lesser sciatic notch of the hip bone, the sacrospinous ligament, and the sacrotuberous ligament

lesser sciatic notch shallow indentation along the posterior margin of the ischium, inferior to the ischial spine

lesser trochanter small, bony projection on the medial side of the proximal femur, at the base of the femoral neck

lesser tubercle small, bony prominence located on anterior side of the proximal humerus

ligament of the head of the femur ligament that spans the acetabulum of the hip bone and the fovea capitis of the femoral head

limb bud small elevation that appears on the lateral side of the embryo during the fourth or fifth week of development, which gives rise to an upper or lower limb

linea aspera longitudinally running bony ridge located in the middle third of the posterior femur

lunate from the lateral side, the second of the four proximal carpal bones; articulates with the radius proximally, the capitate and hamate distally, the scaphoid laterally, and the triquetrum medially

medial border of the scapula elongated, medial margin of the scapula

medial condyle of the femur smooth, articulating surface that forms the distal and posterior sides of the medial expansion of the distal femur

medial condyle of the tibia medial, expanded region of the proximal tibia that includes the smooth surface that articulates with the medial condyle of the femur as part of the knee joint

medial cuneiform most medial of the three cuneiform tarsal bones; articulates posteriorly with the navicular bone, laterally with the intermediate cuneiform bone, and anteriorly with the first and second metatarsal bones

medial epicondyle of the femur roughened area of the distal femur located on the medial side of the medial condyle

medial epicondyle of the humerus enlarged projection located on the medial side of the distal humerus

medial malleolus bony expansion located on the medial side of the distal tibia

metacarpal bone one of the five long bones that form the palm of the hand; numbered 1–5, starting on the lateral (thumb) side of the hand

metacarpophalangeal joint articulation between the distal end of a metacarpal bone of the hand and a proximal phalanx bone of the thumb or a finger

metatarsal bone one of the five elongated bones that forms the anterior half of the foot; numbered 1–5, starting on the medial side of the foot

metatarsophalangeal joint articulation between a metatarsal bone of the foot and the proximal phalanx bone of a toe

midcarpal joint articulation between the proximal and distal rows of the carpal bones; contributes to movements of the hand at the wrist

navicular tarsal bone that articulates posteriorly with the talus bone, laterally with the cuboid bone, and anteriorly with the medial, intermediate, and lateral cuneiform bones

neck of the femur narrowed region located inferior to the head of the femur

neck of the radius narrowed region immediately distal to the head of the radius

obturator foramen large opening located in the anterior hip bone, between the pubis and ischium regions

olecranon fossa large depression located on the posterior side of the distal humerus; this space receives the olecranon process of the ulna when the elbow is fully extended

olecranon process expanded posterior and superior portions of the proximal ulna; forms the bony tip of the elbow

patella kneecap; the largest sesamoid bone of the body; articulates with the distal femur

patellar surface smooth groove located on the anterior side of the distal femur, between the medial and lateral condyles; site of articulation for the patella

pectineal line narrow ridge located on the superior surface of the superior pubic ramus

pectoral girdle shoulder girdle; the set of bones, consisting of the scapula and clavicle, which attaches each upper limb to the axial skeleton

pelvic brim pelvic inlet; the dividing line between the greater and lesser pelvic regions; formed by the superior margin of the pubic symphysis, the pectineal lines of each pubis, the arcuate lines of each ilium, and the sacral promontory

pelvic girdle hip girdle; consists of a single hip bone, which attaches a lower limb to the sacrum of the axial skeleton

pelvic inlet pelvic brim

pelvic outlet inferior opening of the lesser pelvis; formed by the inferior margin of the pubic symphysis, right and left ischiopubic rami and sacrotuberous ligaments, and the tip of the coccyx

pelvis ring of bone consisting of the right and left hip bones, the sacrum, and the coccyx

phalanx bone of the foot (plural = phalanges) one of the 14 bones that form the toes; these include the proximal and distal phalanges of the big toe, and the proximal, middle, and distal phalanx bones of toes two through five

phalanx bone of the hand (plural = phalanges) one of the 14 bones that form the thumb and fingers; these include the proximal and distal phalanges of the thumb, and the proximal, middle, and distal phalanx bones of the fingers two through five

pisiform from the lateral side, the fourth of the four proximal carpal bones; articulates with the anterior surface of the triquetrum

pollex (also, thumb) digit 1 of the hand

posterior inferior iliac spine small, bony projection located at the inferior margin of the auricular surface on the posterior ilium

posterior sacroiliac ligament strong ligament spanning the sacrum and ilium of the hip bone that supports the posterior side of the sacroiliac joint

posterior superior iliac spine rounded, posterior end of the iliac crest

proximal radioulnar joint articulation formed by the radial notch of the ulna and the head of the radius

proximal tibiofibular joint articulation between the head of the fibula and the inferior aspect of the lateral condyle of the tibia

pubic arch bony structure formed by the pubic symphysis, and the bodies and inferior pubic rami of the right and left pubic bones

pubic body enlarged, medial portion of the pubis region of the hip bone

pubic symphysis joint formed by the articulation between the pubic bodies of the right and left hip bones

pubic tubercle small bump located on the superior aspect of the pubic body

pubis anterior portion of the hip bone

radial fossa small depression located on the anterior humerus above the capitulum; this space receives the head of the radius when the elbow is maximally flexed

radial notch of the ulna small, smooth area on the lateral side of the proximal ulna; articulates with the head of the radius as part of the proximal radioulnar joint

radial tuberosity oval-shaped, roughened protuberance located on the medial side of the proximal radius

radiocarpal joint wrist joint, located between the forearm and hand regions of the upper limb; articulation formed proximally by the distal end of the radius and the fibrocartilaginous pad that unites the distal radius and ulna bone, and distally by the scaphoid, lunate, and triquetrum carpal bones

radius bone located on the lateral side of the forearm

sacroiliac joint joint formed by the articulation between the auricular surfaces of the sacrum and ilium

sacrospinous ligament ligament that spans the sacrum to the ischial spine of the hip bone

sacrotuberous ligament ligament that spans the sacrum to the ischial tuberosity of the hip bone

scaphoid from the lateral side, the first of the four proximal carpal bones; articulates with the radius proximally, the trapezoid, trapezium, and capitate distally, and the lunate medially

scapula shoulder blade bone located on the posterior side of the shoulder

shaft of the femur cylindrically shaped region that forms the central portion of the femur

shaft of the fibula elongated, slender portion located between the expanded ends of the fibula

shaft of the humerus narrow, elongated, central region of the humerus

shaft of the radius narrow, elongated, central region of the radius

shaft of the tibia triangular-shaped, central portion of the tibia

shaft of the ulna narrow, elongated, central region of the ulna

soleal line small, diagonally running ridge located on the posterior side of the proximal tibia

spine of the scapula prominent ridge passing mediolaterally across the upper portion of the posterior scapular surface

sternal end of the clavicle medial end of the clavicle that articulates with the manubrium of the sternum

sternoclavicular joint articulation between the manubrium of the sternum and the sternal end of the clavicle; forms the only bony attachment between the pectoral girdle of the upper limb and the axial skeleton

styloid process of the radius pointed projection located on the lateral end of the distal radius

styloid process of the ulna short, bony projection located on the medial end of the distal ulna

subpubic angle inverted V-shape formed by the convergence of the right and left ischiopubic rami; this angle is greater than 80 degrees in females and less than 70 degrees in males

subscapular fossa broad depression located on the anterior (deep) surface of the scapula

superior angle of the scapula corner of the scapula between the superior and medial borders of the scapula

superior border of the scapula superior margin of the scapula

superior pubic ramus narrow segment of bone that passes laterally from the pubic body to join the ilium

supraglenoid tubercle small bump located at the superior margin of the glenoid cavity

suprascapular notch small notch located along the superior border of the scapula, medial to the coracoid process

supraspinous fossa narrow depression located on the posterior scapula, superior to the spine

surgical neck region of the humerus where the expanded, proximal end joins with the narrower shaft

sustentaculum tali bony ledge extending from the medial side of the calcaneus bone

talus tarsal bone that articulates superiorly with the tibia and fibula at the ankle joint; also articulates inferiorly with the calcaneus bone and anteriorly with the navicular bone

tarsal bone one of the seven bones that make up the posterior foot; includes the calcaneus, talus, navicular, cuboid, medial cuneiform, intermediate cuneiform, and lateral cuneiform bones

thigh portion of the lower limb located between the hip and knee joints

tibia shin bone; the large, weight-bearing bone located on the medial side of the leg

tibial tuberosity elevated area on the anterior surface of the proximal tibia

trapezium from the lateral side, the first of the four distal carpal bones; articulates with the scaphoid proximally, the first and second metacarpals distally, and the trapezoid medially

trapezoid from the lateral side, the second of the four distal carpal bones; articulates with the scaphoid proximally, the second metacarpal distally, the trapezium laterally, and the capitate medially

triquetrum from the lateral side, the third of the four proximal carpal bones; articulates with the lunate laterally, the hamate distally, and has a facet for the pisiform

trochlea pulley-shaped region located medially at the distal end of the humerus; articulates at the elbow with the trochlear notch of the ulna

trochlear notch large, C-shaped depression located on the anterior side of the proximal ulna; articulates at the elbow with the trochlea of the humerus

ulna bone located on the medial side of the forearm

ulnar notch of the radius shallow, smooth area located on the medial side of the distal radius; articulates with the head of the ulna at the distal radioulnar joint

ulnar tuberosity roughened area located on the anterior, proximal ulna inferior to the coronoid process

CHAPTER REVIEW

8.1 The Pectoral Girdle

The pectoral girdle, consisting of the clavicle and the scapula, attaches each upper limb to the axial skeleton. The clavicle is an anterior bone whose sternal end articulates with the manubrium of the sternum at the sternoclavicular joint. The sternal end is also anchored to the first rib by the costoclavicular ligament. The acromial end of the clavicle articulates with the acromion of the scapula at the acromioclavicular joint. This end is also anchored to the coracoid process of the scapula by the coracoclavicular ligament, which provides indirect support for the acromioclavicular joint. The clavicle supports the scapula, transmits the weight and forces from the upper limb to the body trunk, and protects the underlying nerves and blood vessels.

The scapula lies on the posterior aspect of the pectoral girdle. It mediates the attachment of the upper limb to the clavicle, and contributes to the formation of the glenohumeral (shoulder) joint. This triangular bone has three sides called the medial, lateral, and superior borders. The suprascapular notch is located on the superior border. The scapula also has three corners, two of which are the superior and inferior angles. The third corner is occupied by the glenoid cavity. Posteriorly, the spine separates the supraspinous and infraspinous fossae, and then extends laterally as the acromion. The subscapular fossa is located on the anterior surface of the scapula. The coracoid process projects anteriorly, passing inferior to the lateral end of the clavicle.

8.2 Bones of the Upper Limb

Each upper limb is divided into three regions and contains a total of 30 bones. The upper arm is the region located between the shoulder and elbow joints. This area contains the humerus. The proximal humerus consists of the head, which articulates with the scapula at the glenohumeral joint, the greater and lesser tubercles separated by the intertubercular (bicipital) groove, and the anatomical and surgical necks. The humeral shaft has the roughened area of the deltoid tuberosity on its lateral side. The distal humerus is flattened, forming a lateral supracondylar ridge that terminates at the small lateral epicondyle. The medial side of the distal humerus has the large, medial epicondyle. The articulating surfaces of the distal humerus consist of the trochlea medially and the capitulum laterally. Depressions on the humerus that accommodate the forearm bones during bending (flexing) and straightening (extending) of the elbow include the coronoid fossa, the radial fossa, and the olecranon fossa.

The forearm is the region of the upper limb located between the elbow and wrist joints. This region contains two bones, the ulna medially and the radius on the lateral (thumb) side. The elbow joint is formed by the articulation between the trochlea of the humerus and the trochlear notch of the ulna, plus the articulation between the capitulum of the humerus and the head of the radius. The proximal radioulnar joint is the articulation between the head of the radius and the radial notch of the ulna. The proximal ulna also has the olecranon process, forming an expanded posterior region, and the coronoid process and ulnar tuberosity on its anterior aspect. On the proximal radius, the narrowed region below the head is the neck; distal to this is the radial tuberosity. The shaft portions of both the ulna and radius have an interosseous border, whereas the distal ends of each bone have a pointed styloid process. The distal radioulnar joint is found between the head of the ulna and the ulnar notch of the radius. The distal end of the radius articulates with the proximal carpal bones, but the ulna does not.

The base of the hand is formed by eight carpal bones. The carpal bones are united into two rows of bones. The proximal row contains (from lateral to medial) the scaphoid, lunate, triquetrum, and pisiform bones. The scaphoid, lunate, and triquetrum bones contribute to the formation of the radiocarpal joint. The distal row of carpal bones contains (from medial to lateral) the hamate, capitate, trapezoid, and trapezium bones ("So Long To Pinky, Here Comes The Thumb"). The anterior hamate has a prominent bony hook. The proximal and distal carpal rows articulate with each other at the midcarpal joint. The carpal bones, together with the flexor retinaculum, also form the carpal tunnel of the wrist.

The five metacarpal bones form the palm of the hand. The metacarpal bones are numbered 1–5, starting with the thumb side. The first metacarpal bone is freely mobile, but the other bones are united as a group. The digits are also numbered 1–5, with the thumb being number 1. The fingers and thumb contain a total of 14 phalanges (phalanx bones). The thumb contains a proximal and a distal phalanx, whereas the remaining digits each contain proximal, middle, and distal phalanges.

8.3 The Pelvic Girdle and Pelvis

The pelvic girdle, consisting of a hip bone, serves to attach a lower limb to the axial skeleton. The hip bone articulates posteriorly at the sacroiliac joint with the sacrum, which is part of the axial skeleton. The right and left hip bones converge anteriorly and articulate with each other at the pubic symphysis. The combination of the hip bone, the sacrum, and the coccyx forms the pelvis. The pelvis has a pronounced anterior tilt. The primary function of the pelvis is to support the upper body and transfer body weight to the lower limbs. It also serves as the site of attachment for multiple muscles.

The hip bone consists of three regions: the ilium, ischium, and pubis. The ilium forms the large, fan-like region of the hip bone. The superior margin of this area is the iliac crest. Located at either end of the iliac crest are the anterior superior and posterior superior iliac spines. Inferior to these are the anterior inferior and posterior inferior iliac spines. The auricular surface of the ilium articulates with the sacrum to form the sacroiliac joint. The medial surface of the upper ilium forms the iliac fossa, with the arcuate line marking the inferior limit of this area. The posterior margin of the ilium has the large greater sciatic notch.

The posterolateral portion of the hip bone is the ischium. It has the expanded ischial tuberosity, which supports body weight when sitting. The ischial ramus projects anteriorly and superiorly. The posterior margin of the ischium has the shallow lesser sciatic notch and the ischial spine, which separates the greater and lesser sciatic notches.

The pubis forms the anterior portion of the hip bone. The body of the pubis articulates with the pubis of the opposite hip bone at the pubic symphysis. The superior margin of the pubic body has the pubic tubercle. The pubis is joined to the ilium by the superior pubic ramus, the superior surface of which forms the pectineal line. The inferior pubic ramus projects inferiorly and laterally. The pubic arch is formed by the pubic symphysis, the bodies of the adjacent pubic bones, and the two inferior pubic rami. The inferior pubic ramus joins the ischial ramus to form the ischiopubic ramus. The subpubic angle is formed by the medial convergence of the right and left ischiopubic rami.

The lateral side of the hip bone has the cup-like acetabulum, which is part of the hip joint. The large anterior opening is the obturator foramen. The sacroiliac joint is supported by the anterior and posterior sacroiliac ligaments. The sacrum is also joined to the hip bone by the sacrospinous ligament, which attaches to the ischial spine, and the sacrotuberous ligament, which attaches to the ischial tuberosity. The sacrospinous and sacrotuberous ligaments contribute to the formation of the greater and lesser sciatic foramina.

The broad space of the upper pelvis is the greater pelvis, and the narrow, inferior space is the lesser pelvis. These areas are separated by the pelvic brim (pelvic inlet). The inferior opening of the pelvis is the pelvic outlet. Compared to the male, the female pelvis is wider to accommodate childbirth, has a larger subpubic angle, and a broader greater sciatic notch.

8.4 Bones of the Lower Limb

The lower limb is divided into three regions. These are the thigh, located between the hip and knee joints; the leg, located between the knee and ankle joints; and distal to the ankle, the foot. There are 30 bones in each lower limb. These are the femur, patella, tibia, fibula, seven tarsal bones, five metatarsal bones, and 14 phalanges.

The femur is the single bone of the thigh. Its rounded head articulates with the acetabulum of the hip bone to form the hip joint. The head has the fovea capitis for attachment of the ligament of the head of the femur. The narrow neck joins inferiorly with the greater and lesser trochanters. Passing between these bony expansions are the intertrochanteric line on the anterior femur and the larger intertrochanteric crest on the posterior femur. On the posterior shaft of the femur is the gluteal tuberosity proximally and the linea aspera in the mid-shaft region. The expanded distal end consists of three articulating surfaces: the medial and lateral condyles, and the patellar surface. The outside margins of the condyles are the medial and lateral epicondyles. The adductor tubercle is on the superior aspect of the medial epicondyle.

The patella is a sesamoid bone located within a muscle tendon. It articulates with the patellar surface on the anterior side of the distal femur, thereby protecting the muscle tendon from rubbing against the femur.

The leg contains the large tibia on the medial side and the slender fibula on the lateral side. The tibia bears the weight of the body, whereas the fibula does not bear weight. The interosseous border of each bone is the attachment site for the interosseous membrane of the leg, the connective tissue sheet that unites the tibia and fibula.

The proximal tibia consists of the expanded medial and lateral condyles, which articulate with the medial and lateral condyles of the femur to form the knee joint. Between the tibial condyles is the intercondylar eminence. On the anterior side of the proximal tibia is the tibial tuberosity, which is continuous inferiorly with the anterior border of the tibia. On the posterior side, the proximal tibia has the curved soleal line. The bony expansion on the medial side of the distal tibia is the medial malleolus. The groove on the lateral side of the distal tibia is the fibular notch.

The head of the fibula forms the proximal end and articulates with the underside of the lateral condyle of the tibia. The distal fibula articulates with the fibular notch of the tibia. The expanded distal end of the fibula is the lateral malleolus.

The posterior foot is formed by the seven tarsal bones. The talus articulates superiorly with the distal tibia, the medial malleolus of the tibia, and the lateral malleolus of the fibula to form the ankle joint. The talus articulates inferiorly with the calcaneus bone. The sustentaculum tali of the calcaneus helps to support the talus. Anterior to the talus is the navicular bone, and anterior to this are the medial, intermediate, and lateral cuneiform bones. The cuboid bone is anterior to the calcaneus.

The five metatarsal bones form the anterior foot. The base of these bones articulate with the cuboid or cuneiform bones. The metatarsal heads, at their distal ends, articulate with the proximal phalanges of the toes. The big toe (toe number 1) has proximal and distal phalanx bones. The remaining toes have proximal, middle, and distal phalanges.

8.5 Development of the Appendicular Skeleton

The bones of the appendicular skeleton arise from embryonic mesenchyme. Limb buds appear at the end of the fourth week. The apical ectodermal ridge, located at the end of the limb bud, stimulates growth and elongation of the limb. During the sixth week, the distal end of the limb bud becomes paddle-shaped, and selective cell death separates the developing fingers and toes. At the same time, mesenchyme within the limb bud begins to differentiate into hyaline cartilage, forming models for future bones. During the seventh week, the upper limbs rotate laterally and the lower limbs rotate medially, bringing the limbs into their final positions.

Endochondral ossification, the process that converts the hyaline cartilage model into bone, begins in most appendicular bones by the twelfth fetal week. This begins as a primary ossification center in the diaphysis, followed by the later appearance of one or more secondary ossifications centers in the regions of the epiphyses. Each secondary ossification center is separated from the primary ossification center by an epiphyseal plate. Continued growth of the epiphyseal plate cartilage provides for bone lengthening. Disappearance of the epiphyseal plate is followed by fusion of the bony components to form a single, adult bone.

The clavicle develops via intramembranous ossification, in which mesenchyme is converted directly into bone tissue. Ossification within the clavicle begins during the fifth week of development and continues until 25 years of age.

INTERACTIVE LINK QUESTIONS

1. Watch this video (http://openstaxcollege.org/l/fractures) to see how fractures of the distal radius bone can affect the wrist joint. Explain the problems that may occur if a fracture of the distal radius involves the joint surface of the radiocarpal joint of the wrist.

2. Visit this site (http://openstaxcollege.org/l/handbone) to explore the bones and joints of the hand. What are the three arches of the hand, and what is the importance of these during the gripping of an object?

3. Watch this video (http://openstaxcollege.org/l/colles) to learn about a Colles fracture, a break of the distal radius, usually caused by falling onto an outstretched hand. When would surgery be required and how would the fracture be repaired in this case?

4. Watch this video (http://openstaxcollege.org/l/3Dpelvis) for a 3-D view of the pelvis and its associated ligaments. What is the large opening in the bony pelvis, located between the ischium and pubic regions, and what two parts of the pubis contribute to the formation of this opening?

5. Watch this video (http://openstaxcollege.org/l/midfemur) to view how a fracture of the mid-femur is surgically repaired. How are the two portions of the broken femur stabilized during surgical repair of a fractured femur?

6. Visit this site (http://openstaxcollege.org/l/kneesurgery) to perform a virtual knee replacement surgery. The prosthetic knee components must be properly aligned to function properly. How is this alignment ensured?

7. Use this tutorial (http://openstaxcollege.org/l/footbones) to review the bones of the foot. Which tarsal bones are in the proximal, intermediate, and distal groups?

8. View this link (http://openstaxcollege.org/l/bunion) to learn about a bunion, a localized swelling on the medial side of the foot, next to the first metatarsophalangeal joint, at the base of the big toe. What is a bunion and what type of shoe is most likely to cause this to develop?

9. Watch this animation (http://openstaxcollege.org/l/limbbuds) to follow the development and growth of the upper and lower limb buds. On what days of embryonic development do these events occur: (a) first appearance of the upper limb bud (limb ridge); (b) the flattening of the distal limb to form the handplate or footplate; and (c) the beginning of limb rotation?

REVIEW QUESTIONS

10. Which part of the clavicle articulates with the manubrium?
- a. shaft
- b. sternal end
- c. acromial end
- d. coracoid process

11. A shoulder separation results from injury to the _____.
- a. glenohumeral joint
- b. costoclavicular joint
- c. acromioclavicular joint
- d. sternoclavicular joint

12. Which feature lies between the spine and superior border of the scapula?
- a. suprascapular notch
- b. glenoid cavity
- c. superior angle
- d. supraspinous fossa

13. What structure is an extension of the spine of the scapula?
- a. acromion
- b. coracoid process
- c. supraglenoid tubercle
- d. glenoid cavity

14. Name the short, hook-like bony process of the scapula that projects anteriorly.
- a. acromial process
- b. clavicle
- c. coracoid process
- d. glenoid fossa

15. How many bones are there in the upper limbs combined?
- a. 20
- b. 30
- c. 40
- d. 60

16. Which bony landmark is located on the lateral side of the proximal humerus?
    a. greater tubercle
    b. trochlea
    c. lateral epicondyle
    d. lesser tubercle

17. Which region of the humerus articulates with the radius as part of the elbow joint?
    a. trochlea
    b. styloid process
    c. capitulum
    d. olecranon process

18. Which is the lateral-most carpal bone of the proximal row?
    a. trapezium
    b. hamate
    c. pisiform
    d. scaphoid

19. The radius bone _____.
    a. is found on the medial side of the forearm
    b. has a head that articulates with the radial notch of the ulna
    c. does not articulate with any of the carpal bones
    d. has the radial tuberosity located near its distal end

20. How many bones fuse in adulthood to form the hip bone?
    a. 2
    b. 3
    c. 4
    d. 5

21. Which component forms the superior part of the hip bone?
    a. ilium
    b. pubis
    c. ischium
    d. sacrum

22. Which of the following supports body weight when sitting?
    a. iliac crest
    b. ischial tuberosity
    c. ischiopubic ramus
    d. pubic body

23. The ischial spine is found between which of the following structures?
    a. inferior pubic ramus and ischial ramus
    b. pectineal line and arcuate line
    c. lesser sciatic notch and greater sciatic notch
    d. anterior superior iliac spine and posterior superior iliac spine

24. The pelvis _____.
    a. has a subpubic angle that is larger in females
    b. consists of the two hip bones, but does not include the sacrum or coccyx
    c. has an obturator foramen, an opening that is defined in part by the sacrospinous and sacrotuberous ligaments
    d. has a space located inferior to the pelvic brim called the greater pelvis

25. Which bony landmark of the femur serves as a site for muscle attachments?
    a. fovea capitis
    b. lesser trochanter
    c. head
    d. medial condyle

26. What structure contributes to the knee joint?
    a. lateral malleolus of the fibula
    b. tibial tuberosity
    c. medial condyle of the tibia
    d. lateral epicondyle of the femur

27. Which tarsal bone articulates with the tibia and fibula?

    a. calcaneus
    b. cuboid
    c. navicular
    d. talus

28. What is the total number of bones found in the foot and toes?
    a. 7
    b. 14
    c. 26
    d. 30

29. The tibia _____.
    a. has an expanded distal end called the lateral malleolus
    b. is not a weight-bearing bone
    c. is firmly anchored to the fibula by an interosseous membrane
    d. can be palpated (felt) under the skin only at its proximal and distal ends

30. Which event takes place during the seventh week of development?
    a. appearance of the upper and lower limb buds
    b. flattening of the distal limb bud into a paddle shape
    c. the first appearance of hyaline cartilage models of future bones
    d. the rotation of the limbs

31. During endochondral ossification of a long bone, _____.

   a. a primary ossification center will develop within the epiphysis

   b. mesenchyme will differentiate directly into bone tissue

   c. growth of the epiphyseal plate will produce bone lengthening

   d. all epiphyseal plates will disappear before birth

32. The clavicle _____.

   a. develops via intramembranous ossification

   b. develops via endochondral ossification

   c. is the last bone of the body to begin ossification

   d. is fully ossified at the time of birth

CRITICAL THINKING QUESTIONS

33. Describe the shape and palpable line formed by the clavicle and scapula.

34. Discuss two possible injuries of the pectoral girdle that may occur following a strong blow to the shoulder or a hard fall onto an outstretched hand.

35. Your friend runs out of gas and you have to help push his car. Discuss the sequence of bones and joints that convey the forces passing from your hand, through your upper limb and your pectoral girdle, and to your axial skeleton.

36. Name the bones in the wrist and hand, and describe or sketch out their locations and articulations.

37. Describe the articulations and ligaments that unite the four bones of the pelvis to each other.

38. Discuss the ways in which the female pelvis is adapted for childbirth.

39. Define the regions of the lower limb, name the bones found in each region, and describe the bony landmarks that articulate together to form the hip, knee, and ankle joints.

40. The talus bone of the foot receives the weight of the body from the tibia. The talus bone then distributes this weight toward the ground in two directions: one-half of the body weight is passed in a posterior direction and one-half of the weight is passed in an anterior direction. Describe the arrangement of the tarsal and metatarsal bones that are involved in both the posterior and anterior distribution of body weight.

41. How can a radiograph of a child's femur be used to determine the approximate age of that child?

42. How does the development of the clavicle differ from the development of other appendicular skeleton bones?

9 | JOINTS

Figure 9.1 Girl Kayaking   Without joints, body movements would be impossible. (credit: Graham Richardson/ flickr.com)

Introduction

Chapter Objectives

After this chapter, you will be able to:

- Discuss both functional and structural classifications for body joints
- Describe the characteristic features for fibrous, cartilaginous, and synovial joints and give examples of each
- Define and identify the different body movements
- Discuss the structure of specific body joints and the movements allowed by each
- Explain the development of body joints

The adult human body has 206 bones, and with the exception of the hyoid bone in the neck, each bone is connected to at least one other bone. Joints are the location where bones come together. Many joints allow for movement between the bones. At these joints, the articulating surfaces of the adjacent bones can move smoothly against each other. However, the bones of other joints may be joined to each other by connective tissue or cartilage. These joints are designed for stability and provide for little or no movement. Importantly, joint stability and movement are related to each other. This means that stable joints allow for little or no mobility between the adjacent bones. Conversely, joints that provide the most movement between bones are the least stable. Understanding the relationship between joint structure and function will help to explain why particular types of joints are found in certain areas of the body.

The articulating surfaces of bones at stable types of joints, with little or no mobility, are strongly united to each other. For example, most of the joints of the skull are held together by fibrous connective tissue and do not allow for movement between the adjacent bones. This lack of mobility is important, because the skull bones serve to protect the brain. Similarly, other joints united by fibrous connective tissue allow for very little movement, which provides stability and weight-bearing support for the body. For example, the tibia and fibula of the leg are tightly united to give stability to the body when standing. At other joints, the bones are held together by cartilage, which permits limited movements between the bones. Thus, the joints of the vertebral column only allow for small movements between adjacent vertebrae, but when added together, these movements provide the flexibility that allows your body to twist, or bend to the front, back, or side. In contrast, at joints that allow for wide ranges of motion, the articulating surfaces of the bones are not directly united to each other. Instead, these surfaces are enclosed within a space filled with lubricating fluid, which allows the bones to move smoothly against each other. These joints provide greater mobility, but since the bones are free to move in relation to each other, the joint is less stable. Most of the joints between the bones of the appendicular skeleton are this freely moveable type of joint. These joints allow the muscles of the body to pull on a bone and thereby produce movement of that body region. Your ability to kick a soccer ball, pick up a fork, and dance the tango depend on mobility at these types of joints.

9.1 | Classification of Joints

By the end of this section, you will be able to:

- Distinguish between the functional and structural classifications for joints
- Describe the three functional types of joints and give an example of each
- List the three types of diarthrodial joints

A **joint**, also called an **articulation**, is any place where adjacent bones or bone and cartilage come together (articulate with each other) to form a connection. Joints are classified both structurally and functionally. Structural classifications of joints take into account whether the adjacent bones are strongly anchored to each other by fibrous connective tissue or cartilage, or whether the adjacent bones articulate with each other within a fluid-filled space called a **joint cavity**. Functional classifications describe the degree of movement available between the bones, ranging from immobile, to slightly mobile, to freely moveable joints. The amount of movement available at a particular joint of the body is related to the functional requirements for that joint. Thus immobile or slightly moveable joints serve to protect internal organs, give stability to the body, and allow for limited body movement. In contrast, freely moveable joints allow for much more extensive movements of the body and limbs.

Structural Classification of Joints

The structural classification of joints is based on whether the articulating surfaces of the adjacent bones are directly connected by fibrous connective tissue or cartilage, or whether the articulating surfaces contact each other within a fluid-filled joint cavity. These differences serve to divide the joints of the body into three structural classifications. A **fibrous joint** is where the adjacent bones are united by fibrous connective tissue. At a **cartilaginous joint**, the bones are joined by hyaline cartilage or fibrocartilage. At a **synovial joint**, the articulating surfaces of the bones are not directly connected, but instead come into contact with each other within a joint cavity that is filled with a lubricating fluid. Synovial joints allow for free movement between the bones and are the most common joints of the body.

Functional Classification of Joints

The functional classification of joints is determined by the amount of mobility found between the adjacent bones. Joints are thus functionally classified as a synarthrosis or immobile joint, an amphiarthrosis or slightly moveable joint, or as a diarthrosis, which is a freely moveable joint (arthroun = "to fasten by a joint"). Depending on their location, fibrous joints may be functionally classified as a synarthrosis (immobile joint) or an amphiarthrosis (slightly mobile joint). Cartilaginous joints are also functionally classified as either a synarthrosis or an amphiarthrosis joint. All synovial joints are functionally classified as a diarthrosis joint.

Synarthrosis

An immobile or nearly immobile joint is called a **synarthrosis**. The immobile nature of these joints provide for a strong union between the articulating bones. This is important at locations where the bones provide protection for internal organs. Examples include sutures, the fibrous joints between the bones of the skull that surround and protect the brain (Figure 9.2), and the manubriosternal joint, the cartilaginous joint that unites the manubrium and body of the sternum for protection of the heart.

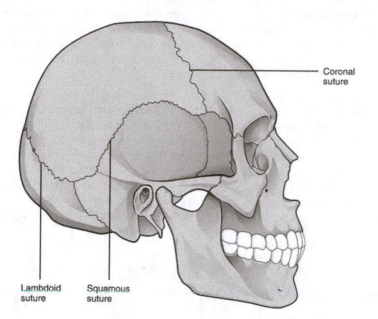

Figure 9.2 Suture Joints of Skull The suture joints of the skull are an example of a synarthrosis, an immobile or essentially immobile joint.

Amphiarthrosis

An **amphiarthrosis** is a joint that has limited mobility. An example of this type of joint is the cartilaginous joint that unites the bodies of adjacent vertebrae. Filling the gap between the vertebrae is a thick pad of fibrocartilage called an intervertebral disc (Figure 9.3). Each intervertebral disc strongly unites the vertebrae but still allows for a limited amount of movement between them. However, the small movements available between adjacent vertebrae can sum together along the length of the vertebral column to provide for large ranges of body movements.

Another example of an amphiarthrosis is the pubic symphysis of the pelvis. This is a cartilaginous joint in which the pubic regions of the right and left hip bones are strongly anchored to each other by fibrocartilage. This joint normally has very little mobility. The strength of the pubic symphysis is important in conferring weight-bearing stability to the pelvis.

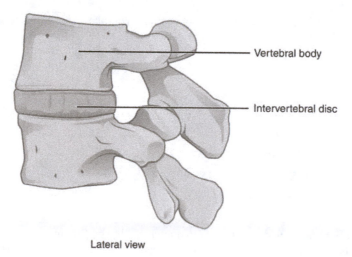

Lateral view

Figure 9.3 Intervertebral Disc An intervertebral disc unites the bodies of adjacent vertebrae within the vertebral column. Each disc allows for limited movement between the vertebrae and thus functionally forms an amphiarthrosis type of joint. Intervertebral discs are made of fibrocartilage and thereby structurally form a symphysis type of cartilaginous joint.

Diarthrosis

A freely mobile joint is classified as a **diarthrosis**. These types of joints include all synovial joints of the body, which provide the majority of body movements. Most diarthrotic joints are found in the appendicular skeleton and thus give the limbs a wide range of motion. These joints are divided into three categories, based on the number of axes of motion provided by each. An axis in anatomy is described as the movements in reference to the three anatomical planes: transverse, frontal, and sagittal. Thus, diarthroses are classified as uniaxial (for movement in one plane), biaxial (for movement in two planes), or multiaxial joints (for movement in all three anatomical planes).

A **uniaxial joint** only allows for a motion in a single plane (around a single axis). The elbow joint, which only allows for bending or straightening, is an example of a uniaxial joint. A **biaxial joint** allows for motions within two planes. An example of a biaxial joint is a metacarpophalangeal joint (knuckle joint) of the hand. The joint allows for movement along one axis to produce bending or straightening of the finger, and movement along a second axis, which allows for spreading of the fingers away from each other and bringing them together. A joint that allows for the several directions of movement is called a **multiaxial joint** (polyaxial or triaxial joint). This type of diarthrotic joint allows for movement along three axes (Figure 9.4). The shoulder and hip joints are multiaxial joints. They allow the upper or lower limb to move in an anterior-posterior direction and a medial-lateral direction. In addition, the limb can also be rotated around its long axis. This third movement results in rotation of the limb so that its anterior surface is moved either toward or away from the midline of the body.

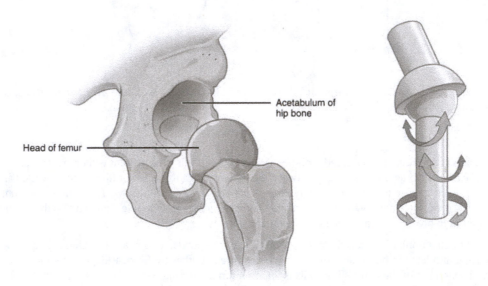

Figure 9.4 Multiaxial Joint A multiaxial joint, such as the hip joint, allows for three types of movement: anterior-posterior, medial-lateral, and rotational.

9.2 | Fibrous Joints

By the end of this section, you will be able to:

- Describe the structural features of fibrous joints
- Distinguish between a suture, syndesmosis, and gomphosis
- Give an example of each type of fibrous joint

At a fibrous joint, the adjacent bones are directly connected to each other by fibrous connective tissue, and thus the bones do not have a joint cavity between them (Figure 9.5). The gap between the bones may be narrow or wide. There are three types of fibrous joints. A suture is the narrow fibrous joint found between most bones of the skull. At a syndesmosis joint, the bones are more widely separated but are held together by a narrow band of fibrous connective tissue called a **ligament** or a wide sheet of connective tissue called an interosseous membrane. This type of fibrous joint is found between the shaft regions of the long bones in the forearm and in the leg. Lastly, a gomphosis is the narrow fibrous joint between the roots of a tooth and the bony socket in the jaw into which the tooth fits.

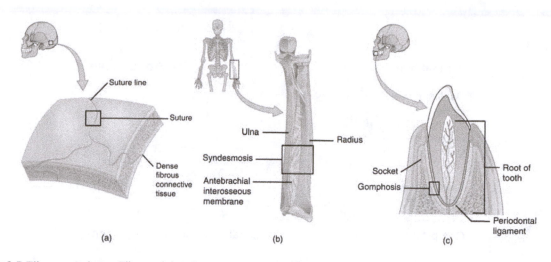

Figure 9.5 Fibrous Joints Fibrous joints form strong connections between bones. (a) Sutures join most bones of the skull. (b) An interosseous membrane forms a syndesmosis between the radius and ulna bones of the forearm. (c) A gomphosis is a specialized fibrous joint that anchors a tooth to its socket in the jaw.

Suture

All the bones of the skull, except for the mandible, are joined to each other by a fibrous joint called a **suture**. The fibrous connective tissue found at a suture ("to bind or sew") strongly unites the adjacent skull bones and thus helps to protect the brain and form the face. In adults, the skull bones are closely opposed and fibrous connective tissue fills the narrow gap between the bones. The suture is frequently convoluted, forming a tight union that prevents most movement between the bones. (See **Figure 9.5a**.) Thus, skull sutures are functionally classified as a synarthrosis, although some sutures may allow for slight movements between the cranial bones.

In newborns and infants, the areas of connective tissue between the bones are much wider, especially in those areas on the top and sides of the skull that will become the sagittal, coronal, squamous, and lambdoid sutures. These broad areas of connective tissue are called **fontanelles** (**Figure 9.6**). During birth, the fontanelles provide flexibility to the skull, allowing the bones to push closer together or to overlap slightly, thus aiding movement of the infant's head through the birth canal. After birth, these expanded regions of connective tissue allow for rapid growth of the skull and enlargement of the brain. The fontanelles greatly decrease in width during the first year after birth as the skull bones enlarge. When the connective tissue between the adjacent bones is reduced to a narrow layer, these fibrous joints are now called sutures. At some sutures, the connective tissue will ossify and be converted into bone, causing the adjacent bones to fuse to each other. This fusion between bones is called a **synostosis** ("joined by bone"). Examples of synostosis fusions between cranial bones are found both early and late in life. At the time of birth, the frontal and maxillary bones consist of right and left halves joined together by sutures, which disappear by the eighth year as the halves fuse together to form a single bone. Late in life, the sagittal, coronal, and lambdoid sutures of the skull will begin to ossify and fuse, causing the suture line to gradually disappear.

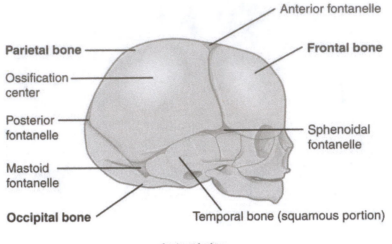

Figure 9.6 The Newborn Skull The fontanelles of a newborn's skull are broad areas of fibrous connective tissue that form fibrous joints between the bones of the skull.

Syndesmosis

A **syndesmosis** ("fastened with a band") is a type of fibrous joint in which two parallel bones are united to each other by fibrous connective tissue. The gap between the bones may be narrow, with the bones joined by ligaments, or the gap may be wide and filled in by a broad sheet of connective tissue called an **interosseous membrane**.

In the forearm, the wide gap between the shaft portions of the radius and ulna bones are strongly united by an interosseous membrane (see Figure 9.5**b**). Similarly, in the leg, the shafts of the tibia and fibula are also united by an interosseous membrane. In addition, at the distal tibiofibular joint, the articulating surfaces of the bones lack cartilage and the narrow gap between the bones is anchored by fibrous connective tissue and ligaments on both the anterior and posterior aspects of the joint. Together, the interosseous membrane and these ligaments form the tibiofibular syndesmosis.

The syndesmoses found in the forearm and leg serve to unite parallel bones and prevent their separation. However, a syndesmosis does not prevent all movement between the bones, and thus this type of fibrous joint is functionally classified as an amphiarthrosis. In the leg, the syndesmosis between the tibia and fibula strongly unites the bones, allows for little movement, and firmly locks the talus bone in place between the tibia and fibula at the ankle joint. This provides strength and stability to the leg and ankle, which are important during weight bearing. In the forearm, the interosseous membrane is flexible enough to allow for rotation of the radius bone during forearm movements. Thus in contrast to the stability provided by the tibiofibular syndesmosis, the flexibility of the antebrachial interosseous membrane allows for the much greater mobility of the forearm.

The interosseous membranes of the leg and forearm also provide areas for muscle attachment. Damage to a syndesmotic joint, which usually results from a fracture of the bone with an accompanying tear of the interosseous membrane, will produce pain, loss of stability of the bones, and may damage the muscles attached to the interosseous membrane. If the fracture site is not properly immobilized with a cast or splint, contractile activity by these muscles can cause improper alignment of the broken bones during healing.

Gomphosis

A **gomphosis** ("fastened with bolts") is the specialized fibrous joint that anchors the root of a tooth into its bony socket within the maxillary bone (upper jaw) or mandible bone (lower jaw) of the skull. A gomphosis is also known as a peg-and-socket joint. Spanning between the bony walls of the socket and the root of the tooth are numerous short bands of dense connective tissue, each of which is called a **periodontal ligament** (see Figure 9.5**c**). Due to the immobility of a gomphosis, this type of joint is functionally classified as a synarthrosis.

9.3 | Cartilaginous Joints

By the end of this section, you will be able to:

- Describe the structural features of cartilaginous joints
- Distinguish between a synchondrosis and symphysis
- Give an example of each type of cartilaginous joint

As the name indicates, at a cartilaginous joint, the adjacent bones are united by cartilage, a tough but flexible type of connective tissue. These types of joints lack a joint cavity and involve bones that are joined together by either hyaline cartilage or fibrocartilage (Figure 9.7). There are two types of cartilaginous joints. A synchondrosis is a cartilaginous joint where the bones are joined by hyaline cartilage. Also classified as a synchondrosis are places where bone is united to a cartilage structure, such as between the anterior end of a rib and the costal cartilage of the thoracic cage. The second type of cartilaginous joint is a symphysis, where the bones are joined by fibrocartilage.

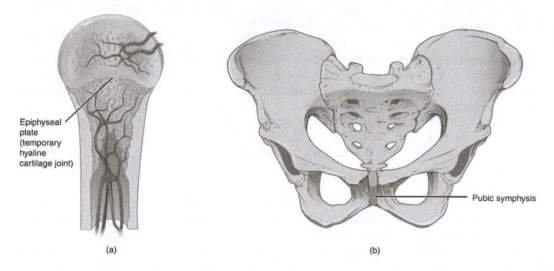

Figure 9.7 Cartiliginous Joints   At cartilaginous joints, bones are united by hyaline cartilage to form a synchondrosis or by fibrocartilage to form a symphysis. (a) The hyaline cartilage of the epiphyseal plate (growth plate) forms a synchondrosis that unites the shaft (diaphysis) and end (epiphysis) of a long bone and allows the bone to grow in length. (b) The pubic portions of the right and left hip bones of the pelvis are joined together by fibrocartilage, forming the pubic symphysis.

Synchondrosis

A **synchondrosis** ("joined by cartilage") is a cartilaginous joint where bones are joined together by hyaline cartilage, or where bone is united to hyaline cartilage. A synchondrosis may be temporary or permanent. A temporary synchondrosis is the epiphyseal plate (growth plate) of a growing long bone. The epiphyseal plate is the region of growing hyaline cartilage that unites the diaphysis (shaft) of the bone to the epiphysis (end of the bone). Bone lengthening involves growth of the epiphyseal plate cartilage and its replacement by bone, which adds to the diaphysis. For many years during childhood growth, the rates of cartilage growth and bone formation are equal and thus the epiphyseal plate does not change in overall thickness as the bone lengthens. During the late teens and early 20s, growth of the cartilage slows and eventually stops. The epiphyseal plate is then completely replaced by bone, and the diaphysis and epiphysis portions of the bone fuse together to form a single adult bone. This fusion of the diaphysis and epiphysis is a synostosis. Once this occurs, bone lengthening ceases. For this reason, the epiphyseal plate is considered to be a temporary synchondrosis. Because cartilage is softer than bone tissue, injury to a growing long bone can damage the epiphyseal plate cartilage, thus stopping bone growth and preventing additional bone lengthening.

Growing layers of cartilage also form synchondroses that join together the ilium, ischium, and pubic portions of the hip bone during childhood and adolescence. When body growth stops, the cartilage disappears and is replaced by bone, forming synostoses and fusing the bony components together into the single hip bone of the adult. Similarly, synostoses unite the sacral vertebrae that fuse together to form the adult sacrum.

Visit this **website (http://openstaxcollege.org/l/childhand)** to view a radiograph (X-ray image) of a child's hand and wrist. The growing bones of child have an epiphyseal plate that forms a synchondrosis between the shaft and end of a long bone. Being less dense than bone, the area of epiphyseal cartilage is seen on this radiograph as the dark epiphyseal gaps located near the ends of the long bones, including the radius, ulna, metacarpal, and phalanx bones. Which of the bones in this image do not show an epiphyseal plate (epiphyseal gap)?

Examples of permanent synchondroses are found in the thoracic cage. One example is the first sternocostal joint, where the first rib is anchored to the manubrium by its costal cartilage. (The articulations of the remaining costal cartilages to the sternum are all synovial joints.) Additional synchondroses are formed where the anterior end of the other 11 ribs is joined to its costal cartilage. Unlike the temporary synchondroses of the epiphyseal plate, these permanent synchondroses retain their hyaline cartilage and thus do not ossify with age. Due to the lack of movement between the bone and cartilage, both temporary and permanent synchondroses are functionally classified as a synarthrosis.

Symphysis

A cartilaginous joint where the bones are joined by fibrocartilage is called a **symphysis** ("growing together"). Fibrocartilage is very strong because it contains numerous bundles of thick collagen fibers, thus giving it a much greater ability to resist pulling and bending forces when compared with hyaline cartilage. This gives symphyses the ability to strongly unite the adjacent bones, but can still allow for limited movement to occur. Thus, a symphysis is functionally classified as an amphiarthrosis.

The gap separating the bones at a symphysis may be narrow or wide. Examples in which the gap between the bones is narrow include the pubic symphysis and the manubriosternal joint. At the pubic symphysis, the pubic portions of the right and left hip bones of the pelvis are joined together by fibrocartilage across a narrow gap. Similarly, at the manubriosternal joint, fibrocartilage unites the manubrium and body portions of the sternum.

The intervertebral symphysis is a wide symphysis located between the bodies of adjacent vertebrae of the vertebral column. Here a thick pad of fibrocartilage called an intervertebral disc strongly unites the adjacent vertebrae by filling the gap between them. The width of the intervertebral symphysis is important because it allows for small movements between the adjacent vertebrae. In addition, the thick intervertebral disc provides cushioning between the vertebrae, which is important when carrying heavy objects or during high-impact activities such as running or jumping.

9.4 | Synovial Joints

By the end of this section, you will be able to:

- Describe the structural features of a synovial joint
- Discuss the function of additional structures associated with synovial joints
- List the six types of synovial joints and give an example of each

Synovial joints are the most common type of joint in the body (**Figure 9.8**). A key structural characteristic for a synovial joint that is not seen at fibrous or cartilaginous joints is the presence of a joint cavity. This fluid-filled space is the site at which the articulating surfaces of the bones contact each other. Also unlike fibrous or cartilaginous joints, the articulating bone surfaces at a synovial joint are not directly connected to each other with fibrous connective tissue or cartilage. This gives the bones of a synovial joint the ability to move smoothly against each other, allowing for increased joint mobility.

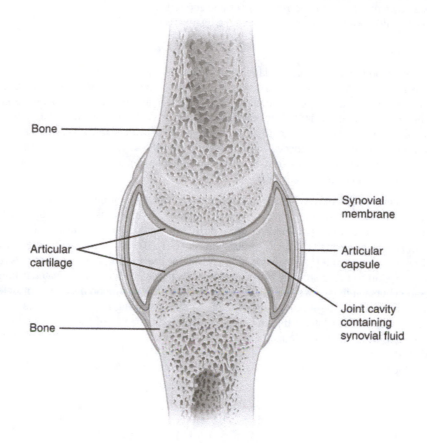

Figure 9.8 Synovial Joints Synovial joints allow for smooth movements between the adjacent bones. The joint is surrounded by an articular capsule that defines a joint cavity filled with synovial fluid. The articulating surfaces of the bones are covered by a thin layer of articular cartilage. Ligaments support the joint by holding the bones together and resisting excess or abnormal joint motions.

Structural Features of Synovial Joints

Synovial joints are characterized by the presence of a joint cavity. The walls of this space are formed by the **articular capsule**, a fibrous connective tissue structure that is attached to each bone just outside the area of the bone's articulating surface. The bones of the joint articulate with each other within the joint cavity.

Friction between the bones at a synovial joint is prevented by the presence of the **articular cartilage**, a thin layer of hyaline cartilage that covers the entire articulating surface of each bone. However, unlike at a cartilaginous joint, the articular cartilages of each bone are not continuous with each other. Instead, the articular cartilage acts like a Teflon® coating over the bone surface, allowing the articulating bones to move smoothly against each other without damaging the underlying bone tissue. Lining the inner surface of the articular capsule is a thin **synovial membrane**. The cells of this membrane secrete **synovial fluid** (synovia = "a thick fluid"), a thick, slimy fluid that provides lubrication to further reduce friction between the bones of the joint. This fluid also provides nourishment to the articular cartilage, which does not contain blood vessels. The ability of the bones to move smoothly against each other within the joint cavity, and the freedom of joint movement this provides, means that each synovial joint is functionally classified as a diarthrosis.

Outside of their articulating surfaces, the bones are connected together by ligaments, which are strong bands of fibrous connective tissue. These strengthen and support the joint by anchoring the bones together and preventing their separation. Ligaments allow for normal movements at a joint, but limit the range of these motions, thus preventing excessive or abnormal joint movements. Ligaments are classified based on their relationship to the fibrous articular capsule. An **extrinsic ligament** is located outside of the articular capsule, an **intrinsic ligament** is fused to or incorporated into the wall of the articular capsule, and an **intracapsular ligament** is located inside of the articular capsule.

At many synovial joints, additional support is provided by the muscles and their tendons that act across the joint. A **tendon** is the dense connective tissue structure that attaches a muscle to bone. As forces acting on a joint increase, the body will automatically increase the overall strength of contraction of the muscles crossing that joint, thus allowing the muscle and its tendon to serve as a "dynamic ligament" to resist forces and support the joint. This type of indirect support by muscles is very important at the shoulder joint, for example, where the ligaments are relatively weak.

Additional Structures Associated with Synovial Joints

A few synovial joints of the body have a fibrocartilage structure located between the articulating bones. This is called an **articular disc**, which is generally small and oval-shaped, or a **meniscus**, which is larger and C-shaped. These structures can serve several functions, depending on the specific joint. In some places, an articular disc may act to strongly unite the bones of the joint to each other. Examples of this include the articular discs found at the sternoclavicular joint or between the distal ends of the radius and ulna bones. At other synovial joints, the disc can provide shock absorption and cushioning between the bones, which is the function of each meniscus within the knee joint. Finally, an articular disc can serve to smooth the movements between the articulating bones, as seen at the temporomandibular joint. Some synovial joints also have a fat pad, which can serve as a cushion between the bones.

Additional structures located outside of a synovial joint serve to prevent friction between the bones of the joint and the overlying muscle tendons or skin. A **bursa** (plural = bursae) is a thin connective tissue sac filled with lubricating liquid. They are located in regions where skin, ligaments, muscles, or muscle tendons can rub against each other, usually near a body joint (**Figure 9.9**). Bursae reduce friction by separating the adjacent structures, preventing them from rubbing directly against each other. Bursae are classified by their location. A **subcutaneous bursa** is located between the skin and an underlying bone. It allows skin to move smoothly over the bone. Examples include the prepatellar bursa located over the kneecap and the olecranon bursa at the tip of the elbow. A **submuscular bursa** is found between a muscle and an underlying bone, or between adjacent muscles. These prevent rubbing of the muscle during movements. A large submuscular bursa, the trochanteric bursa, is found at the lateral hip, between the greater trochanter of the femur and the overlying gluteus maximus muscle. A **subtendinous bursa** is found between a tendon and a bone. Examples include the subacromial bursa that protects the tendon of shoulder muscle as it passes under the acromion of the scapula, and the suprapatellar bursa that separates the tendon of the large anterior thigh muscle from the distal femur just above the knee.

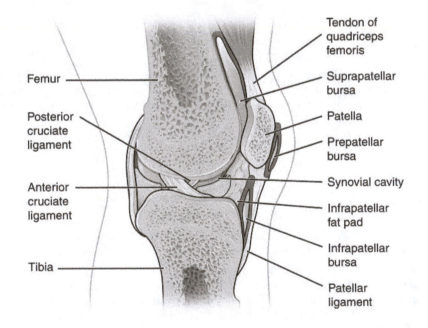

Figure 9.9 Bursae Bursae are fluid-filled sacs that serve to prevent friction between skin, muscle, or tendon and an underlying bone. Three major bursae and a fat pad are part of the complex joint that unites the femur and tibia of the leg.

A **tendon sheath** is similar in structure to a bursa, but smaller. It is a connective tissue sac that surrounds a muscle tendon at places where the tendon crosses a joint. It contains a lubricating fluid that allows for smooth motions of the tendon during muscle contraction and joint movements.

Homeostatic IMBALANCES

Bursitis

Bursitis is the inflammation of a bursa near a joint. This will cause pain, swelling, or tenderness of the bursa and surrounding area, and may also result in joint stiffness. Bursitis is most commonly associated with the bursae found at or near the shoulder, hip, knee, or elbow joints. At the shoulder, subacromial bursitis may occur in the bursa that separates the acromion of the scapula from the tendon of a shoulder muscle as it passes deep to the acromion. In the hip region, trochanteric bursitis can occur in the bursa that overlies the greater trochanter of the femur, just below the lateral side of the hip. Ischial bursitis occurs in the bursa that separates the skin from the ischial tuberosity of the pelvis, the bony structure that is weight bearing when sitting. At the knee, inflammation and swelling of the bursa located between the skin and patella bone is prepatellar bursitis ("housemaid's knee"), a condition more commonly seen today in roofers or floor and carpet installers who do not use knee pads. At the elbow, olecranon bursitis is inflammation of the bursa between the skin and olecranon process of the ulna. The olecranon forms the bony tip of the elbow, and bursitis here is also known as "student's elbow."

Bursitis can be either acute (lasting only a few days) or chronic. It can arise from muscle overuse, trauma, excessive or prolonged pressure on the skin, rheumatoid arthritis, gout, or infection of the joint. Repeated acute episodes of bursitis can result in a chronic condition. Treatments for the disorder include antibiotics if the bursitis is caused by an infection, or anti-inflammatory agents, such as nonsteroidal anti-inflammatory drugs (NSAIDs) or corticosteroids if the bursitis is due to trauma or overuse. Chronic bursitis may require that fluid be drained, but additional surgery is usually not required.

Types of Synovial Joints

Synovial joints are subdivided based on the shapes of the articulating surfaces of the bones that form each joint. The six types of synovial joints are pivot, hinge, condyloid, saddle, plane, and ball-and socket-joints (Figure 9.10).

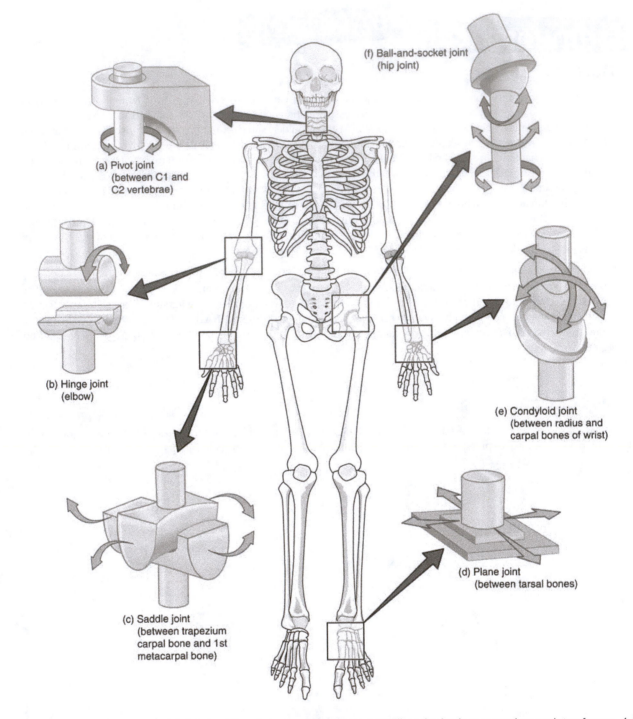

Figure 9.10 Types of Synovial Joints The six types of synovial joints allow the body to move in a variety of ways. (a) Pivot joints allow for rotation around an axis, such as between the first and second cervical vertebrae, which allows for side-to-side rotation of the head. (b) The hinge joint of the elbow works like a door hinge. (c) The articulation between the trapezium carpal bone and the first metacarpal bone at the base of the thumb is a saddle joint. (d) Plane joints, such as those between the tarsal bones of the foot, allow for limited gliding movements between bones. (e) The radiocarpal joint of the wrist is a condyloid joint. (f) The hip and shoulder joints are the only ball-and-socket joints of the body.

Pivot Joint

At a **pivot joint**, a rounded portion of a bone is enclosed within a ring formed partially by the articulation with another bone and partially by a ligament (see **Figure 9.10a**). The bone rotates within this ring. Since the rotation is around a single axis, pivot joints are functionally classified as a uniaxial diarthrosis type of joint. An example of a pivot joint is the atlantoaxial joint, found between the C1 (atlas) and C2 (axis) vertebrae. Here, the upward projecting dens of the axis articulates with the inner aspect of the atlas, where it is held in place by a ligament. Rotation at this joint allows you to turn your head from side to side. A second pivot joint is found at the **proximal radioulnar joint**. Here, the head of the radius is largely encircled by a ligament that holds it in place as it articulates with the radial notch of the ulna. Rotation of the radius allows for forearm movements.

Hinge Joint

In a **hinge joint**, the convex end of one bone articulates with the concave end of the adjoining bone (see Figure 9.10b). This type of joint allows only for bending and straightening motions along a single axis, and thus hinge joints are functionally classified as uniaxial joints. A good example is the elbow joint, with the articulation between the trochlea of the humerus and the trochlear notch of the ulna. Other hinge joints of the body include the knee, ankle, and interphalangeal joints between the phalanx bones of the fingers and toes.

Condyloid Joint

At a **condyloid joint** (ellipsoid joint), the shallow depression at the end of one bone articulates with a rounded structure from an adjacent bone or bones (see Figure 9.10e). The knuckle (metacarpophalangeal) joints of the hand between the distal end of a metacarpal bone and the proximal phalanx bone are condyloid joints. Another example is the radiocarpal joint of the wrist, between the shallow depression at the distal end of the radius bone and the rounded scaphoid, lunate, and triquetrum carpal bones. In this case, the articulation area has a more oval (elliptical) shape. Functionally, condyloid joints are biaxial joints that allow for two planes of movement. One movement involves the bending and straightening of the fingers or the anterior-posterior movements of the hand. The second movement is a side-to-side movement, which allows you to spread your fingers apart and bring them together, or to move your hand in a medial-going or lateral-going direction.

Saddle Joint

At a **saddle joint**, both of the articulating surfaces for the bones have a saddle shape, which is concave in one direction and convex in the other (see Figure 9.10c). This allows the two bones to fit together like a rider sitting on a saddle. Saddle joints are functionally classified as biaxial joints. The primary example is the first carpometacarpal joint, between the trapezium (a carpal bone) and the first metacarpal bone at the base of the thumb. This joint provides the thumb the ability to move away from the palm of the hand along two planes. Thus, the thumb can move within the same plane as the palm of the hand, or it can jut out anteriorly, perpendicular to the palm. This movement of the first carpometacarpal joint is what gives humans their distinctive "opposable" thumbs. The sternoclavicular joint is also classified as a saddle joint.

Plane Joint

At a **plane joint** (gliding joint), the articulating surfaces of the bones are flat or slightly curved and of approximately the same size, which allows the bones to slide against each other (see Figure 9.10d). The motion at this type of joint is usually small and tightly constrained by surrounding ligaments. Based only on their shape, plane joints can allow multiple movements, including rotation. Thus plane joints can be functionally classified as a multiaxial joint. However, not all of these movements are available to every plane joint due to limitations placed on it by ligaments or neighboring bones. Thus, depending upon the specific joint of the body, a plane joint may exhibit only a single type of movement or several movements. Plane joints are found between the carpal bones (intercarpal joints) of the wrist or tarsal bones (intertarsal joints) of the foot, between the clavicle and acromion of the scapula (acromioclavicular joint), and between the superior and inferior articular processes of adjacent vertebrae (zygapophysial joints).

Ball-and-Socket Joint

The joint with the greatest range of motion is the **ball-and-socket joint**. At these joints, the rounded head of one bone (the ball) fits into the concave articulation (the socket) of the adjacent bone (see Figure 9.10f). The hip joint and the glenohumeral (shoulder) joint are the only ball-and-socket joints of the body. At the hip joint, the head of the femur articulates with the acetabulum of the hip bone, and at the shoulder joint, the head of the humerus articulates with the glenoid cavity of the scapula.

Ball-and-socket joints are classified functionally as multiaxial joints. The femur and the humerus are able to move in both anterior-posterior and medial-lateral directions and they can also rotate around their long axis. The shallow socket formed by the glenoid cavity allows the shoulder joint an extensive range of motion. In contrast, the deep socket of the acetabulum and the strong supporting ligaments of the hip joint serve to constrain movements of the femur, reflecting the need for stability and weight-bearing ability at the hip.

Interactive LINK

Watch this **video (http://openstaxcollege.org/l/synjoints)** to see an animation of synovial joints in action. Synovial joints are places where bones articulate with each other inside of a joint cavity. The different types of synovial joints are the ball-and-socket joint (shoulder joint), hinge joint (knee), pivot joint (atlantoaxial joint, between C1 and C2 vertebrae of the neck), condyloid joint (radiocarpal joint of the wrist), saddle joint (first carpometacarpal joint, between the trapezium carpal bone and the first metacarpal bone, at the base of the thumb), and plane joint (facet joints of vertebral column, between superior and inferior articular processes). Which type of synovial joint allows for the widest range of motion?

Aging AND THE...

Joints

Arthritis is a common disorder of synovial joints that involves inflammation of the joint. This often results in significant joint pain, along with swelling, stiffness, and reduced joint mobility. There are more than 100 different forms of arthritis. Arthritis may arise from aging, damage to the articular cartilage, autoimmune diseases, bacterial or viral infections, or unknown (probably genetic) causes.

The most common type of arthritis is osteoarthritis, which is associated with aging and "wear and tear" of the articular cartilage (Figure 9.11). Risk factors that may lead to osteoarthritis later in life include injury to a joint; jobs that involve physical labor; sports with running, twisting, or throwing actions; and being overweight. These factors put stress on the articular cartilage that covers the surfaces of bones at synovial joints, causing the cartilage to gradually become thinner. As the articular cartilage layer wears down, more pressure is placed on the bones. The joint responds by increasing production of the lubricating synovial fluid, but this can lead to swelling of the joint cavity, causing pain and joint stiffness as the articular capsule is stretched. The bone tissue underlying the damaged articular cartilage also responds by thickening, producing irregularities and causing the articulating surface of the bone to become rough or bumpy. Joint movement then results in pain and inflammation. In its early stages, symptoms of osteoarthritis may be reduced by mild activity that "warms up" the joint, but the symptoms may worsen following exercise. In individuals with more advanced osteoarthritis, the affected joints can become more painful and therefore are difficult to use effectively, resulting in increased immobility. There is no cure for osteoarthritis, but several treatments can help alleviate the pain. Treatments may include lifestyle changes, such as weight loss and low-impact exercise, and over-the-counter or prescription medications that help to alleviate the pain and inflammation. For severe cases, joint replacement surgery (arthroplasty) may be required.

Joint replacement is a very invasive procedure, so other treatments are always tried before surgery. However arthroplasty can provide relief from chronic pain and can enhance mobility within a few months following the surgery. This type of surgery involves replacing the articular surfaces of the bones with prosthesis (artificial components). For example, in hip arthroplasty, the worn or damaged parts of the hip joint, including the head and neck of the femur and the acetabulum of the pelvis, are removed and replaced with artificial joint components. The replacement head for the femur consists of a rounded ball attached to the end of a shaft that is inserted inside the diaphysis of the femur. The acetabulum of the pelvis is reshaped and a replacement socket is fitted into its place. The parts, which are always built in advance of the surgery, are sometimes custom made to produce the best possible fit for a patient.

Gout is a form of arthritis that results from the deposition of uric acid crystals within a body joint. Usually only one or a few joints are affected, such as the big toe, knee, or ankle. The attack may only last a few days, but may return to the same or another joint. Gout occurs when the body makes too much uric acid or the kidneys do not properly excrete it. A diet with excessive fructose has been implicated in raising the chances of a susceptible individual developing gout.

Other forms of arthritis are associated with various autoimmune diseases, bacterial infections of the joint, or unknown genetic causes. Autoimmune diseases, including rheumatoid arthritis, scleroderma, or systemic lupus erythematosus, produce arthritis because the immune system of the body attacks the body joints. In rheumatoid arthritis, the joint capsule and synovial membrane become inflamed. As the disease progresses, the articular cartilage is severely damaged or destroyed, resulting in joint deformation, loss of movement, and severe disability. The most commonly involved joints are the hands, feet, and cervical spine, with corresponding joints on both sides of the body usually affected, though not always to the same extent. Rheumatoid arthritis is also associated with lung fibrosis, vasculitis (inflammation of blood vessels), coronary heart disease, and premature mortality. With no known cure, treatments are aimed at alleviating symptoms. Exercise, anti-inflammatory and pain medications, various specific disease-modifying anti-rheumatic drugs, or surgery are used to treat rheumatoid arthritis.

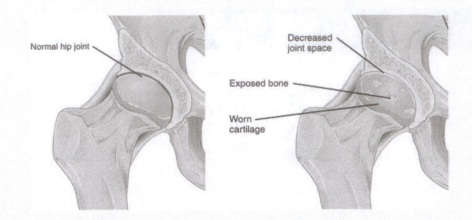

Figure 9.11 Osteoarthritis Osteoarthritis of a synovial joint results from aging or prolonged joint wear and tear. These cause erosion and loss of the articular cartilage covering the surfaces of the bones, resulting in inflammation that causes joint stiffness and pain.

Visit this website (http://openstaxcollege.org/l/gout) to learn about a patient who arrives at the hospital with joint pain and weakness in his legs. What caused this patient's weakness?

Watch this animation (http://openstaxcollege.org/l/hipreplace) to observe hip replacement surgery (total hip arthroplasty), which can be used to alleviate the pain and loss of joint mobility associated with osteoarthritis of the hip joint. What is the most common cause of hip disability?

Watch this **video (http://openstaxcollege.org/l/rheuarthritis)** to learn about the symptoms and treatments for rheumatoid arthritis. Which system of the body malfunctions in rheumatoid arthritis and what does this cause?

9.5 | Types of Body Movements

By the end of this section, you will be able to:

- Define the different types of body movements
- Identify the joints that allow for these motions

Synovial joints allow the body a tremendous range of movements. Each movement at a synovial joint results from the contraction or relaxation of the muscles that are attached to the bones on either side of the articulation. The type of movement that can be produced at a synovial joint is determined by its structural type. While the ball-and-socket joint gives the greatest range of movement at an individual joint, in other regions of the body, several joints may work together to produce a particular movement. Overall, each type of synovial joint is necessary to provide the body with its great flexibility and mobility. There are many types of movement that can occur at synovial joints (Table 9.1). Movement types are generally paired, with one being the opposite of the other. Body movements are always described in relation to the anatomical position of the body: upright stance, with upper limbs to the side of body and palms facing forward. Refer to Figure 9.12 as you go through this section.

Watch this **video (http://openstaxcollege.org/l/anatomical)** to learn about anatomical motions. What motions involve increasing or decreasing the angle of the foot at the ankle?

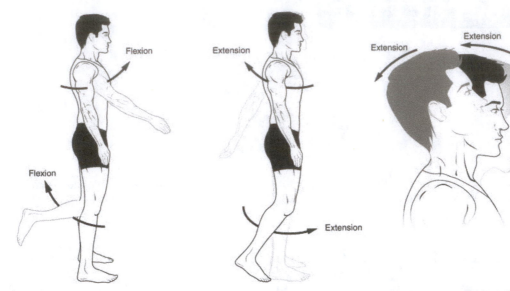

(a) and (b) Angular movements: flexion and extension at the shoulder and knees

(c) Angular movements: flexion and extension of the neck

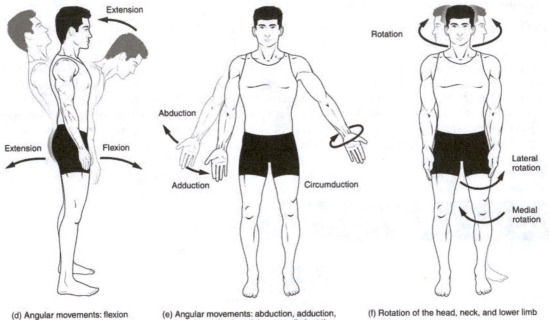

(d) Angular movements: flexion and extension of the vertebral column

(e) Angular movements: abduction, adduction, and circumduction of the upper limb at the shoulder

(f) Rotation of the head, neck, and lower limb

Figure 9.12 Movements of the Body, Part 1 Synovial joints give the body many ways in which to move. (a)–(b) Flexion and extension motions are in the sagittal (anterior–posterior) plane of motion. These movements take place at the shoulder, hip, elbow, knee, wrist, metacarpophalangeal, metatarsophalangeal, and interphalangeal joints. (c)–(d) Anterior bending of the head or vertebral column is flexion, while any posterior-going movement is extension. (e) Abduction and adduction are motions of the limbs, hand, fingers, or toes in the coronal (medial–lateral) plane of movement. Moving the limb or hand laterally away from the body, or spreading the fingers or toes, is abduction. Adduction brings the limb or hand toward or across the midline of the body, or brings the fingers or toes together. Circumduction is the movement of the limb, hand, or fingers in a circular pattern, using the sequential combination of flexion, adduction, extension, and abduction motions. Adduction/abduction and circumduction take place at the shoulder, hip, wrist, metacarpophalangeal, and metatarsophalangeal joints. (f) Turning of the head side to side or twisting of the body is rotation. Medial and lateral rotation of the upper limb at the shoulder or lower limb at the hip involves turning the anterior surface of the limb toward the midline of the body (medial or internal rotation) or away from the midline (lateral or external rotation).

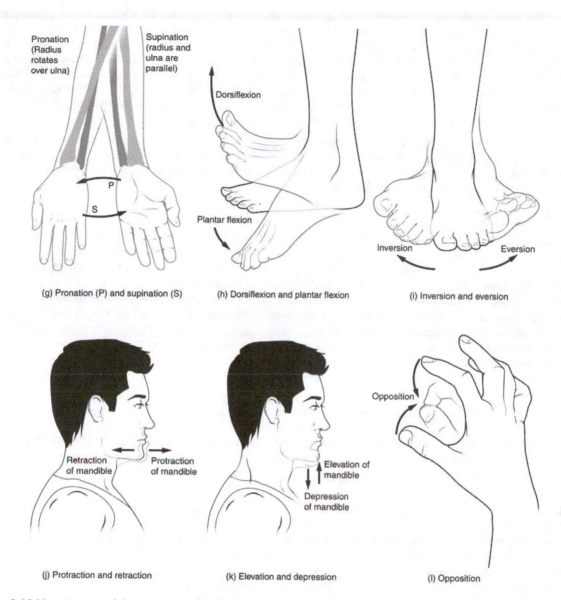

(g) Pronation (P) and supination (S)

(h) Dorsiflexion and plantar flexion

(i) Inversion and eversion

(j) Protraction and retraction

(k) Elevation and depression

(l) Opposition

Figure 9.13 Movements of the Body, Part 2 (g) Supination of the forearm turns the hand to the palm forward position in which the radius and ulna are parallel, while forearm pronation turns the hand to the palm backward position in which the radius crosses over the ulna to form an "X." (h) Dorsiflexion of the foot at the ankle joint moves the top of the foot toward the leg, while plantar flexion lifts the heel and points the toes. (i) Eversion of the foot moves the bottom (sole) of the foot away from the midline of the body, while foot inversion faces the sole toward the midline. (j) Protraction of the mandible pushes the chin forward, and retraction pulls the chin back. (k) Depression of the mandible opens the mouth, while elevation closes it. (l) Opposition of the thumb brings the tip of the thumb into contact with the tip of the fingers of the same hand and reposition brings the thumb back next to the index finger.

Flexion and Extension

Flexion and **extension** are movements that take place within the sagittal plane and involve anterior or posterior movements of the body or limbs. For the vertebral column, flexion (anterior flexion) is an anterior (forward) bending of the neck or body, while extension involves a posterior-directed motion, such as straightening from a flexed position or bending backward. **Lateral flexion** is the bending of the neck or body toward the right or left side. These movements of the vertebral column involve both the symphysis joint formed by each intervertebral disc, as well as the plane type of synovial joint formed between the inferior articular processes of one vertebra and the superior articular processes of the next lower vertebra.

In the limbs, flexion decreases the angle between the bones (bending of the joint), while extension increases the angle and straightens the joint. For the upper limb, all anterior-going motions are flexion and all posterior-going motions are extension.

These include anterior-posterior movements of the arm at the shoulder, the forearm at the elbow, the hand at the wrist, and the fingers at the metacarpophalangeal and interphalangeal joints. For the thumb, extension moves the thumb away from the palm of the hand, within the same plane as the palm, while flexion brings the thumb back against the index finger or into the palm. These motions take place at the first carpometacarpal joint. In the lower limb, bringing the thigh forward and upward is flexion at the hip joint, while any posterior-going motion of the thigh is extension. Note that extension of the thigh beyond the anatomical (standing) position is greatly limited by the ligaments that support the hip joint. Knee flexion is the bending of the knee to bring the foot toward the posterior thigh, and extension is the straightening of the knee. Flexion and extension movements are seen at the hinge, condyloid, saddle, and ball-and-socket joints of the limbs (see Figure 9.12a-d).

Hyperextension is the abnormal or excessive extension of a joint beyond its normal range of motion, thus resulting in injury. Similarly, **hyperflexion** is excessive flexion at a joint. Hyperextension injuries are common at hinge joints such as the knee or elbow. In cases of "whiplash" in which the head is suddenly moved backward and then forward, a patient may experience both hyperextension and hyperflexion of the cervical region.

Abduction and Adduction

Abduction and **adduction** motions occur within the coronal plane and involve medial-lateral motions of the limbs, fingers, toes, or thumb. Abduction moves the limb laterally away from the midline of the body, while adduction is the opposing movement that brings the limb toward the body or across the midline. For example, abduction is raising the arm at the shoulder joint, moving it laterally away from the body, while adduction brings the arm down to the side of the body. Similarly, abduction and adduction at the wrist moves the hand away from or toward the midline of the body. Spreading the fingers or toes apart is also abduction, while bringing the fingers or toes together is adduction. For the thumb, abduction is the anterior movement that brings the thumb to a 90° perpendicular position, pointing straight out from the palm. Adduction moves the thumb back to the anatomical position, next to the index finger. Abduction and adduction movements are seen at condyloid, saddle, and ball-and-socket joints (see Figure 9.12e).

Circumduction

Circumduction is the movement of a body region in a circular manner, in which one end of the body region being moved stays relatively stationary while the other end describes a circle. It involves the sequential combination of flexion, adduction, extension, and abduction at a joint. This type of motion is found at biaxial condyloid and saddle joints, and at multiaxial ball-and-sockets joints (see Figure 9.12e).

Rotation

Rotation can occur within the vertebral column, at a pivot joint, or at a ball-and-socket joint. Rotation of the neck or body is the twisting movement produced by the summation of the small rotational movements available between adjacent vertebrae. At a pivot joint, one bone rotates in relation to another bone. This is a uniaxial joint, and thus rotation is the only motion allowed at a pivot joint. For example, at the atlantoaxial joint, the first cervical (C1) vertebra (atlas) rotates around the dens, the upward projection from the second cervical (C2) vertebra (axis). This allows the head to rotate from side to side as when shaking the head "no." The proximal radioulnar joint is a pivot joint formed by the head of the radius and its articulation with the ulna. This joint allows for the radius to rotate along its length during pronation and supination movements of the forearm.

Rotation can also occur at the ball-and-socket joints of the shoulder and hip. Here, the humerus and femur rotate around their long axis, which moves the anterior surface of the arm or thigh either toward or away from the midline of the body. Movement that brings the anterior surface of the limb toward the midline of the body is called **medial (internal) rotation**. Conversely, rotation of the limb so that the anterior surface moves away from the midline is **lateral (external) rotation** (see Figure 9.12f). Be sure to distinguish medial and lateral rotation, which can only occur at the multiaxial shoulder and hip joints, from circumduction, which can occur at either biaxial or multiaxial joints.

Supination and Pronation

Supination and pronation are movements of the forearm. In the anatomical position, the upper limb is held next to the body with the palm facing forward. This is the **supinated position** of the forearm. In this position, the radius and ulna are parallel to each other. When the palm of the hand faces backward, the forearm is in the **pronated position**, and the radius and ulna form an X-shape.

Supination and pronation are the movements of the forearm that go between these two positions. **Pronation** is the motion that moves the forearm from the supinated (anatomical) position to the pronated (palm backward) position. This motion is produced by rotation of the radius at the proximal radioulnar joint, accompanied by movement of the radius at the distal radioulnar joint. The proximal radioulnar joint is a pivot joint that allows for rotation of the head of the radius. Because of the slight curvature of the shaft of the radius, this rotation causes the distal end of the radius to cross over the distal ulna at the distal radioulnar joint. This crossing over brings the radius and ulna into an X-shape position. **Supination** is the opposite motion, in which rotation of the radius returns the bones to their parallel positions and moves the palm to the anterior facing (supinated) position. It helps to remember that supination is the motion you use when scooping up soup with a spoon (see Figure 9.13g).

Dorsiflexion and Plantar Flexion

Dorsiflexion and **plantar flexion** are movements at the ankle joint, which is a hinge joint. Lifting the front of the foot, so that the top of the foot moves toward the anterior leg is dorsiflexion, while lifting the heel of the foot from the ground or pointing the toes downward is plantar flexion. These are the only movements available at the ankle joint (see Figure 9.13h).

Inversion and Eversion

Inversion and eversion are complex movements that involve the multiple plane joints among the tarsal bones of the posterior foot (intertarsal joints) and thus are not motions that take place at the ankle joint. **Inversion** is the turning of the foot to angle the bottom of the foot toward the midline, while **eversion** turns the bottom of the foot away from the midline. The foot has a greater range of inversion than eversion motion. These are important motions that help to stabilize the foot when walking or running on an uneven surface and aid in the quick side-to-side changes in direction used during active sports such as basketball, racquetball, or soccer (see Figure 9.13i).

Protraction and Retraction

Protraction and **retraction** are anterior-posterior movements of the scapula or mandible. Protraction of the scapula occurs when the shoulder is moved forward, as when pushing against something or throwing a ball. Retraction is the opposite motion, with the scapula being pulled posteriorly and medially, toward the vertebral column. For the mandible, protraction occurs when the lower jaw is pushed forward, to stick out the chin, while retraction pulls the lower jaw backward. (See Figure 9.13j.)

Depression and Elevation

Depression and **elevation** are downward and upward movements of the scapula or mandible. The upward movement of the scapula and shoulder is elevation, while a downward movement is depression. These movements are used to shrug your shoulders. Similarly, elevation of the mandible is the upward movement of the lower jaw used to close the mouth or bite on something, and depression is the downward movement that produces opening of the mouth (see Figure 9.13k).

Excursion

Excursion is the side to side movement of the mandible. **Lateral excursion** moves the mandible away from the midline, toward either the right or left side. **Medial excursion** returns the mandible to its resting position at the midline.

Superior Rotation and Inferior Rotation

Superior and inferior rotation are movements of the scapula and are defined by the direction of movement of the glenoid cavity. These motions involve rotation of the scapula around a point inferior to the scapular spine and are produced by combinations of muscles acting on the scapula. During **superior rotation**, the glenoid cavity moves upward as the medial end of the scapular spine moves downward. This is a very important motion that contributes to upper limb abduction. Without superior rotation of the scapula, the greater tubercle of the humerus would hit the acromion of the scapula, thus preventing any abduction of the arm above shoulder height. Superior rotation of the scapula is thus required for full abduction of the upper limb. Superior rotation is also used without arm abduction when carrying a heavy load with your hand or on your shoulder. You can feel this rotation when you pick up a load, such as a heavy book bag and carry it on only one shoulder. To increase its weight-bearing support for the bag, the shoulder lifts as the scapula superiorly rotates. **Inferior rotation** occurs during limb adduction and involves the downward motion of the glenoid cavity with upward movement of the medial end of the scapular spine.

Opposition and Reposition

Opposition is the thumb movement that brings the tip of the thumb in contact with the tip of a finger. This movement is produced at the first carpometacarpal joint, which is a saddle joint formed between the trapezium carpal bone and the first metacarpal bone. Thumb opposition is produced by a combination of flexion and abduction of the thumb at this joint. Returning the thumb to its anatomical position next to the index finger is called **reposition** (see Figure 9.13l).

Movements of the Joints

Type of Joint	Movement	Example
Pivot	Uniaxial joint; allows rotational movement	Atlantoaxial joint (C1–C2 vertebrae articulation); proximal radioulnar joint
Hinge	Uniaxial joint; allows flexion/extension movements	Knee; elbow; ankle; interphalangeal joints of fingers and toes
Condyloid	Biaxial joint; allows flexion/extension, abduction/adduction, and circumduction movements	Metacarpophalangeal (knuckle) joints of fingers; radiocarpal joint of wrist; metatarsophalangeal joints for toes
Saddle	Biaxial joint; allows flexion/extension, abduction/adduction, and circumduction movements	First carpometacarpal joint of the thumb; sternoclavicular joint
Plane	Multiaxial joint; allows inversion and eversion of foot, or flexion, extension, and lateral flexion of the vertebral column	Intertarsal joints of foot; superior-inferior articular process articulations between vertebrae
Ball-and-socket	Multiaxial joint; allows flexion/extension, abduction/adduction, circumduction, and medial/lateral rotation movements	Shoulder and hip joints

Table 9.1

9.6 | Anatomy of Selected Synovial Joints

By the end of this section, you will be able to:

- Describe the bones that articulate together to form selected synovial joints
- Discuss the movements available at each joint
- Describe the structures that support and prevent excess movements at each joint

Each synovial joint of the body is specialized to perform certain movements. The movements that are allowed are determined by the structural classification for each joint. For example, a multiaxial ball-and-socket joint has much more mobility than a uniaxial hinge joint. However, the ligaments and muscles that support a joint may place restrictions on the total range of motion available. Thus, the ball-and-socket joint of the shoulder has little in the way of ligament support, which gives the shoulder a very large range of motion. In contrast, movements at the hip joint are restricted by strong ligaments, which reduce its range of motion but confer stability during standing and weight bearing.

This section will examine the anatomy of selected synovial joints of the body. Anatomical names for most joints are derived from the names of the bones that articulate at that joint, although some joints, such as the elbow, hip, and knee joints are exceptions to this general naming scheme.

Articulations of the Vertebral Column

In addition to being held together by the intervertebral discs, adjacent vertebrae also articulate with each other at synovial joints formed between the superior and inferior articular processes called **zygapophysial joints** (facet joints) (see Figure 9.3). These are plane joints that provide for only limited motions between the vertebrae. The orientation of the articular processes at these joints varies in different regions of the vertebral column and serves to determine the types of motions available in each vertebral region. The cervical and lumbar regions have the greatest ranges of motions.

In the neck, the articular processes of cervical vertebrae are flattened and generally face upward or downward. This orientation provides the cervical vertebral column with extensive ranges of motion for flexion, extension, lateral flexion, and rotation. In the thoracic region, the downward projecting and overlapping spinous processes, along with the attached thoracic cage, greatly limit flexion, extension, and lateral flexion. However, the flattened and vertically positioned thoracic articular processes allow for the greatest range of rotation within the vertebral column. The lumbar region allows for considerable extension, flexion, and lateral flexion, but the orientation of the articular processes largely prohibits rotation.

The articulations formed between the skull, the atlas (C1 vertebra), and the axis (C2 vertebra) differ from the articulations in other vertebral areas and play important roles in movement of the head. The **atlanto-occipital joint** is formed by the articulations between the superior articular processes of the atlas and the occipital condyles on the base of the skull. This articulation has a pronounced U-shaped curvature, oriented along the anterior-posterior axis. This allows the skull to rock forward and backward, producing flexion and extension of the head. This moves the head up and down, as when shaking your head "yes."

The **atlantoaxial joint**, between the atlas and axis, consists of three articulations. The paired superior articular processes of the axis articulate with the inferior articular processes of the atlas. These articulating surfaces are relatively flat and oriented horizontally. The third articulation is the pivot joint formed between the dens, which projects upward from the body of the axis, and the inner aspect of the anterior arch of the atlas (Figure 9.14). A strong ligament passes posterior to the dens to hold it in position against the anterior arch. These articulations allow the atlas to rotate on top of the axis, moving the head toward the right or left, as when shaking your head "no."

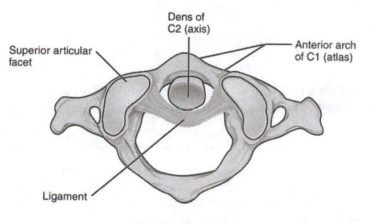

Superior view of atlas

Figure 9.14 Atlantoaxial Joint   The atlantoaxial joint is a pivot type of joint between the dens portion of the axis (C2 vertebra) and the anterior arch of the atlas (C1 vertebra), with the dens held in place by a ligament.

Temporomandibular Joint

The **temporomandibular joint (TMJ)** is the joint that allows for opening (mandibular depression) and closing (mandibular elevation) of the mouth, as well as side-to-side and protraction/retraction motions of the lower jaw. This joint involves the articulation between the mandibular fossa and articular tubercle of the temporal bone, with the condyle (head) of the mandible. Located between these bony structures, filling the gap between the skull and mandible, is a flexible articular disc (Figure 9.15). This disc serves to smooth the movements between the temporal bone and mandibular condyle.

Movement at the TMJ during opening and closing of the mouth involves both gliding and hinge motions of the mandible. With the mouth closed, the mandibular condyle and articular disc are located within the mandibular fossa of the temporal bone. During opening of the mouth, the mandible hinges downward and at the same time is pulled anteriorly, causing both the condyle and the articular disc to glide forward from the mandibular fossa onto the downward projecting articular tubercle. The net result is a forward and downward motion of the condyle and mandibular depression. The temporomandibular joint is supported by an extrinsic ligament that anchors the mandible to the skull. This ligament spans the distance between the base of the skull and the lingula on the medial side of the mandibular ramus.

Dislocation of the TMJ may occur when opening the mouth too wide (such as when taking a large bite) or following a blow to the jaw, resulting in the mandibular condyle moving beyond (anterior to) the articular tubercle. In this case, the individual would not be able to close his or her mouth. Temporomandibular joint disorder is a painful condition that may arise due to arthritis, wearing of the articular cartilage covering the bony surfaces of the joint, muscle fatigue from overuse or grinding of the teeth, damage to the articular disc within the joint, or jaw injury. Temporomandibular joint disorders can also cause headache, difficulty chewing, or even the inability to move the jaw (lock jaw). Pharmacologic agents for pain or other therapies, including bite guards, are used as treatments.

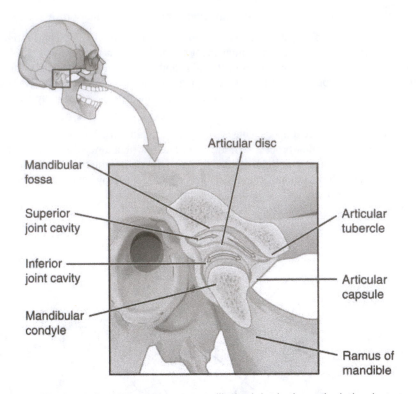

Figure 9.15 Temporomandibular Joint The temporomandibular joint is the articulation between the temporal bone of the skull and the condyle of the mandible, with an articular disc located between these bones. During depression of the mandible (opening of the mouth), the mandibular condyle moves both forward and hinges downward as it travels from the mandibular fossa onto the articular tubercle.

Watch this **video (http://openstaxcollege.org/l/TMJ)** to learn about TMJ. Opening of the mouth requires the combination of two motions at the temporomandibular joint, an anterior gliding motion of the articular disc and mandible and the downward hinging of the mandible. What is the initial movement of the mandible during opening and how much mouth opening does this produce?

Shoulder Joint

The shoulder joint is called the **glenohumeral joint**. This is a ball-and-socket joint formed by the articulation between the head of the humerus and the glenoid cavity of the scapula (**Figure 9.16**). This joint has the largest range of motion of any joint in the body. However, this freedom of movement is due to the lack of structural support and thus the enhanced mobility is offset by a loss of stability.

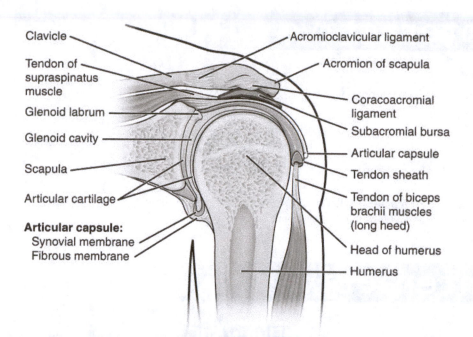

Figure 9.16 Glenohumeral Joint The glenohumeral (shoulder) joint is a ball-and-socket joint that provides the widest range of motions. It has a loose articular capsule and is supported by ligaments and the rotator cuff muscles.

The large range of motions at the shoulder joint is provided by the articulation of the large, rounded humeral head with the small and shallow glenoid cavity, which is only about one third of the size of the humeral head. The socket formed by the glenoid cavity is deepened slightly by a small lip of fibrocartilage called the **glenoid labrum**, which extends around the outer margin of the cavity. The articular capsule that surrounds the glenohumeral joint is relatively thin and loose to allow for large motions of the upper limb. Some structural support for the joint is provided by thickenings of the articular capsule wall that form weak intrinsic ligaments. These include the **coracohumeral ligament**, running from the coracoid process of the scapula to the anterior humerus, and three ligaments, each called a **glenohumeral ligament**, located on the anterior side of the articular capsule. These ligaments help to strengthen the superior and anterior capsule walls.

However, the primary support for the shoulder joint is provided by muscles crossing the joint, particularly the four rotator cuff muscles. These muscles (supraspinatus, infraspinatus, teres minor, and subscapularis) arise from the scapula and attach to the greater or lesser tubercles of the humerus. As these muscles cross the shoulder joint, their tendons encircle the head of the humerus and become fused to the anterior, superior, and posterior walls of the articular capsule. The thickening of the capsule formed by the fusion of these four muscle tendons is called the **rotator cuff**. Two bursae, the **subacromial bursa** and the **subscapular bursa**, help to prevent friction between the rotator cuff muscle tendons and the scapula as these tendons cross the glenohumeral joint. In addition to their individual actions of moving the upper limb, the rotator cuff muscles also serve to hold the head of the humerus in position within the glenoid cavity. By constantly adjusting their strength of contraction to resist forces acting on the shoulder, these muscles serve as "dynamic ligaments" and thus provide the primary structural support for the glenohumeral joint.

Injuries to the shoulder joint are common. Repetitive use of the upper limb, particularly in abduction such as during throwing, swimming, or racquet sports, may lead to acute or chronic inflammation of the bursa or muscle tendons, a tear of the glenoid labrum, or degeneration or tears of the rotator cuff. Because the humeral head is strongly supported by muscles and ligaments around its anterior, superior, and posterior aspects, most dislocations of the humerus occur in an inferior direction. This can occur when force is applied to the humerus when the upper limb is fully abducted, as when diving to catch a baseball and landing on your hand or elbow. Inflammatory responses to any shoulder injury can lead to the formation of scar tissue between the articular capsule and surrounding structures, thus reducing shoulder mobility, a condition called adhesive capsulitis ("frozen shoulder").

Watch this **video (http://openstaxcollege.org/l/shoulderjoint1)** for a tutorial on the anatomy of the shoulder joint. What movements are available at the shoulder joint?

Watch this **video (http://openstaxcollege.org/l/shoulderjoint2)** to learn more about the anatomy of the shoulder joint, including bones, joints, muscles, nerves, and blood vessels. What is the shape of the glenoid labrum in cross-section, and what is the importance of this shape?

Elbow Joint

The **elbow joint** is a uniaxial hinge joint formed by the **humeroulnar joint**, the articulation between the trochlea of the humerus and the trochlear notch of the ulna. Also associated with the elbow are the **humeroradial joint** and the proximal radioulnar joint. All three of these joints are enclosed within a single articular capsule (**Figure 9.17**).

The articular capsule of the elbow is thin on its anterior and posterior aspects, but is thickened along its outside margins by strong intrinsic ligaments. These ligaments prevent side-to-side movements and hyperextension. On the medial side is the triangular **ulnar collateral ligament**. This arises from the medial epicondyle of the humerus and attaches to the medial side of the proximal ulna. The strongest part of this ligament is the anterior portion, which resists hyperextension of the elbow. The ulnar collateral ligament may be injured by frequent, forceful extensions of the forearm, as is seen in baseball pitchers. Reconstructive surgical repair of this ligament is referred to as Tommy John surgery, named for the former major league pitcher who was the first person to have this treatment.

The lateral side of the elbow is supported by the **radial collateral ligament**. This arises from the lateral epicondyle of the humerus and then blends into the lateral side of the annular ligament. The **annular ligament** encircles the head of the radius. This ligament supports the head of the radius as it articulates with the radial notch of the ulna at the proximal radioulnar joint. This is a pivot joint that allows for rotation of the radius during supination and pronation of the forearm.

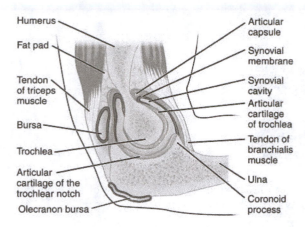

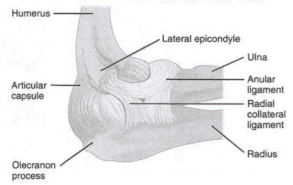

(a) Medial sagittal section through right elbow (lateral view)

(b) Lateral view of right elbow joint

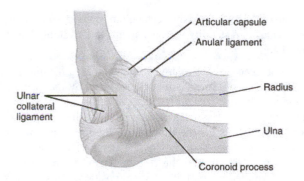

(c) Medial view of right elbow joint

Figure 9.17 Elbow Joint (a) The elbow is a hinge joint that allows only for flexion and extension of the forearm. (b) It is supported by the ulnar and radial collateral ligaments. (c) The annular ligament supports the head of the radius at the proximal radioulnar joint, the pivot joint that allows for rotation of the radius.

☞Interactive LINK

Watch this **animation (http://openstaxcollege.org/l/elbowjoint1)** to learn more about the anatomy of the elbow joint. Which structures provide the main stability for the elbow?

Interactive LINK

Watch this video (http://openstaxcollege.org/l/elbowjoint2) to learn more about the anatomy of the elbow joint, including bones, joints, muscles, nerves, and blood vessels. What are the functions of the articular cartilage?

Hip Joint

The hip joint is a multiaxial ball-and-socket joint between the head of the femur and the acetabulum of the hip bone (Figure 9.18). The hip carries the weight of the body and thus requires strength and stability during standing and walking. For these reasons, its range of motion is more limited than at the shoulder joint.

The acetabulum is the socket portion of the hip joint. This space is deep and has a large articulation area for the femoral head, thus giving stability and weight bearing ability to the joint. The acetabulum is further deepened by the **acetabular labrum**, a fibrocartilage lip attached to the outer margin of the acetabulum. The surrounding articular capsule is strong, with several thickened areas forming intrinsic ligaments. These ligaments arise from the hip bone, at the margins of the acetabulum, and attach to the femur at the base of the neck. The ligaments are the **iliofemoral ligament**, **pubofemoral ligament**, and **ischiofemoral ligament**, all of which spiral around the head and neck of the femur. The ligaments are tightened by extension at the hip, thus pulling the head of the femur tightly into the acetabulum when in the upright, standing position. Very little additional extension of the thigh is permitted beyond this vertical position. These ligaments thus stabilize the hip joint and allow you to maintain an upright standing position with only minimal muscle contraction. Inside of the articular capsule, the **ligament of the head of the femur** (ligamentum teres) spans between the acetabulum and femoral head. This intracapsular ligament is normally slack and does not provide any significant joint support, but it does provide a pathway for an important artery that supplies the head of the femur.

The hip is prone to osteoarthritis, and thus was the first joint for which a replacement prosthesis was developed. A common injury in elderly individuals, particularly those with weakened bones due to osteoporosis, is a "broken hip," which is actually a fracture of the femoral neck. This may result from a fall, or it may cause the fall. This can happen as one lower limb is taking a step and all of the body weight is placed on the other limb, causing the femoral neck to break and producing a fall. Any accompanying disruption of the blood supply to the femoral neck or head can lead to necrosis of these areas, resulting in bone and cartilage death. Femoral fractures usually require surgical treatment, after which the patient will need mobility assistance for a prolonged period, either from family members or in a long-term care facility. Consequentially, the associated health care costs of "broken hips" are substantial. In addition, hip fractures are associated with increased rates of morbidity (incidences of disease) and mortality (death). Surgery for a hip fracture followed by prolonged bed rest may lead to life-threatening complications, including pneumonia, infection of pressure ulcers (bedsores), and thrombophlebitis (deep vein thrombosis; blood clot formation) that can result in a pulmonary embolism (blood clot within the lung).

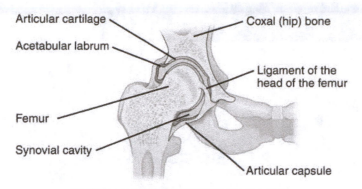

Articular cartilage

Coxal (hip) bone

Acetabular labrum

Ligament of the
head of the femur

Femur

Synovial cavity

Articular capsule

(a) Frontal section through the right hip joint

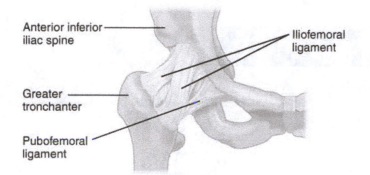

Anterior inferior
iliac spine

Iliofemoral
ligament

Greater
tronchanter

Pubofemoral
ligament

(b) Anterior view of right hip joint, capsule in place

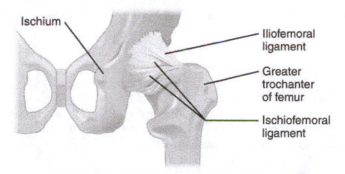

Ischium

Iliofemoral
ligament

Greater
trochanter
of femur

Ischiofemoral
ligament

(c) Posterior view of right hip joint, capsule in place

Figure 9.18 Hip Joint (a) The ball-and-socket joint of the hip is a multiaxial joint that provides both stability and a wide range of motion. (b–c) When standing, the supporting ligaments are tight, pulling the head of the femur into the acetabulum.

Watch this **video (http://openstaxcollege.org/l/hipjoint1)** for a tutorial on the anatomy of the hip joint. What is a possible consequence following a fracture of the femoral neck within the capsule of the hip joint?

Watch this **video (http://openstaxcollege.org/l/hipjoint2)** to learn more about the anatomy of the hip joint, including bones, joints, muscles, nerves, and blood vessels. Where is the articular cartilage thickest within the hip joint?

Knee Joint

The knee joint is the largest joint of the body (Figure 9.19). It actually consists of three articulations. The **femoropatellar joint** is found between the patella and the distal femur. The **medial tibiofemoral joint** and **lateral tibiofemoral joint** are located between the medial and lateral condyles of the femur and the medial and lateral condyles of the tibia. All of these articulations are enclosed within a single articular capsule. The knee functions as a hinge joint, allowing flexion and extension of the leg. This action is generated by both rolling and gliding motions of the femur on the tibia. In addition, some rotation of the leg is available when the knee is flexed, but not when extended. The knee is well constructed for weight bearing in its extended position, but is vulnerable to injuries associated with hyperextension, twisting, or blows to the medial or lateral side of the joint, particularly while weight bearing.

At the femoropatellar joint, the patella slides vertically within a groove on the distal femur. The patella is a sesamoid bone incorporated into the tendon of the quadriceps femoris muscle, the large muscle of the anterior thigh. The patella serves to protect the quadriceps tendon from friction against the distal femur. Continuing from the patella to the anterior tibia just below the knee is the **patellar ligament**. Acting via the patella and patellar ligament, the quadriceps femoris is a powerful muscle that acts to extend the leg at the knee. It also serves as a "dynamic ligament" to provide very important support and stabilization for the knee joint.

The medial and lateral tibiofemoral joints are the articulations between the rounded condyles of the femur and the relatively flat condyles of the tibia. During flexion and extension motions, the condyles of the femur both roll and glide over the surfaces of the tibia. The rolling action produces flexion or extension, while the gliding action serves to maintain the femoral condyles centered over the tibial condyles, thus ensuring maximal bony, weight-bearing support for the femur in all knee positions. As the knee comes into full extension, the femur undergoes a slight medial rotation in relation to tibia. The rotation results because the lateral condyle of the femur is slightly smaller than the medial condyle. Thus, the lateral condyle finishes its rolling motion first, followed by the medial condyle. The resulting small medial rotation of the femur serves to "lock" the knee into its fully extended and most stable position. Flexion of the knee is initiated by a slight lateral rotation of the femur on the tibia, which "unlocks" the knee. This lateral rotation motion is produced by the popliteus muscle of the posterior leg.

Located between the articulating surfaces of the femur and tibia are two articular discs, the **medial meniscus** and **lateral meniscus** (see Figure 9.19b). Each is a C-shaped fibrocartilage structure that is thin along its inside margin and thick along the outer margin. They are attached to their tibial condyles, but do not attach to the femur. While both menisci are free to move during knee motions, the medial meniscus shows less movement because it is anchored at its outer margin to the articular capsule and tibial collateral ligament. The menisci provide padding between the bones and help to fill the gap between the round femoral condyles and flattened tibial condyles. Some areas of each meniscus lack an arterial blood supply and thus these areas heal poorly if damaged.

The knee joint has multiple ligaments that provide support, particularly in the extended position (see Figure 9.19c). Outside of the articular capsule, located at the sides of the knee, are two extrinsic ligaments. The **fibular collateral ligament** (lateral collateral ligament) is on the lateral side and spans from the lateral epicondyle of the femur to the head of the fibula. The **tibial collateral ligament** (medial collateral ligament) of the medial knee runs from the medial epicondyle of the femur to the medial tibia. As it crosses the knee, the tibial collateral ligament is firmly attached on its deep side to the articular capsule and to the medial meniscus, an important factor when considering knee injuries. In the fully extended knee position, both collateral ligaments are taut (tight), thus serving to stabilize and support the extended knee and preventing side-to-side or rotational motions between the femur and tibia.

The articular capsule of the posterior knee is thickened by intrinsic ligaments that help to resist knee hyperextension. Inside the knee are two intracapsular ligaments, the **anterior cruciate ligament** and **posterior cruciate ligament**. These ligaments are anchored inferiorly to the tibia at the intercondylar eminence, the roughened area between the tibial condyles. The cruciate ligaments are named for whether they are attached anteriorly or posteriorly to this tibial region. Each ligament runs diagonally upward to attach to the inner aspect of a femoral condyle. The cruciate ligaments are named for the X-shape formed as they pass each other (cruciate means "cross"). The posterior cruciate ligament is the stronger ligament. It serves to support the knee when it is flexed and weight bearing, as when walking downhill. In this position, the posterior cruciate ligament prevents the femur from sliding anteriorly off the top of the tibia. The anterior cruciate ligament becomes tight when the knee is extended, and thus resists hyperextension.

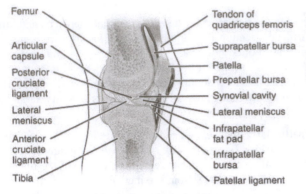

(a) Sagittal section through the right knee joint

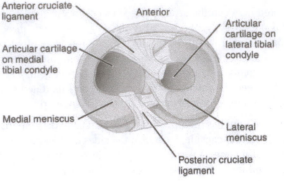

(b) Superior view of the right tibia in the knee joint, showing the menisci and cruciate ligaments

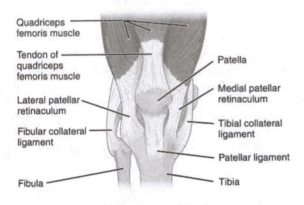

(c) Anterior view of right knee

Figure 9.19 Knee Joint　(a) The knee joint is the largest joint of the body. (b)–(c) It is supported by the tibial and fibular collateral ligaments located on the sides of the knee outside of the articular capsule, and the anterior and posterior cruciate ligaments found inside the capsule. The medial and lateral menisci provide padding and support between the femoral condyles and tibial condyles.

Watch this **video (http://openstaxcollege.org/l/flexext)** to learn more about the flexion and extension of the knee, as the femur both rolls and glides on the tibia to maintain stable contact between the bones in all knee positions. The patella glides along a groove on the anterior side of the distal femur. The collateral ligaments on the sides of the knee become tight in the fully extended position to help stabilize the knee. The posterior cruciate ligament supports the knee when flexed and the anterior cruciate ligament becomes tight when the knee comes into full extension to resist hyperextension. What are the ligaments that support the knee joint?

Interactive LINK

Watch this video (http://openstaxcollege.org/l/kneejoint1) to learn more about the anatomy of the knee joint, including bones, joints, muscles, nerves, and blood vessels. Which ligament of the knee keeps the tibia from sliding too far forward in relation to the femur and which ligament keeps the tibia from sliding too far backward?

isorders OF THE...

Joints

Injuries to the knee are common. Since this joint is primarily supported by muscles and ligaments, injuries to any of these structures will result in pain or knee instability. Injury to the posterior cruciate ligament occurs when the knee is flexed and the tibia is driven posteriorly, such as falling and landing on the tibial tuberosity or hitting the tibia on the dashboard when not wearing a seatbelt during an automobile accident. More commonly, injuries occur when forces are applied to the extended knee, particularly when the foot is planted and unable to move. Anterior cruciate ligament injuries can result with a forceful blow to the anterior knee, producing hyperextension, or when a runner makes a quick change of direction that produces both twisting and hyperextension of the knee.

A worse combination of injuries can occur with a hit to the lateral side of the extended knee (Figure 9.20). A moderate blow to the lateral knee will cause the medial side of the joint to open, resulting in stretching or damage to the tibial collateral ligament. Because the medial meniscus is attached to the tibial collateral ligament, a stronger blow can tear the ligament and also damage the medial meniscus. This is one reason that the medial meniscus is 20 times more likely to be injured than the lateral meniscus. A powerful blow to the lateral knee produces a "terrible triad" injury, in which there is a sequential injury to the tibial collateral ligament, medial meniscus, and anterior cruciate ligament.

Arthroscopic surgery has greatly improved the surgical treatment of knee injuries and reduced subsequent recovery times. This procedure involves a small incision and the insertion into the joint of an arthroscope, a pencil-thin instrument that allows for visualization of the joint interior. Small surgical instruments are also inserted via additional incisions. These tools allow a surgeon to remove or repair a torn meniscus or to reconstruct a ruptured cruciate ligament. The current method for anterior cruciate ligament replacement involves using a portion of the patellar ligament. Holes are drilled into the cruciate ligament attachment points on the tibia and femur, and the patellar ligament graft, with small areas of attached bone still intact at each end, is inserted into these holes. The bone-to-bone sites at each end of the graft heal rapidly and strongly, thus enabling a rapid recovery.

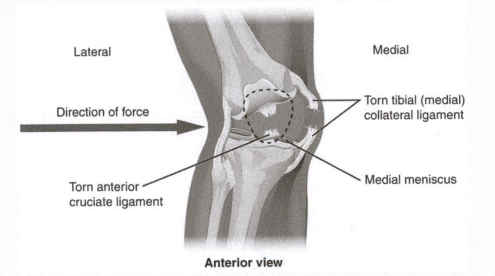

Anterior view

Figure 9.20 Knee Injury A strong blow to the lateral side of the extended knee will cause three injuries, in sequence: tearing of the tibial collateral ligament, damage to the medial meniscus, and rupture of the anterior cruciate ligament.

Interactive LINK

Watch this video (http://openstaxcollege.org/l/kneeinjury) to learn more about different knee injuries and diagnostic testing of the knee. What are the most common causes of anterior cruciate ligament injury?

Ankle and Foot Joints

The ankle is formed by the **talocrural joint** (Figure 9.21). It consists of the articulations between the talus bone of the foot and the distal ends of the tibia and fibula of the leg (crural = "leg"). The superior aspect of the talus bone is square-shaped and has three areas of articulation. The top of the talus articulates with the inferior tibia. This is the portion of the ankle joint that carries the body weight between the leg and foot. The sides of the talus are firmly held in position by the articulations with the medial malleolus of the tibia and the lateral malleolus of the fibula, which prevent any side-to-side motion of the talus. The ankle is thus a uniaxial hinge joint that allows only for dorsiflexion and plantar flexion of the foot.

Additional joints between the tarsal bones of the posterior foot allow for the movements of foot inversion and eversion. Most important for these movements is the **subtalar joint**, located between the talus and calcaneus bones. The joints between the talus and navicular bones and the calcaneus and cuboid bones are also important contributors to these movements. All of the joints between tarsal bones are plane joints. Together, the small motions that take place at these joints all contribute to the production of inversion and eversion foot motions.

Like the hinge joints of the elbow and knee, the talocrural joint of the ankle is supported by several strong ligaments located on the sides of the joint. These ligaments extend from the medial malleolus of the tibia or lateral malleolus of the fibula and anchor to the talus and calcaneus bones. Since they are located on the sides of the ankle joint, they allow for dorsiflexion and plantar flexion of the foot. They also prevent abnormal side-to-side and twisting movements of the talus and calcaneus bones during eversion and inversion of the foot. On the medial side is the broad **deltoid ligament**. The deltoid ligament supports the ankle joint and also resists excessive eversion of the foot. The lateral side of the ankle has several smaller ligaments. These include the **anterior talofibular ligament** and the **posterior talofibular ligament**, both of which span between the talus bone and the lateral malleolus of the fibula, and the **calcaneofibular ligament**, located between the calcaneus bone and fibula. These ligaments support the ankle and also resist excess inversion of the foot.

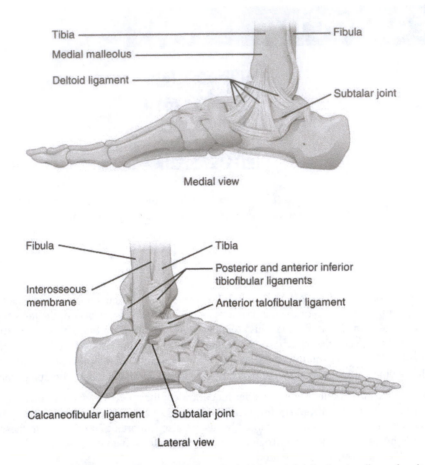

Medial view

Lateral view

Figure 9.21 Ankle Joint The talocrural (ankle) joint is a uniaxial hinge joint that only allows for dorsiflexion or plantar flexion of the foot. Movements at the subtalar joint, between the talus and calcaneus bones, combined with motions at other intertarsal joints, enables eversion/inversion movements of the foot. Ligaments that unite the medial or lateral malleolus with the talus and calcaneus bones serve to support the talocrural joint and to resist excess eversion or inversion of the foot.

Watch this **video (http://openstaxcollege.org/l/anklejoint1)** for a tutorial on the anatomy of the ankle joint. What are the three ligaments found on the lateral side of the ankle joint?

Interactive LINK

Watch this **video (http://openstaxcollege.org/l/anklejoint2)** to learn more about the anatomy of the ankle joint, including bones, joints, muscles, nerves, and blood vessels. Which type of joint used in woodworking does the ankle joint resemble?

Disorders OF THE...

Joints

The ankle is the most frequently injured joint in the body, with the most common injury being an inversion ankle sprain. A sprain is the stretching or tearing of the supporting ligaments. Excess inversion causes the talus bone to tilt laterally, thus damaging the ligaments on the lateral side of the ankle. The anterior talofibular ligament is most commonly injured, followed by the calcaneofibular ligament. In severe inversion injuries, the forceful lateral movement of the talus not only ruptures the lateral ankle ligaments, but also fractures the distal fibula.

Less common are eversion sprains of the ankle, which involve stretching of the deltoid ligament on the medial side of the ankle. Forcible eversion of the foot, for example, with an awkward landing from a jump or when a football player has a foot planted and is hit on the lateral ankle, can result in a Pott's fracture and dislocation of the ankle joint. In this injury, the very strong deltoid ligament does not tear, but instead shears off the medial malleolus of the tibia. This frees the talus, which moves laterally and fractures the distal fibula. In extreme cases, the posterior margin of the tibia may also be sheared off.

Above the ankle, the distal ends of the tibia and fibula are united by a strong syndesmosis formed by the interosseous membrane and ligaments at the distal tibiofibular joint. These connections prevent separation between the distal ends of the tibia and fibula and maintain the talus locked into position between the medial malleolus and lateral malleolus. Injuries that produce a lateral twisting of the leg on top of the planted foot can result in stretching or tearing of the tibiofibular ligaments, producing a syndesmotic ankle sprain or "high ankle sprain."

Most ankle sprains can be treated using the RICE technique: Rest, Ice, Compression, and Elevation. Reducing joint mobility using a brace or cast may be required for a period of time. More severe injuries involving ligament tears or bone fractures may require surgery.

☞Interactive LINK

Watch this **video (http://openstaxcollege.org/l/anklejoint3)** to learn more about the ligaments of the ankle joint, ankle sprains, and treatment. During an inversion ankle sprain injury, all three ligaments that resist excessive inversion of the foot may be injured. What is the sequence in which these three ligaments are injured?

9.7 | Development of Joints

By the end of this section, you will be able to:

- Describe the two processes by which mesenchyme can give rise to bone
- Discuss the process by which joints of the limbs are formed

Joints form during embryonic development in conjunction with the formation and growth of the associated bones. The embryonic tissue that gives rise to all bones, cartilages, and connective tissues of the body is called mesenchyme. In the head, mesenchyme will accumulate at those areas that will become the bones that form the top and sides of the skull. The mesenchyme in these areas will develop directly into bone through the process of intramembranous ossification, in which mesenchymal cells differentiate into bone-producing cells that then generate bone tissue. The mesenchyme between the areas of bone production will become the fibrous connective tissue that fills the spaces between the developing bones. Initially, the connective tissue-filled gaps between the bones are wide, and are called fontanelles. After birth, as the skull bones grow and enlarge, the gaps between them decrease in width and the fontanelles are reduced to suture joints in which the bones are united by a narrow layer of fibrous connective tissue.

The bones that form the base and facial regions of the skull develop through the process of endochondral ossification. In this process, mesenchyme accumulates and differentiates into hyaline cartilage, which forms a model of the future bone. The hyaline cartilage model is then gradually, over a period of many years, displaced by bone. The mesenchyme between these developing bones becomes the fibrous connective tissue of the suture joints between the bones in these regions of the skull.

A similar process of endochondral ossification gives rises to the bones and joints of the limbs. The limbs initially develop as small limb buds that appear on the sides of the embryo around the end of the fourth week of development. Starting during the sixth week, as each limb bud continues to grow and elongate, areas of mesenchyme within the bud begin to differentiate into the hyaline cartilage that will form models for of each of the future bones. The synovial joints will form between the adjacent cartilage models, in an area called the **joint interzone**. Cells at the center of this interzone region undergo cell death to form the joint cavity, while surrounding mesenchyme cells will form the articular capsule and supporting ligaments. The process of endochondral ossification, which converts the cartilage models into bone, begins by the twelfth week of embryonic development. At birth, ossification of much of the bone has occurred, but the hyaline cartilage of the epiphyseal plate will remain throughout childhood and adolescence to allow for bone lengthening. Hyaline cartilage is also retained as the articular cartilage that covers the surfaces of the bones at synovial joints.

KEY TERMS

abduction movement in the coronal plane that moves a limb laterally away from the body; spreading of the fingers

acetabular labrum lip of fibrocartilage that surrounds outer margin of the acetabulum on the hip bone

adduction movement in the coronal plane that moves a limb medially toward or across the midline of the body; bringing fingers together

amphiarthrosis slightly mobile joint

annular ligament intrinsic ligament of the elbow articular capsule that surrounds and supports the head of the radius at the proximal radioulnar joint

anterior cruciate ligament intracapsular ligament of the knee; extends from anterior, superior surface of the tibia to the inner aspect of the lateral condyle of the femur; resists hyperextension of knee

anterior talofibular ligament intrinsic ligament located on the lateral side of the ankle joint, between talus bone and lateral malleolus of fibula; supports talus at the talocrural joint and resists excess inversion of the foot

articular capsule connective tissue structure that encloses the joint cavity of a synovial joint

articular cartilage thin layer of hyaline cartilage that covers the articulating surfaces of bones at a synovial joint

articular disc meniscus; a fibrocartilage structure found between the bones of some synovial joints; provides padding or smooths movements between the bones; strongly unites the bones together

articulation joint of the body

atlanto-occipital joint articulation between the occipital condyles of the skull and the superior articular processes of the atlas (C1 vertebra)

atlantoaxial joint series of three articulations between the atlas (C1) vertebra and the axis (C2) vertebra, consisting of the joints between the inferior articular processes of C1 and the superior articular processes of C2, and the articulation between the dens of C2 and the anterior arch of C1

ball-and-socket joint synovial joint formed between the spherical end of one bone (the ball) that fits into the depression of a second bone (the socket); found at the hip and shoulder joints; functionally classified as a multiaxial joint

biaxial joint type of diarthrosis; a joint that allows for movements within two planes (two axes)

bursa connective tissue sac containing lubricating fluid that prevents friction between adjacent structures, such as skin and bone, tendons and bone, or between muscles

calcaneofibular ligament intrinsic ligament located on the lateral side of the ankle joint, between the calcaneus bone and lateral malleolus of the fibula; supports the talus bone at the ankle joint and resists excess inversion of the foot

cartilaginous joint joint at which the bones are united by hyaline cartilage (synchondrosis) or fibrocartilage (symphysis)

circumduction circular motion of the arm, thigh, hand, thumb, or finger that is produced by the sequential combination of flexion, abduction, extension, and adduction

condyloid joint synovial joint in which the shallow depression at the end of one bone receives a rounded end from a second bone or a rounded structure formed by two bones; found at the metacarpophalangeal joints of the fingers or the radiocarpal joint of the wrist; functionally classified as a biaxial joint

coracohumeral ligament intrinsic ligament of the shoulder joint; runs from the coracoid process of the scapula to the anterior humerus

deltoid ligament broad intrinsic ligament located on the medial side of the ankle joint; supports the talus at the talocrural joint and resists excess eversion of the foot

depression downward (inferior) motion of the scapula or mandible

diarthrosis freely mobile joint

dorsiflexion movement at the ankle that brings the top of the foot toward the anterior leg

elbow joint humeroulnar joint

elevation upward (superior) motion of the scapula or mandible

eversion foot movement involving the intertarsal joints of the foot in which the bottom of the foot is turned laterally, away from the midline

extension movement in the sagittal plane that increases the angle of a joint (straightens the joint); motion involving posterior bending of the vertebral column or returning to the upright position from a flexed position

extrinsic ligament ligament located outside of the articular capsule of a synovial joint

femoropatellar joint portion of the knee joint consisting of the articulation between the distal femur and the patella

fibrous joint joint where the articulating areas of the adjacent bones are connected by fibrous connective tissue

fibular collateral ligament extrinsic ligament of the knee joint that spans from the lateral epicondyle of the femur to the head of the fibula; resists hyperextension and rotation of the extended knee

flexion movement in the sagittal plane that decreases the angle of a joint (bends the joint); motion involving anterior bending of the vertebral column

fontanelles expanded areas of fibrous connective tissue that separate the braincase bones of the skull prior to birth and during the first year after birth

glenohumeral joint shoulder joint; articulation between the glenoid cavity of the scapula and head of the humerus; multiaxial ball-and-socket joint that allows for flexion/extension, abduction/adduction, circumduction, and medial/lateral rotation of the humerus

glenohumeral ligament one of the three intrinsic ligaments of the shoulder joint that strengthen the anterior articular capsule

glenoid labrum lip of fibrocartilage located around the outside margin of the glenoid cavity of the scapula

gomphosis type of fibrous joint in which the root of a tooth is anchored into its bony jaw socket by strong periodontal ligaments

hinge joint synovial joint at which the convex surface of one bone articulates with the concave surface of a second bone; includes the elbow, knee, ankle, and interphalangeal joints; functionally classified as a uniaxial joint

humeroradial joint articulation between the capitulum of the humerus and head of the radius

humeroulnar joint articulation between the trochlea of humerus and the trochlear notch of the ulna; uniaxial hinge joint that allows for flexion/extension of the forearm

hyperextension excessive extension of joint, beyond the normal range of movement

hyperflexion excessive flexion of joint, beyond the normal range of movement

iliofemoral ligament intrinsic ligament spanning from the ilium of the hip bone to the femur, on the superior-anterior aspect of the hip joint

inferior rotation movement of the scapula during upper limb adduction in which the glenoid cavity of the scapula moves in a downward direction as the medial end of the scapular spine moves in an upward direction

interosseous membrane wide sheet of fibrous connective tissue that fills the gap between two parallel bones, forming a syndesmosis; found between the radius and ulna of the forearm and between the tibia and fibula of the leg

intracapsular ligament ligament that is located within the articular capsule of a synovial joint

intrinsic ligament ligament that is fused to or incorporated into the wall of the articular capsule of a synovial joint

inversion foot movement involving the intertarsal joints of the foot in which the bottom of the foot is turned toward the midline

ischiofemoral ligament intrinsic ligament spanning from the ischium of the hip bone to the femur, on the posterior aspect of the hip joint

joint site at which two or more bones or bone and cartilage come together (articulate)

joint cavity space enclosed by the articular capsule of a synovial joint that is filled with synovial fluid and contains the articulating surfaces of the adjacent bones

joint interzone site within a growing embryonic limb bud that will become a synovial joint

lateral (external) rotation movement of the arm at the shoulder joint or the thigh at the hip joint that moves the anterior surface of the limb away from the midline of the body

lateral excursion side-to-side movement of the mandible away from the midline, toward either the right or left side

lateral flexion bending of the neck or body toward the right or left side

lateral meniscus C-shaped fibrocartilage articular disc located at the knee, between the lateral condyle of the femur and the lateral condyle of the tibia

lateral tibiofemoral joint portion of the knee consisting of the articulation between the lateral condyle of the tibia and the lateral condyle of the femur; allows for flexion/extension at the knee

ligament strong band of dense connective tissue spanning between bones

ligament of the head of the femur intracapsular ligament that runs from the acetabulum of the hip bone to the head of the femur

medial (internal) rotation movement of the arm at the shoulder joint or the thigh at the hip joint that brings the anterior surface of the limb toward the midline of the body

medial excursion side-to-side movement that returns the mandible to the midline

medial meniscus C-shaped fibrocartilage articular disc located at the knee, between the medial condyle of the femur and medial condyle of the tibia

medial tibiofemoral joint portion of the knee consisting of the articulation between the medial condyle of the tibia and the medial condyle of the femur; allows for flexion/extension at the knee

meniscus articular disc

multiaxial joint type of diarthrosis; a joint that allows for movements within three planes (three axes)

opposition thumb movement that brings the tip of the thumb in contact with the tip of a finger

patellar ligament ligament spanning from the patella to the anterior tibia; serves as the final attachment for the quadriceps femoris muscle

periodontal ligament band of dense connective tissue that anchors the root of a tooth into the bony jaw socket

pivot joint synovial joint at which the rounded portion of a bone rotates within a ring formed by a ligament and an articulating bone; functionally classified as uniaxial joint

plane joint synovial joint formed between the flattened articulating surfaces of adjacent bones; functionally classified as a multiaxial joint

plantar flexion foot movement at the ankle in which the heel is lifted off of the ground

posterior cruciate ligament intracapsular ligament of the knee; extends from the posterior, superior surface of the tibia to the inner aspect of the medial condyle of the femur; prevents anterior displacement of the femur when the knee is flexed and weight bearing

posterior talofibular ligament intrinsic ligament located on the lateral side of the ankle joint, between the talus bone and lateral malleolus of the fibula; supports the talus at the talocrural joint and resists excess inversion of the foot

pronated position forearm position in which the palm faces backward

pronation forearm motion that moves the palm of the hand from the palm forward to the palm backward position

protraction anterior motion of the scapula or mandible

proximal radioulnar joint articulation between head of radius and radial notch of ulna; uniaxial pivot joint that allows for rotation of radius during pronation/supination of forearm

pubofemoral ligament intrinsic ligament spanning from the pubis of the hip bone to the femur, on the anterior-inferior aspect of the hip joint

radial collateral ligament intrinsic ligament on the lateral side of the elbow joint; runs from the lateral epicondyle of humerus to merge with the annular ligament

reposition movement of the thumb from opposition back to the anatomical position (next to index finger)

retraction posterior motion of the scapula or mandible

rotation movement of a bone around a central axis (atlantoaxial joint) or around its long axis (proximal radioulnar joint; shoulder or hip joint); twisting of the vertebral column resulting from the summation of small motions between adjacent vertebrae

rotator cuff strong connective tissue structure formed by the fusion of four rotator cuff muscle tendons to the articular capsule of the shoulder joint; surrounds and supports superior, anterior, lateral, and posterior sides of the humeral head

saddle joint synovial joint in which the articulating ends of both bones are convex and concave in shape, such as at the first carpometacarpal joint at the base of the thumb; functionally classified as a biaxial joint

subacromial bursa bursa that protects the supraspinatus muscle tendon and superior end of the humerus from rubbing against the acromion of the scapula

subcutaneous bursa bursa that prevents friction between skin and an underlying bone

submuscular bursa bursa that prevents friction between bone and a muscle or between adjacent muscles

subscapular bursa bursa that prevents rubbing of the subscapularis muscle tendon against the scapula

subtalar joint articulation between the talus and calcaneus bones of the foot; allows motions that contribute to inversion/eversion of the foot

subtendinous bursa bursa that prevents friction between bone and a muscle tendon

superior rotation movement of the scapula during upper limb abduction in which the glenoid cavity of the scapula moves in an upward direction as the medial end of the scapular spine moves in a downward direction

supinated position forearm position in which the palm faces anteriorly (anatomical position)

supination forearm motion that moves the palm of the hand from the palm backward to the palm forward position

suture fibrous joint that connects the bones of the skull (except the mandible); an immobile joint (synarthrosis)

symphysis type of cartilaginous joint where the bones are joined by fibrocartilage

synarthrosis immobile or nearly immobile joint

synchondrosis type of cartilaginous joint where the bones are joined by hyaline cartilage

syndesmosis type of fibrous joint in which two separated, parallel bones are connected by an interosseous membrane

synostosis site at which adjacent bones or bony components have fused together

synovial fluid thick, lubricating fluid that fills the interior of a synovial joint

synovial joint joint at which the articulating surfaces of the bones are located within a joint cavity formed by an articular capsule

synovial membrane thin layer that lines the inner surface of the joint cavity at a synovial joint; produces the synovial fluid

talocrural joint ankle joint; articulation between the talus bone of the foot and medial malleolus of the tibia, distal tibia, and lateral malleolus of the fibula; a uniaxial hinge joint that allows only for dorsiflexion and plantar flexion of the foot

temporomandibular joint (TMJ) articulation between the condyle of the mandible and the mandibular fossa and articular tubercle of the temporal bone of the skull; allows for depression/elevation (opening/closing of mouth), protraction/retraction, and side-to-side motions of the mandible

tendon dense connective tissue structure that anchors a muscle to bone

tendon sheath connective tissue that surrounds a tendon at places where the tendon crosses a joint; contains a lubricating fluid to prevent friction and allow smooth movements of the tendon

tibial collateral ligament extrinsic ligament of knee joint that spans from the medial epicondyle of the femur to the medial tibia; resists hyperextension and rotation of extended knee

ulnar collateral ligament intrinsic ligament on the medial side of the elbow joint; spans from the medial epicondyle of the humerus to the medial ulna

uniaxial joint type of diarthrosis; joint that allows for motion within only one plane (one axis)

zygapophysial joints facet joints; plane joints between the superior and inferior articular processes of adjacent vertebrae that provide for only limited motions between the vertebrae

CHAPTER REVIEW

9.1 Classification of Joints

Structural classifications of the body joints are based on how the bones are held together and articulate with each other. At fibrous joints, the adjacent bones are directly united to each other by fibrous connective tissue. Similarly, at a cartilaginous joint, the adjacent bones are united by cartilage. In contrast, at a synovial joint, the articulating bone surfaces are not directly united to each other, but come together within a fluid-filled joint cavity.

The functional classification of body joints is based on the degree of movement found at each joint. A synarthrosis is a joint that is essentially immobile. This type of joint provides for a strong connection between the adjacent bones, which serves to protect internal structures such as the brain or heart. Examples include the fibrous joints of the skull sutures and the cartilaginous manubriosternal joint. A joint that allows for limited movement is an amphiarthrosis. An example is the pubic symphysis of the pelvis, the cartilaginous joint that strongly unites the right and left hip bones of the pelvis. The cartilaginous joints in which vertebrae are united by intervertebral discs provide for small movements between the adjacent vertebrae and are also an amphiarthrosis type of joint. Thus, based on their movement ability, both fibrous and cartilaginous joints are functionally classified as a synarthrosis or amphiarthrosis.

The most common type of joint is the diarthrosis, which is a freely moveable joint. All synovial joints are functionally classified as diarthroses. A uniaxial diarthrosis, such as the elbow, is a joint that only allows for movement within a single anatomical plane. Joints that allow for movements in two planes are biaxial joints, such as the metacarpophalangeal joints of the fingers. A multiaxial joint, such as the shoulder or hip joint, allows for three planes of motions.

9.2 Fibrous Joints

Fibrous joints are where adjacent bones are strongly united by fibrous connective tissue. The gap filled by connective tissue may be narrow or wide. The three types of fibrous joints are sutures, gomphoses, and syndesmoses. A suture is the narrow fibrous joint that unites most bones of the skull. At a gomphosis, the root of a tooth is anchored across a narrow gap by periodontal ligaments to the walls of its socket in the bony jaw. A syndesmosis is the type of fibrous joint found between parallel bones. The gap between the bones may be wide and filled with a fibrous interosseous membrane, or it may narrow with ligaments spanning between the bones. Syndesmoses are found between the bones of the forearm (radius and ulna) and the leg (tibia and fibula). Fibrous joints strongly unite adjacent bones and thus serve to provide protection for internal organs, strength to body regions, or weight-bearing stability.

9.3 Cartilaginous Joints

There are two types of cartilaginous joints. A synchondrosis is formed when the adjacent bones are united by hyaline cartilage. A temporary synchondrosis is formed by the epiphyseal plate of a growing long bone, which is lost when the epiphyseal plate ossifies as the bone reaches maturity. The synchondrosis is thus replaced by a synostosis. Permanent synchondroses that do not ossify are found at the first sternocostal joint and between the anterior ends of the bony ribs and the junction with their costal cartilage. A symphysis is where the bones are joined by fibrocartilage and the gap between the bones may be narrow or wide. A narrow symphysis is found at the manubriosternal joint and at the pubic symphysis. A wide symphysis is the intervertebral symphysis in which the bodies of adjacent vertebrae are united by an intervertebral disc.

9.4 Synovial Joints

Synovial joints are the most common type of joints in the body. They are characterized by the presence of a joint cavity, inside of which the bones of the joint articulate with each other. The articulating surfaces of the bones at a synovial joint are not directly connected to each other by connective tissue or cartilage, which allows the bones to move freely against each other. The walls of the joint cavity are formed by the articular capsule. Friction between the bones is reduced by a thin layer of articular cartilage covering the surfaces of the bones, and by a lubricating synovial fluid, which is secreted by the synovial membrane.

Synovial joints are strengthened by the presence of ligaments, which hold the bones together and resist excessive or abnormal movements of the joint. Ligaments are classified as extrinsic ligaments if they are located outside of the articular capsule, intrinsic ligaments if they are fused to the wall of the articular capsule, or intracapsular ligaments if they are located inside the articular capsule. Some synovial joints also have an articular disc (meniscus), which can provide padding between the bones, smooth their movements, or strongly join the bones together to strengthen the joint. Muscles and their tendons acting across a joint can also increase their contractile strength when needed, thus providing indirect support for the joint.

Bursae contain a lubricating fluid that serves to reduce friction between structures. Subcutaneous bursae prevent friction between the skin and an underlying bone, submuscular bursae protect muscles from rubbing against a bone or another muscle, and a subtendinous bursa prevents friction between bone and a muscle tendon. Tendon sheaths contain a lubricating fluid and surround tendons to allow for smooth movement of the tendon as it crosses a joint.

Based on the shape of the articulating bone surfaces and the types of movement allowed, synovial joints are classified into six types. At a pivot joint, one bone is held within a ring by a ligament and its articulation with a second bone. Pivot joints only allow for rotation around a single axis. These are found at the articulation between the C1 (atlas) and the dens of the C2 (axis) vertebrae, which provides the side-to-side rotation of the head, or at the proximal radioulnar joint between the head of the radius and the radial notch of the ulna, which allows for rotation of the radius during forearm movements. Hinge joints, such as at the elbow, knee, ankle, or interphalangeal joints between phalanx bones of the fingers and toes, allow only for bending and straightening of the joint. Pivot and hinge joints are functionally classified as uniaxial joints.

Condyloid joints are found where the shallow depression of one bone receives a rounded bony area formed by one or two bones. Condyloid joints are found at the base of the fingers (metacarpophalangeal joints) and at the wrist (radiocarpal joint). At a saddle joint, the articulating bones fit together like a rider and a saddle. An example is the first carpometacarpal joint located at the base of the thumb. Both condyloid and saddle joints are functionally classified as biaxial joints.

Plane joints are formed between the small, flattened surfaces of adjacent bones. These joints allow the bones to slide or rotate against each other, but the range of motion is usually slight and tightly limited by ligaments or surrounding bones. This type of joint is found between the articular processes of adjacent vertebrae, at the acromioclavicular joint, or at the intercarpal joints of the hand and intertarsal joints of the foot. Ball-and-socket joints, in which the rounded head of a bone fits into a large depression or socket, are found at the shoulder and hip joints. Both plane and ball-and-sockets joints are classified functionally as multiaxial joints. However, ball-and-socket joints allow for large movements, while the motions between bones at a plane joint are small.

9.5 Types of Body Movements

The variety of movements provided by the different types of synovial joints allows for a large range of body motions and gives you tremendous mobility. These movements allow you to flex or extend your body or limbs, medially rotate and adduct your arms and flex your elbows to hold a heavy object against your chest, raise your arms above your head, rotate or shake your head, and bend to touch the toes (with or without bending your knees).

Each of the different structural types of synovial joints also allow for specific motions. The atlantoaxial pivot joint provides side-to-side rotation of the head, while the proximal radioulnar articulation allows for rotation of the radius during pronation and supination of the forearm. Hinge joints, such as at the knee and elbow, allow only for flexion and extension. Similarly, the hinge joint of the ankle only allows for dorsiflexion and plantar flexion of the foot.

Condyloid and saddle joints are biaxial. These allow for flexion and extension, and abduction and adduction. The sequential combination of flexion, adduction, extension, and abduction produces circumduction. Multiaxial plane joints provide for only small motions, but these can add together over several adjacent joints to produce body movement, such as inversion and eversion of the foot. Similarly, plane joints allow for flexion, extension, and lateral flexion movements of the vertebral column. The multiaxial ball and socket joints allow for flexion-extension, abduction-adduction, and circumduction. In addition, these also allow for medial (internal) and lateral (external) rotation. Ball-and-socket joints have the greatest range of motion of all synovial joints.

9.6 Anatomy of Selected Synovial Joints

Although synovial joints share many common features, each joint of the body is specialized for certain movements and activities. The joints of the upper limb provide for large ranges of motion, which give the upper limb great mobility, thus enabling actions such as the throwing of a ball or typing on a keyboard. The joints of the lower limb are more robust, giving them greater strength and the stability needed to support the body weight during running, jumping, or kicking activities.

The joints of the vertebral column include the symphysis joints formed by each intervertebral disc and the plane synovial joints between the superior and inferior articular processes of adjacent vertebrae. Each of these joints provide for limited motions, but these sum together to produce flexion, extension, lateral flexion, and rotation of the neck and body. The range of motions available in each region of the vertebral column varies, with all of these motions available in the cervical region. Only rotation is allowed in the thoracic region, while the lumbar region has considerable extension, flexion, and lateral flexion, but rotation is prevented. The atlanto-occipital joint allows for flexion and extension of the head, while the atlantoaxial joint is a pivot joint that provides for rotation of the head.

The temporomandibular joint is the articulation between the condyle of the mandible and the mandibular fossa and articular tubercle of the skull temporal bone. An articular disc is located between the bony components of this joint. A combination of gliding and hinge motions of the mandibular condyle allows for elevation/depression, protraction/retraction, and side-to-side motions of the lower jaw.

The glenohumeral (shoulder) joint is a multiaxial ball-and-socket joint that provides flexion/extension, abduction/adduction, circumduction, and medial/lateral rotation of the humerus. The head of the humerus articulates with the glenoid cavity of the scapula. The glenoid labrum extends around the margin of the glenoid cavity. Intrinsic ligaments, including the coracohumeral ligament and glenohumeral ligaments, provide some support for the shoulder joint. However, the primary support comes from muscles crossing the joint whose tendons form the rotator cuff. These muscle tendons are protected from friction against the scapula by the subacromial bursa and subscapular bursa.

The elbow is a uniaxial hinge joint that allows for flexion/extension of the forearm. It includes the humeroulnar joint and the humeroradial joint. The medial elbow is supported by the ulnar collateral ligament and the radial collateral ligament supports the lateral side. These ligaments prevent side-to-side movements and resist hyperextension of the elbow. The proximal radioulnar joint is a pivot joint that allows for rotation of the radius during pronation/supination of the forearm. The annular ligament surrounds the head of the radius to hold it in place at this joint.

The hip joint is a ball-and-socket joint whose motions are more restricted than at the shoulder to provide greater stability during weight bearing. The hip joint is the articulation between the head of the femur and the acetabulum of the hip bone. The acetabulum is deepened by the acetabular labrum. The iliofemoral, pubofemoral, and ischiofemoral ligaments strongly support the hip joint in the upright, standing position. The ligament of the head of the femur provides little support but carries an important artery that supplies the femur.

The knee includes three articulations. The femoropatellar joint is between the patella and distal femur. The patella, a sesamoid bone incorporated into the tendon of the quadriceps femoris muscle of the anterior thigh, serves to protect this tendon from rubbing against the distal femur during knee movements. The medial and lateral tibiofemoral joints, between the condyles of the femur and condyles of the tibia, are modified hinge joints that allow for knee extension and flexion. During these movements, the condyles of the femur both roll and glide over the surface of the tibia. As the knee comes into full extension, a slight medial rotation of the femur serves to "lock" the knee into its most stable, weight-bearing position. The reverse motion, a small lateral rotation of the femur, is required to initiate knee flexion. When the knee is flexed, some rotation of the leg is available.

Two extrinsic ligaments, the tibial collateral ligament on the medial side and the fibular collateral ligament on the lateral side, serve to resist hyperextension or rotation of the extended knee joint. Two intracapsular ligaments, the anterior cruciate ligament and posterior cruciate ligament, span between the tibia and the inner aspects of the femoral condyles. The anterior cruciate ligament resists hyperextension of the knee, while the posterior cruciate ligament prevents anterior sliding of the femur, thus supporting the knee when it is flexed and weight bearing. The medial and lateral menisci, located between the femoral and tibial condyles, are articular discs that provide padding and improve the fit between the bones.

The talocrural joint forms the ankle. It consists of the articulation between the talus bone and the medial malleolus of the tibia, the distal end of the tibia, and the lateral malleolus of the fibula. This is a uniaxial hinge joint that allows only dorsiflexion and plantar flexion of the foot. Gliding motions at the subtalar and intertarsal joints of the foot allow for inversion/eversion of the foot. The ankle joint is supported on the medial side by the deltoid ligament, which prevents side-to-side motions of the talus at the talocrural joint and resists excessive eversion of the foot. The lateral ankle is supported by the anterior and posterior talofibular ligaments and the calcaneofibular ligament. These support the ankle joint and also resist excess inversion of the foot. An inversion ankle sprain, a common injury, will result in injury to one or more of these lateral ankle ligaments.

9.7 Development of Joints

During embryonic growth, bones and joints develop from mesenchyme, an embryonic tissue that gives rise to bone, cartilage, and fibrous connective tissues. In the skull, the bones develop either directly from mesenchyme through the process of intramembranous ossification, or indirectly through endochondral ossification, which initially forms a hyaline cartilage model of the future bone, which is later converted into bone. In both cases, the mesenchyme between the developing bones differentiates into fibrous connective tissue that will unite the skull bones at suture joints. In the limbs, mesenchyme accumulations within the growing limb bud will become a hyaline cartilage model for each of the limb bones. A joint interzone will develop between these areas of cartilage. Mesenchyme cells at the margins of the interzone will give rise to the articular capsule, while cell death at the center forms the space that will become the joint cavity of the future synovial joint. The hyaline cartilage model of each limb bone will eventually be converted into bone via the process of endochondral ossification. However, hyaline cartilage will remain, covering the ends of the adult bone as the articular cartilage.

INTERACTIVE LINK QUESTIONS

1. Go to this website (http://openstaxcollege.org/l/childhand) to view a radiograph (X-ray image) of a child's hand and wrist. The growing bones of child have an epiphyseal plate that forms a synchondrosis between the shaft and end of a long bone. Being less dense than bone, the area of epiphyseal cartilage is seen on this radiograph as the dark epiphyseal gaps located near the ends of the long bones, including the radius, ulna, metacarpal, and phalanx bones. Which of the bones in this image do not show an epiphyseal plate (epiphyseal gap)?

2. Watch this video (http://openstaxcollege.org/l/synjoints) to see an animation of synovial joints in action. Synovial joints are places where bones articulate with each other inside of a joint cavity. The different types of synovial joints are the ball-and-socket joint (shoulder joint), hinge joint (knee), pivot joint (atlantoaxial joint, between C1 and C2 vertebrae of the neck), condyloid joint (radiocarpal joint of the wrist), saddle joint (first carpometacarpal joint, between the trapezium carpal bone and the first metacarpal bone, at the base of the thumb), and plane joint (facet joints of vertebral column, between superior and inferior articular processes). Which type of synovial joint allows for the widest ranges of motion?

3. Visit this website (http://openstaxcollege.org/l/gout) to read about a patient who arrives at the hospital with joint pain and weakness in his legs. What caused this patient's weakness?

4. Watch this animation (http://openstaxcollege.org/l/hipreplace) to observe hip replacement surgery (total hip arthroplasty), which can be used to alleviate the pain and loss of joint mobility associated with osteoarthritis of the hip joint. What is the most common cause of hip disability?

5. Watch this video (http://openstaxcollege.org/l/rheuarthritis) to learn about the symptoms and treatments for rheumatoid arthritis. Which system of the body malfunctions in rheumatoid arthritis and what does this cause?

6. Watch this video (http://openstaxcollege.org/l/anatomical) to learn about anatomical motions. What motions involve increasing or decreasing the angle of the foot at the ankle?

7. Watch this video (http://openstaxcollege.org/l/TMJ) to learn about TMJ. Opening of the mouth requires the combination of two motions at the temporomandibular joint, an anterior gliding motion of the articular disc and mandible and the downward hinging of the mandible. What is the initial movement of the mandible during opening and how much mouth opening does this produce?

8. Watch this video (http://openstaxcollege.org/l/shoulderjoint1) for a tutorial on the anatomy of the shoulder joint. What movements are available at the shoulder joint?

9. Watch this video (http://openstaxcollege.org/l/shoulderjoint2) to learn about the anatomy of the shoulder joint, including bones, joints, muscles, nerves, and blood vessels. What is the shape of the glenoid labrum in cross-section, and what is the importance of this shape?

10. Watch this animation (http://openstaxcollege.org/l/elbowjoint1) to learn more about the anatomy of the elbow joint. What structures provide the main stability for the elbow?

11. Watch this video (http://openstaxcollege.org/l/elbowjoint2) to learn more about the anatomy of the elbow joint, including bones, joints, muscles, nerves, and blood vessels. What are the functions of the articular cartilage?

12. Watch this video (http://openstaxcollege.org/l/hipjoint1) for a tutorial on the anatomy of the hip joint. What is a possible consequence following a fracture of the femoral neck within the capsule of the hip joint?

13. Watch this video (http://openstaxcollege.org/l/hipjoint2) to learn more about the anatomy of the hip joint, including bones, joints, muscles, nerves, and blood vessels. Where is the articular cartilage thickest within the hip joint?

14. Watch this video (http://openstaxcollege.org/l/flexext) to learn more about the flexion and extension of the knee, as the femur both rolls and glides on the tibia to maintain stable contact between the bones in all knee positions. The patella glides along a groove on the anterior side of the distal femur. The collateral ligaments on the sides of the knee become tight in the fully extended position to help stabilize the knee. The posterior cruciate ligament supports the knee when flexed and the anterior cruciate ligament becomes tight when the knee comes into full extension to resist hyperextension. What are the ligaments that support the knee joint?

15. Watch this video (http://openstaxcollege.org/l/kneejoint1) to learn more about the anatomy of the knee joint, including bones, joints, muscles, nerves, and blood vessels. Which ligament of the knee keeps the tibia from sliding too far forward in relation to the femur and which ligament keeps the tibia from sliding too far backward?

16. Watch this video (http://openstaxcollege.org/l/kneeinjury) to learn more about different knee injuries and diagnostic testing of the knee. What are the most causes of anterior cruciate ligament injury?

17. Watch this video (http://openstaxcollege.org/l/anklejoint1) for a tutorial on the anatomy of the ankle joint. What are the three ligaments found on the lateral side of the ankle joint?

18. Watch this video (http://openstaxcollege.org/l/anklejoint2) to learn more about the anatomy of the ankle joint, including bones, joints, muscles, nerves, and blood vessels. The ankle joint resembles what type of joint used in woodworking?

19. Watch this video (http://openstaxcollege.org/l/anklejoint3) to learn about the ligaments of the ankle joint, ankle sprains, and treatment. During an inversion ankle sprain injury, all three ligaments that resist excessive inversion of the foot may be injured. What is the sequence in which these three ligaments are injured?

REVIEW QUESTIONS

20. The joint between adjacent vertebrae that includes an invertebral disc is classified as which type of joint?

    a. diarthrosis
    b. multiaxial
    c. amphiarthrosis
    d. synarthrosis

21. Which of these joints is classified as a synarthrosis?

    a. the pubic symphysis
    b. the manubriosternal joint
    c. an invertebral disc
    d. the shoulder joint

22. Which of these joints is classified as a biaxial diarthrosis?
    a. the metacarpophalangeal joint
    b. the hip joint
    c. the elbow joint
    d. the pubic symphysis

23. Synovial joints _____.
    a. may be functionally classified as a synarthrosis
    b. are joints where the bones are connected to each other by hyaline cartilage
    c. may be functionally classified as a amphiarthrosis
    d. are joints where the bones articulate with each other within a fluid-filled joint cavity

24. Which type of fibrous joint connects the tibia and fibula?
    a. syndesmosis
    b. symphysis
    c. suture
    d. gomphosis

25. An example of a wide fibrous joint is _____.

    a. the interosseous membrane of the forearm
    b. a gomphosis
    c. a suture joint
    d. a synostosis

26. A gomphosis _____.
    a. is formed by an interosseous membrane
    b. connects the tibia and fibula bones of the leg
    c. contains a joint cavity
    d. anchors a tooth to the jaw

27. A syndesmosis is _____.
    a. a narrow fibrous joint
    b. the type of joint that unites bones of the skull
    c. a fibrous joint that unites parallel bones
    d. the type of joint that anchors the teeth in the jaws

28. A cartilaginous joint _____.
    a. has a joint cavity
    b. is called a symphysis when the bones are united by fibrocartilage
    c. anchors the teeth to the jaws
    d. is formed by a wide sheet of fibrous connective tissue

29. A synchondrosis is _____.
    a. found at the pubic symphysis
    b. where bones are connected together with fibrocartilage
    c. a type of fibrous joint
    d. found at the first sternocostal joint of the thoracic cage

30. Which of the following are joined by a symphysis?
    a. adjacent vertebrae
    b. the first rib and the sternum
    c. the end and shaft of a long bone
    d. the radius and ulna bones

31. The epiphyseal plate of a growing long bone in a child is classified as a _____.
    a. synchondrosis
    b. synostosis
    c. symphysis
    d. syndesmosis

32. Which type of joint provides the greatest range of motion?
    a. ball-and-socket
    b. hinge
    c. condyloid
    d. plane

33. Which type of joint allows for only uniaxial movement?
    a. saddle joint
    b. hinge joint
    c. condyloid joint
    d. ball-and-socket joint

34. Which of the following is a type of synovial joint?

    a. a synostosis
    b. a suture
    c. a plane joint
    d. a synchondrosis

35. A bursa _____.
    a. surrounds a tendon at the point where the tendon crosses a joint
    b. secretes the lubricating fluid for a synovial joint
    c. prevents friction between skin and bone, or a muscle tendon and bone
    d. is the strong band of connective tissue that holds bones together at a synovial joint

36. At synovial joints, _____.
    a. the articulating ends of the bones are directly connected by fibrous connective tissue
    b. the ends of the bones are enclosed within a space called a subcutaneous bursa
    c. intrinsic ligaments are located entirely inside of the articular capsule
    d. the joint cavity is filled with a thick, lubricating fluid

37. At a synovial joint, the synovial membrane _____.

    a. forms the fibrous connective walls of the joint cavity
    b. is the layer of cartilage that covers the articulating surfaces of the bones
    c. forms the intracapsular ligaments
    d. secretes the lubricating synovial fluid

38. Condyloid joints _____.
   a. are a type of ball-and-socket joint
   b. include the radiocarpal joint
   c. are a uniaxial diarthrosis joint
   d. are found at the proximal radioulnar joint

39. A meniscus is _____.
   a. a fibrocartilage pad that provides padding between bones
   b. a fluid-filled space that prevents friction between a muscle tendon and underlying bone
   c. the articular cartilage that covers the ends of a bone at a synovial joint
   d. the lubricating fluid within a synovial joint

40. The joints between the articular processes of adjacent vertebrae can contribute to which movement?
   a. lateral flexion
   b. circumduction
   c. dorsiflexion
   d. abduction

41. Which motion moves the bottom of the foot away from the midline of the body?
   a. elevation
   b. dorsiflexion
   c. eversion
   d. plantar flexion

42. Movement of a body region in a circular movement at a condyloid joint is what type of motion?
   a. rotation
   b. elevation
   c. abduction
   d. circumduction

43. Supination is the motion that moves the _____.
   a. hand from the palm backward position to the palm forward position
   b. foot so that the bottom of the foot faces the midline of the body
   c. hand from the palm forward position to the palm backward position
   d. scapula in an upward direction

44. Movement at the shoulder joint that moves the upper limb laterally away from the body is called _____.
   a. elevation
   b. eversion
   c. abduction
   d. lateral rotation

45. The primary support for the glenohumeral joint is provided by the _____.
   a. coracohumeral ligament
   b. glenoid labrum
   c. rotator cuff muscles
   d. subacromial bursa

46. The proximal radioulnar joint _____.
   a. is supported by the annular ligament
   b. contains an articular disc that strongly unites the bones
   c. is supported by the ulnar collateral ligament
   d. is a hinge joint that allows for flexion/extension of the forearm

47. Which statement is true concerning the knee joint?
   a. The lateral meniscus is an intrinsic ligament located on the lateral side of the knee joint.
   b. Hyperextension is resisted by the posterior cruciate ligament.
   c. The anterior cruciate ligament supports the knee when it is flexed and weight bearing.
   d. The medial meniscus is attached to the tibial collateral ligament.

48. The ankle joint _____.
   a. is also called the subtalar joint
   b. allows for gliding movements that produce inversion/eversion of the foot
   c. is a uniaxial hinge joint
   d. is supported by the tibial collateral ligament on the lateral side

49. Which region of the vertebral column has the *greatest* range of motion for rotation?
   a. cervical
   b. thoracic
   c. lumbar
   d. sacral

50. Intramembranous ossification _____.
   a. gives rise to the bones of the limbs
   b. produces the bones of the top and sides of the skull
   c. produces the bones of the face and base of the skull
   d. involves the conversion of a hyaline cartilage model into bone

51. Synovial joints _____.
   a. are derived from fontanelles
   b. are produced by intramembranous ossification
   c. develop at an interzone site
   d. are produced by endochondral ossification

52. Endochondral ossification is _____.
   a. the process that replaces hyaline cartilage with bone tissue
   b. the process by which mesenchyme differentiates directly into bone tissue
   c. completed before birth
   d. the process that gives rise to the joint interzone and future joint cavity

CRITICAL THINKING QUESTIONS

53. Define how joints are classified based on function. Describe and give an example for each functional type of joint.

54. Explain the reasons for why joints differ in their degree of mobility.

55. Distinguish between a narrow and wide fibrous joint and give an example of each.

56. The periodontal ligaments are made of collagen fibers and are responsible for connecting the roots of the teeth to the jaws. Describe how scurvy, a disease that inhibits collagen production, can affect the teeth.

57. Describe the two types of cartilaginous joints and give examples of each.

58. Both functional and structural classifications can be used to describe an individual joint. Define the first sternocostal joint and the pubic symphysis using both functional and structural characteristics.

59. Describe the characteristic structures found at all synovial joints.

60. Describe the structures that provide direct and indirect support for a synovial joint.

61. Briefly define the types of joint movements available at a ball-and-socket joint.

62. Discuss the joints involved and movements required for you to cross your arms together in front of your chest.

63. Discuss the structures that contribute to support of the shoulder joint.

64. Describe the sequence of injuries that may occur if the extended, weight-bearing knee receives a very strong blow to the lateral side of the knee.

65. Describe how synovial joints develop within the embryonic limb.

66. Differentiate between endochondral and intramembranous ossification.

10 | MUSCLE TISSUE

Figure 10.1 Tennis Player Athletes rely on toned skeletal muscles to supply the force required for movement. (credit: Emmanuel Huybrechts/flickr)

Introduction

Chapter Objectives

After studying this chapter, you will be able to:

- Explain the organization of muscle tissue
- Describe the function and structure of skeletal, cardiac muscle, and smooth muscle
- Explain how muscles work with tendons to move the body
- Describe how muscles contract and relax
- Define the process of muscle metabolism
- Explain how the nervous system controls muscle tension
- Relate the connections between exercise and muscle performance
- Explain the development and regeneration of muscle tissue

When most people think of muscles, they think of the muscles that are visible just under the skin, particularly of the limbs. These are skeletal muscles, so-named because most of them move the skeleton. But there are two other types of muscle in the body, with distinctly different jobs. Cardiac muscle, found in the heart, is concerned with pumping blood through the circulatory system. Smooth muscle is concerned with various involuntary movements, such as having one's hair stand on end when cold or frightened, or moving food through the digestive system. This chapter will examine the structure and function of these three types of muscles.

10.1 | Overview of Muscle Tissues

By the end of this section, you will be able to:

- Describe the different types of muscle
- Explain contractibility and extensibility

Muscle is one of the four primary tissue types of the body, and the body contains three types of muscle tissue: skeletal muscle, cardiac muscle, and smooth muscle (Figure 10.2). All three muscle tissues have some properties in common; they all exhibit a quality called **excitability** as their plasma membranes can change their electrical states (from polarized to depolarized) and send an electrical wave called an action potential along the entire length of the membrane. While the nervous system can influence the excitability of cardiac and smooth muscle to some degree, skeletal muscle completely depends on signaling from the nervous system to work properly. On the other hand, both cardiac muscle and smooth muscle can respond to other stimuli, such as hormones and local stimuli.

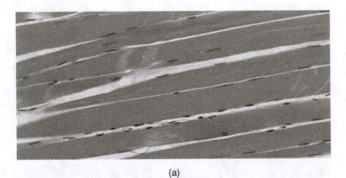

(a)

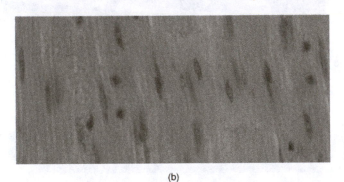

(b)

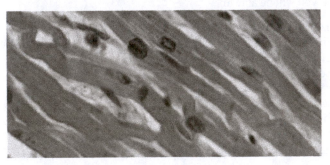

(c)

Figure 10.2 The Three Types of Muscle Tissue   The body contains three types of muscle tissue: (a) skeletal muscle, (b) smooth muscle, and (c) cardiac muscle. From top, LM × 1600, LM × 1600, LM × 1600. (Micrographs provided by the Regents of University of Michigan Medical School © 2012)

The muscles all begin the actual process of contracting (shortening) when a protein called actin is pulled by a protein called myosin. This occurs in striated muscle (skeletal and cardiac) after specific binding sites on the actin have been exposed in response to the interaction between calcium ions (Ca^{++}) and proteins (troponin and tropomyosin) that "shield" the actin-binding sites. Ca^{++} also is required for the contraction of smooth muscle, although its role is different: here Ca^{++} activates enzymes, which in turn activate myosin heads. All muscles require adenosine triphosphate (ATP) to continue the process of contracting, and they all relax when the Ca^{++} is removed and the actin-binding sites are re-shielded.

A muscle can return to its original length when relaxed due to a quality of muscle tissue called **elasticity**. It can recoil back to its original length due to elastic fibers. Muscle tissue also has the quality of **extensibility**; it can stretch or extend. **Contractility** allows muscle tissue to pull on its attachment points and shorten with force.

Differences among the three muscle types include the microscopic organization of their contractile proteins—actin and myosin. The actin and myosin proteins are arranged very regularly in the cytoplasm of individual muscle cells (referred to as fibers) in both skeletal muscle and cardiac muscle, which creates a pattern, or stripes, called striations. The striations are visible with a light microscope under high magnification (see Figure 10.2). **Skeletal muscle** fibers are multinucleated structures that compose the skeletal muscle. **Cardiac muscle** fibers each have one to two nuclei and are physically and electrically connected to each other so that the entire heart contracts as one unit (called a syncytium).

Because the actin and myosin are not arranged in such regular fashion in **smooth muscle**, the cytoplasm of a smooth muscle fiber (which has only a single nucleus) has a uniform, nonstriated appearance (resulting in the name smooth muscle). However, the less organized appearance of smooth muscle should not be interpreted as less efficient. Smooth muscle in the walls of arteries is a critical component that regulates blood pressure necessary to push blood through the circulatory system; and smooth muscle in the skin, visceral organs, and internal passageways is essential for moving all materials through the body.

10.2 | Skeletal Muscle

By the end of this section, you will be able to:

- Describe the layers of connective tissues packaging skeletal muscle
- Explain how muscles work with tendons to move the body
- Identify areas of the skeletal muscle fibers
- Describe excitation-contraction coupling

The best-known feature of skeletal muscle is its ability to contract and cause movement. Skeletal muscles act not only to produce movement but also to stop movement, such as resisting gravity to maintain posture. Small, constant adjustments of the skeletal muscles are needed to hold a body upright or balanced in any position. Muscles also prevent excess movement of the bones and joints, maintaining skeletal stability and preventing skeletal structure damage or deformation. Joints can become misaligned or dislocated entirely by pulling on the associated bones; muscles work to keep joints stable. Skeletal muscles are located throughout the body at the openings of internal tracts to control the movement of various substances. These muscles allow functions, such as swallowing, urination, and defecation, to be under voluntary control. Skeletal muscles also protect internal organs (particularly abdominal and pelvic organs) by acting as an external barrier or shield to external trauma and by supporting the weight of the organs.

Skeletal muscles contribute to the maintenance of homeostasis in the body by generating heat. Muscle contraction requires energy, and when ATP is broken down, heat is produced. This heat is very noticeable during exercise, when sustained muscle movement causes body temperature to rise, and in cases of extreme cold, when shivering produces random skeletal muscle contractions to generate heat.

Each skeletal muscle is an organ that consists of various integrated tissues. These tissues include the skeletal muscle fibers, blood vessels, nerve fibers, and connective tissue. Each skeletal muscle has three layers of connective tissue (called "mysia") that enclose it and provide structure to the muscle as a whole, and also compartmentalize the muscle fibers within the muscle (Figure 10.3). Each muscle is wrapped in a sheath of dense, irregular connective tissue called the **epimysium**, which allows a muscle to contract and move powerfully while maintaining its structural integrity. The epimysium also separates muscle from other tissues and organs in the area, allowing the muscle to move independently.

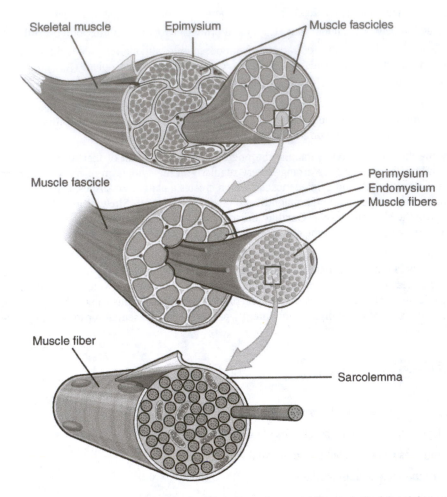

Figure 10.3 The Three Connective Tissue Layers Bundles of muscle fibers, called fascicles, are covered by the perimysium. Muscle fibers are covered by the endomysium.

Inside each skeletal muscle, muscle fibers are organized into individual bundles, each called a **fascicle**, by a middle layer of connective tissue called the **perimysium**. This fascicular organization is common in muscles of the limbs; it allows the nervous system to trigger a specific movement of a muscle by activating a subset of muscle fibers within a bundle, or fascicle of the muscle. Inside each fascicle, each muscle fiber is encased in a thin connective tissue layer of collagen and reticular fibers called the **endomysium**. The endomysium contains the extracellular fluid and nutrients to support the muscle fiber. These nutrients are supplied via blood to the muscle tissue.

In skeletal muscles that work with tendons to pull on bones, the collagen in the three tissue layers (the mysia) intertwines with the collagen of a tendon. At the other end of the tendon, it fuses with the periosteum coating the bone. The tension created by contraction of the muscle fibers is then transferred though the mysia, to the tendon, and then to the periosteum to pull on the bone for movement of the skeleton. In other places, the mysia may fuse with a broad, tendon-like sheet called an **aponeurosis**, or to fascia, the connective tissue between skin and bones. The broad sheet of connective tissue in the lower back that the latissimus dorsi muscles (the "lats") fuse into is an example of an aponeurosis.

Every skeletal muscle is also richly supplied by blood vessels for nourishment, oxygen delivery, and waste removal. In addition, every muscle fiber in a skeletal muscle is supplied by the axon branch of a somatic motor neuron, which signals the fiber to contract. Unlike cardiac and smooth muscle, the only way to functionally contract a skeletal muscle is through signaling from the nervous system.

Skeletal Muscle Fibers

Because skeletal muscle cells are long and cylindrical, they are commonly referred to as muscle fibers. Skeletal muscle fibers can be quite large for human cells, with diameters up to 100 μm and lengths up to 30 cm (11.8 in) in the Sartorius of the upper leg. During early development, embryonic myoblasts, each with its own nucleus, fuse with up to hundreds of other myoblasts to form the multinucleated skeletal muscle fibers. Multiple nuclei mean multiple copies of genes, permitting the production of the large amounts of proteins and enzymes needed for muscle contraction.

Some other terminology associated with muscle fibers is rooted in the Greek *sarco*, which means "flesh." The plasma membrane of muscle fibers is called the **sarcolemma**, the cytoplasm is referred to as **sarcoplasm**, and the specialized smooth endoplasmic reticulum, which stores, releases, and retrieves calcium ions (Ca^{++}) is called the **sarcoplasmic reticulum (SR)** (Figure 10.4). As will soon be described, the functional unit of a skeletal muscle fiber is the sarcomere, a highly organized arrangement of the contractile myofilaments **actin** (thin filament) and **myosin** (thick filament), along with other support proteins.

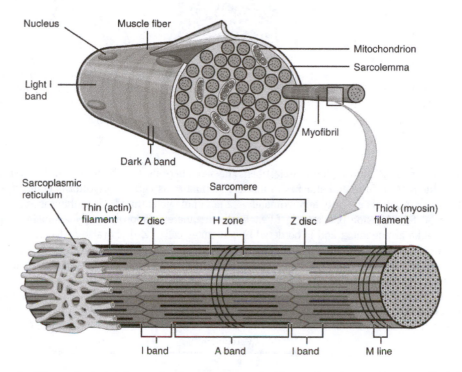

Figure 10.4 Muscle Fiber A skeletal muscle fiber is surrounded by a plasma membrane called the sarcolemma, which contains sarcoplasm, the cytoplasm of muscle cells. A muscle fiber is composed of many fibrils, which give the cell its striated appearance.

The Sarcomere

The striated appearance of skeletal muscle fibers is due to the arrangement of the myofilaments of actin and myosin in sequential order from one end of the muscle fiber to the other. Each packet of these microfilaments and their regulatory proteins, **troponin** and **tropomyosin** (along with other proteins) is called a **sarcomere**.

Interactive LINK

Watch this video (http://openstaxcollege.org/l/micromacro) to learn more about macro- and microstructures of skeletal muscles. (a) What are the names of the "junction points" between sarcomeres? (b) What are the names of the "subunits" within the myofibrils that run the length of skeletal muscle fibers? (c) What is the "double strand of pearls" described in the video? (d) What gives a skeletal muscle fiber its striated appearance?

The sarcomere is the functional unit of the muscle fiber. The sarcomere itself is bundled within the myofibril that runs the entire length of the muscle fiber and attaches to the sarcolemma at its end. As myofibrils contract, the entire muscle cell contracts. Because myofibrils are only approximately 1.2 μm in diameter, hundreds to thousands (each with thousands of sarcomeres) can be found inside one muscle fiber. Each sarcomere is approximately 2 μm in length with a three-dimensional cylinder-like arrangement and is bordered by structures called Z-discs (also called Z-lines, because pictures are two-dimensional), to which the actin myofilaments are anchored (Figure 10.5). Because the actin and its troponin-tropomyosin complex (projecting from the Z-discs toward the center of the sarcomere) form strands that are thinner than the myosin, it is called the **thin filament** of the sarcomere. Likewise, because the myosin strands and their multiple heads (projecting from the center of the sarcomere, toward but not all to way to, the Z-discs) have more mass and are thicker, they are called the **thick filament** of the sarcomere.

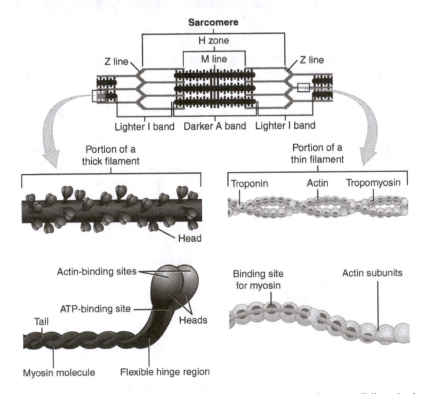

Figure 10.5 The Sarcomere   The sarcomere, the region from one Z-line to the next Z-line, is the functional unit of a skeletal muscle fiber.

The Neuromuscular Junction

Another specialization of the skeletal muscle is the site where a motor neuron's terminal meets the muscle fiber—called the **neuromuscular junction (NMJ)**. This is where the muscle fiber first responds to signaling by the motor neuron. Every skeletal muscle fiber in every skeletal muscle is innervated by a motor neuron at the NMJ. Excitation signals from the neuron are the only way to functionally activate the fiber to contract.

Every skeletal muscle fiber is supplied by a motor neuron at the NMJ. Watch this video (http://openstaxcollege.org/l/skelmuscfiber) to learn more about what happens at the NMJ. (a) What is the definition of a motor unit? (b) What is the structural and functional difference between a large motor unit and a small motor unit? (c) Can you give an example of each? (d) Why is the neurotransmitter acetylcholine degraded after binding to its receptor?

Excitation-Contraction Coupling

All living cells have membrane potentials, or electrical gradients across their membranes. The inside of the membrane is usually around -60 to -90 mV, relative to the outside. This is referred to as a cell's membrane potential. Neurons and muscle cells can use their membrane potentials to generate electrical signals. They do this by controlling the movement of charged particles, called ions, across their membranes to create electrical currents. This is achieved by opening and closing specialized proteins in the membrane called ion channels. Although the currents generated by ions moving through these channel proteins are very small, they form the basis of both neural signaling and muscle contraction.

Both neurons and skeletal muscle cells are electrically excitable, meaning that they are able to generate action potentials. An action potential is a special type of electrical signal that can travel along a cell membrane as a wave. This allows a signal to be transmitted quickly and faithfully over long distances.

Although the term **excitation-contraction coupling** confuses or scares some students, it comes down to this: for a skeletal muscle fiber to contract, its membrane must first be "excited"—in other words, it must be stimulated to fire an action potential. The muscle fiber action potential, which sweeps along the sarcolemma as a wave, is "coupled" to the actual contraction through the release of calcium ions (Ca^{++}) from the SR. Once released, the Ca^{++} interacts with the shielding proteins, forcing them to move aside so that the actin-binding sites are available for attachment by myosin heads. The myosin then pulls the actin filaments toward the center, shortening the muscle fiber.

In skeletal muscle, this sequence begins with signals from the somatic motor division of the nervous system. In other words, the "excitation" step in skeletal muscles is always triggered by signaling from the nervous system (Figure 10.6).

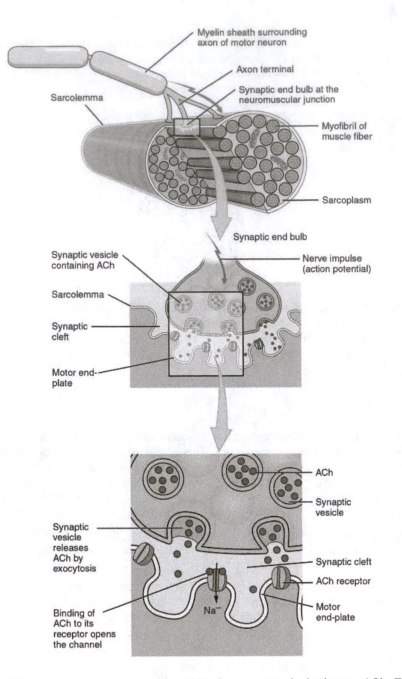

Figure 10.6 Motor End-Plate and Innervation At the NMJ, the axon terminal releases ACh. The motor end-plate is the location of the ACh-receptors in the muscle fiber sarcolemma. When ACh molecules are released, they diffuse across a minute space called the synaptic cleft and bind to the receptors.

The motor neurons that tell the skeletal muscle fibers to contract originate in the spinal cord, with a smaller number located in the brainstem for activation of skeletal muscles of the face, head, and neck. These neurons have long processes, called axons, which are specialized to transmit action potentials long distances— in this case, all the way from the spinal cord to the muscle itself (which may be up to three feet away). The axons of multiple neurons bundle together to form nerves, like wires bundled together in a cable.

Signaling begins when a neuronal **action potential** travels along the axon of a motor neuron, and then along the individual branches to terminate at the NMJ. At the NMJ, the axon terminal releases a chemical messenger, or **neurotransmitter**, called **acetylcholine (ACh)**. The ACh molecules diffuse across a minute space called the **synaptic cleft** and bind to ACh receptors located within the **motor end-plate** of the sarcolemma on the other side of the synapse. Once ACh binds, a channel in the ACh receptor opens and positively charged ions can pass through into the muscle fiber, causing it to **depolarize**, meaning that the membrane potential of the muscle fiber becomes less negative (closer to zero.)

As the membrane depolarizes, another set of ion channels called **voltage-gated sodium channels** are triggered to open. Sodium ions enter the muscle fiber, and an action potential rapidly spreads (or "fires") along the entire membrane to initiate excitation-contraction coupling.

Things happen very quickly in the world of excitable membranes (just think about how quickly you can snap your fingers as soon as you decide to do it). Immediately following depolarization of the membrane, it repolarizes, re-establishing the negative membrane potential. Meanwhile, the ACh in the synaptic cleft is degraded by the enzyme acetylcholinesterase (AChE) so that the ACh cannot rebind to a receptor and reopen its channel, which would cause unwanted extended muscle excitation and contraction.

Propagation of an action potential along the sarcolemma is the excitation portion of excitation-contraction coupling. Recall that this excitation actually triggers the release of calcium ions (Ca^{++}) from its storage in the cell's SR. For the action potential to reach the membrane of the SR, there are periodic invaginations in the sarcolemma, called **T-tubules** ("T" stands for "transverse"). You will recall that the diameter of a muscle fiber can be up to 100 μm, so these T-tubules ensure that the membrane can get close to the SR in the sarcoplasm. The arrangement of a T-tubule with the membranes of SR on either side is called a **triad** (Figure 10.7). The triad surrounds the cylindrical structure called a **myofibril**, which contains actin and myosin.

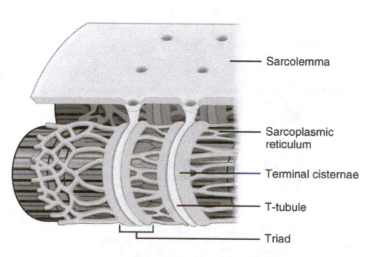

Figure 10.7 The T-tubule Narrow T-tubules permit the conduction of electrical impulses. The SR functions to regulate intracellular levels of calcium. Two terminal cisternae (where enlarged SR connects to the T-tubule) and one T-tubule comprise a triad—a "threesome" of membranes, with those of SR on two sides and the T-tubule sandwiched between them.

The T-tubules carry the action potential into the interior of the cell, which triggers the opening of calcium channels in the membrane of the adjacent SR, causing Ca^{++} to diffuse out of the SR and into the sarcoplasm. It is the arrival of Ca^{++} in the sarcoplasm that initiates contraction of the muscle fiber by its contractile units, or sarcomeres.

10.3 | Muscle Fiber Contraction and Relaxation

By the end of this section, you will be able to:

- Describe the components involved in a muscle contraction
- Explain how muscles contract and relax
- Describe the sliding filament model of muscle contraction

The sequence of events that result in the contraction of an individual muscle fiber begins with a signal—the neurotransmitter, ACh—from the motor neuron innervating that fiber. The local membrane of the fiber will depolarize as positively charged sodium ions (Na^+) enter, triggering an action potential that spreads to the rest of the membrane will depolarize, including the T-tubules. This triggers the release of calcium ions (Ca^{++}) from storage in the sarcoplasmic reticulum (SR). The Ca^{++} then initiates contraction, which is sustained by ATP (Figure 10.8). As long as Ca^{++} ions remain in the sarcoplasm to bind to troponin, which keeps the actin-binding sites "unshielded," and as long as ATP is available to drive the cross-bridge cycling and the pulling of actin strands by myosin, the muscle fiber will continue to shorten to an anatomical limit.

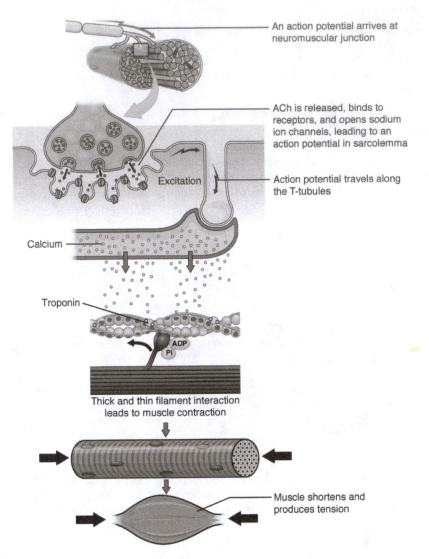

An action potential arrives at neuromuscular junction

ACh is released, binds to receptors, and opens sodium ion channels, leading to an action potential in sarcolemma

Action potential travels along the T-tubules

Excitation

Calcium

Troponin

ADP
Pi

Thick and thin filament interaction leads to muscle contraction

Muscle shortens and produces tension

Figure 10.8 Contraction of a Muscle Fiber A cross-bridge forms between actin and the myosin heads triggering contraction. As long as Ca^{++} ions remain in the sarcoplasm to bind to troponin, and as long as ATP is available, the muscle fiber will continue to shorten.

Muscle contraction usually stops when signaling from the motor neuron ends, which repolarizes the sarcolemma and T-tubules, and closes the voltage-gated calcium channels in the SR. Ca^{++} ions are then pumped back into the SR, which causes the tropomyosin to reshield (or re-cover) the binding sites on the actin strands. A muscle also can stop contracting when it runs out of ATP and becomes fatigued (**Figure 10.9**).

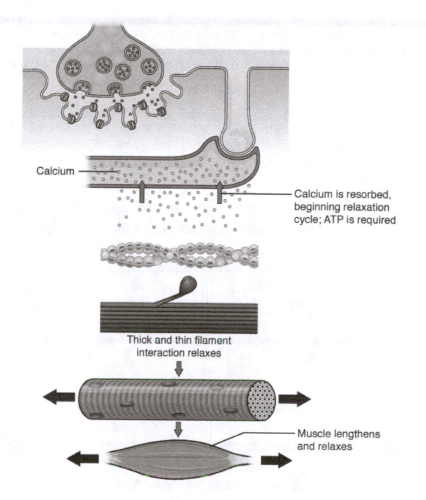

Figure 10.9 Relaxation of a Muscle Fiber Ca^{++} ions are pumped back into the SR, which causes the tropomyosin to reshield the binding sites on the actin strands. A muscle may also stop contracting when it runs out of ATP and becomes fatigued.

The release of calcium ions initiates muscle contractions. Watch this **video (http://openstaxcollege.org/l/calciumrole)** to learn more about the role of calcium. (a) What are "T-tubules" and what is their role? (b) Please describe how actin-binding sites are made available for cross-bridging with myosin heads during contraction.

The molecular events of muscle fiber shortening occur within the fiber's sarcomeres (see **Figure 10.10**). The contraction of a striated muscle fiber occurs as the sarcomeres, linearly arranged within myofibrils, shorten as myosin heads pull on the actin filaments.

The region where thick and thin filaments overlap has a dense appearance, as there is little space between the filaments.

This zone where thin and thick filaments overlap is very important to muscle contraction, as it is the site where filament movement starts. Thin filaments, anchored at their ends by the Z-discs, do not extend completely into the central region that only contains thick filaments, anchored at their bases at a spot called the M-line. A myofibril is composed of many sarcomeres running along its length; thus, myofibrils and muscle cells contract as the sarcomeres contract.

The Sliding Filament Model of Contraction

When signaled by a motor neuron, a skeletal muscle fiber contracts as the thin filaments are pulled and then slide past the thick filaments within the fiber's sarcomeres. This process is known as the sliding filament model of muscle contraction (Figure 10.10). The sliding can only occur when myosin-binding sites on the actin filaments are exposed by a series of steps that begins with Ca^{++} entry into the sarcoplasm.

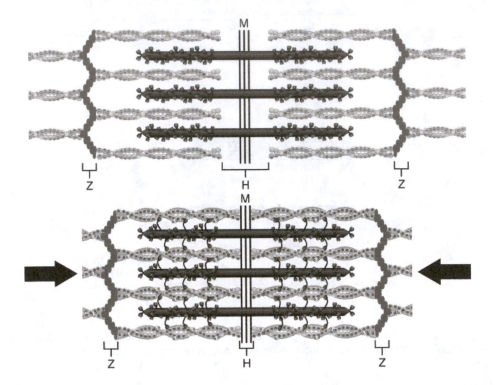

Figure 10.10 The Sliding Filament Model of Muscle Contraction   When a sarcomere contracts, the Z lines move closer together, and the I band becomes smaller. The A band stays the same width. At full contraction, the thin and thick filaments overlap completely.

Tropomyosin is a protein that winds around the chains of the actin filament and covers the myosin-binding sites to prevent actin from binding to myosin. Tropomyosin binds to troponin to form a troponin-tropomyosin complex. The troponin-tropomyosin complex prevents the myosin "heads" from binding to the active sites on the actin microfilaments. Troponin also has a binding site for Ca^{++} ions.

To initiate muscle contraction, tropomyosin has to expose the myosin-binding site on an actin filament to allow cross-bridge formation between the actin and myosin microfilaments. The first step in the process of contraction is for Ca^{++} to bind to troponin so that tropomyosin can slide away from the binding sites on the actin strands. This allows the myosin heads to bind to these exposed binding sites and form cross-bridges. The thin filaments are then pulled by the myosin heads to slide past the thick filaments toward the center of the sarcomere. But each head can only pull a very short distance before it has reached its limit and must be "re-cocked" before it can pull again, a step that requires ATP.

ATP and Muscle Contraction

For thin filaments to continue to slide past thick filaments during muscle contraction, myosin heads must pull the actin at the binding sites, detach, re-cock, attach to more binding sites, pull, detach, re-cock, etc. This repeated movement is known as the cross-bridge cycle. This motion of the myosin heads is similar to the oars when an individual rows a boat: The paddle of the oars (the myosin heads) pull, are lifted from the water (detach), repositioned (re-cocked) and then immersed again to pull (Figure 10.11). Each cycle requires energy, and the action of the myosin heads in the sarcomeres repetitively pulling on the thin filaments also requires energy, which is provided by ATP.

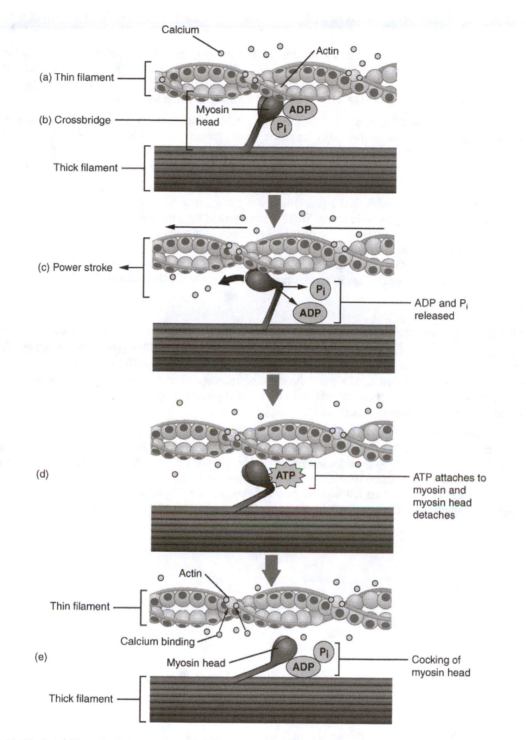

Figure 10.11 Skeletal Muscle Contraction   (a) The active site on actin is exposed as calcium binds to troponin. (b) The myosin head is attracted to actin, and myosin binds actin at its actin-binding site, forming the cross-bridge. (c) During the power stroke, the phosphate generated in the previous contraction cycle is released. This results in the myosin head pivoting toward the center of the sarcomere, after which the attached ADP and phosphate group are released. (d) A new molecule of ATP attaches to the myosin head, causing the cross-bridge to detach. (e) The myosin head hydrolyzes ATP to ADP and phosphate, which returns the myosin to the cocked position.

Cross-bridge formation occurs when the myosin head attaches to the actin while adenosine diphosphate (ADP) and inorganic phosphate (P_i) are still bound to myosin (**Figure 10.11a,b**). P_i is then released, causing myosin to form a stronger attachment to the actin, after which the myosin head moves toward the M-line, pulling the actin along with it. As actin is pulled, the filaments move approximately 10 nm toward the M-line. This movement is called the **power stroke**, as movement of the thin filament occurs at this step (Figure 10.11c). In the absence of ATP, the myosin head will not detach from actin.

One part of the myosin head attaches to the binding site on the actin, but the head has another binding site for ATP. ATP binding causes the myosin head to detach from the actin (Figure 10.11d). After this occurs, ATP is converted to ADP and P_i by the intrinsic **ATPase** activity of myosin. The energy released during ATP hydrolysis changes the angle of the myosin head into a cocked position (Figure 10.11e). The myosin head is now in position for further movement.

When the myosin head is cocked, myosin is in a high-energy configuration. This energy is expended as the myosin head moves through the power stroke, and at the end of the power stroke, the myosin head is in a low-energy position. After the power stroke, ADP is released; however, the formed cross-bridge is still in place, and actin and myosin are bound together. As long as ATP is available, it readily attaches to myosin, the cross-bridge cycle can recur, and muscle contraction can continue.

Note that each thick filament of roughly 300 myosin molecules has multiple myosin heads, and many cross-bridges form and break continuously during muscle contraction. Multiply this by all of the sarcomeres in one myofibril, all the myofibrils in one muscle fiber, and all of the muscle fibers in one skeletal muscle, and you can understand why so much energy (ATP) is needed to keep skeletal muscles working. In fact, it is the loss of ATP that results in the rigor mortis observed soon after someone dies. With no further ATP production possible, there is no ATP available for myosin heads to detach from the actin-binding sites, so the cross-bridges stay in place, causing the rigidity in the skeletal muscles.

Sources of ATP

ATP supplies the energy for muscle contraction to take place. In addition to its direct role in the cross-bridge cycle, ATP also provides the energy for the active-transport Ca^{++} pumps in the SR. Muscle contraction does not occur without sufficient amounts of ATP. The amount of ATP stored in muscle is very low, only sufficient to power a few seconds worth of contractions. As it is broken down, ATP must therefore be regenerated and replaced quickly to allow for sustained contraction. There are three mechanisms by which ATP can be regenerated: creatine phosphate metabolism, anaerobic glycolysis, and fermentation and aerobic respiration.

Creatine phosphate is a molecule that can store energy in its phosphate bonds. In a resting muscle, excess ATP transfers its energy to creatine, producing ADP and creatine phosphate. This acts as an energy reserve that can be used to quickly create more ATP. When the muscle starts to contract and needs energy, creatine phosphate transfers its phosphate back to ADP to form ATP and creatine. This reaction is catalyzed by the enzyme creatine kinase and occurs very quickly; thus, creatine phosphate-derived ATP powers the first few seconds of muscle contraction. However, creatine phosphate can only provide approximately 15 seconds worth of energy, at which point another energy source has to be used (Figure 10.12).

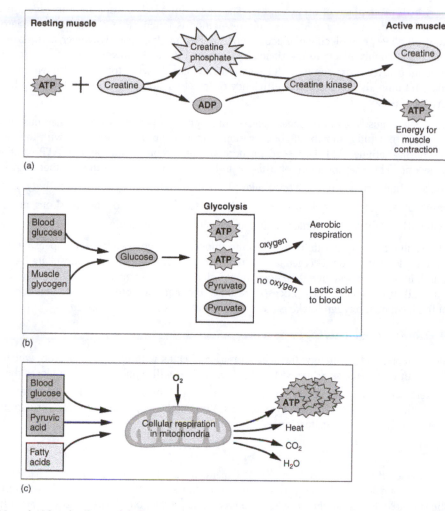

Figure 10.12 Muscle Metabolism (a) Some ATP is stored in a resting muscle. As contraction starts, it is used up in seconds. More ATP is generated from creatine phosphate for about 15 seconds. (b) Each glucose molecule produces two ATP and two molecules of pyruvic acid, which can be used in aerobic respiration or converted to lactic acid. If oxygen is not available, pyruvic acid is converted to lactic acid, which may contribute to muscle fatigue. This occurs during strenuous exercise when high amounts of energy are needed but oxygen cannot be sufficiently delivered to muscle. (c) Aerobic respiration is the breakdown of glucose in the presence of oxygen (O_2) to produce carbon dioxide, water, and ATP. Approximately 95 percent of the ATP required for resting or moderately active muscles is provided by aerobic respiration, which takes place in mitochondria.

As the ATP produced by creatine phosphate is depleted, muscles turn to glycolysis as an ATP source. **Glycolysis** is an anaerobic (non-oxygen-dependent) process that breaks down glucose (sugar) to produce ATP; however, glycolysis cannot generate ATP as quickly as creatine phosphate. Thus, the switch to glycolysis results in a slower rate of ATP availability to the muscle. The sugar used in glycolysis can be provided by blood glucose or by metabolizing glycogen that is stored in the muscle. The breakdown of one glucose molecule produces two ATP and two molecules of **pyruvic acid**, which can be used in aerobic respiration or when oxygen levels are low, converted to lactic acid (**Figure 10.12b**).

If oxygen is available, pyruvic acid is used in aerobic respiration. However, if oxygen is not available, pyruvic acid is converted to **lactic acid**, which may contribute to muscle fatigue. This conversion allows the recycling of the enzyme NAD^+ from NADH, which is needed for glycolysis to continue. This occurs during strenuous exercise when high amounts of energy are needed but oxygen cannot be sufficiently delivered to muscle. Glycolysis itself cannot be sustained for very long (approximately 1 minute of muscle activity), but it is useful in facilitating short bursts of high-intensity output. This is because glycolysis does not utilize glucose very efficiently, producing a net gain of two ATPs per molecule of glucose, and the end product of lactic acid, which may contribute to muscle fatigue as it accumulates.

Aerobic respiration is the breakdown of glucose or other nutrients in the presence of oxygen (O_2) to produce carbon dioxide, water, and ATP. Approximately 95 percent of the ATP required for resting or moderately active muscles is provided by aerobic respiration, which takes place in mitochondria. The inputs for aerobic respiration include glucose circulating in the bloodstream, pyruvic acid, and fatty acids. Aerobic respiration is much more efficient than anaerobic glycolysis, producing approximately 36 ATPs per molecule of glucose versus four from glycolysis. However, aerobic respiration cannot be sustained without a steady supply of O_2 to the skeletal muscle and is much slower (Figure 10.12c). To compensate, muscles store small amount of excess oxygen in proteins call myoglobin, allowing for more efficient muscle contractions and less fatigue. Aerobic training also increases the efficiency of the circulatory system so that O_2 can be supplied to the muscles for longer periods of time.

Muscle fatigue occurs when a muscle can no longer contract in response to signals from the nervous system. The exact causes of muscle fatigue are not fully known, although certain factors have been correlated with the decreased muscle contraction that occurs during fatigue. ATP is needed for normal muscle contraction, and as ATP reserves are reduced, muscle function may decline. This may be more of a factor in brief, intense muscle output rather than sustained, lower intensity efforts. Lactic acid buildup may lower intracellular pH, affecting enzyme and protein activity. Imbalances in Na^+ and K^+ levels as a result of membrane depolarization may disrupt Ca^{++} flow out of the SR. Long periods of sustained exercise may damage the SR and the sarcolemma, resulting in impaired Ca^{++} regulation.

Intense muscle activity results in an **oxygen debt**, which is the amount of oxygen needed to compensate for ATP produced without oxygen during muscle contraction. Oxygen is required to restore ATP and creatine phosphate levels, convert lactic acid to pyruvic acid, and, in the liver, to convert lactic acid into glucose or glycogen. Other systems used during exercise also require oxygen, and all of these combined processes result in the increased breathing rate that occurs after exercise. Until the oxygen debt has been met, oxygen intake is elevated, even after exercise has stopped.

Relaxation of a Skeletal Muscle

Relaxing skeletal muscle fibers, and ultimately, the skeletal muscle, begins with the motor neuron, which stops releasing its chemical signal, ACh, into the synapse at the NMJ. The muscle fiber will repolarize, which closes the gates in the SR where Ca^{++} was being released. ATP-driven pumps will move Ca^{++} out of the sarcoplasm back into the SR. This results in the "reshielding" of the actin-binding sites on the thin filaments. Without the ability to form cross-bridges between the thin and thick filaments, the muscle fiber loses its tension and relaxes.

Muscle Strength

The number of skeletal muscle fibers in a given muscle is genetically determined and does not change. Muscle strength is directly related to the amount of myofibrils and sarcomeres within each fiber. Factors, such as hormones and stress (and artificial anabolic steroids), acting on the muscle can increase the production of sarcomeres and myofibrils within the muscle fibers, a change called hypertrophy, which results in the increased mass and bulk in a skeletal muscle. Likewise, decreased use of a skeletal muscle results in atrophy, where the number of sarcomeres and myofibrils disappear (but not the number of muscle fibers). It is common for a limb in a cast to show atrophied muscles when the cast is removed, and certain diseases, such as polio, show atrophied muscles.

Disorders OF THE...

Muscular System

Duchenne muscular dystrophy (DMD) is a progressive weakening of the skeletal muscles. It is one of several diseases collectively referred to as "muscular dystrophy." DMD is caused by a lack of the protein dystrophin, which helps the thin filaments of myofibrils bind to the sarcolemma. Without sufficient dystrophin, muscle contractions cause the sarcolemma to tear, causing an influx of Ca^{++}, leading to cellular damage and muscle fiber degradation. Over time, as muscle damage accumulates, muscle mass is lost, and greater functional impairments develop.

DMD is an inherited disorder caused by an abnormal X chromosome. It primarily affects males, and it is usually diagnosed in early childhood. DMD usually first appears as difficulty with balance and motion, and then progresses to an inability to walk. It continues progressing upward in the body from the lower extremities to the upper body, where it affects the muscles responsible for breathing and circulation. It ultimately causes death due to respiratory failure, and those afflicted do not usually live past their 20s.

Because DMD is caused by a mutation in the gene that codes for dystrophin, it was thought that introducing healthy myoblasts into patients might be an effective treatment. Myoblasts are the embryonic cells responsible for muscle development, and ideally, they would carry healthy genes that could produce the dystrophin needed for normal muscle contraction. This approach has been largely unsuccessful in humans. A recent approach has involved attempting to boost the muscle's production of utrophin, a protein similar to dystrophin that may be able to assume the role of dystrophin and prevent cellular damage from occurring.

10.4 | Nervous System Control of Muscle Tension

By the end of this section, you will be able to:

- Explain concentric, isotonic, and eccentric contractions
- Describe the length-tension relationship
- Describe the three phases of a muscle twitch
- Define wave summation, tetanus, and treppe

To move an object, referred to as load, the sarcomeres in the muscle fibers of the skeletal muscle must shorten. The force generated by the contraction of the muscle (or shortening of the sarcomeres) is called **muscle tension**. However, muscle tension also is generated when the muscle is contracting against a load that does not move, resulting in two main types of skeletal muscle contractions: isotonic contractions and isometric contractions.

In **isotonic contractions**, where the tension in the muscle stays constant, a load is moved as the length of the muscle changes (shortens). There are two types of isotonic contractions: concentric and eccentric. A **concentric contraction** involves the muscle shortening to move a load. An example of this is the biceps brachii muscle contracting when a hand weight is brought upward with increasing muscle tension. As the biceps brachii contract, the angle of the elbow joint decreases as the forearm is brought toward the body. Here, the biceps brachii contracts as sarcomeres in its muscle fibers are shortening and cross-bridges form; the myosin heads pull the actin. An **eccentric contraction** occurs as the muscle tension diminishes and the muscle lengthens. In this case, the hand weight is lowered in a slow and controlled manner as the amount of cross-bridges being activated by nervous system stimulation decreases. In this case, as tension is released from the biceps brachii, the angle of the elbow joint increases. Eccentric contractions are also used for movement and balance of the body.

An **isometric contraction** occurs as the muscle produces tension without changing the angle of a skeletal joint. Isometric contractions involve sarcomere shortening and increasing muscle tension, but do not move a load, as the force produced cannot overcome the resistance provided by the load. For example, if one attempts to lift a hand weight that is too heavy, there will be sarcomere activation and shortening to a point, and ever-increasing muscle tension, but no change in the angle of the elbow joint. In everyday living, isometric contractions are active in maintaining posture and maintaining bone and joint stability. However, holding your head in an upright position occurs not because the muscles cannot move the head, but because the goal is to remain stationary and not produce movement. Most actions of the body are the result of a combination of isotonic and isometric contractions working together to produce a wide range of outcomes (Figure 10.13).

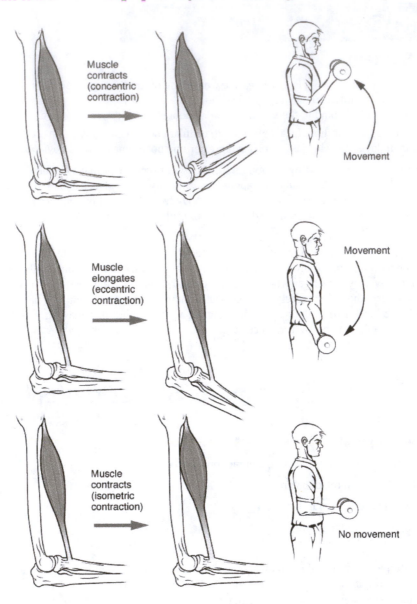

Figure 10.13 Types of Muscle Contractions   During isotonic contractions, muscle length changes to move a load. During isometric contractions, muscle length does not change because the load exceeds the tension the muscle can generate.

All of these muscle activities are under the exquisite control of the nervous system. Neural control regulates concentric, eccentric and isometric contractions, muscle fiber recruitment, and muscle tone. A crucial aspect of nervous system control of skeletal muscles is the role of motor units.

Motor Units

As you have learned, every skeletal muscle fiber must be innervated by the axon terminal of a motor neuron in order to contract. Each muscle fiber is innervated by only one motor neuron. The actual group of muscle fibers in a muscle innervated by a single motor neuron is called a **motor unit**. The size of a motor unit is variable depending on the nature of the muscle.

A small motor unit is an arrangement where a single motor neuron supplies a small number of muscle fibers in a muscle. Small motor units permit very fine motor control of the muscle. The best example in humans is the small motor units of the extraocular eye muscles that move the eyeballs. There are thousands of muscle fibers in each muscle, but every six or so fibers are supplied by a single motor neuron, as the axons branch to form synaptic connections at their individual NMJs.

This allows for exquisite control of eye movements so that both eyes can quickly focus on the same object. Small motor units are also involved in the many fine movements of the fingers and thumb of the hand for grasping, texting, etc.

A large motor unit is an arrangement where a single motor neuron supplies a large number of muscle fibers in a muscle. Large motor units are concerned with simple, or "gross," movements, such as powerfully extending the knee joint. The best example is the large motor units of the thigh muscles or back muscles, where a single motor neuron will supply thousands of muscle fibers in a muscle, as its axon splits into thousands of branches.

There is a wide range of motor units within many skeletal muscles, which gives the nervous system a wide range of control over the muscle. The small motor units in the muscle will have smaller, lower-threshold motor neurons that are more excitable, firing first to their skeletal muscle fibers, which also tend to be the smallest. Activation of these smaller motor units, results in a relatively small degree of contractile strength (tension) generated in the muscle. As more strength is needed, larger motor units, with bigger, higher-threshold motor neurons are enlisted to activate larger muscle fibers. This increasing activation of motor units produces an increase in muscle contraction known as **recruitment**. As more motor units are recruited, the muscle contraction grows progressively stronger. In some muscles, the largest motor units may generate a contractile force of 50 times more than the smallest motor units in the muscle. This allows a feather to be picked up using the biceps brachii arm muscle with minimal force, and a heavy weight to be lifted by the same muscle by recruiting the largest motor units.

When necessary, the maximal number of motor units in a muscle can be recruited simultaneously, producing the maximum force of contraction for that muscle, but this cannot last for very long because of the energy requirements to sustain the contraction. To prevent complete muscle fatigue, motor units are generally not all simultaneously active, but instead some motor units rest while others are active, which allows for longer muscle contractions. The nervous system uses recruitment as a mechanism to efficiently utilize a skeletal muscle.

The Length-Tension Range of a Sarcomere

When a skeletal muscle fiber contracts, myosin heads attach to actin to form cross-bridges followed by the thin filaments sliding over the thick filaments as the heads pull the actin, and this results in sarcomere shortening, creating the tension of the muscle contraction. The cross-bridges can only form where thin and thick filaments already overlap, so that the length of the sarcomere has a direct influence on the force generated when the sarcomere shortens. This is called the length-tension relationship.

The ideal length of a sarcomere to produce maximal tension occurs at 80 percent to 120 percent of its resting length, with 100 percent being the state where the medial edges of the thin filaments are just at the most-medial myosin heads of the thick filaments (Figure 10.14). This length maximizes the overlap of actin-binding sites and myosin heads. If a sarcomere is stretched past this ideal length (beyond 120 percent), thick and thin filaments do not overlap sufficiently, which results in less tension produced. If a sarcomere is shortened beyond 80 percent, the zone of overlap is reduced with the thin filaments jutting beyond the last of the myosin heads and shrinks the H zone, which is normally composed of myosin tails. Eventually, there is nowhere else for the thin filaments to go and the amount of tension is diminished. If the muscle is stretched to the point where thick and thin filaments do not overlap at all, no cross-bridges can be formed, and no tension is produced in that sarcomere. This amount of stretching does not usually occur, as accessory proteins and connective tissue oppose extreme stretching.

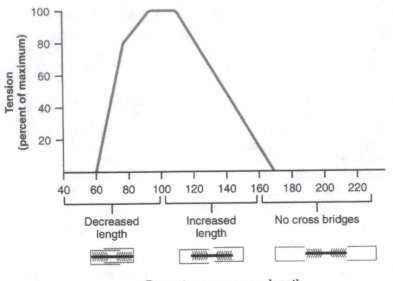

Figure 10.14 The Ideal Length of a Sarcomere   Sarcomeres produce maximal tension when thick and thin filaments overlap between about 80 percent to 120 percent.

The Frequency of Motor Neuron Stimulation

A single action potential from a motor neuron will produce a single contraction in the muscle fibers of its motor unit. This isolated contraction is called a **twitch**. A twitch can last for a few milliseconds or 100 milliseconds, depending on the muscle type. The tension produced by a single twitch can be measured by a **myogram**, an instrument that measures the amount of tension produced over time (Figure 10.15). Each twitch undergoes three phases. The first phase is the **latent period**, during which the action potential is being propagated along the sarcolemma and Ca^{++} ions are released from the SR. This is the phase during which excitation and contraction are being coupled but contraction has yet to occur. The **contraction phase** occurs next. The Ca^{++} ions in the sarcoplasm have bound to troponin, tropomyosin has shifted away from actin-binding sites, cross-bridges formed, and sarcomeres are actively shortening to the point of peak tension. The last phase is the **relaxation phase**, when tension decreases as contraction stops. Ca^{++} ions are pumped out of the sarcoplasm into the SR, and cross-bridge cycling stops, returning the muscle fibers to their resting state.

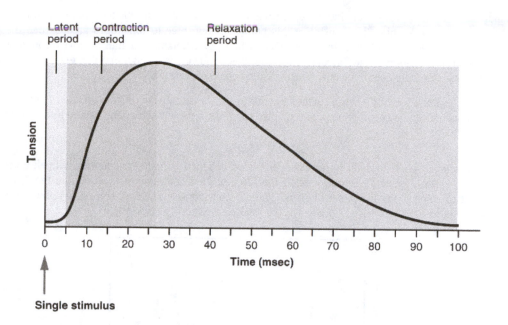

Figure 10.15 A Myogram of a Muscle Twitch A single muscle twitch has a latent period, a contraction phase when tension increases, and a relaxation phase when tension decreases. During the latent period, the action potential is being propagated along the sarcolemma. During the contraction phase, Ca^{++} ions in the sarcoplasm bind to troponin, tropomyosin moves from actin-binding sites, cross-bridges form, and sarcomeres shorten. During the relaxation phase, tension decreases as Ca^{++} ions are pumped out of the sarcoplasm and cross-bridge cycling stops.

Although a person can experience a muscle "twitch," a single twitch does not produce any significant muscle activity in a living body. A series of action potentials to the muscle fibers is necessary to produce a muscle contraction that can produce work. Normal muscle contraction is more sustained, and it can be modified by input from the nervous system to produce varying amounts of force; this is called a **graded muscle response**. The frequency of action potentials (nerve impulses) from a motor neuron and the number of motor neurons transmitting action potentials both affect the tension produced in skeletal muscle.

The rate at which a motor neuron fires action potentials affects the tension produced in the skeletal muscle. If the fibers are stimulated while a previous twitch is still occurring, the second twitch will be stronger. This response is called **wave summation**, because the excitation-contraction coupling effects of successive motor neuron signaling is summed, or added together (**Figure 10.16a**). At the molecular level, summation occurs because the second stimulus triggers the release of more Ca^{++} ions, which become available to activate additional sarcomeres while the muscle is still contracting from the first stimulus. Summation results in greater contraction of the motor unit.

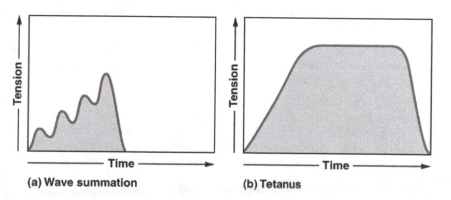

Figure 10.16 Wave Summation and Tetanus (a) The excitation-contraction coupling effects of successive motor neuron signaling is added together which is referred to as wave summation. The bottom of each wave, the end of the relaxation phase, represents the point of stimulus. (b) When the stimulus frequency is so high that the relaxation phase disappears completely, the contractions become continuous; this is called tetanus.

If the frequency of motor neuron signaling increases, summation and subsequent muscle tension in the motor unit continues to rise until it reaches a peak point. The tension at this point is about three to four times greater than the tension of a single twitch, a state referred to as incomplete tetanus. During incomplete tetanus, the muscle goes through quick cycles of contraction with a short relaxation phase for each. If the stimulus frequency is so high that the relaxation phase disappears completely, contractions become continuous in a process called complete **tetanus** (Figure 10.16**b**).

During tetanus, the concentration of Ca^{++} ions in the sarcoplasm allows virtually all of the sarcomeres to form cross-bridges and shorten, so that a contraction can continue uninterrupted (until the muscle fatigues and can no longer produce tension).

Treppe

When a skeletal muscle has been dormant for an extended period and then activated to contract, with all other things being equal, the initial contractions generate about one-half the force of later contractions. The muscle tension increases in a graded manner that to some looks like a set of stairs. This tension increase is called **treppe**, a condition where muscle contractions become more efficient. It's also known as the "staircase effect" (Figure 10.17).

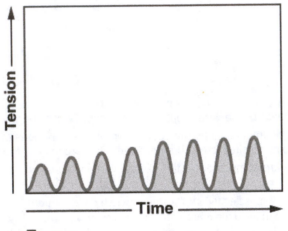

Figure 10.17 Treppe   When muscle tension increases in a graded manner that looks like a set of stairs, it is called treppe. The bottom of each wave represents the point of stimulus.

It is believed that treppe results from a higher concentration of Ca^{++} in the sarcoplasm resulting from the steady stream of signals from the motor neuron. It can only be maintained with adequate ATP.

Muscle Tone

Skeletal muscles are rarely completely relaxed, or flaccid. Even if a muscle is not producing movement, it is contracted a small amount to maintain its contractile proteins and produce **muscle tone**. The tension produced by muscle tone allows muscles to continually stabilize joints and maintain posture.

Muscle tone is accomplished by a complex interaction between the nervous system and skeletal muscles that results in the activation of a few motor units at a time, most likely in a cyclical manner. In this manner, muscles never fatigue completely, as some motor units can recover while others are active.

The absence of the low-level contractions that lead to muscle tone is referred to as **hypotonia**, and can result from damage to parts of the central nervous system (CNS), such as the cerebellum, or from loss of innervations to a skeletal muscle, as in poliomyelitis. Hypotonic muscles have a flaccid appearance and display functional impairments, such as weak reflexes. Conversely, excessive muscle tone is referred to as **hypertonia**, accompanied by hyperreflexia (excessive reflex responses), often the result of damage to upper motor neurons in the CNS. Hypertonia can present with muscle rigidity (as seen in Parkinson's disease) or spasticity, a phasic change in muscle tone, where a limb will "snap" back from passive stretching (as seen in some strokes).

10.5 | Types of Muscle Fibers

By the end of this section, you will be able to:

- Describe the types of skeletal muscle fibers
- Explain fast and slow muscle fibers

Two criteria to consider when classifying the types of muscle fibers are how fast some fibers contract relative to others, and how fibers produce ATP. Using these criteria, there are three main types of skeletal muscle fibers. **Slow oxidative (SO)** fibers contract relatively slowly and use aerobic respiration (oxygen and glucose) to produce ATP. **Fast oxidative (FO)** fibers have fast contractions and primarily use aerobic respiration, but because they may switch to anaerobic respiration (glycolysis), can fatigue more quickly than SO fibers. Lastly, **fast glycolytic (FG)** fibers have fast contractions and primarily use anaerobic glycolysis. The FG fibers fatigue more quickly than the others. Most skeletal muscles in a human contain(s) all three types, although in varying proportions.

The speed of contraction is dependent on how quickly myosin's ATPase hydrolyzes ATP to produce cross-bridge action. Fast fibers hydrolyze ATP approximately twice as quickly as slow fibers, resulting in much quicker cross-bridge cycling (which pulls the thin filaments toward the center of the sarcomeres at a faster rate). The primary metabolic pathway used by a muscle fiber determines whether the fiber is classified as oxidative or glycolytic. If a fiber primarily produces ATP through aerobic pathways it is oxidative. More ATP can be produced during each metabolic cycle, making the fiber more resistant to fatigue. Glycolytic fibers primarily create ATP through anaerobic glycolysis, which produces less ATP per cycle. As a result, glycolytic fibers fatigue at a quicker rate.

The oxidative fibers contain many more mitochondria than the glycolytic fibers, because aerobic metabolism, which uses oxygen (O_2) in the metabolic pathway, occurs in the mitochondria. The SO fibers possess a large number of mitochondria and are capable of contracting for longer periods because of the large amount of ATP they can produce, but they have a relatively small diameter and do not produce a large amount of tension. SO fibers are extensively supplied with blood capillaries to supply O_2 from the red blood cells in the bloodstream. The SO fibers also possess myoglobin, an O_2-carrying molecule similar to O_2-carrying hemoglobin in the red blood cells. The myoglobin stores some of the needed O_2 within the fibers themselves (and gives SO fibers their red color). All of these features allow SO fibers to produce large quantities of ATP, which can sustain muscle activity without fatiguing for long periods of time.

The fact that SO fibers can function for long periods without fatiguing makes them useful in maintaining posture, producing isometric contractions, stabilizing bones and joints, and making small movements that happen often but do not require large amounts of energy. They do not produce high tension, and thus they are not used for powerful, fast movements that require high amounts of energy and rapid cross-bridge cycling.

FO fibers are sometimes called intermediate fibers because they possess characteristics that are intermediate between fast fibers and slow fibers. They produce ATP relatively quickly, more quickly than SO fibers, and thus can produce relatively high amounts of tension. They are oxidative because they produce ATP aerobically, possess high amounts of mitochondria, and do not fatigue quickly. However, FO fibers do not possess significant myoglobin, giving them a lighter color than the red SO fibers. FO fibers are used primarily for movements, such as walking, that require more energy than postural control but less energy than an explosive movement, such as sprinting. FO fibers are useful for this type of movement because they produce more tension than SO fibers but they are more fatigue-resistant than FG fibers.

FG fibers primarily use anaerobic glycolysis as their ATP source. They have a large diameter and possess high amounts of glycogen, which is used in glycolysis to generate ATP quickly to produce high levels of tension. Because they do not primarily use aerobic metabolism, they do not possess substantial numbers of mitochondria or significant amounts of myoglobin and therefore have a white color. FG fibers are used to produce rapid, forceful contractions to make quick, powerful movements. These fibers fatigue quickly, permitting them to only be used for short periods. Most muscles possess a mixture of each fiber type. The predominant fiber type in a muscle is determined by the primary function of the muscle.

10.6 | Exercise and Muscle Performance

By the end of this section, you will be able to:

- Describe hypertrophy and atrophy
- Explain how resistance exercise builds muscle
- Explain how performance-enhancing substances affect muscle

Physical training alters the appearance of skeletal muscles and can produce changes in muscle performance. Conversely, a lack of use can result in decreased performance and muscle appearance. Although muscle cells can change in size, new cells are not formed when muscles grow. Instead, structural proteins are added to muscle fibers in a process called **hypertrophy**, so cell diameter increases. The reverse, when structural proteins are lost and muscle mass decreases, is called **atrophy**. Age-related muscle atrophy is called **sarcopenia**. Cellular components of muscles can also undergo changes in response to changes in muscle use.

Endurance Exercise

Slow fibers are predominantly used in endurance exercises that require little force but involve numerous repetitions. The aerobic metabolism used by slow-twitch fibers allows them to maintain contractions over long periods. Endurance training modifies these slow fibers to make them even more efficient by producing more mitochondria to enable more aerobic metabolism and more ATP production. Endurance exercise can also increase the amount of myoglobin in a cell, as increased aerobic respiration increases the need for oxygen. Myoglobin is found in the sarcoplasm and acts as an oxygen storage supply for the mitochondria.

The training can trigger the formation of more extensive capillary networks around the fiber, a process called **angiogenesis**, to supply oxygen and remove metabolic waste. To allow these capillary networks to supply the deep portions of the muscle, muscle mass does not greatly increase in order to maintain a smaller area for the diffusion of nutrients and gases. All of these cellular changes result in the ability to sustain low levels of muscle contractions for greater periods without fatiguing.

The proportion of SO muscle fibers in muscle determines the suitability of that muscle for endurance, and may benefit those participating in endurance activities. Postural muscles have a large number of SO fibers and relatively few FO and FG fibers, to keep the back straight (**Figure 10.18**). Endurance athletes, like marathon-runners also would benefit from a larger proportion of SO fibers, but it is unclear if the most-successful marathoners are those with naturally high numbers of SO fibers, or whether the most successful marathon runners develop high numbers of SO fibers with repetitive training. Endurance training can result in overuse injuries such as stress fractures and joint and tendon inflammation.

Figure 10.18 Marathoners Long-distance runners have a large number of SO fibers and relatively few FO and FG fibers. (credit: "Tseo2"/Wikimedia Commons)

Resistance Exercise

Resistance exercises, as opposed to endurance exercise, require large amounts of FG fibers to produce short, powerful movements that are not repeated over long periods. The high rates of ATP hydrolysis and cross-bridge formation in FG fibers result in powerful muscle contractions. Muscles used for power have a higher ratio of FG to SO/FO fibers, and trained athletes possess even higher levels of FG fibers in their muscles. Resistance exercise affects muscles by increasing the formation of myofibrils, thereby increasing the thickness of muscle fibers. This added structure causes hypertrophy, or the enlargement of muscles, exemplified by the large skeletal muscles seen in body builders and other athletes (Figure 10.19). Because this muscular enlargement is achieved by the addition of structural proteins, athletes trying to build muscle mass often ingest large amounts of protein.

Figure 10.19 Hypertrophy   Body builders have a large number of FG fibers and relatively few FO and SO fibers. (credit: Lin Mei/flickr)

Except for the hypertrophy that follows an increase in the number of sarcomeres and myofibrils in a skeletal muscle, the cellular changes observed during endurance training do not usually occur with resistance training. There is usually no significant increase in mitochondria or capillary density. However, resistance training does increase the development of connective tissue, which adds to the overall mass of the muscle and helps to contain muscles as they produce increasingly powerful contractions. Tendons also become stronger to prevent tendon damage, as the force produced by muscles is transferred to tendons that attach the muscle to bone.

For effective strength training, the intensity of the exercise must continually be increased. For instance, continued weight lifting without increasing the weight of the load does not increase muscle size. To produce ever-greater results, the weights lifted must become increasingly heavier, making it more difficult for muscles to move the load. The muscle then adapts to this heavier load, and an even heavier load must be used if even greater muscle mass is desired.

If done improperly, resistance training can lead to overuse injuries of the muscle, tendon, or bone. These injuries can occur if the load is too heavy or if the muscles are not given sufficient time between workouts to recover or if joints are not aligned properly during the exercises. Cellular damage to muscle fibers that occurs after intense exercise includes damage to the sarcolemma and myofibrils. This muscle damage contributes to the feeling of soreness after strenuous exercise, but muscles gain mass as this damage is repaired, and additional structural proteins are added to replace the damaged ones. Overworking skeletal muscles can also lead to tendon damage and even skeletal damage if the load is too great for the muscles to bear.

Performance-Enhancing Substances

Some athletes attempt to boost their performance by using various agents that may enhance muscle performance. Anabolic steroids are one of the more widely known agents used to boost muscle mass and increase power output. Anabolic steroids are a form of testosterone, a male sex hormone that stimulates muscle formation, leading to increased muscle mass.

Endurance athletes may also try to boost the availability of oxygen to muscles to increase aerobic respiration by using substances such as erythropoietin (EPO), a hormone normally produced in the kidneys, which triggers the production of red blood cells. The extra oxygen carried by these blood cells can then be used by muscles for aerobic respiration. Human growth hormone (hGH) is another supplement, and although it can facilitate building muscle mass, its main role is to promote the healing of muscle and other tissues after strenuous exercise. Increased hGH may allow for faster recovery after muscle damage, reducing the rest required after exercise, and allowing for more sustained high-level performance.

Although performance-enhancing substances often do improve performance, most are banned by governing bodies in sports and are illegal for nonmedical purposes. Their use to enhance performance raises ethical issues of cheating because they give users an unfair advantage over nonusers. A greater concern, however, is that their use carries serious health risks. The side effects of these substances are often significant, nonreversible, and in some cases fatal. The physiological strain caused by these substances is often greater than what the body can handle, leading to effects that are unpredictable and dangerous. Anabolic steroid use has been linked to infertility, aggressive behavior, cardiovascular disease, and brain cancer.

Similarly, some athletes have used creatine to increase power output. Creatine phosphate provides quick bursts of ATP to muscles in the initial stages of contraction. Increasing the amount of creatine available to cells is thought to produce more ATP and therefore increase explosive power output, although its effectiveness as a supplement has been questioned.

Everyday CONNECTION

Aging and Muscle Tissue

Although atrophy due to disuse can often be reversed with exercise, muscle atrophy with age, referred to as sarcopenia, is irreversible. This is a primary reason why even highly trained athletes succumb to declining performance with age. This decline is noticeable in athletes whose sports require strength and powerful movements, such as sprinting, whereas the effects of age are less noticeable in endurance athletes such as marathon runners or long-distance cyclists. As muscles age, muscle fibers die, and they are replaced by connective tissue and adipose tissue (Figure 10.20). Because those tissues cannot contract and generate force as muscle can, muscles lose the ability to produce powerful contractions. The decline in muscle mass causes a loss of strength, including the strength required for posture and mobility. This may be caused by a reduction in FG fibers that hydrolyze ATP quickly to produce short, powerful contractions. Muscles in older people sometimes possess greater numbers of SO fibers, which are responsible for longer contractions and do not produce powerful movements. There may also be a reduction in the size of motor units, resulting in fewer fibers being stimulated and less muscle tension being produced.

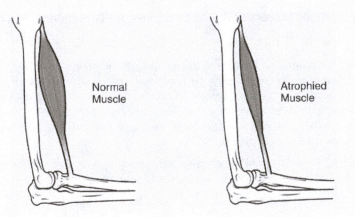

Figure 10.20 Atrophy Muscle mass is reduced as muscles atrophy with disuse.

Sarcopenia can be delayed to some extent by exercise, as training adds structural proteins and causes cellular changes that can offset the effects of atrophy. Increased exercise can produce greater numbers of cellular mitochondria, increase capillary density, and increase the mass and strength of connective tissue. The effects of age-related atrophy are especially pronounced in people who are sedentary, as the loss of muscle cells is displayed as functional impairments such as trouble with locomotion, balance, and posture. This can lead to a decrease in quality of life and medical problems, such as joint problems because the muscles that stabilize bones and joints are weakened. Problems with locomotion and balance can also cause various injuries due to falls.

10.7 | Cardiac Muscle Tissue

By the end of this section, you will be able to:

- Describe intercalated discs and gap junctions
- Describe a desmosome

Cardiac muscle tissue is only found in the heart. Highly coordinated contractions of cardiac muscle pump blood into the vessels of the circulatory system. Similar to skeletal muscle, cardiac muscle is striated and organized into sarcomeres, possessing the same banding organization as skeletal muscle (Figure 10.21). However, cardiac muscle fibers are shorter than skeletal muscle fibers and usually contain only one nucleus, which is located in the central region of the cell. Cardiac muscle fibers also possess many mitochondria and myoglobin, as ATP is produced primarily through aerobic metabolism. Cardiac muscle fibers cells also are extensively branched and are connected to one another at their ends by intercalated discs. An **intercalated disc** allows the cardiac muscle cells to contract in a wave-like pattern so that the heart can work as a pump.

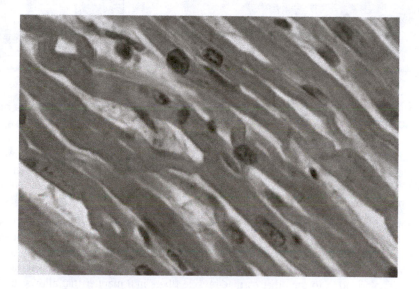

Figure 10.21 Cardiac Muscle Tissue   Cardiac muscle tissue is only found in the heart. LM × 1600. (Micrograph provided by the Regents of University of Michigan Medical School © 2012)

View the University of Michigan WebScope at http://virtualslides.med.umich.edu/Histology/Cardiovascular%20System/305_HISTO_40X.svs/view.apml (http://openstaxcollege.org/l/cardmuscleMG) to explore the tissue sample in greater detail.

Intercalated discs are part of the sarcolemma and contain two structures important in cardiac muscle contraction: gap junctions and desmosomes. A gap junction forms channels between adjacent cardiac muscle fibers that allow the depolarizing current produced by cations to flow from one cardiac muscle cell to the next. This joining is called electric coupling, and in cardiac muscle it allows the quick transmission of action potentials and the coordinated contraction of the entire heart. This network of electrically connected cardiac muscle cells creates a functional unit of contraction called a syncytium. The remainder of the intercalated disc is composed of desmosomes. A **desmosome** is a cell structure that anchors the ends of cardiac muscle fibers together so the cells do not pull apart during the stress of individual fibers contracting (Figure 10.22).

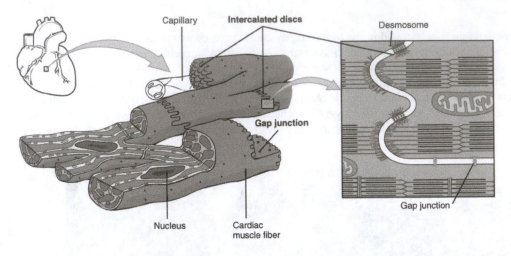

Figure 10.22 Cardiac Muscle   Intercalated discs are part of the cardiac muscle sarcolemma and they contain gap junctions and desmosomes.

Contractions of the heart (heartbeats) are controlled by specialized cardiac muscle cells called pacemaker cells that directly control heart rate. Although cardiac muscle cannot be consciously controlled, the pacemaker cells respond to signals from the autonomic nervous system (ANS) to speed up or slow down the heart rate. The pacemaker cells can also respond to various hormones that modulate heart rate to control blood pressure.

The wave of contraction that allows the heart to work as a unit, called a functional syncytium, begins with the pacemaker cells. This group of cells is self-excitable and able to depolarize to threshold and fire action potentials on their own, a feature called **autorhythmicity**; they do this at set intervals which determine heart rate. Because they are connected with gap junctions to surrounding muscle fibers and the specialized fibers of the heart's conduction system, the pacemaker cells are able to transfer the depolarization to the other cardiac muscle fibers in a manner that allows the heart to contract in a coordinated manner.

Another feature of cardiac muscle is its relatively long action potentials in its fibers, having a sustained depolarization "plateau." The plateau is produced by Ca^{++} entry though voltage-gated calcium channels in the sarcolemma of cardiac muscle fibers. This sustained depolarization (and Ca^{++} entry) provides for a longer contraction than is produced by an action potential in skeletal muscle. Unlike skeletal muscle, a large percentage of the Ca^{++} that initiates contraction in cardiac muscles comes from outside the cell rather than from the SR.

10.8 | Smooth Muscle

By the end of this section, you will be able to:

- Describe a dense body
- Explain how smooth muscle works with internal organs and passageways through the body
- Explain how smooth muscles differ from skeletal and cardiac muscles
- Explain the difference between single-unit and multi-unit smooth muscle

Smooth muscle (so-named because the cells do not have striations) is present in the walls of hollow organs like the urinary bladder, uterus, stomach, intestines, and in the walls of passageways, such as the arteries and veins of the circulatory system, and the tracts of the respiratory, urinary, and reproductive systems (Figure 10.23ab). Smooth muscle is also present in the eyes, where it functions to change the size of the iris and alter the shape of the lens; and in the skin where it causes hair to stand erect in response to cold temperature or fear.

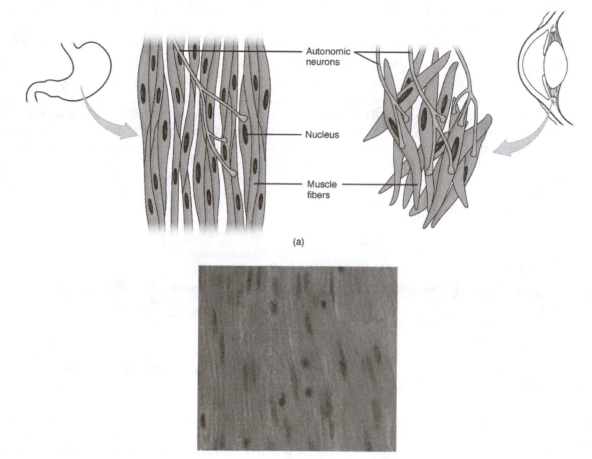

(a)

(b)

Figure 10.23 Smooth Muscle Tissue Smooth muscle tissue is found around organs in the digestive, respiratory, reproductive tracts and the iris of the eye. LM × 1600. (Micrograph provided by the Regents of University of Michigan Medical School © 2012)

Interactive LINK

View the University of Michigan WebScope at http://virtualslides.med.umich.edu/Histology/Digestive%20System/Intestines/169_HISTO_40X.svs/view.apml (http://openstaxcollege.org/l/smoothmuscMG) to explore the tissue sample in greater detail.

Smooth muscle fibers are spindle-shaped (wide in the middle and tapered at both ends, somewhat like a football) and have a single nucleus; they range from about 30 to 200 μm (thousands of times shorter than skeletal muscle fibers), and they produce their own connective tissue, endomysium. Although they do not have striations and sarcomeres, smooth muscle fibers do have actin and myosin contractile proteins, and thick and thin filaments. These thin filaments are anchored by dense bodies. A **dense body** is analogous to the Z-discs of skeletal and cardiac muscle fibers and is fastened to the sarcolemma. Calcium ions are supplied by the SR in the fibers and by sequestration from the extracellular fluid through membrane indentations called calveoli.

Because smooth muscle cells do not contain troponin, cross-bridge formation is not regulated by the troponin-tropomyosin complex but instead by the regulatory protein **calmodulin**. In a smooth muscle fiber, external Ca^{++} ions passing through opened calcium channels in the sarcolemma, and additional Ca^{++} released from SR, bind to calmodulin. The Ca^{++}-calmodulin complex then activates an enzyme called myosin (light chain) kinase, which, in turn, activates the myosin heads by phosphorylating them (converting ATP to ADP and P_i, with the P_i attaching to the head). The heads can then attach to actin-binding sites and pull on the thin filaments. The thin filaments also are anchored to the dense bodies; the structures invested in the inner membrane of the sarcolemma (at adherens junctions) that also have cord-like intermediate filaments attached to them. When the thin filaments slide past the thick filaments, they pull on the dense bodies, structures tethered to the sarcolemma, which then pull on the intermediate filaments networks throughout the sarcoplasm. This arrangement causes the entire muscle fiber to contract in a manner whereby the ends are pulled toward the center, causing the midsection to bulge in a corkscrew motion (Figure 10.24).

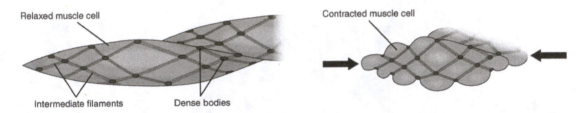
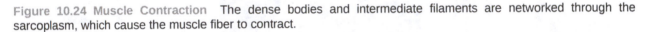

Figure 10.24 Muscle Contraction The dense bodies and intermediate filaments are networked through the sarcoplasm, which cause the muscle fiber to contract.

Although smooth muscle contraction relies on the presence of Ca^{++} ions, smooth muscle fibers have a much smaller diameter than skeletal muscle cells. T-tubules are not required to reach the interior of the cell and therefore not necessary to transmit an action potential deep into the fiber. Smooth muscle fibers have a limited calcium-storing SR but have calcium channels in the sarcolemma (similar to cardiac muscle fibers) that open during the action potential along the sarcolemma. The influx of extracellular Ca^{++} ions, which diffuse into the sarcoplasm to reach the calmodulin, accounts for most of the Ca^{++} that triggers contraction of a smooth muscle cell.

Muscle contraction continues until ATP-dependent calcium pumps actively transport Ca^{++} ions back into the SR and out of the cell. However, a low concentration of calcium remains in the sarcoplasm to maintain muscle tone. This remaining calcium keeps the muscle slightly contracted, which is important in certain tracts and around blood vessels.

Because most smooth muscles must function for long periods without rest, their power output is relatively low, but contractions can continue without using large amounts of energy. Some smooth muscle can also maintain contractions even as Ca^{++} is removed and myosin kinase is inactivated/dephosphorylated. This can happen as a subset of cross-bridges between myosin heads and actin, called **latch-bridges**, keep the thick and thin filaments linked together for a prolonged period, and without the need for ATP. This allows for the maintaining of muscle "tone" in smooth muscle that lines arterioles and other visceral organs with very little energy expenditure.

Smooth muscle is not under voluntary control; thus, it is called involuntary muscle. The triggers for smooth muscle contraction include hormones, neural stimulation by the ANS, and local factors. In certain locations, such as the walls of visceral organs, stretching the muscle can trigger its contraction (the stress-relaxation response).

Axons of neurons in the ANS do not form the highly organized NMJs with smooth muscle, as seen between motor neurons and skeletal muscle fibers. Instead, there is a series of neurotransmitter-filled bulges called varicosities as an axon courses through smooth muscle, loosely forming motor units (Figure 10.25). A **varicosity** releases neurotransmitters into the synaptic cleft. Also, visceral muscle in the walls of the hollow organs (except the heart) contains pacesetter cells. A **pacesetter cell** can spontaneously trigger action potentials and contractions in the muscle.

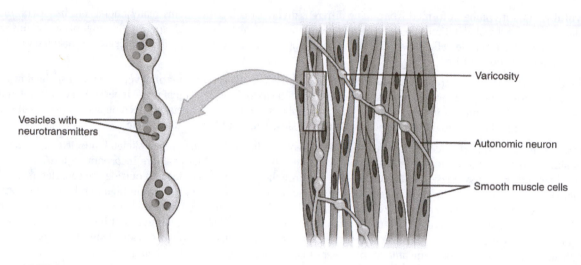

Figure 10.25 Motor Units A series of axon-like swelling, called varicosities or "boutons," from autonomic neurons form motor units through the smooth muscle.

Smooth muscle is organized in two ways: as single-unit smooth muscle, which is much more common; and as multiunit smooth muscle. The two types have different locations in the body and have different characteristics. Single-unit muscle has its muscle fibers joined by gap junctions so that the muscle contracts as a single unit. This type of smooth muscle is found in the walls of all visceral organs except the heart (which has cardiac muscle in its walls), and so it is commonly called **visceral muscle**. Because the muscle fibers are not constrained by the organization and stretchability limits of sarcomeres, visceral smooth muscle has a **stress-relaxation response**. This means that as the muscle of a hollow organ is stretched when it fills, the mechanical stress of the stretching will trigger contraction, but this is immediately followed by relaxation so that the organ does not empty its contents prematurely. This is important for hollow organs, such as the stomach or urinary bladder, which continuously expand as they fill. The smooth muscle around these organs also can maintain a muscle tone when the organ empties and shrinks, a feature that prevents "flabbiness" in the empty organ. In general, visceral smooth muscle produces slow, steady contractions that allow substances, such as food in the digestive tract, to move through the body.

Multiunit smooth muscle cells rarely possess gap junctions, and thus are not electrically coupled. As a result, contraction does not spread from one cell to the next, but is instead confined to the cell that was originally stimulated. Stimuli for multiunit smooth muscles come from autonomic nerves or hormones but not from stretching. This type of tissue is found around large blood vessels, in the respiratory airways, and in the eyes.

Hyperplasia in Smooth Muscle

Similar to skeletal and cardiac muscle cells, smooth muscle can undergo hypertrophy to increase in size. Unlike other muscle, smooth muscle can also divide to produce more cells, a process called **hyperplasia**. This can most evidently be observed in the uterus at puberty, which responds to increased estrogen levels by producing more uterine smooth muscle fibers, and greatly increases the size of the myometrium.

10.9 | Development and Regeneration of Muscle Tissue

By the end of this section, you will be able to:

- Describe the function of satellite cells
- Define fibrosis
- Explain which muscle has the greatest regeneration ability

Most muscle tissue of the body arises from embryonic mesoderm. Paraxial mesodermal cells adjacent to the neural tube form blocks of cells called **somites**. Skeletal muscles, excluding those of the head and limbs, develop from mesodermal somites, whereas skeletal muscle in the head and limbs develop from general mesoderm. Somites give rise to myoblasts. A **myoblast** is a muscle-forming stem cell that migrates to different regions in the body and then fuse(s) to form a syncytium, or **myotube**. As a myotube is formed from many different myoblast cells, it contains many nuclei, but has a continuous cytoplasm. This is why skeletal muscle cells are multinucleate, as the nucleus of each contributing myoblast remains intact in the mature skeletal muscle cell. However, cardiac and smooth muscle cells are not multinucleate because the myoblasts that form their cells do not fuse.

Gap junctions develop in the cardiac and single-unit smooth muscle in the early stages of development. In skeletal muscles, ACh receptors are initially present along most of the surface of the myoblasts, but spinal nerve innervation causes the release of growth factors that stimulate the formation of motor end-plates and NMJs. As neurons become active, electrical signals that are sent through the muscle influence the distribution of slow and fast fibers in the muscle.

Although the number of muscle cells is set during development, satellite cells help to repair skeletal muscle cells. A **satellite cell** is similar to a myoblast because it is a type of stem cell; however, satellite cells are incorporated into muscle cells and facilitate the protein synthesis required for repair and growth. These cells are located outside the sarcolemma and are stimulated to grow and fuse with muscle cells by growth factors that are released by muscle fibers under certain forms of stress. Satellite cells can regenerate muscle fibers to a very limited extent, but they primarily help to repair damage in living cells. If a cell is damaged to a greater extent than can be repaired by satellite cells, the muscle fibers are replaced by scar tissue in a process called **fibrosis**. Because scar tissue cannot contract, muscle that has sustained significant damage loses strength and cannot produce the same amount of power or endurance as it could before being damaged.

Smooth muscle tissue can regenerate from a type of stem cell called a **pericyte**, which is found in some small blood vessels. Pericytes allow smooth muscle cells to regenerate and repair much more readily than skeletal and cardiac muscle tissue. Similar to skeletal muscle tissue, cardiac muscle does not regenerate to a great extent. Dead cardiac muscle tissue is replaced by scar tissue, which cannot contract. As scar tissue accumulates, the heart loses its ability to pump because of the loss of contractile power. However, some minor regeneration may occur due to stem cells found in the blood that occasionally enter cardiac tissue.

Career CONNECTION

Physical Therapist

As muscle cells die, they are not regenerated but instead are replaced by connective tissue and adipose tissue, which do not possess the contractile abilities of muscle tissue. Muscles atrophy when they are not used, and over time if atrophy is prolonged, muscle cells die. It is therefore important that those who are susceptible to muscle atrophy exercise to maintain muscle function and prevent the complete loss of muscle tissue. In extreme cases, when movement is not possible, electrical stimulation can be introduced to a muscle from an external source. This acts as a substitute for endogenous neural stimulation, stimulating the muscle to contract and preventing the loss of proteins that occurs with a lack of use.

Physiotherapists work with patients to maintain muscles. They are trained to target muscles susceptible to atrophy, and to prescribe and monitor exercises designed to stimulate those muscles. There are various causes of atrophy, including mechanical injury, disease, and age. After breaking a limb or undergoing surgery, muscle use is impaired and can lead to disuse atrophy. If the muscles are not exercised, this atrophy can lead to long-term muscle weakness. A stroke can also cause muscle impairment by interrupting neural stimulation to certain muscles. Without neural inputs, these muscles do not contract and thus begin to lose structural proteins. Exercising these muscles can help to restore muscle function and minimize functional impairments. Age-related muscle loss is also a target of physical therapy, as exercise can reduce the effects of age-related atrophy and improve muscle function.

The goal of a physiotherapist is to improve physical functioning and reduce functional impairments; this is achieved by understanding the cause of muscle impairment and assessing the capabilities of a patient, after which a program to enhance these capabilities is designed. Some factors that are assessed include strength, balance, and endurance, which are continually monitored as exercises are introduced to track improvements in muscle function. Physiotherapists can also instruct patients on the proper use of equipment, such as crutches, and assess whether someone has sufficient strength to use the equipment and when they can function without it.

KEY TERMS

acetylcholine (ACh) neurotransmitter that binds at a motor end-plate to trigger depolarization

actin protein that makes up most of the thin myofilaments in a sarcomere muscle fiber

action potential change in voltage of a cell membrane in response to a stimulus that results in transmission of an electrical signal; unique to neurons and muscle fibers

aerobic respiration production of ATP in the presence of oxygen

angiogenesis formation of blood capillary networks

aponeurosis broad, tendon-like sheet of connective tissue that attaches a skeletal muscle to another skeletal muscle or to a bone

ATPase enzyme that hydrolyzes ATP to ADP

atrophy loss of structural proteins from muscle fibers

autorhythmicity heart's ability to control its own contractions

calmodulin regulatory protein that facilitates contraction in smooth muscles

cardiac muscle striated muscle found in the heart; joined to one another at intercalated discs and under the regulation of pacemaker cells, which contract as one unit to pump blood through the circulatory system. Cardiac muscle is under involuntary control.

concentric contraction muscle contraction that shortens the muscle to move a load

contractility ability to shorten (contract) forcibly

contraction phase twitch contraction phase when tension increases

creatine phosphate phosphagen used to store energy from ATP and transfer it to muscle

dense body sarcoplasmic structure that attaches to the sarcolemma and shortens the muscle as thin filaments slide past thick filaments

depolarize to reduce the voltage difference between the inside and outside of a cell's plasma membrane (the sarcolemma for a muscle fiber), making the inside less negative than at rest

desmosome cell structure that anchors the ends of cardiac muscle fibers to allow contraction to occur

eccentric contraction muscle contraction that lengthens the muscle as the tension is diminished

elasticity ability to stretch and rebound

endomysium loose, and well-hydrated connective tissue covering each muscle fiber in a skeletal muscle

epimysium outer layer of connective tissue around a skeletal muscle

excitability ability to undergo neural stimulation

excitation-contraction coupling sequence of events from motor neuron signaling to a skeletal muscle fiber to contraction of the fiber's sarcomeres

extensibility ability to lengthen (extend)

fascicle bundle of muscle fibers within a skeletal muscle

fast glycolytic (FG) muscle fiber that primarily uses anaerobic glycolysis

fast oxidative (FO) intermediate muscle fiber that is between slow oxidative and fast glycolytic fibers

fibrosis replacement of muscle fibers by scar tissue

glycolysis anaerobic breakdown of glucose to ATP

graded muscle response modification of contraction strength

hyperplasia process in which one cell splits to produce new cells

hypertonia abnormally high muscle tone

hypertrophy addition of structural proteins to muscle fibers

hypotonia abnormally low muscle tone caused by the absence of low-level contractions

intercalated disc part of the sarcolemma that connects cardiac tissue, and contains gap junctions and desmosomes

isometric contraction muscle contraction that occurs with no change in muscle length

isotonic contraction muscle contraction that involves changes in muscle length

lactic acid product of anaerobic glycolysis

latch-bridges subset of a cross-bridge in which actin and myosin remain locked together

latent period the time when a twitch does not produce contraction

motor end-plate sarcolemma of muscle fiber at the neuromuscular junction, with receptors for the neurotransmitter acetylcholine

motor unit motor neuron and the group of muscle fibers it innervates

muscle tension force generated by the contraction of the muscle; tension generated during isotonic contractions and isometric contractions

muscle tone low levels of muscle contraction that occur when a muscle is not producing movement

myoblast muscle-forming stem cell

myofibril long, cylindrical organelle that runs parallel within the muscle fiber and contains the sarcomeres

myogram instrument used to measure twitch tension

myosin protein that makes up most of the thick cylindrical myofilament within a sarcomere muscle fiber

myotube fusion of many myoblast cells

neuromuscular junction (NMJ) synapse between the axon terminal of a motor neuron and the section of the membrane of a muscle fiber with receptors for the acetylcholine released by the terminal

neurotransmitter signaling chemical released by nerve terminals that bind to and activate receptors on target cells

oxygen debt amount of oxygen needed to compensate for ATP produced without oxygen during muscle contraction

pacesetter cell cell that triggers action potentials in smooth muscle

pericyte stem cell that regenerates smooth muscle cells

perimysium connective tissue that bundles skeletal muscle fibers into fascicles within a skeletal muscle

power stroke action of myosin pulling actin inward (toward the M line)

pyruvic acid product of glycolysis that can be used in aerobic respiration or converted to lactic acid

recruitment increase in the number of motor units involved in contraction

relaxation phase period after twitch contraction when tension decreases

sarcolemma plasma membrane of a skeletal muscle fiber

sarcomere longitudinally, repeating functional unit of skeletal muscle, with all of the contractile and associated proteins involved in contraction

sarcopenia age-related muscle atrophy

sarcoplasm cytoplasm of a muscle cell

sarcoplasmic reticulum (SR) specialized smooth endoplasmic reticulum, which stores, releases, and retrieves Ca^{++}

satellite cell stem cell that helps to repair muscle cells

skeletal muscle striated, multinucleated muscle that requires signaling from the nervous system to trigger contraction; most skeletal muscles are referred to as voluntary muscles that move bones and produce movement

slow oxidative (SO) muscle fiber that primarily uses aerobic respiration

smooth muscle nonstriated, mononucleated muscle in the skin that is associated with hair follicles; assists in moving materials in the walls of internal organs, blood vessels, and internal passageways

somites blocks of paraxial mesoderm cells

stress-relaxation response relaxation of smooth muscle tissue after being stretched

synaptic cleft space between a nerve (axon) terminal and a motor end-plate

T-tubule projection of the sarcolemma into the interior of the cell

tetanus a continuous fused contraction

thick filament the thick myosin strands and their multiple heads projecting from the center of the sarcomere toward, but not all to way to, the Z-discs

thin filament thin strands of actin and its troponin-tropomyosin complex projecting from the Z-discs toward the center of the sarcomere

treppe stepwise increase in contraction tension

triad the grouping of one T-tubule and two terminal cisternae

tropomyosin regulatory protein that covers myosin-binding sites to prevent actin from binding to myosin

troponin regulatory protein that binds to actin, tropomyosin, and calcium

twitch single contraction produced by one action potential

varicosity enlargement of neurons that release neurotransmitters into synaptic clefts

visceral muscle smooth muscle found in the walls of visceral organs

voltage-gated sodium channels membrane proteins that open sodium channels in response to a sufficient voltage change, and initiate and transmit the action potential as Na^+ enters through the channel

wave summation addition of successive neural stimuli to produce greater contraction

CHAPTER REVIEW

10.1 Overview of Muscle Tissues

Muscle is the tissue in animals that allows for active movement of the body or materials within the body. There are three types of muscle tissue: skeletal muscle, cardiac muscle, and smooth muscle. Most of the body's skeletal muscle produces movement by acting on the skeleton. Cardiac muscle is found in the wall of the heart and pumps blood through the circulatory system.

Smooth muscle is found in the skin, where it is associated with hair follicles; it also is found in the walls of internal organs, blood vessels, and internal passageways, where it assists in moving materials.

10.2 Skeletal Muscle

Skeletal muscles contain connective tissue, blood vessels, and nerves. There are three layers of connective tissue: epimysium, perimysium, and endomysium. Skeletal muscle fibers are organized into groups called fascicles. Blood vessels and nerves enter the connective tissue and branch in the cell. Muscles attach to bones directly or through tendons or aponeuroses. Skeletal muscles maintain posture, stabilize bones and joints, control internal movement, and generate heat.

Skeletal muscle fibers are long, multinucleated cells. The membrane of the cell is the sarcolemma; the cytoplasm of the cell is the sarcoplasm. The sarcoplasmic reticulum (SR) is a form of endoplasmic reticulum. Muscle fibers are composed of myofibrils. The striations are created by the organization of actin and myosin resulting in the banding pattern of myofibrils.

10.3 Muscle Fiber Contraction and Relaxation

A sarcomere is the smallest contractile portion of a muscle. Myofibrils are composed of thick and thin filaments. Thick filaments are composed of the protein myosin; thin filaments are composed of the protein actin. Troponin and tropomyosin are regulatory proteins.

Muscle contraction is described by the sliding filament model of contraction. ACh is the neurotransmitter that binds at the neuromuscular junction (NMJ) to trigger depolarization, and an action potential travels along the sarcolemma to trigger calcium release from SR. The actin sites are exposed after Ca^{++} enters the sarcoplasm from its SR storage to activate the troponin-tropomyosin complex so that the tropomyosin shifts away from the sites. The cross-bridging of myposin heads docking into actin-binding sites is followed by the "power stroke"—the sliding of the thin filaments by thick filaments. The power strokes are powered by ATP. Ultimately, the sarcomeres, myofibrils, and muscle fibers shorten to produce movement.

10.4 Nervous System Control of Muscle Tension

The number of cross-bridges formed between actin and myosin determines the amount of tension produced by a muscle. The length of a sarcomere is optimal when the zone of overlap between thin and thick filaments is greatest. Muscles that are stretched or compressed too greatly do not produce maximal amounts of power. A motor unit is formed by a motor neuron and all of the muscle fibers that are innervated by that same motor neuron. A single contraction is called a twitch. A muscle twitch has a latent period, a contraction phase, and a relaxation phase. A graded muscle response allows variation in muscle tension. Summation occurs as successive stimuli are added together to produce a stronger muscle contraction. Tetanus is the fusion of contractions to produce a continuous contraction. Increasing the number of motor neurons involved increases the amount of motor units activated in a muscle, which is called recruitment. Muscle tone is the constant low-level contractions that allow for posture and stability.

10.5 Types of Muscle Fibers

ATP provides the energy for muscle contraction. The three mechanisms for ATP regeneration are creatine phosphate, anaerobic glycolysis, and aerobic metabolism. Creatine phosphate provides about the first 15 seconds of ATP at the beginning of muscle contraction. Anaerobic glycolysis produces small amounts of ATP in the absence of oxygen for a short period. Aerobic metabolism utilizes oxygen to produce much more ATP, allowing a muscle to work for longer periods. Muscle fatigue, which has many contributing factors, occurs when muscle can no longer contract. An oxygen debt is created as a result of muscle use. The three types of muscle fiber are slow oxidative (SO), fast oxidative (FO) and fast glycolytic (FG). SO fibers use aerobic metabolism to produce low power contractions over long periods and are slow to fatigue. FO fibers use aerobic metabolism to produce ATP but produce higher tension contractions than SO fibers. FG fibers use anaerobic metabolism to produce powerful, high-tension contractions but fatigue quickly.